Great Lives from History

Scientists and Science

Scientists and Science

Volume III
Cecilia Payne-Gaposchkin – Fritz Zwicky

Editor
Joseph L. Spradley
Wheaton College

SALEM PRESS
A Division of EBSCO Publishing
Ipswich, Massachusetts

The paper used in these volumes conforms to the American National Standard for Permanence of Paper for Printed Library Materials, X39.48-1992 (R1997).

Library of Congress Cataloging-in-Publication Data

Great lives from history : scientists and science / editor, Joseph L. Spradley, Wheaton College.
    pages cm
  Includes bibliographical references and index.
  ISBN 978-1-58765-968-3 (set) — ISBN 978-1-58765-969-0 (volume 1) — ISBN 978-1-58765-970-6 (volume 2) — ISBN 978-1-58765-971-3 (volume 3) — ISBN 978-1-58765-972-0 (ebook set) (print) 1. Scientists--Biography. 2. Science—History. I. Spradley, Joseph L., editor.
  Q141.G7667 2013
  509.2'2—dc23
                                                                                    2012032366

PRINTED IN THE UNITED STATES OF AMERICA

Contents

Volume 3

Appendixes

Indexes

KEY TO PRONUNCIATION

Many of the names of personages covered in *Great Lives from History: Scientists and Science* may be unfamiliar to students and general readers. For difficult-to-pronounce names, guidelines to pronunciation have been provided upon first mention of the name in each essay. These guidelines do not purport to achieve the subleties of all languages but will offer readers a rough equivalent of how English speakers may approximate the proper pronunciation.

Vowel Sounds

Symbol	Spelled (Pronounced)
a	answer (AN-suhr), laugh (laf), sample (SAM-puhl), that (that)
ah	father (FAH-thur), hospital (HAHS-pih-tuhl)
aw	awful (AW-fuhl), caught (kawt)
ay	blaze (blayz), fade (fayd), waiter (WAYT-ur), weigh (way)
ee	believe (bee-LEEV), cedar (SEE-dur), leader (LEED-ur), liter (LEE-tur)
eh	bed (behd), head (hehd), said (sehd)
ew	boot (bewt), lose (lewz)
i	buy (bi), height (hit), lie (li), surprise (sur-PRIZ)
ih	bitter (BIH-tur), pill (pihl)
o	cotton (KO-tuhn), hot (hot)
oh	below (bee-LOH), coat (koht), note (noht), wholesome (HOHL-suhm)
oo	good (good), look (look)
ow	couch (kowch), how (how)
oy	boy (boy), coin (koyn)
uh	about (uh-BOWT), butter (BUH-tuhr), enough (ee-NUHF), other (UH-thur)

Consonant Sounds

Symbol	Spelled (Pronounced)
ch	beach (beech), chimp (chihmp)
g	beg (behg), disguise (dihs-GIZ), get (geht)
j	digit (DIH-juht), edge (ehj), jet (jeht)
k	cat (kat), kitten (KIH-tuhn), hex (hehks)
s	cellar (SEHL-ur), save (sayv), scent (sehnt)
sh	champagne (sham-PAYN), issue (IH-shew), shop (shop)
ur	birth (burth), disturb (dihs-TURB), earth (urth), letter (LEH-tur)
y	useful (YEWS-fuhl), young (yuhng)
z	business (BIHZ-nehs), zest (zehst)
zh	vision (VIH-zhuhn)

COMPLETE LIST OF CONTENTS

VOLUME 1

VOLUME 2

VOLUME 3

LIST OF DISCOVERIES

Scientists and Science

Cecilia Payne-Gaposchkin

English American astronomer

Astronomer Cecilia Payne-Gaposchkin was the first person to receive a PhD in astronomy from Harvard University and the first female professor there. While studying stellar atmospheres and the composition of stars, she suggested that their most abundant element is hydrogen.

Born: May 10, 1900; Wendover, England
Died: December 7, 1979; Cambridge, Massachusetts
Primary field: Astronomy
Specialties: Observational astronomy; astrophysics

EARLY LIFE

Cecilia Helena Payne was born in Wendover, Buckinghamshire, England, on May 10, 1900, the oldest of the three children of Edward Payne and Emma Pertz. Her father, a scholar, musician, and lawyer, died when she was four, and she and her two siblings were raised by their mother.

For six years, Payne-Gaposchkin attended a small private elementary school near her home. When she was about eight years old, she saw her first meteorite and immediately became interested in astronomy. In 1910, she witnessed both the great daylight comet (C/1910 A1) and Halley's comet, which further fueled her interest.

In 1912, Payne-Gaposchkin's family moved to London, where she attended a school run by the Church of England. Her education there concentrated on classical languages; preferring science, Payne-Gaposchkin studied botany and math on her own. She insisted on being examined in botany and scored top marks on the exam. She also found a tutor to help her learn German, a language vital for scientists at the time.

In 1917, Payne-Gaposchkin transferred to St. Paul's Girls' School, where she was able to study science. In 1919, thanks to a scholarship, she entered Newnham College at Cambridge University, where she majored in biology. After attending a lecture by English astrophysicist Arthur Eddington, Payne-Gaposchkin's interest shifted to the physical sciences. She was the only woman to attend astronomy lectures and worked on her own at the college observatory, where she met future English astronomer Edward A. Milne. After graduating in 1923, Payne-Gaposchkin won a National Research Council fellowship, which she used to pursue graduate work at Radcliffe College, a women's college affiliated with Harvard University.

LIFE'S WORK

Payne-Gaposchkin was assigned to the Harvard College Observatory under its new director, Harlow Shapley, who became her thesis advisor and mentor and persuaded her to work toward her PhD. In the absence of an astronomy program, Payne-Gaposchkin completed her research at the observatory.

At the time, the sun was believed to be composed mostly of iron. Spectroscopic readings, or measurements of the composition of matter in a celestial body, can overlap, and the results may depend on how they are broken apart; in the course of her research, Payne-Gaposchkin interpreted the spectroscopic readings in a new way and reached the conclusion that the sun is primarily composed of hydrogen, with helium being the second most abundant element. Numerous astronomers, including Eddington, insisted that she was wrong. Only Milne supported her thesis. Payne-Gaposchkin fought for her conclusion, but in order to have her thesis accepted, she was forced to include a statement that the presence of hydrogen in the sun was highly unlikely.

Payne-Gaposchkin's doctoral thesis, *Stellar Atmospheres: A Contribution to the Observational Study of Matter at High Temperatures*, was published in 1925. In it, she established a stellar temperature scale and affirmed that in spite of seeming variations, all stars have essentially the same composition. Payne-Gaposchkin was granted a PhD in astronomy at the age of twenty-five, making her the first person to receive a doctorate in the subject from either Harvard University or Radcliffe College. The following year, she became the youngest astronomer to appear in the biographical reference *American Men of Science*.

By 1929, the work of independent scientists, particularly Russian astronomer Otto Struve, had proved Payne-Gaposchkin's theory of the sun's composition correct. Struve offered to credit her for the discovery, but she felt that she did not deserve recognition because she had capitulated even when she knew she was right. However, she has since been recognized as the first to discover the composition of the sun.

Payne-Gaposchkin became a United States citizen in 1931. In 1933, she traveled to Russia and Germany. At an astronomy conference at the University of Göttingen, Germany, she met astronomer Sergei I. Gaposchkin, a

Cecilia Payne-Gaposchkin Develops a Stellar Temperature Scale

In addition to her assertion that the sun is composed largely of hydrogen, Cecilia Payne-Gaposchkin made large contributions to our knowledge of stellar atmospheres during her career. In her 1925 thesis, she developed a temperature scale that correlates with the spectral classification system created by American astronomer Annie Jump Cannon. This scale was inspired by the work of Indian astrophysicist Meghnad Saha, who had recently developed a theory of ionization—the process by which particles gain or lose electrons to become electrically charged. Payne-Gaposchkin applied Saha's theory to the measure and density of the stellar atmosphere. This marriage of quantum mechanics and astronomy, Payne-Gaposchkin later wrote in her autobiography, gave birth to modern astrophysics.

At the time of Payne-Gaposchkin's research, the Harvard College Observatory boasted the world's largest collection of stellar spectra on photographic plates. The images had been achieved by spectroscope, an instrument attached to a telescope that captured the various wavelengths of starlight on a color spectrum. In the resulting photograph, most stellar spectra had dark gaps where light at certain wavelengths was missing; these gaps are known as absorption lines, representing the chemical elements in a star's atmosphere that absorb the light.

Payne-Gaposchkin began to study these absorption lines in an effort to determine the chemicals that created them, applying her knowledge of quantum physics to the task. She knew that the features of an atom are determined by the configuration of its electrons and that atoms lose electrons at high temperatures, at which point they become ions. Saha had earlier related this theory to the temperature and density of stars, but Payne-Gaposchkin further stretched the theory to explain the wide variance of stellar spectra shown by the spectroscopes. She asserted that the variation is due to the different ionization rates of stars, and by extension their different temperatures—not, as was widely hypothesized at the time, to different amounts of elements. Payne-Gaposchkin's temperature scale led her to further discover that the elemental makeup of stars is largely uniform and that the most common elements are also the lightest elements, hydrogen and helium.

Payne-Gaposchkin's temperature scale made it possible for the first time to extrapolate a star's surface temperature, caused by ionization, from stellar spectra. The scale further proved that Cannon's star-classification system organizes stars according to decreasing temperature. Cannon had arranged the stars according to their separate spectral features, and it had long been hypothesized that the classification ranked stars in order of decreasing temperature, but Payne-Gaposchkin was the first person to demonstrate this quantitatively.

Russian refugee. He had come to the meeting specifically to meet Payne-Gaposchkin but was unable to stay in Germany because of the recent Nazi takeover. When Payne-Gaposchkin returned to Harvard, she used her influence to bring Gaposchkin to the United States, where he was given a position at Harvard. The couple married in 1934 and went on to have three children. Payne-Gaposchkin's daughter, Katherine, would later become an astronomer and collaborate with her mother on several papers.

Payne-Gaposchkin also collaborated with her husband on many astronomical investigations and publications. Over the course of their study of variable stars, which are stars that change in magnitude (brightness) over time, the two examined 1,500 specimens and reported their preliminary findings in three monographs in 1935. In a 1936 report to the National Academy of Sciences, Payne-Gaposchkin suggested that supernovas differ from normal novas only in size, and in 1938, she and her husband published *Variable Stars* to provide evidence to support their preliminary conclusions. That year, Payne-Gaposchkin was named Phillips Astronomer at Harvard College Observatory and became a lecturer in astronomy.

During the 1940s, Payne-Gaposchkin continued her research projects with her husband, independently, and with other staff members at the Harvard Observatory. In 1946, she reported in the *Astrophysical Journal* on the variable binary star RT Andromedae. Two years later, she and her husband presented their final report on variable stars to the American Philosophical Society. In 1949, at an energy conference at Wellesley College in Massachusetts, Payne-Gaposchkin explained how the sun consumes its own substance and then renews its energy from the atomic cores, or nuclei, with hydrogen as the fuel and helium the "ash." She compared this process to that which occurs in an atomic bomb.

Throughout the 1950s, Payne-Gaposchkin published several works, including *Stars in the Making* (1952); *Variable Stars and Galactic Structure* (1954), a synopsis of a presentation at the University of London; *Introduction to Astronomy* (1954, 1956); and *The Galactic Novae* (1957). She also wrote numerous articles on spiral galaxies and other subjects. In 1956, she was made a full professor of astronomy at Harvard and was promoted to chair of the astronomy department, the first woman appointed to both positions. She battled for increased pay, but although her salary was raised, she still made less than beginning male lecturers.

In the late 1960s, Payne-Gaposchkin collaborated with her daughter on a revised second edition of *Introduction to Astronomy*, which was published in 1970. Nine years later, she collected and collated family correspondence dating back to 1830. She completed the collection, which she called *The Garnet Letters*, in 1979.

Payne-Gaposchkin received honorary degrees from Wilson College, Smith College, the Western College for Women, Colby College, the Women's Medical College of Philadelphia, and Cambridge University. She was the first to receive the Annie Jump Cannon Award from the American Astronomical Society in 1934. She was also granted the Radcliffe Award of Merit for outstanding scientific achievements in 1952 and the American Astronomical Society's Henry Norris Russell Prize in 1976. She was a member of the Royal Astronomical Society, the American Academy of Arts and Sciences, the American Astronomical Society, and the American Philosophical Society.

Payne-Gaposchkin died of lung cancer on December 7, 1979.

IMPACT

The asteroid 2039 Payne-Gaposchkin, discovered in 1974, was named in Payne-Gaposchkin's honor in 1977. As the first astronomer to graduate with a doctoral degree in astronomy from Harvard University and the first female professor and department chair at Harvard, Payne-Gaposchkin helped establish both the field of astronomy at a postgraduate level and a place for women in that field. In her determination to study what she loved, she was able to contribute prolifically to astronomy, and she earned respect in a scientific community overwhelmingly dominated by men.

Payne-Gaposchkin determined the sun's composition and the composition of stars in general, and her collection of stellar data resulted in numerous publications for astronomers and students of astronomy. This, in turn, impacted scientists' understanding of the nature of variable stars, stellar atmospheric temperature, and the elemental composition of stars. By combining stellar astronomy with atomic physics, Payne-Gaposchkin's research helped develop the study of stellar composition within the field of astrophysics. Understanding a star's composition can help scientists determine that star's evolution, thus contributing to our basic understanding of the universe.

Ellen Bailey

FURTHER READING

Kaler, James B. *Stars and Their Spectra: An Introduction to the Spectral Sequence*. 2nd ed. New York: Cambridge UP, 2011. Print. An overview of stellar spectroscopy. Covers the fundamental properties of various types of stars and their spectra.

Payne-Gaposchkin, Cecilia. *Cecilia Payne-Gaposchkin: An Autobiography and Other Recollections*. 1984. New York: Cambridge UP, 1996. Print. Payne-Gaposchkin's life and work. Includes her bibliography and introductory material by her daughter and other female astronomers.

Percy, John R. *Understanding Variable Stars*. New York: Cambridge UP, 2004. Print. Overview of variable stars and the information their variations in magnitude provide about the stars' properties, composition, and evolution.

MAX PERUTZ

Austrian molecular biologist

Max Perutz developed the procedure by which the atomic structure of proteins can be determined by the pattern of X-ray diffraction they produce. He later applied similar techniques of X-ray diffraction to explain the structure of hemoglobin.

Born: May 19, 1914; Vienna, Austria
Died: February 6, 2002; Cambridge, England
Primary field: Biology
Specialties: Molecular biology; biochemistry

EARLY LIFE

Max Ferdinand Perutz was born May 19, 1914 in Vienna, the capital of what was then the Austro-Hungarian Empire. His father, Hugo Perutz, was a textile manufacturer of Czechoslovakian ancestry. His mother, Adele Goldschmidt Perutz, was Viennese. Her family was also in the textile business. Perutz was the youngest of their three children.

World War I and its aftereffects significantly disrupted the Perutz family. Two of Perutz's uncles were killed in the war. His father served as a member of a mortar unit on the Italian front. Starvation was common after the war, and the Perutz family moved to Reichenau in order to exchange clothing for food. Textile products remained in significant demand after the war, allowing the Perutz family first to survive and then to become relatively prosperous. Anti-Semitism was widespread in Viennese society during this period, and consequently some members of the family, including Perutz, were baptized as Christians.

At age ten, Perutz enrolled at the Theresianum, an exclusive preparatory school established in 1746 for training the sons of the aristocracy. He was also educated by private tutors. The curriculum at the school changed during the eight years in which Perutz was enrolled. The school's emphasis on Latin and Greek was replaced with French. The school continued to have strong mathematics and science programs, and Perutz developed a growing interest in chemistry during these years. He was strongly encouraged by his family to pursue law, but he convinced his parents to allow him to study chemistry instead.

LIFE'S WORK

In 1932, Perutz enrolled at the University of Vienna to pursue a degree in chemistry. As a student, he found a course in organic biochemistry of particular interest. References to the work being carried out by biochemist and Nobel laureate Frederick Hopkins at Cambridge University in London inspired Perutz to pursue his doctoral work in London.

In September 1936, Perutz joined the Cavendish Laboratory at Cambridge, where he began working with Bernal on X-ray crystallography. Perutz became fascinated with crystallography, believing the key to understanding living matter lay in an understanding of protein. Although Perutz requested he be given a project analyzing biological material, he was instead given chips of silicate to analyze. To conduct the analysis, Perutz worked with an old X-ray apparatus. Another of

Perutz Deciphers the Molecular Structure of Hemoglobin

The application of X-ray diffraction as a means to analyze protein was first reported in 1914, when physicist Max von Laue demonstrated such patterns using protein crystals; von Laue was awarded the Nobel Prize in Physics that year for his work. The father and son team of William and Lawrence Bragg (joint Nobel laureates in 1915) applied the properties of X-ray diffraction to analyze lattice structures of simple crystals such as salt. However, it was not until the 1930s that similar analysis of more complex structures was undertaken.

In 1937, Max Perutz presented his first X-ray analysis of horse hemoglobin, jointly published with Lawrence Bragg and Isidor Fankuchen. After the interruption necessitated by the war years, Perutz resumed his analysis of hemoglobin using highly purified crystals. By shining a beam of X-rays through a rotating crystal of hemoglobin Perutz was able to produce a pattern of spots on film, with a position and intensity influenced by the position of the atoms in the crystal. As the crystal was rotated, the pattern produced different intensities (circles), with sometimes alternating dark-light-dark intensities called "fringes." The pattern revealed some aspects of the crystal's atomic makeup but provided little information about the phase angles produced in the rotation.

Perutz solved the problem through the creation of isomorphous crystals, in which he attached a heavy atom to the protein in different positions. The benefit of using a heavy atom was that it provided a reference point for analysis of the fringes. By comparing diffraction patterns of hemoglobin without the presence of a heavy atom with those patterns in which heavy atoms were placed in various positions, Perutz was able to determine the atomic structure of the hemoglobin molecule. While Perutz was unable to demonstrate the precise positions of individual amino acids prior to being awarded the Nobel Prize, he was able to depict the relative positions of the polypeptide chains that make up the globin, and to demonstrate the changes in molecular structure in the oxygenated and deoxygenated forms. The hemoglobin molecule consists in part of four polypeptide chains whose relative positions Perutz was also able to determine.

Bernal's associates instructed Perutz in the use of the instrument, while Bernal provided the interpretation of the data. Bernal and British chemist Dorothy Hodgkin demonstrated that X-ray diffraction patterns obtained when using crystals of protein could be applied in measurements of distance between atoms. Perutz theorized that the same principles could be used for atomic analysis of other larger molecules.

In the summer of 1937, Perutz travelled to Prague, where he met with a cousin who was married to biochemist Felix Haurowitz. Haurowitz had been studying horse hemoglobin (the molecule carrying oxygen in red blood cells) and showed Perutz how purple crystals of deoxyhemoglobin became scarlet-colored when exposed to oxygen. The demonstration peaked Perutz's interest, and Haurowitz suggested that he contact the protein scientist Gilbert Adair at Cambridge in order to obtain his own crystalline samples of hemoglobin for analysis. In 1938, Bernal, Perutz, and a third scientist, Isidor Fankuchen, published a paper describing the X-ray diffraction pattern of hemoglobin.

In 1938, Austria and portions of Czechoslovakia were annexed to Germany by Nazi leader Adolf Hitler. Since the Perutz family was of Jewish ancestry, their businesses were appropriated by the Nazis, who had begun enforcing a strict anti-Semitic social policy. Although Perutz lost the funding for his work that was provided by his family, he was able to obtain a grant through the Rockefeller Foundation in New York, which allowed him to continue working as a research assistant to physicist Lawrence Bragg, a 1915 Nobel laureate who by 1938 had replaced Bernal as Cavendish Professor in Cambridge. In 1940, Perutz earned his PhD.

Following the beginning of the Second World War in September 1939, and the subsequent election of Winston Churchill as British prime minister the following year, Perutz was among 7,500 people of German or Austrian ancestry interned in England as "enemy aliens." Perutz was subsequently exiled to Canada, though he was later allowed to return to Cambridge. Despite the treatment he received at the hands of the British government, Perutz participated in the Allied war effort, and was associated with Project Habakkuk. The project, proposed by scientist Geoffrey Pike, suggested using large ice flows in the Atlantic as floating aircraft carriers for Allied forces. Although the proposal never came to fruition, Perutz's contribution included a study of crystal formations in glaciers.

Perutz married Gisela Peiser in 1942; they would have two children, one of whom, Robin Perutz, became a professor of chemistry.

Following the Allied victory in 1945, Perutz continued his X-ray diffraction studies. Bernal had departed from Cambridge prior to the beginning of the war, becoming Chair of Physics at Birkbeck College in London. Perutz had earlier shown Bragg his diffraction photographs of hemoglobin, and Bragg remained among the strongest supporters of Perutz's research for the remainder of his tenure.

In 1946, biochemist and crystallographer John Kendrew joined the Cambridge laboratory as Perutz's colleague. Kendrew was primarily involved in the study of myoglobin structure, a molecule found in muscle that functioned in a manner similar to hemoglobin; the diffraction principles for each were largely identical. The following year Perutz was appointed head of the Medical Research Council Unit for Molecular Biology (MRC), the position he held until 1962 when he became founder and chair of the MRC Laboratory of Molecular Biology. It was as the head of the MRC that Perutz oversaw the work of geneticists James Watson and Francis Crick in the early 1950s as they deciphered the structure of DNA.

One challenge Perutz faced in trying to decipher the X-ray diffraction patterns was that of phase variation, which prevented the superimposing of images necessary to understand the atomic pattern. Perutz solved the problem by 1954 through what he called isomorphous replacement, which was the attachment of heavy atoms to a structure that allowed for the determination of a reference point. Within five years both the structures of hemoglobin (by Perutz) and myoglobin (by Kendrew) had been determined. In 1962 they shared the Nobel Prize in Chemistry for their work.

Perutz's later research focused on changes in hemoglobin structure that took place as a result of oxygen binding (oxyhemoglobin) and detachment of oxygen (deoxyhemoglobin). He applied this to the study of genetic diseases associated with hemoglobin. Perutz also studied Huntington's disease, a genetic abnormality involving the degeneration of nerve cells in the brain. He had just completed a manuscript proposing a mechanism underlying the pathology of Huntington's disease when he died on February 6, 2002.

IMPACT

Perutz's analysis of hemoglobin represented the first time a protein structure was understood at the atomic level. He further applied this in his description of structural changes taking place in the binding or release of oxygen, as well as structural changes inherent in mutations of hemoglobin, opening a new field of molecular pathology. The result was an understanding of the mechanisms by which hemoglobin attaches to oxygen and subsequently releases the molecule into tissue, a linking of structure with function.

Other scientists quickly applied the isomorphous technique introduced by Perutz in their respective three-dimensional analyses of other proteins. In the years immediately following Perutz's and Kendrew's publications, the structures of lysozyme (an enzyme that hydrolyzes carbohydrates), the digestive enzyme α-chymotrypsin, carboxypeptidase B (a pancreatic enzyme that hydrolyzes protein), and ribonuclease A were all determined.

Richard Adler

FURTHER READING

Brown, Andrew. *J. D. Bernal: The Sage of Science.* New York: Oxford UP, 2005. Print. Presents a biography of Bernal, Perutz's mentor and colleague. Perutz was one of several students of Bernal's to be awarded a Nobel Prize.

Ferry, Georgina. *Max Perutz and the Secret of Life.* Cold Spring Harbor: Cold Spring Harbor P, 2007. Print. Biography of Perutz. Discusses his ancestry and continues with both his personal life and scientific career. Includes a discussion of his significance as a mentor to other scientists.

Watson, James D. *The Double Helix: A Personal Account of the Discovery of the Structure of DNA.* New York: Touchstone, 2001. Print. Autobiography of one of the scientists who deciphered the structure of DNA. Perutz was head of the unit in the Medical Research Council that oversaw Watson and Francis Crick's work at Cambridge.

MAX PLANCK

German physicist

Planck's 1900 discovery that light consists of infinitesimal "quanta" and his articulation of quantum theory replaced classical physics with modern quantum physics. This work not only resulted in Planck's receiving the Nobel Prize in Physics in 1918 but also laid the groundwork for the achievements of many other Nobel laureates.

Born: April 23, 1858; Kiel, Denmark (now Germany)
Died: October 4, 1947; Göttingen, West Germany (now Germany)
Primary field: Physics
Specialties: Theoretical physics; quantum mechanics

EARLY LIFE

Born into an intellectual family, Max Planck spent most of his early life in Munich, where the family moved in the spring of 1867. Planck's father was a professor of civil law at the university in Kiel. Planck's forebears included many lawyers and clergymen, which may have contributed to his lifelong respect for the law and interest in religion.

In May 1867, Planck was enrolled in Munich's Königliche Maximilian-Gymnasium, where he came under the tutelage of Hermann Muller, a mathematician who took an interest in the youth and taught him astronomy and mechanics as well as mathematics. It was from Muller that Planck first learned the principle of the conservation of energy that underlay much of his eventual work in thermodynamics and quantum theory.

When Planck entered the University of Munich in October 1874, he concentrated on mathematics, even though he was widely gifted in the arts. At Munich, his interest in physics grew. However, his mathematics professors believed that nothing new remained to be discovered in the field.

Planck became ill during his first year at Munich and missed two years of school. In the winter term of 1877–78, when he was well enough to resume his studies, he entered the University of Berlin, where he decided to study theoretical physics, as he was interested in the nature of the universe.

In Berlin, Planck studied with physicists Hermann von Helmholtz, Gustav Kirchhoff, and Rudolf Clausius. Although his doctoral dissertation on the second law of thermodynamics was undistinguished, he graduated summa cum laude in 1879. He taught mathematics and physics briefly at his former secondary school in Munich and, in 1880, received a teaching position at the University of Munich. At that time, theoretical physics was viewed as an unpromising field.

In 1885, Planck became an associate professor of physics at the University of Kiel, where he remained until 1888. He was then appointed assistant professor and

Planck Introduces Quantum Theory

By the end of the nineteenth century, many physicists believed that the study of physics was complete. Several experimental oddities, however, could not be explained. One of these was blackbody radiation. When a piece of metal becomes very hot, it begins to turn a dull red that gets redder as it gets hotter. There is a continual shift of the color of a heated object from red through white to blue as it is heated to higher and higher temperatures. In terms of frequency (the number of waves of radiation that pass a given point per unit of time), the radiation emitted from the heated object goes from a lower to a higher frequency as the temperature increases because red is in a lower-frequency range of the spectrum than blue.

The observed colors are the frequencies being emitted in the greatest proportion. Moreover, any heated body will exhibit a frequency spectrum (a range of different intensities for each frequency). A theoretical body that can completely absorb all the radiation falling upon it is called a blackbody; the radiation it gives off when it is heated is called blackbody radiation.

In theory, if the blackbody were heated past the blue stage, it would give off an invisible light, called ultraviolet light, which has an even higher frequency than that of blue light. Strangely, this was not observed to happen in experiments.

Max Planck offered a solution by suggesting that the metal does not absorb energy in a continuous way but only in certain fixed amounts, or *quanta*. It had previously been assumed that light waves behaved like mechanical waves. Mechanical waves, much like waves in a pond, are a collection of all possible waves at all frequencies, with higher-frequency waves being the most visible. In the mechanical wave theory, all waves appear when energy is introduced, with high-frequency waves naturally being present in greater amounts. The lack of ultraviolet light observed in blackbody radiation showed this theory to be incorrect for light.

Planck stated that light waves do not behave like mechanical waves. He postulated that the discrepancy is due to the relationship between energy and wave frequency. To prove his point, Planck created a formula that showed energy and frequency as directly proportional, related by a proportionality constant (now called "Planck's constant"). Higher frequency means higher energy. Consequently, unless the energy of the heated body was high enough, the higher-frequency light would not seen. In other words, only a fixed amount of energy is available at a given temperature.

Moreover, the release of that energy could be made only in exact amounts, by dividing the energy exactly. Small divisions of the energy, resulting in large numbers of units, are favored over large divisions of small numbers of units. Lower frequencies (small units of energy) are favored over higher frequencies, thus explaining blackbody radiation.

Planck's new idea was so revolutionary that even he had trouble believing it. In 1905, however, Albert Einstein used the quantum theory to explain the photoelectric effect, in which electrons are ejected when light strikes the surface of a piece of metal. Einstein observed that the number of ejected electrons depends not on the intensity of the light but on its frequency. This explanation won Einstein the 1921 Nobel Prize in Physics.

director of the Institute for Theoretical Physics to replace the deceased Kirchhoff. Planck rose to professor in 1892 and remained at Berlin until his retirement in 1926.

LIFE'S WORK

Planck's early work in the laws of thermodynamics and his early interest in the principle of the conservation of energy figured largely in his research from his early teaching days at Kiel through his first decades at the University of Berlin. Although he had been reared on classical physics, Planck began to realize that the laws of classical physics deviated greatly from results obtained in experimental physics. He found the greatest disparities not in the field of optics but rather in thermodynamics. The problems stemmed from the measurement of radiant energy in the frequency spectrum of blackbodies.

Kirchhoff had deduced that radiant energy is independent of the nature of its radiating substance, reasoning that blackbodies, which absorb all frequencies of light, should therefore radiate all frequencies of light. Energy at that time was considered infinitely divisible, a theory that led to many anomalies and seeming contradictions in physics. Problems arose because of the emission discrepancies between lower-frequency ranges and higher-frequency ranges.

International physicists working on this problem reached conflicting conclusions. Work in the field was at an impasse when Planck devised a classically simple equation that explained the distribution of radiation over the full range of frequencies, basing his equation on the daring supposition that energy is not an indivisible flow but composed of tiny particles, which he named *quanta* after the Latin word meaning "How many?" Incidental to this discovery was his determination of a way to measure the absolute weight of molecules and atoms.

Planck's theory showed that the energy of various frequencies of light from violet to red contain different energies, a quantum of violet containing twice the energy of a quantum of red and requiring twice the energy to radiate from a blackbody, making such radiation improbable. Although Planck initially doubted his findings, other scientists began to realize his theory's validity. Soon fellow physicist Albert Einstein based much of his work on photoelectric effect, which classical physics could not explain, on quantum theory. Planck embraced Einstein's theory of relativity eagerly because of its absolutism and because of its presentation of the velocity of light.

Now firmly established at the University of Berlin, Planck was instrumental in bringing Einstein to the Berliner Akademie in 1914 as a professor without teaching obligations and as director of the Kaiser Wilhelm Institute for Physics, which Planck eventually headed. Planck also nominated Einstein for the Nobel Prize in Physics in 1921, and Einstein received the prize one year later.

Quantum mechanics became the most important field of physics in the first half of the twentieth century, followed closely by the field of quantum electrodynamics; both were developments that evolved from Planck's original insights and from his expression of the ratio between the size of a quantum and its frequency (represented by the symbol h).

With Nazi leader Adolf Hitler's rise to power, Planck decided to remain in Germany, although he deplored what was happening. His respect for the law was deeply ingrained, and he felt duty-bound as a citizen to live within the laws but to work from within to change them. He intervened unsuccessfully for Jewish friends and colleagues who were being sent to death camps.

As a Nobel laureate of enormous prestige, Planck scheduled an interview with Hitler and tried to dissuade him from the genocide that was overwhelming Nazi Germany. Planck's intervention did not deter Hitler from his disastrous course, however. Before the end of the war, Planck had lost his home and all of his papers to a bombing raid, had once been trapped for several hours in a collapsed air-raid shelter, and had suffered the Nazis' execution of his son Erwin, a former secretary of state accused of plotting to assassinate Hitler.

When the Allies came into Germany in May 1945, Planck and his second wife, who had fled to Magdeburg after the destruction of their home near Berlin, were again homeless. American soldiers rescued Planck and had him sent to a hospital in Göttingen, where he lived for his few remaining years. He continued his professional activities, giving his last public lecture on scientific pseudoproblems in 1946.

IMPACT

Planck lived another twenty-one years after his retirement. His search for the meaning of the universe and for the nature of existence persisted in his later years. He wrote on general subjects, developing some of his earlier lectures and essays into fuller works. Five volumes of Planck's work in theoretical physics were published in English under the title *Introduction to Theoretical Physics* (1932–33). His highly philosophical *Physikalische Gesetzlichkeit im Lichte neuer Forschung* (1926) and *Das Weltbild der neuen Physik* (1929; combined in *The Universe in the Light of Modern Physics*, 1931) exhibited Planck's search for absolutes in a broadly religious context.

His general works *Where Is Science Going?* (1932) and *Wege zur Physikalischen Erkenntnis* (1933; *The Philosophy of Physics*, 1936) were combined with *The Universe in the Light of Modern Physics* and published in English under the title *The New Science* (1959). Planck's autobiography *Wissenschaftliche Selbstbiographie* (1948; *Scientific Autobiography and Other Papers*, 1949) was published posthumously.

In 1930, Planck had become president of the Kaiser Wilhelm Society of Berlin, which was renamed the Max Planck Society in his honor. In his final years, he again became president of the society.

R. Baird Shuman

FURTHER READING

Heilbron, J. L. *The Dilemmas of an Upright Man: Max Planck and the Fortunes of German Science*. Cambridge: Harvard UP, 2000. Print. Biography focusing on Planck's career. After rising to the pinnacle of German scientific achievement, Planck suffered morally and intellectually as he continued to serve his country during World Wars I and II.

Hermann, Armin. *The Genesis of Quantum Theory (1899–1913)*. Cambridge: MIT P, 1971. Print. Presents a study of the pioneering work Planck did in the late 1880s and early 1890s as he moved toward the discovery of quanta.

Planck, Max. *A Survey of Physical Theory*. Trans. R. Jones and D. H. Williams. 1925. New York: Dover, 2011. Print. An overview of developments and theories in physics, featuring a detailed account of Planck's work with quantum theory.

SIMÉON DENIS POISSON

French mathematician and physicist

Nineteenth-century French mathematician Siméon Denis Poisson made important contributions in the areas of statistics and physics. A student of French astronomer Pierre Laplace, Poisson is one of seventy-two French scientists, engineers and notables who have their names engraved on the Eiffel Tower in recognition of their work.

Born: June 21, 1781; Pithiviers, France
Died: April 25, 1840; Sceaux, France
Primary fields: Mathematics; physics
Specialties: Electromagnetism; probability theory

EARLY LIFE

Siméon Denis Poisson was born in Pithiviers, France on June 21, 1781. His father, Siméon Poisson, was a soldier and neither he nor Poisson's mother was from a noble family. However, changes in French society that came about as a result of the French Revolution in 1789 would result in unprecedented educational opportunities for Poisson as a young man.

Poisson was the first of the children in his family to survive beyond infancy. Because he was not of good health, his family put him in the care of a nurse to ensure his survival. His father taught him to read and write and wished for him to study medicine.

As a young man, Poisson was sent to Fontainebleau in Paris to apprentice with an uncle who was a surgeon. However, he found that he lacked the necessary hand coordination required for conducting surgery, and had little interest in being a physician.

In 1796, Poisson returned to Fontainebleau, this time to the École Centrale, where he quickly distinguished himself as a student of mathematics. At the urging of his teachers, he sat for the exam for École Polytechnique in Paris. Despite his lack of a formal education in mathematics, Poisson was named first in his class in 1798. His work in mathematics drew the attention of two men whose work was deeply respected: astronomer Pierre-Simon Laplace and mathematician Joseph-Louis Lagrange. Poisson's lack of fine motor skills was again an impediment, as it made drawing mathematical diagrams tedious and difficult. This was especially problematic for geometry. Nonetheless, Poisson had an interest in pure mathematics and was able to work around this limitation.

LIFE'S WORK

Poisson's greatest achievements lay in his work as a theoretical mathematician and educator. By 1802, Poisson was a deputy director at École Polytechnique. Upon his graduation in 1800, he was appointed to the position of teaching assistant. He was also published twice in the École Polytechnique's *Recueil des savants étrangers* (Reports of foreign scientists), a great honor for an eighteen-year-old student.

In 1802, Poisson became an assistant professor. He attained a professorship in 1806, when Jean Baptiste Joseph Fourier vacated the position. In 1808, Poisson was appointed as an astronomer at the Bureau des Longitudes. He also had a treatise on celestial mechanics published. This work, *Sur les inégalités séculaires des moyens mouvements des planets* (On the motions of planets), examined the stability of planetary orbits. By 1811, Poisson had begun his work on the application of mathematics to electricity and magnetism, mechanics, and other areas of physics. He published *Traité de mécanique* (Treatise of mechanics) in 1811. This work served as a standard reference on the subject for many years.

In 1812, Poisson became a member of the Institut de France, an academic society. He also published a memoir on his two-fluid theory of electricity. In this theory, Poisson posited that electricity was made up of two fluids that contained particles, which repelled like particles and attracted unlike particles. He calculated the reactive force as inversely proportional to the square of the distance between them.

Poisson developed his probability theory, which became known as the Poisson equation, in 1813. He was named examiner for the military school at Saint-Cyr in 1815. In 1816, he was named graduation examiner at

The Poisson Distribution

Siméon Denis Poisson was intrigued by the possibility that an event could occur in a given period of time, during repeated trials, whose outcomes did not influence the outcomes of the other trials. To explore this phenomenon, he focused on events that occurred with enough frequency that even an unlikely event would happen from time to time. His work culminated *Recherches sur la probabilité des jugements en matière criminelle et matière civile* (Research on the probability of judgments in criminal and civil matters), published in 1837. Poisson examined criminal and civil trial outcomes, describing the probability that a specific type of outcome will occur within a certain timeframe, independently of the outcome of previous trials. The resulting theory and formula are known as the Poisson distribution.

Poisson based his research on the outcome of criminal and civil trails because the trials took place on an ongoing basis, the specific outcomes were independent from one another, and outcomes of a specific type occurred infrequently. His work in probability theory went largely unnoticed until 1898, when a paper by Ladislaus von Bortkiewicz showed that the number of Prussian soldiers killed by horse kicks could be accurately estimated with the use of Poisson's formula.

Von Bortkiewicz's application fit the parameters of the distribution because, although infrequently, soldiers in the Prussian cavalry were killed by horse kick and the opportunity for such deaths to occur took place on a regular basis. Von Bortkiewicz used over two hundred observations to find the absolute and relative frequency distribution and then used this value in the Poisson formula. When his findings and the Poisson distribution tables agreed, it elevated Poisson's work from the purely theoretical realm to one of practical value.

In the present day, the Poisson distribution is used in numerous ways. For example, it helps companies determine optimal staffing levels, and it is used to determine the number and configuration of toll-booths on a toll road or the amount of equipment to have on hand in the event of unlikely but possible emergency events.

the École Polytechnique. He married Nancy de Bardi in 1817 and was elected a fellow of the Royal Society of London in 1818.

Poisson became a fellow of the Royal Society of Edinburgh in 1820. That same year, he accepted a nomination to the Conseil Royal de L'Université. During this time, professional science and science education were falling into disregard in France because of political instability, and Poisson used his position to defend the role of science in everyday life and in the academy.

He published *Sur la libération de la lune*, another work on celestial mechanics, in 1821. In 1822, he was elected a foreign member of the Royal Swedish Academy of Sciences. In 1924, he published a paper on his two-fluid theory of magnetic potential, and in 1825 he published his views on the wave theory of light.

When his longtime mentor Lagrange died in 1827, Poisson replaced him as geometer of the Bureau des Longitudes, a scientific association dedicated to navigational standards. In the interest of advancing Lagrange's work as well as his own, Poisson undertook the task of writing a comprehensive mathematical text made up of various volumes. He would not live to complete this task, but his work did produce another publication on celestial mechanics, *Sur le mouvement de la terre autour de son centre de gravité* (On the movement of the Earth around its center of gravity), released in 1827.

In 1829, Poisson published *Sur l'attraction des spheroids* (On the attraction of spheroids). In 1832, he received the prestigious Copley Medal for his contributions to science form the Royal Society of London. He published a memoir on the movement of the moon in 1833.

IMPACT

Poisson's passion for mathematics is summed up in a statement attributed to him by French mathematician and politician Dominique François Jean Arago: "Life is good for only two things, discovering mathematics and teaching mathematics." In all, Poisson published over three hundred works in pure mathematics, applied mathematics, mathematical physics, and rational mechanics. His contributions to the field of electricity and magnetism were fundamental to the creation of a new branch of mathematical physics. Poisson's work on attractive forces influenced British mathematical physicist George Green's work on electricity and magnetism. He is equally well remembered for his work in celestial mechanics. The Poisson distribution, dealing with the law of large numbers, is still used to predict the occurrence of such unlikely events as airplane crashes.

Gina Hagler

FURTHER READING

Falk, Michael, Jürg Hüsler, and Rolf-Dieter Reiss. *Laws of Small Numbers: Extremes and Rare Events.* Basel: Birkhäuser, 1994. Print. Explores the theory and applications of probability theory, including information about Poisson approximations.

Gekhtman, Michael, Michael Shapiro, and Alek Vainshtein. *Cluster Algebras and Poisson Geometry.* Providence: American Mathematical Society, 2010. Print. Examines cluster algebra, as introduced by Fomin and Zelevinsky, and as it applies to Poisson geometry and the theory of integrable systems.

Karasev, M. V., Maria Shishkova, Elena Novikova, and Yu M. Vorobjev. *Quantum Algebras and Poisson Geometry in Mathematical Physics.* Providence: American Mathematical Society, 2005. Print. Explores new applications of Poisson geometry, noncommutative algebra theory, and representation theory to well-known problems in mathematical physics.

FREDA PORTER-LOCKLEAR

American environmental scientist and mathematician

Environmental scientist Freda Porter-Locklear is widely known for her application of mathematical models in groundwater analysis and water pollution control systems. A member of the Lumbee American Indian tribe, Porter has also played a well-publicized role in the advocacy of science and mathematics education for students in the United States, particularly for those of American Indian and minority descent.

Born: October 14, 1957; Lumberton, North Carolina
Primary fields: Mathematics; computer science; Earth sciences
Specialties: Mathematical analysis; ecology

EARLY LIFE

Freda Porter-Locklear was born in the town of Lumberton, North Carolina, to parents from the Lumbee American Indian tribe, the ninth-largest American Indian tribe in the United States. She grew up on her parents' farm and attended primary and secondary schools that were predominantly Indian. Graduating at the top of her high school class, she earned a scholarship to Pembroke State University—later the University of North Carolina (UNC) at Pembroke—a historically American Indian public college. She received her bachelor's degree in applied mathematics in 1978.

After her time at Pembroke, Porter-Locklear was accepted into a graduate internship program at IBM. There, she honed her interests in computational mathematics, computer science, and digital engineering, assisting on projects in IBM laboratories under the guidance of senior staff members.

Through a National Science Foundation fellowship, Porter-Locklear was able to enroll in the applied mathematics graduate program the North Carolina State University in Raleigh upon the culmination of her internship work. She completed the program with a master's degree in applied mathematics and minor in computer science in 1981.

Porter-Locklear then spent a couple years as a graduate researcher in circuit verification with the Microelectronics Center of North Carolina in Research Triangle Park. There, she analyzed data to help identify computational errors in large-scale electrical power grid systems.

By the time Porter-Locklear was accepted into the Duke University doctoral program in applied mathematical and computational sciences, she was already married to Milton Locklear, a fellow Lumbee Indian, and had two children. Her doctoral thesis focused on the mathematical arena of hyperbolic partial differential equations. Upon her completion of the program in 1991, Porter-Locklear was one of just twelve American Indian women to have received a doctorate in mathematics.

LIFE'S WORK

Following her departure from Duke, Porter-Locklear began a career as a college math teacher. She was first an instructor at her alma mater and then at UNC Chapel Hill. In the early 1990s, she immersed herself in what would become her patron cause: improving the opportunities for American Indian and other minority students to enter into degree programs in science, engineering, and mathematics.

Porter-Locklear Founds Porter Scientific, Inc.

Porter Scientific, Inc., is a multifaceted environmental services and consulting agency headquartered in Pembroke, North Carolina. The firm has a unique history as it was founded in June 1997 by Freda Porter-Locklear, a Pembroke native and member of the Lumbee American Indian tribe. Company president and CEO Porter started the firm after becoming one of a small number American Indian woman to earn a doctorate in mathematical and computational science.

Porter Scientific began as a provider of technological services geared toward the protection and restoration of contaminated water sources. However, the firm soon grew to encompass a variety of environmental service capabilities, spanning engineering, preventative maintenance, consulting, and human resource development.

The firm's environmental services division provides planning services, evaluative environmental surveys, and data analysis to large-scale construction and infrastructure projects in both the public and private sector. The firm has also provided a wide range of information technology and environmental impact support services to civic agencies and local municipalities ranging from state and local governments, Departments of Defense and Transportation, and the Environmental Protection Agency (EPA).

Porter Scientific has also been home to groundbreaking technological development. The firm was one of a small group of environmental service firms who worked collaboratively on the development and implementation of specially designed spreaders for Vac-Con dispersal units. The patented invention was prominent in reducing the cost and increasing the efficiency of biosolid applications in agriculture throughout the world.

True to the community-focused background of its founder, Porter Scientific also facilitates a mentor-protégé program that encourages federal- and state-recognized minorities, women, and other disadvantaged business enterprises to enter into and compete in the highway construction industry. In 2002, Porter-Locklear was appointed by the then secretary of transportation, Norman Mineta, to the North Carolina Department of Transportation Minority Contractor Expansion Council. Her role was to advise the department on how to expand opportunities for minority companies. PSI was also a founding member of the North Carolina American Indian Chamber of Commerce.

Porter Scientific and its staff have received numerous accolades since its founding. In August 2009, Porter-Locklear was named North Carolina Minority Small Business Person of the Year by the United States Small Business Administration.

Porter Scientific continues to build on a unique legacy that is profoundly different from those of other environmental science firms throughout the United States. The company's expertise and diverse capabilities in the field of environmental science notwithstanding, Porter Scientific has also placed importance on the development and prosperity of American Indian– and minority-owned business throughout North Carolina and the United States.

In 1991, she organized a chapter of the American Indian Science and Engineering Society (AISES) at Pembroke. The organization holds informational seminars about career opportunities in science, math, and engineering in addition to conducting summer math and science programs for local high school freshmen. Porter-Locklear's achievements with the AISES program helped to gain her national recognition as one of the nation's leading proponents of the math and science education in American Indian communities.

Porter-Locklear also gained prominence in the realm of environmental science while consulting for the Environmental Protection Agency (EPA) Ecosystems Research Division in Athens, Georgia. Porter-Locklear also served as a consultant to the NASA-Langley Research Center as an American Society for Engineering Education (ASEE) Faculty Fellow from 1994 to 1995. At this time, Porter-Locklear also finished her postdoctoral studies at UNC Chapel Hill, where she researched groundwater contamination.

In 1996, she was featured in a documentary television series produced by the Public Broadcasting Service (PBS) that highlighted the achievements of twenty minority scientists. Entitled *Break Through: The Changing Face of Science in America*, Porter-Locklear illustrated how her interest in math and science was influenced by her Lumbee heritage.

Spurred by the rise of environmental issues such as corporate pollution and industrial manufacturing runoff in and around many American Indian communities,

Porter-Locklear departed from academia to pursue a career in groundwater analysis and environmental science in 1997. The following July, she gained her certification in water pollution control systems operation from North Carolina State University.

Throughout that year, Porter-Locklear co-conducted a study focusing on the application of mathematical theory to the analysis of contaminated water and soil sample data. The study aimed to utilize advanced mathematical theory to better gauge the harmful effects and lifespan of pollution. The findings of the project were published a year later in the *Society for Industrial and Applied Mathematics Review*.

It was also in 1997 that Porter-Locklear found Porter Scientific, Inc., a full-service environmental services organization specializing in industrial environmental consulting, wastewater management as well as waste-related information technology systems. With its blend of technical and environmental expertise, the firm has grown to become one of the southern Atlantic region's most versatile and successful environmental consulting firms, working in projects ranging from construction and renovation to contamination cleanup, facility support, and workforce development.

As the firm's president and CEO, Porter-Locklear continues to bring attention to previously unaddressed environmental issues effecting American Indian communities. She contributed to a 2001 anthology entitled *Science and Native American Communities: Legacies of Pain, Visions of Promise*, which was dedicated to dispelling the legacy of mistrust that has existed between the scientific community and American Indians. Her contribution expounded on the notion of interconnectedness of nature and Indian culture, stressing the need for joint intervention with the scientific community through the cultivation of education and continued adaptation to ever-advancing technology.

IMPACT

Porter-Locklear's accomplishments have spanned the realms of both academics and business. Her career has successfully merged both her mathematical prowess and lifelong interest in the preservation and protection of the natural world. In the process, she has forged pivotal connections between academia and imperiled or damaged wildlife regions. In recognition of her accomplishments, Porter-Locklear was appointed to the board of trustees for the Smithsonian Institution's National Museum of the American Indian in 2010.

Porter-Locklear's career has inspired future generations to explore the potential relationship between advanced mathematics, digital technology, and environmental stewardship. Through her efforts with AISES and Porter Scientific, she has also assisted American Indian and minority students who, without her influence or passion, may have had little access to the academic pursuit of advanced science, technology, and mathematics.

Porter-Locklear remains intricately involved in the university where she was both a student and a teacher. In July 2009, she was appointed the chair of the board of trustees at UNC Pembroke.

John Pritchard

FURTHER READING

Porter-Locklear, Freda. "Water and Water Quality Issues in and for American Indian Communities." *Science and Native American Communities: Legacies of Pain, Visions of Promise*. Ed. Keith James. Lincoln: U of Nebraska P, 2001. 111–19. Print. A piece on the reception of scientific groundwater studies against the backdrop of Lumbee attitudes toward the interconnectedness of the natural world.

Toler, Laura J. "Program Weds Science, Math and Native American Traditions." *News Services*. University of North Carolina at Chapel Hill, 20 June 1997. Web. 9 July 2012. An article detailing the goals and activities of the AISES chapter that Porter-Locklear founded.

Weaver, James, and Freda Porter-Locklear. "Estimating the Rate of Natural Bioattenuation of Ground Water Contaminants by a Mass Conservation Approach." *SIAM Review* 40.1 (1998): 113–17. Print. A study in the Society for Industrial and Applied Mathematics Review offering Porter-Locklear's approach to measuring pollution rates in groundwater.

LUDWIG PRANDTL

German physicist

One of the fathers of theoretical aerodynamics, Ludwig Prandtl is credited with discovering many of the pivotal concepts on which modern aviation is based. He was also the founder of the highly acclaimed school of aerodynamics and hydrodynamics at the University of Göttingen and the first director of what would become the Max Planck Institute for Dynamics and Self-Organization.

Born: February 4, 1875; Freising, Germany
Died: August 15, 1953; Göttingen, West Germany
(now Germany)
Primary field: Physics
Specialty: Mechanics

EARLY LIFE

Ludwig Prandtl took an early interest in the forces and characteristics of nature. His father, Alexander Prandtl, was a professor of engineering at a college in Weihenstephan, Germany. Prandtl's mother played a lesser role in her son's life because of her extended periods of chronic illness. In 1894, Prandtl decided to study engineering at the Munich Technische Hochschule, a facility for higher technical education. His doctoral thesis on the distribution of tension and torque along a beam arranged at right angles from its source became an important work in the field of the mechanics of solids.

After receiving his degree, Prandtl became an engineer in the Augsburg-Nürnberg machine factory, thanks in part to the support of his mentor, German physicist August Foppl. At the factory, he studied the characteristics of the flow of liquids and gases over objects, a field now known as fluid mechanics. This emerging science was in its infancy at the turn of the century, with the first practical wind tunnels and heavier-than-air craft only slowly coming into use. Prandtl's own introduction to the field came as a result of a project to refit a vacuum device used in the factory. Although his work at the factory would be the last he would undertake outside the world of academia, it led to his most important discoveries and a brilliant career as a founder of an emerging modern science.

LIFE'S WORK

In 1901, Prandtl accepted a professorship at the Technische Schule in Hannover. His first observations in fluid mechanics at Hannover involved the flow of thin liquids through a pipe. He noticed that the shape of the liquid flow did not fully conform to the shape of the pipe through which it flowed; a minute layer of liquid would always form between the interior surface of the pipe and the main body of the liquid. This layer between the wall and the fluid actually controlled the pressure and rate of the liquid flow. In practical terms, this boundary of stationary fluid is much the same as the layer of air that forms on a wing in flight, which helps to provide the lift and drag necessary to control a wing's movement through the air. Prandtl's discovery of the boundary layer, as he named it, was his single most meaningful discovery, revolutionizing powered aviation and leading to major innovations in the streamlining of aircraft wing and fuselage designs.

In 1904, shortly before publishing his paper on his boundary layer theory, Prandtl was invited to head the new Institute for Technical Physics at the University of Göttingen. The institute served as Prandtl's primary base of operations for the remainder of his life and became one of the world's leading centers for theoretical research into fluid mechanics. In 1909, Prandtl married Gertrude Foppl, the daughter of his undergraduate mentor; the couple eventually had two daughters.

At Göttingen, Prandtl addressed many of the theoretical questions about piloted flight that were arising as a result of the breakthroughs in aviation technology. He researched the characteristics of airflow around a body traveling at either subsonic or supersonic speeds. He also directed graduate students' research projects on wing drag, the mechanics of solids, and other areas. Additionally, part of his work during the years before World War I involved developing testing procedures for electrical fans for the German government and industry.

Prandtl's mathematical theories also played a significant part in the advent and popular acceptance of the single-winged airplane. He advocated this design concept against the prevailing opinion held by the aircraft design community in favor of bi- and tri-winged aircraft. Through his theoretical discoveries, he also contributed to improvements in the design of lighter-than-air craft known as dirigibles, which were used in the early twentieth century as both civilian and military air carriers.

After World War I, Prandtl published a breakthrough paper on the way air flows around airplane wings of a finite span. The paper, which duplicated

Ludwig Prandtl Discovers the Boundary Layer

In his 1904 paper "Ueber Flüssigkeitsbewegung bei sehr kleiner Reibung" (On fluid motion with very little friction), Ludwig Prandtl described his groundbreaking theory of the boundary layer. Prandtl's theory combined the phenomenon of drag with William John Macquorn Rankine's theory of streamlines to explain a phenomenon known as skin resistance—the resistance, or drag, that takes place in the fluid flow that is nearest to a solid surface.

Prandtl's theory accounts for the way a very thin layer of fluid, known as the boundary layer, "sticks" to the surface of an object because of the degree of friction at that point of contact. This "stickiness," or friction, causes the streamline of fluid closest to the surface to move very slowly. The streamlines farther from the surface move incrementally more swiftly until the normal rate of flow is attained by those streamlines far enough from the surface that the skin friction is not enough of a factor to be considered.

Before Prandtl's boundary-layer theory, there was no practical way to calculate the impact of friction on fluid flows, and fluids were treated as if they flowed without the effects of friction. Theorists knew this could not be the case because if it were, in keeping with Galileo Galilei's law of inertia and Isaac Newton's first law of motion, an object in motion would never slow or stop moving, yet clearly they did.

Prandtl was also able to prove theoretically and experimentally that the boundary layer can separate from the surface of a body immersed in a flowing fluid. When this separation occurs, it will leave the body as an isolated vortex, disrupting the fluid flow. Prandtl likewise demonstrated the way in which some types of flows can cause the aerodynamic boundary layer to separate from the surface of a wing. When this occurs, it creates a different type of drag—a pressure drag caused by the slow-moving air behind the structure with the skin friction.

The boundary-layer theory is a vital concept in fluid dynamics because it explains the resistance experienced at the boundary of a solid and a fluid. The correct calculation of this resistance is key to determining the future performance of the solid object, whether it be the wetted surface of a ship or the shape of a wing or propeller blade. Prandtl's work gave those involved in the study of such objects a way to treat real flows; they no longer had to treat them as inviscid flows (flows with no fluid resistance). Although Prandtl is known for his work in aerodynamics, his discovery of the boundary layer is applicable to other fluids as well.

and expanded on work by British physicist Frederick William Lanchester, became known as the Lanchester-Prandtl wing theory, one of many theoretical innovations that would bear Prandtl's name over the next several years.

In the mid-1920s, Prandtl and other international researchers undertook the study of air turbulence created by a body moving through the air. In conjunction with his former student Theodor von Kármán, Prandtl developed a device for analyzing the distance turbulent air travels before its motion is dissipated. Prandtl's paper on the subject, presented in 1933, led to radical changes in accepted theories about air turbulence and resulted in concepts used by pilots around the world.

Prandtl also conducted extensive studies into the question of how objects traveling at high subsonic speeds are compressed by the airflow over their surfaces. The resulting theory, known as the Prandtl-Glaubert rule, played a vital role in the development of successful designs for supersonic aircraft.

During the same period, Prandtl, already a world-renowned pioneer in his field, was named to head a technical facility in Germany called the Kaiser Wilhelm Institute for Fluid Dynamics, later renamed the Max Planck Institute for Dynamics and Self-Organization. Thanks to Prandtl's leadership and inspiration, part of this institute later became a major engineering design center and an important contributor of spaceflight hardware and support services to the US National Aeronautics and Space Administration (NASA) and the European Space Agency.

Although it was not his area of primary investigation, Prandtl was also interested in questions concerning the elasticity and plasticity of a variety of solids, as well as the reaction of solid structures to torsion forces. He developed a soap-film analogy that was found to be exceptionally useful in analyzing the effects of torsion forces on structures with noncircular cross sections.

Prandtl's work often centered on the equipment and mathematical models used in testing natural reactions and design concepts. He was also instrumental in advancing the development of air-tunnel technology and other equipment used in aerodynamic testing and design.

Unlike many of the scientists in Germany during the years between World War I and the end of World War II, Prandtl managed to avoid responding to political pressure from the ruling Nazi Party and maintain civilian control over his work. He continued to publish technical papers on his work, receiving widespread attention from the international scientific community. In later years, after World War II, Prandtl expanded his efforts to include meteorology, a subject on which he published a paper in 1950. On August 15, 1953, Prandtl died in Göttingen, West Germany.

IMPACT

As the founder of several pivotal theories of fluid mechanics used in the production of aircraft, Prandtl helped create the age of rapid, safe air transportation. He is known as the founder of aerodynamics because he developed some of the fundamental concepts on which modern air travel is based.

Prandtl is also remembered for his problem-solving techniques in the field of theoretical physics. His contributions even extended into education, as he helped build the Institute for Technical Physics at the University of Göttingen and what is now the Max Planck Institute for Dynamics and Self-Organization. As part of an international community of scientists, he focused his efforts on practical, technological questions, the solutions for which could be put to direct use in aircraft design and other areas. In this regard, Prandtl's discoveries are every bit as significant as those of more visible inventors such as Orville and Wilbur Wright.

Eric Christensen

FURTHER READING

Bloor, David. *The Enigma of the Aerofoil: Rival Theories in Aerodynamics, 1909–1930*. Chicago: U of Chicago P, 2011. Print. An overview of early developments in the field of aerodynamics. Features a chapter on Prandtl's contributions.

Eckert, Michael. *The Dawn of Fluid Dynamics: A Discipline between Science and Technology*. Weinheim: Wiley, 2006. Print. Describes the evolution of fluid dynamics in the twentieth century, focusing on Prandtl's work.

Schlichting, Hermann. *Boundary Layer Theory*. Trans. J. Kestin. 4th ed. New York: McGraw, 1960. Print. Includes many references to Prandtl and his students. Discusses his involvement in the viscous-flow theory.

JOSEPH LOUIS PROUST

French chemist

French chemist Joseph Louis Proust flourished during the late eighteenth and early nineteenth centuries. He spent more than twenty years teaching and researching at institutions in Spain, where he conducted numerous experiments with various metals that ultimately resulted in the development of a universal principle in analytical chemistry.

Born: September 26, 1754; Angers, France
Died: July 5, 1826; Angers, France
Primary field: Chemistry
Specialties: Analytical chemistry; organic chemistry; metallurgy

EARLY LIFE

Joseph Louis Proust was born in Angers, an ancient city on the Maine River in western France. He was the second son of Joseph Proust, an apothecary who owned a pharmacy, and his wife Rosalie Sartre Proust.

Young Joseph became interested in science as a boy and learned the basics of chemistry and herbal remedies from his father. His older brother Joachim (born 1751) also profited from their father's knowledge of chemical substances: In the 1790s he worked as a negotiator for local miners of saltpeter, which was used to make gunpowder, and he later had his own pharmacy in Angers. Joseph obtained his early education at the Oratorian Brothers School in Angers, and he supplemented his studies in the laboratory of his father's pharmacy. As a teen, he helped to create a botanical garden in Angers.

Though his father hoped Joseph would remain in Angers and someday take over the family business, the young man had different ambitions. In 1774, he left for Paris, which was about 150 miles away, and took scientific classes at the University of Paris and also studied in the laboratory of chemist Hilaire Marin Rouelle (1718–1779), one of the discoverers of urea and a popular public demonstrator of chemical principles. Through

Proust's Law, or the Law of Definite Proportions

In the eighteenth century, the study of chemistry was not far removed from alchemy, an ancient and medieval philosophical pseudoscience whose practitioners sought such treasures as the elixir of life and the philosopher's stone, said to transmute lead into gold.

As a genuine researcher for most of his adult life, Joseph Louis Proust took an objective, systematic approach to his investigations, paying attention to details that other chemists of the day ignored. He took nothing for granted, and he repeated tests in order to more closely observe and confirm measurement of the results. His work considerably advanced the science of analytical chemistry and made a major contribution to atomic theory.

In the late 1790s, after conducting numerous tests on metals and other substances in the course of his work in Spanish laboratories, Proust proposed a chemical principle, the law of definite proportions. Proust's law (as it also came to be known) stated that the constituents of any compound, regardless of whether it occurred in nature or was artificially produced, were present in fixed proportions in weight. Water (to take a later-identified example) is always two parts hydrogen to one part oxygen, whether produced in a laboratory or appearing in nature.

The publication of Proust's findings was not met with universal acclaim. A prominent French chemist and acquaintance, Claude Louis Berthollet, held a contrary position: He asserted that chemical compounds could be found in various constituent proportions. The disagreement launched a cordial if intense decade-long dispute between Proust and Berthollet.

Proust returned to the lab to conduct further tests in order to prove his contention. He created artificial copper carbonate to compare with the natural compound, and he performed the same operation with tin oxides and iron sulfides. His results showed that the natural and synthetic substances were identical in composition. In 1806, Berthollet finally capitulated under the weight of Proust's findings and admitted defeat. Two years later, Proust's law served as an important foundation for John Dalton's atomic theory, one of the cornerstones of chemistry.

Ironically, in the early twentieth century, several compounds were found to exhibit slight variations in chemical composition and therefore did not strictly adhere to Proust's law. They were formally called nonstoichiometric compounds and informally named Berthollides—a discovery that finally reconciled the conflicting theories of the two French scientists.

Rouelle, Joseph met many leaders in the French scientific community, including chemist-biologist Antoine Lavoisier, physicist-balloonist Jean-François Pilâtre de Rozier, physicist-balloonist Jacques Charles, and chemist Claude Louis Berthollet.

In 1776, after passing a qualification test, Joseph was appointed chief apothecary at Paris's Salpêtrière Hospital. Initially a gunpowder factory ("Salpêtrière" is derived from the French word for "saltpeter"), the facility was converted to a hospital in 1656 and expanded in 1684. During Joseph's tenure, Salpêtrière—later a psychiatric center and currently a modern medical teaching center—had grown into the largest hospital in the world, with more than ten thousand patients, many of whom were poor, prostitutes, criminals, or mentally disabled. Joseph conducted his first research and published his first scientific papers while employed at Salpêtrière.

LIFE'S WORK

In 1778, Proust left France to accept a post as professor of chemistry at a seminary in Vergara, near Bilbao in northern Spain. One of several facilities established under the auspices of the Basque Society of Friends of their Country, the seminary—part of a national effort to improve education—was the first in Spain geared toward research in chemistry and metallurgy.

Disappointed by the small number of students enrolled in his classes, Proust returned to Paris in 1780. He taught chemistry with his colleague de Rozier, and the two men conducted experiments in aerostatics, the study of stationary gases, as applied to hot-air balloons, a craze in France at the time. In 1783, de Rozier became the first person to take flight in a Montgolfier balloon. The following year, in an event witnessed by the kings of France and Sweden and thousands of spectators, Proust accompanied de Rozier in a hot-air balloon dubbed the *Marie Antoinette*. Lifting off from the Palace of Versailles, they rose to nearly ten thousand feet and floated for forty-five minutes before landing safely more than thirty miles away, setting ballooning records for altitude and distance. (De Rozier and a companion were later killed in 1785 when their hot-air balloon crashed while attempting to cross the English Channel, making them the first known fatalities in an air crash.)

On the recommendation of Antoine Lavoisier, King Carlos III of Spain hired Proust in 1786 as the first professor of chemistry and metallurgy at the Royal Artillery School, housed in a twelfth-century castle in the ancient city of Segovia. In addition to his teaching duties, Proust was responsible for researching the properties of platinum, a new metal first extracted in the mid-eighteenth century from mines in Spanish colonies that would later become Ecuador and Colombia. Proust taught until the mid-1790s at Segovia before moving on to teach chemistry and continue his metallurgic research at the University of Salamanca, also in Spain. In 1798, he married compatriot Ana Rosa de Chatelain D'Augigné, a member of an aristocratic French family who had taken refuge in Spain during the French Revolution; the couple produced no children.

In 1799, King Carlos IV (who had succeeded his father in 1788) appointed Proust to succeed another Frenchman, Pierre Chabaneau, as head of a modern, well-equipped laboratory in Madrid. Proust's chief responsibility was to develop a commercial method of purifying platinum, which was then only being mined from the Spanish Empire's colonial holdings. In addition to his metallurgical studies, Proust conducted considerable research into fruit sugars and investigated a wide variety of other subjects of scientific interest.

In 1806, Proust—worn out and possibly ill, perhaps because of his hazardous research—resigned from his position in Madrid. He and his wife left Spain and returned to France to settle in Craon. In 1808, Napoleon's army captured Madrid after a four-day siege, and the emperor's soldiers looted Proust's former lab. Proust never returned to Spain.

In 1810, the French government commissioned Proust to set up a fruit sugar factory, but for most of the decade, despite formal recognition of his scientific accomplishments, he lived in poverty. His wife died in 1817. In 1820, following the death of his brother Joachim, Proust inherited his pharmacy in Angers. The same year, French King Louis XVIII granted Proust an annual pension, which Louis's successor Charles X kept in effect until Proust died in 1826 at the age of seventy-one.

IMPACT

Joseph Louis Proust was well known and respected in Europe during his lifetime. He gained a reputation for the breadth of his scientific interests, for the accuracy of his measurements, for his analytical skills, and for his meticulously repeated experiments. Proust began a forty-year period of serious research while working at

Salpêtrière Hospital in the late 1770s and published papers that were based on his studies of urea, phosphoric acid, and alum.

In 1780, to provide better lighting for reading and conducting experiments, Proust designed—but never patented—an improved oil lamp that burned whale oil or olive oil and produced a brighter light than a single candle. It featured a reservoir containing flammable fuel that was higher than the wick, so the oil's own weight fed the flame. Two men in Proust's circle of acquaintances—both involved in ballooning—copied and improved the lamp and made fortunes from Proust's invention. Chemist Pierre Argand added a glass chimney and patented the Argand lamp in England in 1784; pharmacist Antoine Quinquet introduced the Quinquet lamp in France in the same year.

Much of Proust's work in Spain involved the purification of platinum. To this end, he developed a practical and efficient method—still in use in metal refining—of using aqua regia (nitro-hydrochloric acid) to separate platinum from other metals and produce a pure, malleable platinum powder at the rate of between 14,000 and 18,000 troy ounces per year. In the process, Proust isolated (but never identified, thus is not credited as discoverer) several other noble metals, including osmium, palladium, rhodium, and iridium. In the course of his work, Proust developed hydrogen sulfide as a reagent. The poisonous gas, which may have adversely affected his health, became an important tool in analytical chemistry for causing reactions useful in analyzing mixtures and compounds.

Another important contribution was Proust's 1799 discovery of grape sugar (later called glucose), which he demonstrated was as sweet as sugar derived from honey or cane. This finding was of commercial benefit because grapes were abundant throughout Europe and were cheaper to use in sugar extraction than cane, which was imported from the Caribbean.

Joseph Louis Proust published the results of his research often in Spanish and French scientific journals and wrote several full-length works based on his studies. He was finally recognized for his work late in life and in 1816, he was inducted into the Institut de France and three years later was elected a chevalier (knight) in the French Legion of Honor.

Jack Ewing

FURTHER READING

Aldersey-Williams, Hugh. *Periodic Tales: A Cultural History of the Elements, from Arsenic to Zinc.* New York: Ecco, 2011. Print. Discusses the discovery, characteristics, names, and other facts about the chemical elements, including platinum and the noble metals with which Joseph Louis Proust extensively experimented.

Inkster, Ian, and Angel Calvo, eds. *History of Technology*, Vol. 30. London: Continuum, 2011. Print. An anthology of essays covering the advance of technology in Spain from the late seventeenth century to the present; several chapters, particularly those on mining and sugar technologies and the chemical industry, relate to the work of Joseph Louis Proust during his time in Spain.

Partington, J. R. *A Short History of Chemistry*. New York: Dover, 1989. Print. Provides an explanation of the basic principles of physical and organic chemistry, which include an account of the development of Proust's law, an important component in the formulation of atomic theory.

Schectman, Jonathan. *Groundbreaking Scientific Experiments, Inventions and Discoveries of the Eighteenth Century*. Westport, CT: Greenwood, 2003. Print. A collection of more than fifty essays detailing the most important advancements—including the work of Proust—during the eighteenth century.

PYTHAGORAS

Greek mathematician

Pythagoras set an inspiring example with his energetic search for knowledge and universal order. His many discoveries and accomplishments in philosophy, mathematics, astronomy, and music theory make him an important figure in Western intellectual history.

Born: c. 580 BCE; Samos, Greece
Died: c. 500 BCE; Metapontum, Lucania (now Italy)
Primary fields: Mathematics; astronomy
Specialties: Number theory; geometry; cosmology

EARLY LIFE
Pythagoras was likely born between 597 and 560 BCE. His birthplace was the Greek island of Samos in the Mediterranean Sea. Aside from these details, information about his early life is extremely sketchy.

Aristotle's *Metaphysica* (335–323 BCE; *Metaphysics*, 1801), one source of information about Pythagorean philosophy, never refers to Pythagoras himself but always to "the Pythagoreans." Furthermore, it is known that many ideas attributed to Pythagoras have been filtered through Platonism. Nevertheless, certain doctrines and biographical events can be traced with reasonable certainty to Pythagoras himself. His teachers in Greece are said to have included Creophilus and Pherecydes of Syros; the latter probably encouraged Pythagoras's belief in the transmigration of souls, which became a major tenet of Pythagorean philosophy. Another tradition has Pythagoras also studying under Thales of Miletus, who built a philosophy on rational, positive integers. These integers would lead to Pythagoras's discovery of irrational numbers, such as the square root of two.

Following his studies in Greece, Pythagoras traveled in Egypt, Babylonia, and other Mediterranean lands, learning what passed for geometry at that time. He went on to raise geometry to the level of a true science through his pioneering work on geometric proofs and the axioms, or postulates, from which such proofs are derived.

LIFE'S WORK
When Pythagoras returned to Samos from his studies abroad, he found his native land in the grip of the tyrant Polycrates, who had come to power about 538 BCE. In the meantime, the Greek mainland had been partially overrun by the Persians. Probably because of these developments, Pythagoras migrated to Croton, a Dorian colony in southern Italy, in 529.

At Croton, he founded a school of philosophy that in some ways resembled a monastic order. Its members were pledged to a pure and devout life, close friendship, and political harmony. Modern historians speculate that Pythagoras thought political power would give his organization an opportunity to encourage the disciplines of nonviolence, vegetarianism, personal alignment with the mathematical laws that govern the universe, and the practice of ethics in order to earn a superior reincarnation. (Pythagoras believed in metempsychosis, the transmigration of souls from one body to another.)

Pythagoras divided his adherents into two hierarchical groups. The first was the *akousmatikoi*, or listeners, who were enjoined to remain silent, listen to and absorb Pythagoras's spoken precepts, and practice the special way of life taught by him. The second group

The Pythagorean Society

The ancient Greek philosopher Pythagoras's most significant contribution to philosophy, education, and social and religious movements was his founding of an exclusive religious community commonly known as the Pythagorean society. This ascetic, ritual-based, education-centered society represented a drastic change in the ancient world's religious and social thought. Pythagorean principles and philosophy influenced some of history's most prominent philosophers, astronomers, and scientists. Over time, the Pythagorean society came to inform the structure and ideologies of many important religious and social groups.

In the Pythagorean society, most aspects of daily life, including diet, religious rituals, social habits, and education, were highly structured and regimented. Pythagoreans were not allowed to eat beans or meat, and in order to gain entry into the society, inductees undertook vows of silence for as long as five years. Some rules followed by Pythagoreans seem more arbitrary by modern standards, such as their insistence on putting one's shoes on by starting with the right foot first. Yet despite its restrictive structure, the Pythagorean society grew to have considerable influence in politics and government, particularly in southern Italy. Some scholars see in the Pythagorean community the frameworks for notable future religious and social groups, such as the Shakers and the Freemasons.

Perhaps the most compelling case for the significance of the Pythagorean society is its influence on some of antiquity's most prominent minds. Pythagorean principles influenced the Greek philosopher Plato, in particular his development of the Academy, which was reminiscent of the schools established by the Pythagoreans. Plato's work *The Republic* (c. 330 BCE) also bears the influence of Pythagorean philosophy, and his predecessor Aristotle studied and wrote extensively about the Pythagorean community. Both Plato and Aristotle noted that Pythagoras's significance lies mainly in his "founding" of a "way of life." Also within Pythagoras's scope of influence were some of antiquity's greatest mathematicians and astronomers, including Euclid and Ptolemy, both of whom attended Pythagorean schools that focused on mathematics.

The impact of Pythagorean society was felt not just by individuals but by religious groups as well. Around 300 BCE, many Jewish people fled their homelands and settled in and around Alexandria, Egypt, where Pythagorean society had considerable influence and power. As a result, some prominent Jewish scholars and leaders came under the influence of the ideology and practices of the Pythagoreans. Some scholars contend that this exposure to Pythagorean philosophy was influential in the subsequent development of Jewish mysticism.

Several religious and social ideas generated by the Pythagoreans represented a dramatic break from those common in antiquity. For instance, Pythagoras taught his adherents that numbers and geometric shapes had mystical and sacred powers. He also held the view that the human soul is immortal. Progressive attitudes on gender were another distinguishing aspect of Pythagoras and his followers, as their societies and schools were open to women as well.

was the *mathematikoi* (students of theoretical subjects, or simply "those who know"), who pursued the subjects of arithmetic, music theory, astronomy, and cosmology. The mathematikoi, after a long period of training, could ask questions and express opinions of their own.

Pythagoras developed a philosophy of numbers to account for the essence of all things. This concept rested on three basic observations: the mathematical relationships of musical harmonies, the fact that any triangle whose sides are in a ratio of 3:4:5 is always a right triangle, and the fixed numerical relations among the movement of stars and planets. He also discovered that musical intervals depend on arithmetical ratios among lengths of string on the lyre (the most widely played instrument of the time), provided that these strings are at the same tension. For example, a ratio of 2:1 produces an octave; that is, a string twice as long as another string, at the same tension, produces the same note an octave below the shorter string. Similarly, 3:2 produces a fifth and 4:3 produces a fourth. Using these ratios, now called Pythagorean intervals, one could assign numbers to the four fixed strings of the lyre: 6, 8, 9, and 12. Moreover, if these ratios are transferred to another instrument—such as the flute, also highly popular in that era—the same harmonies will result.

Pythagoras and his followers also exerted a lasting influence on the field of mathematics. The best-known example of this is the Pythagorean theorem, which states that the square of the hypotenuse of a right triangle is equal to the sum of the squares of the other two sides.

Special applications of the theorem were known in Mesopotamia as early as the eighteenth century BCE; however, since the precise ratio of the side of a square to its diagonal could not be expressed as a whole number, Pythagoras found a solution in the relationship between the squares of the sides of a right triangle. The Pythagorean theorem is set forth in book 1 of Euclid's *Stoicheia* (Elements).

In addition, Pythagoras is said to have discovered the theory of proportion and the arithmetic, geometric, and harmonic means. The ancient historian Proclus also credited Pythagoras with discovering the construction of the five regular geometrical solids, though modern scholars think it more likely that he discovered only three: the pyramid, the tetrahedron, and the dodecahedron.

The field of astronomy is also indebted to Pythagoras. He was among the first to contend that the Earth and the universe are spherical. He understood that Earth's sun, moon, and other planets rotate on their own axes and also orbit a central point outside of themselves, though he believed that this central point was Earth. Later Pythagoreans substituted another planet or "central fire" for Earth as the universe's center. Two thousand years later, Nicolaus Copernicus saw the Pythagorean system as anticipating his own.

One tradition regarding the final years of Pythagoras is that a democrat named Cylon led a revolt against the Pythagorean brotherhood and forced him to retire to Metapontum, where he died peacefully about the end of the sixth century BCE. According to the other tradition, Pythagoras perished when his adversaries set fire to his school in Croton in 504 BCE. This story claims that of his vast library of scrolls, only one was brought out of the fire; it contained his most esoteric secrets and was passed on to succeeding generations of Pythagoreans.

Whichever account is true, Pythagoras's followers continued to be powerful until the middle of the fifth century BCE, when they fell out of favor and their meetinghouses were destroyed. The survivors scattered and did not return to Italy until the end of the fifth century. During the ensuing decades, the leading Pythagorean was Philolaus, who wrote the first systematic exposition of Pythagorean philosophy. Philolaus's influence can be traced to Plato through their mutual friend Archytas, who ruled Taras (Tarentum) in Italy for many years. The Platonic dialogue *Timaeus* (360–347 BCE), named for its main character, a young Pythagorean astronomer, describes Pythagorean ideas in detail.

IMPACT

Pythagoras is said to have been the first person to call himself a *philosopher*, or lover of wisdom. He believed the universe to be a logical, symmetrical whole that can be understood in simple terms. For Pythagoras and his students, there was no gap between the scientific or mathematical ideal and the aesthetic.

Quite aside from any of Pythagoras's specific intellectual accomplishments, his belief in universal order and the energy he displayed in seeking it out inspired others. Indirectly, through Pythagoras's disciple Philolaus, his ideas were transmitted to Plato and Aristotle, and from them to the entire Western world. Pythagorean ideals influenced poets, artists, scientists, and philosophers throughout the Renaissance and into the twenty-first century.

Pythagoras is important in Western intellectual history because of his systematic exposition of mathematical principles and contributions to many fields of academic inquiry. Even those ideas of his that are seen as intellectually disreputable have inspired generations of poets and artists. For example, the Pythagorean concept of the harmony of the spheres, suggested by the analogy between musical ratios and those of planetary orbits, became a central metaphor of Renaissance literature.

Thomas Rankin

FURTHER READING

Kahn, Charles H. *Pythagoras and the Pythagoreans*. Indianapolis: Hackett, 2001. Print. Surveys Pythagorean tradition from Pythagoras's time to early modern times, including his influence on early modern math, music, and astronomy. Indexed by ancient and early modern name as well as by modern name.

Riedweg, Christoph, and Steven Rendall. *Pythagoras: His Life, Teaching, and Influence*. Ithaca: Cornell UP, 2005. Print. Offers an overview of Pythagoras's teachings, secret society, and influence on later philosophers and scientists.

Strohmeier, John, and Peter Westbrook. *Divine Harmony: The Life and Teachings of Pythagoras*. Berkeley: Berkeley Hills, 2003. Print. Describes Pythagoras's travels in Egypt, Phoenicia, Babylonia, and Greece and examines Pythagorean ideas as taught at his scholarly community in southern Italy. Illustrations, map, introduction, bibliography.

ISIDOR ISAAC RABI

Austrian American physicist

Austrian-born physicist Isidor Isaac Rabi developed the magnetic-resonance method to measure the properties of atomic nuclei with unprecedented accuracy. After World War II, he used the idea of science's universality to bring peoples of the globe together.

Born: July 29, 1898; Rymanów, Austria-Hungary
    (now Poland)
Died: January 11, 1988; New York, New York
Primary field: Physics
Specialty: Atomic and molecular physics

EARLY LIFE

Isidor Isaac Rabi was born in the town of Rymanów in Galicia, the northeasternmost province of what used to be the Austro-Hungarian Empire. His father, David Rabi, left Galicia soon after Rabi's birth and came to the United States; within a matter of months, Rabi's father sent for his wife, Sheindel, and his infant son. A turning point in Rabi's life came when, as a nine-year-old child in Brooklyn, he discovered a book on astronomy in the public library. He read about the Copernican solar system, in which planets orbit the sun, and recognized a natural explanation for events that previously had been explained to him only in terms of religion.

Rabi entered Cornell University in 1916 and graduated three years later with a major in chemistry. In 1921, he returned to Cornell as a graduate student of chemistry and soon discovered his passion for physics. He transferred to the physics department at Columbia University in 1923 and received his doctorate in 1926.

The day after he submitted his doctoral dissertation, he married Helen Newmark.

In 1927, Rabi obtained a fellowship and went to Europe, where he studied with Niels Bohr, Werner Heisenberg, Wolfgang Pauli, and Otto Stern. While in Zurich with Pauli, he received an offer from Columbia to join the physics faculty there. He returned from Europe in 1929 and began his career as a lecturer.

LIFE'S WORK

In 1931, Rabi applied the molecular-beam method of studying atoms, which he had learned from Stern, to the study of atomic nuclei. In the molecular-beam method, a stream of atoms or molecules moves through a highly evacuated chamber. Within this chamber, the beam passes between the poles of a magnet designed so that magnetic forces are exerted on individual atoms or molecules. Rabi's method allows the responses of atoms or molecules to these subtle magnetic forces to reveal basic and unknown properties of the nucleus. Rabi made modification after modification to Stern's basic method and significantly reduced the percentage of uncertainties in experimental data.

Rabi's molecular-beam work resulted in the molecular-beam magnetic resonance method. In this method, atoms or molecules pass in succession between the poles of three magnets. The second of these magnets produces an oscillating magnetic field. For certain frequencies of the oscillating field, atoms or molecules are ejected from the beam by the third magnet and thus are not registered by the detector. Since frequencies can be measured with great accuracy, this also allows the properties of the nucleus to be determined accurately. For this work, Rabi was awarded the Nobel Prize in Physics in 1944.

World War II brought Rabi's molecular-beam research to a sudden halt. Long before the United States entered the conflict, Jewish physicists in Europe were being displaced, many of them moving to England and the United States. Adding to the concerns of American physicists was the discovery of nuclear fission by the Austrian physicists Lise Meitner and Otto Frisch, which made it apparent that nuclear energy was now a possibility. The most pressing question concerned what German scientists were doing about it.

During the summer of 1940, British physicists brought a magnetron, a powerful source of microwave radiation recently invented in England, to the United States. They wanted to enlist the aid of American physicists in the development of microwave radar. The magnetron was demonstrated, the Massachusetts Institute of Technology (MIT) Radiation Laboratory was established in Cambridge, and Rabi left Columbia for the Radiation Laboratory. There, he became the head of the research division and, later, the associate director of the laboratory. He took it upon himself to anticipate the course of the war and the type of radar that would be needed by the military services. By the time the United States entered the war in December 1941, a variety of radar systems had been developed. As the conflict proceeded, radar systems from the MIT Radiation Laboratory were being used by Allied forces throughout the war.

In 1943, another wartime laboratory was established in Los Alamos, New Mexico, to develop the atomic bomb. Rabi and J. Robert Oppenheimer, the director of the laboratory, shared a friendship of deep mutual respect, but to Rabi, the radar project was more pertinent to the war effort than the atomic bomb. Nevertheless, Rabi became one of two senior advisers to Oppenheimer, along with Niels Bohr, and made important contributions to the development of the atomic bomb.

When the war ended in 1945, the world faced a powerful new energy source and the issue of establishing policies for its control. In December of that year, Rabi and Oppenheimer formulated a set of ideas that, in the spring of 1946, became the Acheson-Lilienthal report. This document proposed placing atomic energy in the hands of an international agency, thereby dissociating it from the interests of any one nation. In June 1946, these ideas were presented to the United Nations. To Rabi's great disappointment, the Russian delegate, Andrei Gromyko, rejected the proposal. Three years later, the Russians detonated their first atomic bomb, and

the arms race was under way.

The Russian achievement prompted a few influential Americans to propose a crash program to develop the hydrogen bomb. Rabi was then a member of the General Advisory Committee of the Atomic Energy Committee. Chaired by Oppenheimer, the committee was called into session to consider the question of a fusion-bomb program. It unanimously opposed the development of such a weapon, and Rabi and Enrico Fermi wrote a minority opinion in which they expressed their moral disapproval for a weapon that cannot be confined to any military target. Once again, Rabi was on the losing side; the United States detonated a fusion bomb in 1952, and nine months later, the Russians followed suit.

Throughout the postwar years, the culture of science was, for Rabi, a means for joining together peoples of the world. In 1950, as a US delegate to the fifth General Assembly of the United Nations Educational, Scientific, and Cultural Organization, Rabi proposed that European nations unite in the formation of a scientific laboratory. Two years later, the decision was made to establish the European Organization for Nuclear Research (CERN) in Geneva, Switzerland.

In 1954, Rabi proposed an international conference on the peaceful uses of atomic energy. This proposal, inspired by a speech given by US president Dwight D. Eisenhower, was presented to the United Nations by Secretary of State John Foster Dulles. Dag Hammarskjöld, secretary-general of the United Nations, was an enthusiastic supporter of the idea, which Rabi and Hammarskjöld together promoted. In 1955, the first International Conference on the Peaceful Uses of Atomic Energy was held in Geneva. According to Hammarskjöld, this conference was the beginning of détente.

During the mid-1950s, Rabi was the chair of the Science Advisory Committee (SAC) of the Office of Defense Mobilization. The Russian launch of Sputnik in 1957 prompted President Eisenhower to consult the SAC. Rabi proposed six specific actions, all of which Eisenhower accepted immediately. Rabi suggested that SAC needed direct access to the president and that the president needed a science adviser. He remained a member of the President's Science Advisory Committee—the new name for the SAC—until the committee was dissolved by the Nixon administration.

Rabi died on January 11, 1989, in New York City.

Impact

As he began his work in the early 1930s, Rabi was determined to bring American physics out of the shadow

Isidor Isaac Rabi Develops Nuclear Magnetic Resonance Techniques

Isidor Isaac Rabi's doctoral research focused on the magnetic properties of Tutton salts, which are nickel and potassium crystals that have unusual electrical properties. For his dissertation, Rabi devised a new and ingenious technique for determining their magnetic susceptibilities, or the degrees to which the materials are magnetized by an applied field. His experimental methods, however, were to have much wider applications.

Rabi had been fascinated to learn of the famous 1922 Stern-Gerlach experiment, in which Stern and Gerlach sent a beam of silver atoms through a magnetic field in a vacuum chamber. The atoms were caught on a piece of plate glass at the end of the tube. Stern and Gerlach found that the atoms were deflected not randomly but in two broad stripes, thus revealing fundamental differences between quantum mechanics and classical macroscopic physics. The experiment also showed that electrons within the atoms sometimes behaved as though they had tiny bar magnets inside them.

In 1931, Rabi, who had joined the physics faculty at Columbia University, began his own series of molecular-beam experiments. He developed a new means of projecting particle beams at different angles through magnetic fields. Between 1931 and 1937, he devised techniques for measuring nuclear magnetic resonance. This was very difficult to do because the magnetic moment, or susceptibility to magnetic fields, of an atom's nucleus is tiny compared to that of the whole atom. Rabi discovered that using very weak magnetic fields produces deflection patterns in the molecular beams that provide a window into the nature of the nucleus. By adding additional deflections to the beams, scientists can compensate for the varying velocities of the particles that make up the beam.

In 1937, Rabi and his assistants succeeded in using this molecular-beam method to discover the nuclear spin of the sodium atom. A further refinement of the apparatus enabled Rabi to use the zero-moment method to determine nuclear magnetic moments as well as nuclear spin. The accuracy of the nuclear resonance method turned out to be extraordinarily high.

Rabi's work on hydrogen gave rise to two particularly important discoveries of physics. One was that deuterons (stable particles consisting of a proton and neutron) have multiple magnetic poles. The other was Rabi's experimental verification of the magnetic moment of the proton. Both of these discoveries are used in the mathematical analyses that underlie the big bang theory of the origin of the universe.

When World War II broke out, Rabi's work in nuclear magnetic resonance was brought to a halt. During the war, he worked extensively on radar at the famous Radiation Laboratory, or "Rad Lab," at MIT and served at Los Alamos as a consultant on the development of the atomic bomb. Because of the war, the Swedish Academy had suspended the granting of Nobel Prizes in 1940. Awards resumed in 1944, and Rabi was awarded the 1944 Nobel Prize in Physics for his work in nuclear magnetic resonance.

of European physics. It was through the work of scientists such as Rabi and Oppenheimer that American physics became preeminent in the early 1940s. Rabi's influence in this regard is particularly pervasive, as his research continues to be cited by contemporary physicists. He is remembered in particular for his use of nuclear magnetic resonances to examine atomic properties. The new precision of his techniques led to such unanticipated discoveries as the quadrupole moment (a description of the nuclear charge distribution) of the heavy hydrogen nucleus.

Rabi saw clearly the role of science and technology in the modern world and worked to promote that role in the interest of international peace. As a diplomat and advisor, Rabi used science to bridge national, religious, and ideological differences. CERN, the organization that he helped found, remains one of the foremost physics laboratories in the world.

John S. Rigden

FURTHER READING

Day, Michael A. "I. I. Rabi: The Two Cultures and the Universal Culture of Science." *Physics in Perspective* 6.4 (2004): 428–76. Print. Examines Rabi's views on the nature of science and society, specifically on the relation of science to government, education, and religion.

Krige, John. "I. I. Rabi and the Birth of CERN." *Physics Today* 57.9 (2004): 44–48. Print. Describes Rabi's role in the conception and creation of the Center for European Nuclear Research (CERN).

Rabi, Isidor Isaac. *Science: The Center of Culture*. New York: World, 1970. Print. A collection of Rabi's articles and speeches.

Rigden, John S. *Rabi: Scientist and Citizen*. 1987. Cambridge, MA: Harvard UP, 2000. Print. A biography tracing Rabi's life and work.

VENKATRAMAN RAMAKRISHNAN

Indian British American biologist

Indian-born biologist Venkatraman Ramakrishnan shared the 2009 Nobel Prize in Chemistry for his contribution to mapping the atomic structure of the ribosome, thus enabling close study of how proteins are built from genetic information. His discovery also led to research into a new generation of antibiotics.

Born: 1952; Chidambaram, India
Also known as: Venki Ramakrishnan
Primary field: Biology
Specialties: Molecular biology; biochemistry; biophysics

EARLY LIFE

Venkatraman Ramakrishnan was born in Chidambaram, in the modern Indian state of Tamil Nadu, in the spring of 1952. He has kept his birth date confidential. Venkatraman, known to his friends as Venki, is the oldest child of biochemist C. V. Ramakrishnan and psychologist R. Rajalakshmi.

In 1955, Ramakrishnan's parents moved to the western Indian town of Baroda, now known as Vadodara. There, Ramakrishnan's father was appointed chair of the biochemistry department at the Maharaja Sayajirao University of Baroda (MSU). The university's language of instruction was English, and Ramakrishnan attended the only English-speaking school in Baroda, the Convent of Jesus and Mary School. In 1959, Ramakrishnan's sister Lalita was born.

The Ramakrishnans spent the academic year of 1960 in the Australian city of Adelaide. After returning to Baroda, Ramakrishnan lost interest in school from seventh to ninth grade. However, a charismatic science and mathematics teacher, T. C. Patel, reignited his academic interests. Ramakrishnan finished high school the second-best student in his class, even having skipped two grades.

In 1968, after a year of pre-science schooling, Ramakrishnan received an Indian National Science Talent Scholarship. He enrolled at MSU and graduated with a bachelor of science in physics in 1971. He then received a fellowship to study physics at the University of Ohio, but once there, he lost interest in physics, preferring experiments over theory. After reading about advances in biology in *Scientific American*, he considered switching fields.

While at the University of Ohio, Ramakrishnan met Vera Rosenberry, a painting major and a fellow vegetarian; the two married in 1975. Rosenberry's daughter, Tanya Kapka, became Ramakrishnan's stepdaughter. Ramakrishnan earned his PhD in physics in 1976. One month after his graduation, his wife gave birth to their son, Raman.

LIFE'S WORK

Serious about his switch to biology, in the fall of 1976, Ramakrishnan enrolled in the graduate biology program at the University of California, San Diego (UCSD), despite already having a PhD. At UCSD the following year, Ramakrishnan began working with American biochemist Mauricio Montal, studying channels formed in cell membranes by the molecule rhodopsin.

Abandoning his quest for a PhD in biology, Ramakrishnan accepted a postdoctoral fellowship working with American chemist Peter B. Moore at Yale University, starting in the fall of 1978. At Moore's lab, Ramakrishnan brought his cell-membrane expertise to Moore's ribosome project, helping to locate the proteins of the small 30S subunit of the ribosome 70S, which is the ribosome present in prokaryotes (organisms without a cell nucleus). Ramakrishnan and his colleagues used a method called neutron scattering to measure the distance of two altered proteins in the ribosome subunit.

In late 1981, Ramakrishnan applied for faculty positions. Because of his unusual academic background, he received no offers. Finally, he obtained a position among the research staff of the Oak Ridge National Laboratory in Tennessee. After arriving at Oak Ridge in February 1982, Ramakrishnan found he was expected to work only at the neutron-scattering facility instead of pursuing more challenging research. Disillusioned, he sought a new position. In 1983, he joined the scientific staff at the Department of Biology of the Brookhaven National Laboratory on Long Island, New York, where he settled into ribosome research.

Venkatraman Ramakrishnan Maps the Small 30S Subunit of the Prokaryote Ribosome

After biologists James D. Watson and Francis Crick discovered the structure of DNA in 1953, Romanian-born biologist George Emil Palade discovered what became known as the ribosome in 1955. By 1970, it was generally understood that in a cell, the DNA contains genetic material that is transcribed onto messenger RNA, which then travels to the ribosome. There, in an act scientists call *translation*, messenger RNA interacts with transfer RNA, carrying amino acids to build (through ribosomal RNA and based on the DNA information) new proteins that are building blocks of life. However, discovering the exact chemical nature of the activities in the ribosome would depend on knowledge of the atomic structure of the ribosome, a problem that Venkatraman Ramakrishnan began to tackle in 1998.

The most challenging aspects of Ramakrishnan's research were the incredibly small size of the atoms and the huge number of molecules present in the ribosome. The sizes were measured in angstroms, with 1 angstrom corresponding to 0.1 nanometers. The ribosomes found in prokaryotes (organisms without cellular nuclei, mainly bacteria) are different from those found in eukaryotes (organisms with cellular nuclei, including all animals, plants, and fungi). Each ribosome has two distinct subunits, which in prokaryotes are the 50S subunit and the 30S subunit. Messenger RNA first enters the small subunit. At its border with the larger subunit, transfer RNA brings in amino acids, from which proteins are assembled in the large subunit.

As a postdoctoral student at Yale, Ramakrishnan contributed to the discovery of the location of the proteins within the small 30S subunit of the prokaryote ribosome. He used neutron scanning to locate the proteins, but this method did not allow for the discovery of the atomic structure of the ribosome molecules. In the late 1970s, however, Israeli crystallographer Ada Yonath decided to apply X-ray crystallography to the study of the ribosome structure. By 1980, Yonath had successfully grown crystals of ribosomes of sufficiently high quality for the analysis Ramakrishnan hoped to carry out.

In 1988, Ramakrishnan learned crystallography. He grew ribosome crystals of sufficient quality and quantity by cloning them within the prolific bacterium *E. coli*. Next, at Cambridge University's Laboratory of Molecular Biology (LMB), he solved the problem of determining the phase of the X-rays used for crystallography at the nano level. The solution enabled him to determine the atomic structure of two ribosome proteins, S5 and H5, in 1992 and 1993.

To map the atomic structure of the entire small ribosome 30S subunit, Ramakrishnan moved on to two different research institutions, but it was only upon returning to LMB in 1999 that he found a scientific environment conducive to his research. In June 1999, he and his team stunned the scientific world by revealing that they had successfully mapped the atomic structure of the prokaryotic ribosome 30S subunit at a resolution of 5.5 angstroms, which was but one step above the threshold to discovering its atomic structure.

Ramakrishnan and his team performed X-ray crystallography on their RNA crystals at the US Argonne National Laboratory in Illinois in February 2000. The experiment yielded a picture of the 30S subunit at 3 angstroms, finally showing its atomic structure. Ramakrishnan's team was able to successfully illustrate its findings just before a rival team under Yonath published its 3.3-angstrom picture of the 30S subunit in September. Ramakrishnan's picture had come first and at a higher resolution.

Also in 2000, American biologist Thomas A. Steitz mapped the large 50S subunit of the prokaryote ribosome, completing the picture. For these achievements, the three scientists shared the 2009 Nobel Prize in Chemistry. Their discoveries allowed humanity to look at basic processes of life at the nano level of atomic structures.

Around 1988, Ramakrishnan began his scientific quest to map the atomic structure of the small 30S subunit of the prokaryote ribosome. Realizing that neutron scattering could not yield sufficient resolution at the atomic level, he followed the advice of fellow Brookhaven biologist Steve White and learned to use a new technique called X-ray crystallography to study the ribosome subunit. He used cloning to produce ribosomal proteins via the bacterium *E. coli* for crystallization. In 1990, Ramakrishnan crystallized the two ribosomal proteins S5 and H5. Also that year, he received tenure at Brookhaven.

For the academic year 1991–92, Ramakrishnan was awarded a Guggenheim Fellowship and a sabbatical, which he used to carry out research at the famous Medical Research Council Laboratory of Molecular Biology (LMB) at the University of Cambridge in England. There, he rejected a proposal for a DNA crystallization project by the laboratory's director, chemist Aaron Klug, and instead succeeded in mapping the structure of the two proteins, publishing the results in *Nature* in 1992 and 1993.

Returning to Brookhaven in the fall of 1992, Ramakrishnan set his research lab to the task of further crystallization and analysis of ribosomal proteins. Dissatisfied with the new direction at Brookhaven, which discouraged individual projects, he became professor of biochemistry at the University of Utah in fall 1995. At Utah, Ramakrishnan continued his research into the structure of the prokaryote ribosome, but uncertainties about funding led him to move back to the LMB in April 1999.

In June of that year, at a conference in Denmark, Ramakrishnan revealed to the scientific community that he and his team had mapped the atomic structure of the ribosome subunit 30S at a resolution of 5.5 angstroms (0.55 nanometers). In February 2000, he and his team were able to assemble a picture of the 30S subunit at 3 angstroms, revealing its atomic structure. Ramakrishnan then turned his research team toward investigating how antibiotics bind to the ribosome and thus block its translation of genetic information into the building of protein.

In 2003, Ramakrishnan was made a fellow of the Royal Society of London. In 2004, he was elected as a member of the US National Academy of Sciences. He received the Louis-Jeantet Prize for medicine in 2007, the same year his mother died. In 2008, Ramakrishnan was elected senior research fellow at Trinity College, Cambridge. On October 7, 2009, he won the Nobel Prize in Chemistry, which he shared with Israeli crystallographer Ada Yonath and American biochemist Thomas A. Steitz, all three having mapped the ribosome at the atomic level. In 2010, Ramakrishnan received India's prestigious Padma Vibhushan medal; in 2012, he was knighted by Queen Elizabeth II.

IMPACT

Ramakrishnan was the first Indian-born scientist to win a Nobel Prize in Chemistry. His success in mapping the small 30S subunit of the prokaryote ribosome at the atomic level enabled significant further research into exactly how the ribosome uses genetic information from DNA to create proteins, a basic process of life, while the X-ray crystallography he used to map it has found significant applications in the search for a new generation of antibiotics. Knowledge of where exactly antibiotic molecules bond within ribosomes' atomic structure can aid in designing new antibiotics, which is especially important as bacteria become immune to classic antibiotics.

R. C. Lutz

FURTHER READING

Nair, Prashant. "Profile of Venkatraman Ramakrishnan." *Proceedings of the National Academy of Sciences of the United States of America* 108.38 (2011): 15676–78. Print. Discusses Ramakrishnan and his road to mapping the ribosome 30S subunit. Written at the general-interest level.

Rodnina, Marina, et al, eds. *Ribosomes Structure, Function, and Dynamics.* New York: Springer, 2011. Print. Collects thirty-three articles from the 2010 Ribosome Meeting at Orvieto, Italy, many of which highlight and reference Ramakrishnan's achievements.

Sanbonmatsu, Karissa, et al. "Information Processing by Nanomachines: Decoding by the Ribosome." *Molecular Machines.* Ed. Benoit Roux. Hackensack: World Scientific, 2011. 67–86. Print. Discusses Ramakrishnan's discovery of the ribosome chemical groups that participate in decoding genetic material from the DNA in the context of information-processing systems.

Sherer, Edward C. "Antibiotics Targeting the Ribosome: Structure-Based Design and the Nobel Prize." *Annual Reports in Computational Chemistry.* Vol. 6. Ed. Ralph A. Wheeler. Boston: Elsevier, 2010. 139–66. Print. Highlights Ramakrishnan's contributions to research into antibiotics, made possible by his mapping of the small ribosome 30S subunit at the atomic level.

CHANDRASEKHARA VENKATA RAMAN

Indian physicist

Chandrasekhara Venkata Raman, the first internationally acclaimed Indian physicist to be entirely educated within India, was awarded the Nobel Prize in Physics in 1930 for his discovery of important characteristics of light scattering. Raman also made significant contributions to Indian education, establishing the Raman Research Institute in Bangalore in 1948.

Born: November 7, 1888; Trichinopoly, India (now
 Tiruchirapalli, India)
Died: November 21, 1970; Bangalore, India
Primary field: Physics
Specialties: Optics; acoustics

EARLY LIFE

Chandrasekhara Venkata Raman was born the second-eldest child of Chandrasekhara Iyer, a professor of mathematics and physics, and Parvathi Ammal, who was from a family of well-known Sanskrit scholars. In 1892, while Raman was still a child, his father accepted a position at Mrs. A. V. N. College in Vishakhapatnam in Andhra Pradesh province. There, Raman demonstrated his academic prowess early, finishing his secondary education at eleven years old and immediately entering Mrs. A. V. N. College. Raman completed two years there and entered Presidency College in Madras, where he received his BA in English and physics with honors at age fifteen. He was

not well enough to study abroad as his peers did. Instead, he pursued his postgraduate education at Presidency College, publishing his first paper on the physics of light in the British *Philosophical Magazine* in November 1906 and completing his MA with honors in 1907.

By then, Raman had exhausted the available educational routes in India. Since he was unable to travel, his academic career essentially ended, and he applied to take the Indian civil service examination, on which he scored top marks. Such positions were highly respected and well paid. Before entering the civil service, Raman married Lokasundari Ammal and, in late 1907, moved his new family to Calcutta, where he had been made assistant accountant general.

Before the end of 1907, Raman discovered that only a few blocks from his residence was the Indian Association for the Cultivation of Science. The association had fallen on hard times, chiefly because of lack of interest and attention. Raman brought new life to the organization, spending

Raman Advances Theories of Vibrations and Acoustics

Much of Indian physicist Chandrasekhara Venkata Raman's early research focused on the vibrations and acoustics of musical instruments. He authored over two dozen journal articles on the subject, as well as a monograph entitled "On the Mechanical Theory of the Vibrations of Bowed Strings and of Musical Instruments of the Violin Family, with Experimental Verifications of the Results, Part I" (1918). His most significant contributions involved studies of Indian instruments, including the tabla (hand drum), the ectara (single-string guitar), the tambura (long-necked lute), the veena (a family of Indian stringed instruments), and the mridangam (two-headed drum). Raman discovered the overtones in the sounds created by the mridangam and the tabla, demonstrating that the richness of sound in the instruments was deeper than stretched Western drums. Further, Raman described five of the harmonies that could be obtained from the mridangam, due to variations in thickness of the stretched membrane that covers most of the instrument. Raman used his observations to publish another paper on the ancient Hindus and their advanced knowledge of acoustics; though a young man, Raman was already considered an expert in musical instruments and sound by this time.

Though Raman was particularly interested in the harmonic nature of the sound of Indian drums, he was also the first to try to describe the dynamics of bowed-string vibration. Raman sought to create a model to describe the motion of a string and, to do so, made several assumptions. A bowed string is peculiar in that, as with a violin, the bow remains in contact with the string, unlike the plucked strings of a guitar. The constant contact with the bow prevents the bowed string from vibrating as freely as strings that are not in contact with a bow. (However, bows allow a musician to hold a note by continuously inputting energy to the string.) Raman based his model on an ideally flexible string, excited by a friction force (bow) applied at a single point. Using his model, Raman was able to determine various hypothetical periodic motions of the string, including the Helmholtz motion. The Helmholtz motion is described as a "slip-stick" motion: In the sticking phase, the bow and string move at approximately the same velocity; during the slipping phase, the string's velocity differs greatly from that of the bow. In his research, Raman worked out the theory of transverse vibration in bowed strings. Depicted visually as a wave, transverse vibration describes the motion of a string moving steadily upward after being struck, only to reach its highest point and suddenly reverse direction and travel downward. This motion is called transverse vibration because it describes a particular point on the string moving transversely (crosswise) in relation to the string's length.

nearly all of his spare time at the association for the next ten years and actively pursuing his own research interests in a carefully defined research program that he designed chiefly on his own initiative. During those years, Raman published frequently on the physics of stringed instruments and acoustics in such publications as *Nature*, *Bulletin of the Indian Association for the Cultivation of Science*, *Physical Review*, and the *Philosophical Magazine*.

LIFE'S WORK

By 1917, Raman's reputation was sufficiently well established that he was offered the Sir Tarakanath Palit chair in physics at the University of Calcutta. Again, however, Raman was required to study abroad, and he refused. Vice Chancellor Asutosh Mookerjee recognized Raman as the ideal person to occupy the new position and was so impressed by Raman's expertise that he waived the travel requirement, allowing Raman to accept the post. Raman was no longer able to maintain his leadership position at the Indian Association for the Cultivation of Science, however, and his salary dropped significantly. He also shifted from studies on the physics of musical instruments to focus on the physics of light and optics.

Four years after he joined the University of Calcutta, Raman became a full professor, teaching, lecturing, and helping to establish a fully developed graduate curriculum. For the first time in his career, in 1921, Raman traveled outside India to the Congress of Universities of the British Empire in Oxford, England. In England, Raman presented the first of his many lectures to be given abroad to the Physical Society of London about his research activities. On his return to Calcutta, he made the observation that would ultimately lead him to win the Nobel Prize in Physics.

As his ship sailed the Mediterranean Sea, Raman commented on its "wonderful blue opalescence." He also recognized that the blue was a result of the scattering of the light by the water itself and not the reflection of the sky, as was widely accepted at the time. En route, Raman conducted a simple experiment that confirmed his hypothesis. Soon after his return to Calcutta, he published a paper in *Proceedings of the Royal Society* entitled "On the Molecular Scattering of Light in Water and the Colour of the Sea." He was so delighted at uncovering this apparently pristine area of scientific investigation that he began to focus nearly all of his research in uncovering other aspects of the physics of light.

In 1923, Raman and graduate student K. R. Ramanathan were conducting observations in light scattering through highly purified glycerine, when a phenomenon that would later be called the Raman effect was first observed. It was a barely detectable trace of light, shifted to either side of the primary optical spectra of the glycerine.

Raman and his associates first suspected that the very weak secondary reflections that were shifted off the primary spectral trace were the result of impurities in the glycerine. They went to great lengths to purify the glycerine before the light was passed through again. Yet the secondary reflections were still present and undiminished no matter how pure the substance. It became obvious to Raman that these secondary reflections were the result of an inherent characteristic of the matter under investigation. Similar results could be observed in liquids, solids, and gases, but the effect was so weak that conventional methods could not magnify the reflections sufficiently for detailed study.

As Raman's group raced to understand the effect, they discovered that if they used a mercury arc lamp, which produced a very intense beam of monochromatic (single wavelength) light, they could study the fractional secondary wavelengths reflected. They soon discovered that these secondary reflections revealed aspects of the molecular structure itself. It was a tool of immense importance to physicists and chemists. In 1928, Raman and his colleagues published their results in the *Indian Journal of Physics*. His discovery was of such consequence that, in only a year's time, he was designated a knight of the British Empire. In 1930, Raman was awarded the Hughes Medal from the Royal Society and the Nobel Prize in Physics.

Raman was ever devoted to the education of Indian students and knew well that the prominence of his nation in the world depended significantly on its scientific literacy. He founded the *Indian Journal of Physics* in the mid-1920s and, in 1934, the Indian Academy of Sciences and its publication *Proceedings*.

In 1933, Raman left his university post to accept the directorship of the Indian Institute of Science in Bangalore, where he gathered a world-class faculty. Unfortunately, he and the board of directors clashed, and after only three years as director, Raman was forced to resign, though remaining a professor until 1948.

That year, Raman accepted the directorship of the newly created Raman Research Institute in Bangalore. India had just gained independence from Great Britain, and Raman was named national professor. Raman and his students continued studies in optics and reflected light. As he studied the reflection of color from roses in his rose gardens, he became fascinated with the physiology of vision. By 1968, he had published forty-three papers on vision in a book entitled *The Physiology of Vision.*

Raman was awarded the highest honor of the Indian people, the Bharat Ratna (Jewel of India), in 1954. He remained active in the education until his death on November 21, 1970, at the age of eighty-two.

IMPACT

Raman has been described as one of the last true natural philosophers of science. He was able to bring a conscious love for nature to rigorous scientific investigation, as evidenced by his observations of the blue of the sea, of stringed musical instruments, and even of the color of roses and its relationship to vision. Raman's guileless approach to science formed the basis for his life's work, which carried other, far-reaching consequences. Raman's insistence on remaining in India to complete his education later became the foundation for his motivation to make Indian educational institutions first rate and to provide world-class institutions of learning for Indian students. Raman's influence on science, education, and the spirit of nationalism in the newly

independent nation of India was far-reaching. His personal work in establishing so many of India's influential publications and institutions has had a profound impact on India's economic development and social evolution in the world. Furthermore, with the advent of laser, a very powerful, monochromatic beam of light, the Raman effect has been used extensively to investigate the molecular characteristics of many substances.

Dennis Chamberland

FURTHER READING

Levathes, Louise. "Everything Is Illuminated." *Atlantic Monthly* 305.4 (2010): 32. Print. Discusses the modern applications of Raman's work, including the Raman effect.

Parameswaran, Uma. *C. V. Raman: A Biography*. New Delhi: Penguin, 2011. Print. A comprehensive biography of Raman, detailing his personal life as well as the scientific achievements of the first Asian Nobel laureate.

Singh, Rajinder. "C. V. Raman and the Discovery of the Raman Effect." *Physics in Perspective* 4.4 (2002): 399–420. Print. A profile of Raman that focuses on his discovery of the Raman effect.

SRINIVASA RAMANUJAN

Indian mathematician

Self-taught Indian mathematician Srinivasa Ramanujan, a famous collaborator of the English mathematician G. H. Hardy, became a Fellow of the Royal Society in 1918 in recognition of his many contributions to the study of pure mathematics, including an approximate formula for deriving the number of partitions of an integer.

Born: December 22, 1887; Erode, India
Died: April 26, 1920; Kumbakonam, India
Also known as: Srinivasa Aaiyangar Ramanujan; Srīnivāsa Rāmānujan Iyengar
Primary field: Mathematics
Specialties: Number theory; mathematical analysis

EARLY LIFE

On December 22, 1887, Srinivasa Ramanujan was born in Erode, a city in the southern Indian state of Tamil Nadu, into a family struggling with poverty. Ramanujan's father worked as a bookkeeper for a textile merchant, and his mother earned a small income as a

devotional singer in a Hindu temple. By the time he was seven, Ramanujan had survived a bout of smallpox and three of his younger siblings had died as infants.

Ramanujan received little early formal education apart from attending various *pials*—classes held by teachers on the raised porches in front of their homes—until enrolling in Kangayan Primary School. Here he studied Tamil (his native language), English, geography, and mathematics. After receiving the highest examination scores in his district in 1897, Ramanujan attended an English-language high school. He soon surpassed his teachers' curricula and began teaching himself fundamental theorems in trigonometry, geometry, algebra, calculus, and differential equations, with the help of an advanced textbook he had acquired. The book, *A Synopsis of Elementary Results in Pure and Applied Mathematics* (1880), by G. S. Carr, contained more than a thousand theorems but almost no proofs. Ramanujan catapulted his mathematical education forward by working through them from scratch.

In 1904, already working on original solutions to problems in areas such as infinite series and prime number theory, Ramanujan won a scholarship to Government College in Kumbakonam, but he lost it and dropped out because of his neglect of his other subjects. His refusal to spend time on anything other than mathematics was also his undoing at Pachaiyappa's College, where in both 1906 and 1907, he failed the final exam that would have granted him a college degree.

Unsuccessful in his early attempts at higher education, Ramanujan devoted all his free time to mathematics, working largely in isolation. He collected his research on topics such as continued fractions and divergent series in a string of notebooks that were published after his death.

Ramanujan was married in 1909 to S. Janaki Ammal; his mother had arranged the match. For several years he subsisted on donations from friends and mathematical colleagues, but in 1912, he began supporting his obsession with mathematical research by working as a clerk with the Madras Port Trust.

LIFE'S WORK

During his twenties, Ramanujan gained several supporters who were interested in mathematics and became invested in supporting his mathematical career. Among these men was S. Narayana Iyer, Ramanujan's manager at the Madras Port Trust. With Iyer's encouragement, Ramanujan sent letters of introduction to a few mathematicians in England. Impressed by the creativity of the one hundred or so theorems Ramanujan had enclosed, and amazed by what Ramanujan had already managed to do without formal mentorship, the renowned mathematician G. H. Hardy arranged for Ramanujan to travel to Trinity College at the University of Cambridge. Ramanujan arrived at Cambridge in April 1914, remaining there until 1919. The period was tremendously productive for him: He published more than thirty papers in five years. (Ramanujan's first professional article, a *Journal of the Indian Mathematical Society* paper that outlined several new properties of Bernoulli numbers, had been published in 1911.)

Ramanujan's work during his Trinity years spanned a wide range of topics in pure mathematics, including continued fractions, elliptic functions, and the theory of partitions. One of his most original lines of research concerned a type of number that he called "highly composite." A highly composite number has more divisors than any other number smaller than itself. For example,

12 is considered a highly composite number because it has six divisors—it can be divided evenly by the numbers 1, 2, 3, 4, 6, and 12—while no smaller number has as many. Ramanujan published a list of about one hundred highly composite numbers and proved that they had various interesting properties. In particular, he showed that when a highly composite number is expressed as the product of increasing prime numbers in exponential form (for example, $144 = 2^4 \times 3^2$), the exponents always decrease in order.

Not all of Ramanujan's ideas were correct, and his association with Hardy provided the young mathematician with an opportunity to recognize his failures. While he was still in India, for example, Ramanujan had developed what he believed was a groundbreaking formula for computing the number of prime numbers between 0 and any number x. His method did generate exact or almost exact numbers of primes for values of x smaller than 1,000, and it also did well for values of x up to several million. However, Ramanujan had not checked his formula on still higher values of x.

When Hardy examined Ramanujan's calculations, he found that they relied on a false and unproven assumption about a certain property of the Riemann zeta function, a famous infinite series that is written in terms of a complex variable (in mathematics, "complex" refers to a variable that has both a real and an imaginary component). Because of this misstep, the errors that Ramanujan's prime number theorem generated at high x values were large. As it turned out, this was an important failure, because it highlighted the limitations of Ramanujan's brilliant but intuitive and sometimes breezy style of solving problems in mathematics. Working with Hardy helped Ramanujan to realize the importance of writing mathematical proofs using scrupulous, detailed reasoning that never skipped a step, and he slowly began to return to his old ideas and work through them with increased rigor.

In 1916, Ramanujan was granted a bachelor of science by research (the degree now known as a PhD) by Cambridge. In 1918, he became a full Fellow of the Royal Society.

Ramanujan struggled with illness throughout his stay in England, something that eventually prevented him from working as much as he desired. He returned to India in 1919 in poor health. Ramanujan planned to accept a position he had been offered as a university professor in Madras when he recovered, but this never came to pass. He died on April 26, 1920, of tuberculosis at only thirty-two years of age.

Ramanujan and Hardy Develop a Formula for Finding $p(n)$

One of Srinivasa Ramanujan's most significant achievements arose out of his collaboration with G. H. Hardy and concerned the theory of partitions. In mathematics, the partition of a number n, written as $p(n)$, is the number of unique ways it can be represented as a sum of positive integers, disregarding the order in which the integers are arranged. For example, $p(4)$ is equal to 5 because there are five unique ways to express the number 4 as a sum of positive integers. These are 1+1+1+1; 1+1+2; 1+3; 2+2; and 4+0 (or simply "4"). Each of these is known as a partition. Although it is simple enough to calculate $p(n)$ for small numbers by mechanically listing and counting possible sums, the number of such partitions rises extremely quickly as numbers grow larger. There are only 42 ways to partition the number 10, for example, but an astonishing 204,226 ways to partition the number 50.

By the time Ramanujan arrived in Cambridge, mathematicians had been trying to come up with a general formula for computing $p(n)$ for a long time. The eighteenth-century Swiss mathematician Leonhard Euler had been the last person to make any significant progress in solving this problem. Euler's "pentagonal number theorem" made use of a recursive formula: one that involves repeatedly applying the same rule, using the result of each application as the next input. The pentagonal number theorem had allowed the exact calculation of $p(1)$ to $p(200)$. However, the method was not a practical way of calculating the partitions of still larger numbers, as doing so required too many steps.

Ramanujan and Hardy's breakthrough in partition theory occurred in 1917. It was to develop a relatively simple formula for finding approximate values of $p(n)$ that could be used to compute the partitions of much larger numbers. Although their method produced results that were not always exact solutions, it had the advantage of being an asymptotic formula. In other words, as n becomes increasingly large, the ratio of the solution produced by Ramanujan and Hardy's method and the exact solution approaches 1:1. In addition, the errors produced by their theorem are always extremely small—so much so that they disappear when the solution is rounded to the nearest integer.

The heart of Ramanujan and Hardy's theorem lay in an original technique of mathematical analysis. They developed a method for expressing a number as a sum of subsets of integers (a subset of integers is a group of integers each of which shares some mathematical relationship). This process, which would later be known by the generalized name the "circle method," is still considered one of the most powerful tools for solving difficult problems in number theory.

IMPACT

Ramanujan is widely regarded as a rare genius whose creativity and natural grasp of the fundamental relationships between numbers would have placed him in the top tier of mathematicians in any era. Although he spent much of his short life rediscovering already-known mathematical concepts, it is hard to overestimate the impact of his original thinking in number theory and mathematical analysis. The work on highly composite numbers for which he was awarded his Cambridge degree, for example, birthed an entirely new line of investigation; no one before him had ever treated these numbers as a special class or examined their properties.

Several mathematical theorems bear Ramanujan's name. The "Ramanujan conjecture," for example, is a statement about the prime values of an infinite series known as the tau function, and there are two equations relating to partition theory that are known as "Rogers-Ramanujan identities" (these were independently discovered by both Ramanujan and, some years earlier, by the British mathematician Leonard James Rogers).

Ramanujan's impact on the world of mathematics did not end with his death; four of his notebooks, containing thousands of original theorems and ideas, were published posthumously. His journals continue to directly stimulate new research as generations of mathematical minds attempt to confirm or expand on their arguments. For example, Ramanujan never wrote any articles on hypergeometric series (a series in which the ratio of any two consecutive terms can be expressed as a ratio of two polynomial functions). However, he wrote many notebook entries on the subject, particularly regarding a specific group of seventeen infinite series that behave in surprising ways and that he called "mock theta functions." These functions have since turned out to be relevant across a broad range of mathematical and scientific disciplines, including superstring theory and the chemistry of polymers. In addition, his theory of modular and elliptic functions has proven to have applications in modern cryptography.

M. Lee

FURTHER READING

Alladi, Krishnaswami, and Frank Garvan, eds. *Partitions, q-Series, and Modular Forms.* New York: Springer, 2012. Print. Collection of papers and survey articles, several of which address elaborations or expansions on Ramanujan's work, such as his method in partition congruences and the Rogers-Ramanujan identities in hypergeometric series. Highly technical and suitable for advanced undergraduates and graduate students of pure mathematics.

Berndt, Bruce C. *Number Theory in the Spirit of Ramanujan.* Providence, RI: American Mathematical Society, 2006. Print. Explores some of Ramanujan's favorite topics in number theory, including hypergeometry, the Eisenstein series, and elliptic functions. Demands a modest knowledge of number theory at a level provided by an introductory undergraduate course.

---, and Robert A. Rankin, eds. *Ramanujan: Essays and Surveys.* Providence, RI: American Mathematical Society, 2002. Print. Varied collection of articles covering aspects of Ramanujan's personal life, including a biography of his wife, S. Janaki Ammal, and his mathematical contributions.

Kanigel, Robert. *The Man Who Knew Infinity: A Life of the Genius Ramanujan.* London: Abacus, 2006. Print. A biography that gives equal weight to conveying the details of Ramanujan's life and introducing the fundamental meaning of his work, with technical explanations accessible even for non-mathematical readers.

NORMAN F. RAMSEY

American physicist

American physicist Norman F. Ramsey was an influential researcher, teacher, and administrator. He contributed to the development of radar and the atomic bomb, served with a number of agencies, and won the Nobel Prize for the Ramsey method of separated oscillatory fields.

Born: August 27, 1915; Washington, DC
Died: November 4, 2011; Wayland, Massachusetts
Also known as: Norman Foster Ramsey Jr.
Primary field: Physics
Specialties: Atomic and molecular physics; nuclear physics; quantum mechanics; theoretical physics

EARLY LIFE

Norman Foster Ramsey Jr. was the son of West Point graduate and Army Ordnance officer Norman Foster Ramsey Sr. and university mathematics instructor Minna Bauer Ramsey. Because of his father's occupation, Ramsey grew up in a variety of places, including Washington, DC; Paris, France; New Jersey; and Kansas. An exceptionally bright student interested in the sciences, he skipped two grades during his early education before graduating at age fifteen from Fort Leavenworth High School in Kansas. Though his father hoped his son would attend West Point, at graduation in 1930, Ramsey was too young to enroll.

Ramsey was awarded a scholarship to Kansas University, but his parents moved in 1930 to New York City. In 1931, he entered Columbia College (later Columbia University) to major in engineering. Ramsey soon switched to mathematics. A perennial winner of math contests, he was allowed in his senior year to become a teaching assistant, a position normally given to graduate students.

After earning a bachelor's degree from Columbia in 1935, Ramsey used a scholarship to attend Cambridge University in England, where as a physics student he conducted research at the world-famous Cavendish Laboratory. Ramsey learned from leading physicists of the day, including many of whom were or would become Nobel laureates. Among his teachers were Edward Victor Appleton, Max Born, Edward Crisp Bullard, James Chadwick, John Cockcroft, Paul Dirac, Arthur Stanley Eddington, Ralph Howard Fowler, Maurice Goldhaber, Ernest Rutherford, and Joseph John Thompson.

Ramsey received a second bachelor's degree from Cambridge in 1937 and returned to Columbia to conduct molecular beam research with Austrian-born physicist Isidor Isaac Rabi. Ramsey received his PhD in physics in 1940.

Life's Work

After earning his doctoral degree, Ramsey studied in Washington, DC, on a Carnegie Institution fellowship. That same year, he married Elinor Jameson, and the couple soon left for the University of Illinois, where a teaching position awaited Ramsey. With World War II already raging in Europe, however, he was asked to participate in an important wartime project and returned to the East Coast. For the next two years, he was at the Massachusetts Institute of Technology (MIT) in Cambridge, Massachusetts, as director of a group that developed microwave radar, a type of electromagnetic energy used for detecting objects. Ramsey contributed British magnetrons—tubes that magnetically control the flow of electrons to generate power—to the laboratory, where they could be replicated and refined. He afterward served in Washington, DC, as an expert radar consultant to Henry L. Stimson, US secretary of war under Franklin D. Roosevelt.

In 1943, Ramsey was tapped as a member of another wartime program: the Manhattan Project, the code name given to the development of the atomic bomb. Ramsey was a member of Project Alberta, which was tasked with perfecting the shape, configuration, and method of delivery of nuclear devices to their eventual targets, Hiroshima and Nagasaki, Japan. In experiments, Ramsey noticed that heavy bombs tumbled when dropped from high altitude, a condition that adversely affected their accuracy. The tumbling was caused by stresses that crumpled bomb fins. Ramsey devised simple fin reinforcements, called drag plates, that made bombs drop straight and on target.

Following the end of the war, Ramsey returned to Columbia as a professor of physics and research scientist working alongside Rabi in the investigation of molecular beams via spectroscopy. In 1947, Ramsey and Rabi cofounded Brookhaven National Laboratory on Long Island, New York, initially a US Atomic Energy Commission (AEC) research facility, now operated under the aegis of the US Department of Energy. Ramsey served as the first head of the physics department at Brookhaven.

In 1947, Ramsey left Columbia for Harvard University, where he remained as physics professor for the next forty years, though he took frequent leaves of absence to serve in a variety of capacities with a number of organizations. For example, he was a visiting professor at such institutions as Oxford University in England, Middlebury College in Vermont, and the University of Virginia. He also helped establish a molecular beam laboratory at Harvard. There, he carried out proton scattering and magnetic resonance experiments, which helped lead to his invention of the oscillatory field method, subsequently called the separated Ramsey method, a breakthrough that later brought him a share of the 1989 Nobel Prize in Physics. Employing the Ramsey method, Ramsey was able to develop the hydrogen maser in 1960, a device that uses atomic frequencies to make accurate measurements.

In the late 1940s and early 1950s, Ramsey was science advisor to the North Atlantic Treaty Organization, in which post he instituted numerous fellowship and research grants. During the same time period, he oversaw the building of the Harvard Cyclotron Laboratory—completed in 1949—and directed the lab in its startup years.

Ramsey in the late 1950s and early 1960s served as chair of a committee managing the construction of the Cambridge Electron Accelerator (CEA). The CEA, funded by the AEC, was a joint Harvard–MIT project completed in 1960 and in operation until 1974. The CEA was used for high-energy physics experiments, such as electron-proton scattering.

Between the mid-1960s and early 1980s, Ramsey was president of the Universities Research Association (URA), a Washington-based organization consisting of more than eighty research universities in the United States, Canada, Italy, and Japan. Under Ramsey's leadership, URA managed the construction and operation of the US Department of Energy–funded Fermi National Accelerator Laboratory—known worldwide as Fermilab—that opened in 1967 outside Chicago, Illinois.

In 1968, Ramsey served as chair of the highly influential General Advisory Committee of the AEC, which set national policy for both peaceful and military uses of nuclear power. Among other organizations with which Ramsey was affiliated were the Carnegie Endowment for International Peace (trustee, 1962–1986), the American Physical Society (president, 1978–1979), the American Institute of Physics (chairman, board of governors, 1980–1986), and the National Research Council (chairman, board of physics and astronomy, 1985–1989).

Ramsey's first wife, Elinor, died in 1983, after which he married Ellie Welch; the couple had a combined family of seven children and numerous grandchildren. In 1986, Ramsey officially retired, becoming professor emeritus at Harvard. He remained active in physics for years afterward, spending several seasons as a research/adjunct research fellow at the Joint Institute for Laboratory Astrophysics at the University of

Practical Applications of Theoretical Atomic Physics

From the late 1930s onward, the bulk of Norman F. Ramsey's research explored nature on an atomic scale. Ramsey studied the properties and characteristics of molecules and their components, and he examined connections between neutrons, protons, electrons, and other elementary particles. In the course of his work, Ramsey made numerous contributions to the understanding of a submicroscopic universe in which the miniscule building blocks of matter have shapes, relationships, energy, and laws governing their behavior.

One key tool in Ramsey's research was molecular beam spectroscopy. Invented in the late 1920s, the technique incorporates a vacuum within which atomic elements are stimulated to generate a concentrated stream of particles that can be collected, analyzed, and measured to determine the magnetism of their nuclei. Ramsey's mentor, Isidor Rabi, improved the apparatus to provide atomic resonance frequencies. In 1949, Ramsey significantly improved the molecular beam device with the invention of separated oscillatory fields—afterward called the Ramsey method—essentially adding magnets at the beginning and end of the vacuum tube. This innovation greatly enhanced measurements of atomic spin, angular momentum, and velocity; because of increased accuracy and resolution, the invention led to the development of many related technologies.

Ramsey's experiments, often in collaboration with graduate students, resulted in the hydrogen microwave amplifier by stimulated emission of radiation (maser). An extremely accurate device that uses atomic frequency for measurements, masers set the standards for modern atomic clocks; the second is now defined as a unit of time equaling the duration of 9,192,631,770 periods of radiation of the cesium atom. Maser-based atomic clocks are also used in radio telescopes to measure the periods of pulsars and binary stars, in physics to test general and special theories of relativity, in navigation via the satellite-assisted Global Positioning System (GPS), and in astrophysics to locate spacecraft. Masers have also been studied as possible high-tech military weapons.

Likewise, lasers, the infrared and optical spin-offs of masers, have been used to accurately determine the speed of light and to define the meter as related to time: The distance light travels in 1/299,792,458 of a second.

The basic principles of Ramsey's atomic experiments have also been applied to the field of medicine. Such techniques as magnetic resonance imaging (MRI), nuclear magnetic resonance imaging (NMRI), and magnetic resonance tomography (MRT) all use variations on the Ramsey method to produce accurate body scans to aid in patient diagnoses.

Colorado. He also served several stints as visiting professor at the University of Chicago, the University of Michigan, and Williams College in Williamstown, Massachusetts.

Author and coauthor of scores of scholarly papers and books from 1939 onward, Ramsey was honored often for his work. In addition to sharing the 1989 Nobel Prize, he received the Lawrence Award (1960), the Davisson-Germer Prize (1974), the IEEE Medal of Honor (1984), the Rabi Prize and Rumford Premium (1985), the Compton Medal (1986), the Oersted Medal (1988), and the National Medal of Science (1988).

Ramsey died in a nursing home on November 4, 2011, at the age of ninety-six.

IMPACT

A researcher, an administrator, and an inspiring teacher to dozens of advanced students, Ramsey was a colleague to some of the foremost teachers and investigators of

molecular physics between the 1930s and the early twenty-first century.

Ramsey's early experiments with microwave electromagnetic energy were crucial to the Allied efforts in World War II. In conjunction with British radiolocation research into longer wavelengths, the studies of Ramsey and others at the MIT Radiation Laboratory led to the development of radar for use in bombers, night fighters, and submarine-spotters. The accurate radar the laboratory produced was instrumental in the successful outcome of the Battle of Britain in 1940. Likewise, Ramsey's role in the Manhattan Project was vital to the precise delivery of the atomic bombs that ended World War II. The drag plates he developed for making bombs drop on target were later adopted for other military hardware.

Ramsey's Nobel Prize–winning separated oscillatory field method led to the development of the most precise type of clock—the maser atomic clock—and to other developments such as magnetic resonance imaging (MRI) therapy and the Global Positioning System (GPS).

Jack Ewing

FURTHER READING

Audoin, Claude, and Bernard Guinot. *The Measurement of Time: Time, Frequency and the Atomic Clock.* Trans. Stephen Lyle. Cambridge: Cambridge UP, 2001. Print. Presents the physics of time and the measurement of time, from historical and modern perspectives. Covers various types and uses of oscillators and atomic clocks. Includes Ramsey's work.

Brodsky, Ira. *The History and Future of Medical Technology.* St. Louis: Telescope, 2010. Print. An illustrated discussion of how advancements in science, such as the Ramsey method that led to the MRI, have assisted medical care over the last 150 years.

Gordin, Michael D. *Five Days in August: How World War II Became a Nuclear War.* Princeton: Princeton UP, 2007. Print. An account of the cultural and political fallout from the Manhattan Project, in which scientists—including Ramsey—developed and delivered the atomic bombs that ended World War II.

JOHN RAY

English naturalist

Seventeenth-century naturalist John Ray made major contributions to the fields of botany, zoology, and natural theology. With his adaptation of a taxonomical scheme based on such factors as habitat and anatomy, Ray pushed the study of flora and fauna toward modern scientific thinking. His comprehensive field guides set new standards for rigor of methodology and precision of content.

Born: November 29, 1627; Black Notley, England
Died: January 17, 1705; Black Notley, England
Primary field: Biology
Specialties: Botany; zoology

EARLY LIFE

John Ray was born in the village of Black Notley, Essex, England, on November 29, 1627. The seed of his lifelong passion for botany may have been planted early in life; Ray's mother enjoyed a reputation as a skilled herbalist and healer. As an adult, Ray would go on to include in his botanical catalogs summaries of the medicinal application of plants.

Ray's interest in botany took a formal turn in 1650. To speed his recovery from an illness, Ray, at that time a graduate student at the University of Cambridge, undertook a regimen of nature walks. His observations of the local flora inspired him, along with his fellow students, to establish a series of small botanical gardens and to publish a catalog of their findings. The resulting *Catalogus Plantarum circa Cantabrigiam Mascentium* (1660) identified more than 550 plant species. Ray is widely credited with the primary authorship of this catalog, even though it was published anonymously.

Ray earned his bachelor's degree from Cambridge in 1648 and his master's degree from the same institution three years later. He rose steadily through the academic ranks, serving in both teaching and administrative roles at Cambridge for a decade. Ray was ordained as an Anglican priest in 1660 but left his fellowship in Cambridge in 1662 when he refused on principle to subscribe to King Charles II's Act of Uniformity. The act required an oath that many clergymen, including Ray, declined to take—a choice that cost them their livings. Ray came to depend on the financial support of his student and fellow naturalist Francis Willughby.

Upon severing his ties with Cambridge, Ray, accompanied by Willughby, made an expedition to study seabirds on the west coast of England, the first of many such scientific journeys they would undertake. For three years, the pair traveled throughout Europe, collecting plant, animal, and rock specimens from the Netherlands, Germany, Switzerland, France, and Italy. In 1666, when they returned to England, Ray and Willughby began the work of preparing to publish their observations.

Early on in their collaboration, the two scientists had formulated an ambitious plan: to produce the first comprehensive catalog of the flora and fauna of Britain. Ray would undertake the study of plants, while Willughby would survey animal, insect, and marine life. In 1670, Ray published his definitive catalog of British flora, the *Catalogus Plantarum Angliae.* Willughby's role in the joint project was cut short by his death two

John Ray's *Historia Plantarum* and Modern Taxonomy

English naturalist John Ray's *Historia Plantarum* (History of plants), published in three volumes in 1686, 1688, and 1704, provided an important foundation for modern taxonomy. Previously, scientific thought had been most influenced by medieval scholasticism, which emphasized dialectical reasoning and inference. Under this mode of scholarly thought, plants were classified under a preconceived system. Ray, an empiricist, observed the similarities and differences between plants and accordingly constructed a new classification system. In the first volume of *Historia Plantarum*, he also became the first person to attempt a scientific definition of what a species is.

Prior to *Historia Plantarum*, the term *species* did not define a precise biological concept but merely referred to a type or kind of organism. The original Latin word had come to be used in common English, but as it lacked a biological definition, debate arose among scientists about its usage. Ray attempted to resolve this debate by providing a clear definition that would function as a foundation for a consistent and logical system of plant taxonomy.

Ray's species description rested on propagation from seed: no matter how much variation there was between individual organisms, if they came from seeds of the same plant, they belonged to the same species. He then extended this concept to animals. By modern standards, this is a generative definition of a species, based on generating the same forms reliably; it does not address interfertility, as the current biological concept of a species does. However, this was a great step forward for biology, providing a useful, commonly understood model that could be built upon by successive generations of taxonomists and other scientists.

Unlike Carl Linnaeus's later system of taxonomy, Ray's system of plant classification assessed the entire morphology of the plant, rather than primarily or exclusively the reproductive organs. In addition to defining a species, Ray was also the first to divide flowering plants into monocotyledonous and dicotyledonous classes. Although the distinction between these classes remains unclear and even contentious, this was still an important step towards a more natural, observation-based system of plant classification.

Ray's system of taxonomy greatly influenced later botanists, and taxonomy based on multiple characters eventually came to supersede and replace single-character or single-organ taxonomy systems such as Linnaeus's. Although the hierarchical nature and nomenclature of Linnaean taxonomy have survived, modern taxonomy owes more to Ray's morphological classification methods than to Linnaeus. *Historia Plantarum* and Ray's other works on taxonomy inspired generations of taxonomists, including Linnaeus, to collect, document, observe, and classify the natural world, ultimately providing the tools used by evolutionary biologists, ecologists, and other scientists to better understand the history of the world and its evolving ecosystems.

years later. The same year Willughby died, Ray married and returned with his wife to his hometown of Black Notley, where they raised four daughters.

LIFE'S WORK

In 1686, when Ray began work on his masterpiece, the *Historia Plantarum* (History of plants), the field of botany was experiencing profound shifts. Ray himself had helped bring about many of these changes in philosophy and methodology. Early British botanical surveys consisted of little more than alphabetically ordered lists of species, often incomplete, the names and descriptions sometimes contradictory and confusing. With the publication of his earlier catalogs, however, Ray had created new models and rules for the composition of such works. He broadened the scope of inquiry with his consideration of both cultivated and wild species, included information on pharmacology,

and critically assessed existing systems for naming plant species.

Ray also grappled with the problem of plant classification. For the revised and updated publication of his 1690 English catalog, the *Synopsis Stirpium Britannicarum*, Ray abandoned the traditional method of listing plants alphabetically and, in his quest for consistent, logical principles by which to categorize species, turned instead to morphology (form and structure). This shift, which laid the groundwork for modern classification schemes and the evolutionary biological principles underlying them, reflected ideas Ray had set forth earlier in the essay collection *Methodus Plantarum* (1682), in which he had proposed reducing the seemingly boundless number of recognized plant species by relying on a narrow range of invariable characteristics.

Ray's motivations for tightening identification standards were religious as well as scientific. As a scientist,

Ray believed that a plant's seed vessel provided the most rational basis for classification; to be recognized as a legitimate species, according to Ray's view, a plant had to be capable of breeding true to seed, or producing, as the result of self-fertilization, offspring with the same traits. As a man of deep faith in a Bible-based version of creation, Ray also believed that a fixed number of species had existed, unchanged, on the Earth from the beginning of time.

This new ways of conceptualizing the study of botany came together in Ray's *Historia Plantarum*, a massive treatise intended to provide a comprehensive guide to the flora of all of Europe. Ray wrote and revised the three-thousand-page work for nearly two decades, stopping in 1704, the year before his death. The *Historia Plantarum* meticulously explains the nomenclature, morphology, habitat, distribution, and pharmacological applications for each species listed. It also offered practical information on topics such as how to propagate seeds and cure plant diseases.

While Ray continued to maintain in the *Historia Plantarum* his conviction that breeding true to seed represents a requirement for classification as a species, he did modify his views on the fixity of species. Confronted with firsthand observation of physical evidence, Ray conceded that a small degree of transmutation was occasionally possible.

At the same time that Ray was producing his landmark botanical treatise, he was also working on the animal-kingdom survey begun by John Willughby. On the basis of notes Willughby had left behind, Ray completed works on birds and fish, both of which he published under his late friend's name. In *Orinthologiae* (1676), Ray followed the classification scheme he would later adopt in his botanical work by attempting to categorize birds on the basis of habitat and anatomical structure. *Historia Piscium* (1686) offers similarly organized descriptions of the anatomy and physiology of English freshwater and saltwater fish.

IMPACT

Ray died on January 17, 1705, but his most significant contribution to the field of zoology took the form of the posthumous publication of his *Historia Insectorum* in 1710. Entomology, or the study of insects, barely existed in Ray's time. Though his catalog of moths, butterflies, bees, wasps, and flies remained incomplete at the time of his death, it nevertheless broke new ground for generations of researchers.

Ray's publications also include a number of influential works of a nonscientific nature. His *Collection of English Words* (1673), for example, lists names of English birds and fishes, among other vocabulary items, and continues to provide invaluable information to scholars about various English dialects. It also contains descriptions of mining and other industrial operations of the era.

In addition, Ray wrote several books of theology and philosophy and the relationship of these disciplines to scientific inquiry. In *Three Physico-Theological Discourses* (1692), he attempted to square evidence contained in the fossil record with biblical accounts of the Creation and the Flood. Unlike many of his contemporaries, Ray was convinced that fossils represent the remains of organisms that were once alive, although he rejected the theory of extinction as incompatible with Christian doctrine. Yet, toward the end of his life, in the face of plant fossils bearing no resemblance to any living plant, Ray conceded evidence pointing to a much older planet than literal interpretations of Genesis would suggest. His work *The Wisdom of God Manifested in the Works of the Creation* (1691), which displays the breadth of his scientific knowledge of geology, paleontology, botany, zoology, and human anatomy and physiology, would be embraced by natural theologians for more than a century after his death.

Ray championed reliance on stringent firsthand observation and evaluation of physical evidence to support scientific theory. At the same time, he remained a staunch advocate of a worldview rooted in deep religious faith. The beauty and intricacies of nature revealed evidence, according to Ray's philosophy, of a divine creator; the study of natural history served as a spiritual exercise meant to demystify and glorify God's creation. Ray is remembered in the twenty-first century as much for his theological and philosophical writings as for his scientific achievements.

Beverly Ballaro

FURTHER READING

Hoskins, Stephen. "Who Was . . . John Ray: The Father of Natural History." *Biologist* 55.1 (2008): 21–22. Print. Discusses the development of Ray's animal and plant classification system and his scientific legacy in the field of natural history.

Huxley, Robert, ed. *The Great Naturalists*. London: Thames, 2007. Print. Contains biographies of notable naturalists and their contributions to the field;

includes information on the life and work of John Ray as the "English Aristotle."

Raven, Charles Earle. *John Ray, Naturalist: His Life and Works*. New York: Cambridge UP, 2009. Print.

A biography of Ray, first published in 1942, that discusses his life and his contributions to modern science and the fields of natural history and theology.

RENÉ-ANTOINE FERCHAULT DE RÉAUMUR

French naturalist

Réaumur markedly improved metallurgical technology in France and performed groundbreaking experiments involving limb regeneration in crustaceans. As a result of his observations of insects, he is considered by some to be the founder of animal-behavior studies.

Born: February 28, 1683; La Rochelle, France
Died: October 17 or 18, 1757; near Saint-Julien-du-Terroux, France
Primary fields: Biology; chemistry
Specialties: Ecology; zoology; metallurgy

EARLY LIFE

René-Antoine Ferchault de Réaumur was born on February 28, 1683, in La Rochelle, a small city on the west coast of France. His family, the Ferchaults, came from a life of commerce, and they entered the ranks of the lesser nobility when they purchased the Réaumur estate. Réaumur's father, who died in 1684, was in the legal profession. Réaumur's early education was most likely with the Jesuits. In 1699, he traveled to Bourges, in central France, to study civil law.

There is no indication that Réaumur's education included any substantial study of science or mathematics until 1703, when he settled in Paris and studied with Guisnée, a mathematician about whom little is known. Réaumur seems to have shown great aptitude for mathematics, and he subsequently furthered his education with Pierre Varignon, who taught him mathematics and physics, two subjects that were to influence Réaumur's later work. Varignon nominated Réaumur for membership in the French Academy of Sciences, an institution founded by Louis XIV to promote scientific research. Réaumur became a member of the academy in 1708 and remained involved with it for the rest of his life.

Réaumur continued to study mathematics until 1709, presenting such promising work to the academy that Varignon thought he would go on to achieve great things in the subject. However, mathematics was not to be the field in which Réaumur would make his contribution to the sciences. In 1709, he read and disagreed with a paper on the growth of mollusk shells, a fateful event that precipitated a shift in his studies and marked the beginning of his lifelong interest in natural history.

LIFE'S WORK

Despite his early training in mathematics, Réaumur devoted the majority of his life to other subjects, including metallurgy and natural history. In the early years of the eighteenth century, the French Academy of Sciences wanted to produce an encyclopedia of industry, and it was Réaumur who took on the project, a fact that might explain the diversity of his scientific studies in the decade following his admission to the academy.

The eclectic subjects that occupied Réaumur from 1710 to 1712 included determining that mollusk shells grow through accretion, rather than expansion; obtaining dye from mollusk shells; investigating the commercial potential of spider silk; and, most important, experimenting with the regeneration of crustacean limbs. Réaumur's work with crustaceans set him apart as a scientist because he created a highly controlled laboratory setting in which he could observe what happened when he cut off the legs of crayfish. At the time, the ability of crayfish to regenerate limbs was considered something of an old wives' tale, but through careful documentation, Réaumur proved the tale true.

Beginning in 1713, Réaumur focused primarily on the encyclopedia, and therefore on matters of technology instead of biology. Ironwork and the making of steel had long been practiced, but the field of metallurgy had not advanced particularly far. Réaumur set about studying iron, steel, and other metals, recording the way they fractured and examining the particles and patterns of fractured surfaces. He linked the patterns he observed to methods and speeds of cooling and connected the pattern and shape of the grain to the properties of the metal. Because iron castings were too hard to be worked, Réaumur began to experiment with methods of making them malleable. He noticed that when placed in a fire, iron develops a layer of oxides, beneath which it is soft; therefore, he intensified the process, deliberately adding oxides to cast iron before heating. He also developed a process to coat iron or steel with tin to render it less vulnerable to rust.

For the most part, the years following Réaumur's metallurgical work were dominated by his natural-history studies, but one of his final contributions to the field of technology was the invention of the thermometric scale known as the Réaumur scale. The thermometer used alcohol and an eighty-degree scale, with the freezing point of water set to zero and the boiling point set to eighty. The thermometer attempted to eliminate accuracy problems with the Fahrenheit scale, but it had other issues and was used in France for only a short time, roughly from the 1730s until the adoption of the Celsius scale in 1794.

During the 1730s and 1740s, Réaumur's worked on his proposed ten-volume *Mémoires pour servir à l'histoire des insects* (Memoirs to illustrate the history of insects, 1734–42). Only six volumes of the work were completed in Réaumur's lifetime, but they contain several groundbreaking studies. Perhaps the most significant is in volume two, which addresses the influence of temperature on the life cycle and development

René-Antoine Ferchault de Réaumur Discovers Carbon's Role in Hardening Steel

René-Antoine Ferchault de Réaumur wrote a treatise on transforming iron ore into steel, revolutionizing metallurgy in France. Réaumur's recommendations and analysis not only made it possible for France to produce steel for itself, rather than having to import the metal, but also helped pave the way for the Industrial Revolution.

Modern industry began to emerge in Europe in the eighteenth century, and one of the major requirements for its full emergence was a plentiful supply of raw materials from which tools and machinery could be manufactured. Pure iron was too soft for such a purpose, but steel was ideally suited to industrial applications. Steel is composed mostly of iron but contains less than 2 percent carbon, which makes it much harder and more resilient than iron alone.

It was Réaumur who determined the role of carbon in forming steel, making it possible to manufacture it on a mass scale. He became obsessed with metal production, perhaps because he had inherited a steel mill on the southwest coast of France. In his survey of crafts, he had noticed that France lagged behind its neighbors in the production of steel. As a result, the French manufacturing industry depended on imported steel from Germany.

Réaumur's discussions with metalworkers led him to a scientific investigation of the principles behind their craft, namely the chemistry of iron ore in its smelted products. It was the first time iron had ever been studied chemically. Réaumur examined the different chemical compositions of iron when smelted from different types of ores, testing cast iron, steel, and wrought iron. He was also the first scientist to use a microscope to observe their different crystalline structures. Ultimately, he discovered that the proportion of carbon in the smelted product is the primary factor determining the product's ductility or lack thereof.

In 1722, Réaumur published the results of twelve years of intense study in *L'Art de convertir le fer forgé* (*Memoirs on Steel and Iron*, 1956). His treatise discusses the methods for producing cast iron, wrought iron, and steel and indicates which minerals should be added to or eliminated from steel to enhance its ductility and resistance. It also introduces a method Réaumur had discovered for producing steel by adding iron oxides to melted iron and recommends cleaning and polishing steel stock before rolling it into sheets. King Louis XV was sufficiently impressed by the work that he awarded Réaumur a large pension, which Réaumur generously forwarded to the French Academy of Sciences to further scientific research.

While steel had long been produced by the time Réaumur published his treatise, the chemical principles underlying its production were unknown. By revealing those principles, Réaumur revolutionized iron and steel production. His practical recommendations made it possible for the French to produce their own steel in much greater quantities, greatly reducing their dependence on foreign imports. It was his theoretical scientific analysis, however, that enabled future metallurgists and engineers to refine manufacturing techniques and ultimately supersede Réaumur's methods, thus helping to establish the general usefulness of scientific analysis for developing modern industrial techniques—one of many developments in the eighteenth century that made possible the Industrial Revolution.

of insects. Réaumur went about exploring this question with his usual thoroughness, keeping pupae in warm and cool conditions and noting the moths' emergence times. Using these observations, he was able to estimate population increases under different conditions. Réaumur also included the impact of parasites and predators on butterfly populations, studying how population increases are controlled and how weather conditions affect both predator and prey.

Volume five of Réaumur's *Mémoires* focuses on bees and flies. His work with bees is particularly noteworthy because he began to delve into the manner in which bees communicate, something that had not been researched before. Methodically, Réaumur tracked individual bees, dissected them and discovered parasites inside them, recorded hibernation temperatures, and elucidated the function of the queen and how the hive responded when she was taken away or when new queens were introduced. In essence, he documented every aspect of bee biology that he could. The seventh volume of *Mémoires* was never finished, but the partial manuscript includes documentation of Réaumur's observations of ant diet and hibernation patterns, ant-aphid interactions, mating biology, and ant predation of flowers of fruit trees.

Réaumur's scientific work consumed his life, and he never married or had a family. The exact date of his death is not known; he died on either October 17 or 18, 1757, of injuries sustained after falling from his horse.

IMPACT

In the eighteenth century, tools such as the microscope had not long been in existence and were not as powerful as they would become. Therefore, little was known about the chemistry or molecular structure of metals. For this and other reasons, France was lagging far behind in the field of metalwork. Thus, Réaumur's studies, particularly his method of creating malleable iron, were tremendously important to advancing French industry.

While Réaumur is not famous for any particular discovery or theory, he had a profound influence on his contemporaries and the scientists who came after him. His methods of observation and experimentation, particularly with regard to regeneration and insect behavior, were unique and groundbreaking, doing much to improve the ways animals were studied.

Réaumur was notable for nurturing the work of other scientists, particularly at the start of their careers. When his observations of aphids led him to conclude that only female aphids existed, he invited others to continue his work in case he was in error. This led to Swiss naturalist Charles Bonnet discovering parthenogenesis in aphids.

Throughout his life, Réaumur was constantly involved with the French Academy of Sciences, serving as either its director or its subdirector, influencing the course of the sciences and technology in France for the span of four decades during a time of immense change and innovation. In this and other ways, he fostered the scientific community. He was incredibly forward thinking in his encouragement of the sharing of research, specimens, and knowledge.

J. D. Ho

FURTHER READING

Egerton, Frank N. "A History of the Ecological Sciences, Part 21: Réaumur and His History of Insects." *Bulletin of the Ecological Society of America* 87.3 (2006): 212–24. Print. Focuses on Réaumur's entomological studies, putting them in the context of the work of his contemporaries and paying particular attention to how he influenced other naturalists. Extensive bibliography.

James, Ioan Mackenzie. *Remarkable Biologists: From Ray to Hamilton.* New York: Cambridge UP, 2009. Print. Provides a solid biographical background and situates Réaumur's work by profiling the scientists who came before and after him, creating a chronology of ideas and influence.

Ratcliff, Marc J. "Experimentation, Communication, and Patronage: A Perspective on René-Antoine Ferchault de Réaumur (1683–1757)." *Biology of the Cell* 97.4 (2005): 231–33. Print. Discusses Réaumur's scientific method, his encouragement of the sharing of information and specimens, and how he helped create a scientific culture that had a lasting impact on other scientists.

Smith, Cyril Stanley. *A History of Metallography: The Development of Ideas on the Structure of Metals before 1890.* Chicago: U of Chicago P, 1960. Print. Focuses solely on Réaumur as an innovator in metallurgy, discussing both the importance of his scientific method and his impact on French industry. Illustrations.

ELLEN SWALLOW RICHARDS
American chemist

Nineteenth-century scientist Ellen Swallow Richards is considered the first female American chemist. In addition to being the first woman admitted to MIT, she is known for her work in environmental chemistry, sanitary engineering, public health, and home economics.

Born: December 3, 1842; Dunstable, Massachusetts
Died: March 30, 1911; Boston, Massachusetts
Primary field: Chemistry
Specialty: Ecology

EARLY LIFE
Ellen Swallow Richards was born Ellen Henrietta Swallow on December 3, 1842, in Dunstable, Massachusetts. Her parents, Fanny Taylor and Peter Swallow, were both professional teachers. Richards received both traditional and practical education from her parents; as the couple's only child, she helped with all of the daily chores on the family farm. When Richards was seventeen, her family moved to Westford, Massachusetts, where she attended the prestigious Westford Academy. Despite being homeschooled for seventeen years, she did well in school, even tutoring her fellow students in her free time.

The term *applied science* means taking scientific, often abstract, principles and applying them to practical problems. Although she was likely unfamiliar with this term, Richards displayed a talent for applied science early in her career. Assisting her father in the shop he had opened in Westford, she began to notice the buying habits of the customers, as well as the effects of water and air pollution on product quality.

In 1863, after graduating from Westford, Richards moved to Littleton, Massachusetts, where she worked as a teacher, housekeeper, cook, and nurse in order to save money to attend school. In 1868, she was accepted for study at Vassar College, a newly opened institution for women. There, she studied astronomy with Maria Mitchell, though she would eventually concentrate mostly on chemistry. At Vassar, Richards studied a radioactive mineral called samarskite and hypothesized that it contained unknown elements. Though she was unable to fully explore this idea, the existence of two previously unknown elements—samarium and gadolinium—was confirmed when they were discovered in the mineral several years later, just as she had predicted.

Richards graduated from Vassar in 1870, at the age of twenty-seven, and immediately sought further education. Unfortunately, at that time there were no scientific colleges that would admit women. Nonetheless, Richards vowed to earn a degree from the prestigious Massachusetts Institute of Technology (MIT).

LIFE'S WORK
Richards wanted nothing more than to be able to study at MIT, but the school would not admit women. She cleaned, sewed, and performed other housework for the professors, hoping to win their favor and gain acceptance to the school, but her plan did not succeed. Fortunately, several of Richards's Vassar professors wrote letters of recommendation to MIT. Eventually, the school agreed to take her on as a special student, allowing her to study there for free to avoid the stigma of officially enrolling a woman. Her tenure as the first female student at a scientific institution was referred to as "the Swallow experiment." After she earned her bachelor of science degree in chemistry in 1873, by which time she had also earned a master of arts degree from Vassar, Richards became MIT's first woman teacher, albeit without a salary or an official title.

Richards's concerns about product purity, which dated from her days working in her father's shop, informed her later studies of air, water, and food purity. During the 1870s, she worked with William Ripley Nichols, widely considered one of the highest authorities on water supplies. When the Massachusetts Board of Health asked for Nichols's help with a statewide survey of water supplies, Richards was enlisted to assist. She devoted her knowledge and enthusiasm to the project, supervising the testing of more than twenty thousand water samples, a massive undertaking at the time. She was appointed chemist to the Board of Health from 1872 to 1875 and served as water analyst from 1887 to 1897. In the course of her studies, Richards determined how much chlorine water normally contains and the extent to which industry increases chlorine levels, work that prompted the city of Lawrence to build Massachusetts's first facility for studying water pollution.

In 1875, Richards married MIT metallurgy professor Robert Hallowell Richards, the head of MIT's Department of Mining Engineering. Though the couple's fields did not intersect, Richards took an interest in her husband's work. She published papers on the mineral

Ellen Swallow Richards Develops Home Economics

Nineteenth-century American chemist Ellen Swallow Richards is considered a pioneer in the fields of eco-feminism and home economics. Not only did Richards found a new branch of science and chemistry with women at its center, but she also carved out a place for the female perspective within the academic world. As an instructor of chemistry, Richards was able to incorporate issues related to women into her scientific curriculum. She introduced ideas including nutrition, clothing, sanitation, and home management, effectively founding the field of home economics. Richards emphasized practical scientific application of domestic concepts through the analysis and understanding of what she first called *municipal housekeeping*.

Richards's goal in opening up the field of home economics was twofold; she hoped to spark the interest of women in academic scientific subjects while also cultivating and augmenting their role within the domestic sphere. She was interested in communicating ideas of physical fitness, good nutrition, organic foods, and the creation of efficient clothing. Focusing on all of these topics, she argued, would enable women to concentrate their domestic efforts not just on cooking and cleaning but also on tasks that were larger and more substantial in scope. In Richards's model, the role of women now aimed to merge domestic work with scientific work.

To effectively teach women about home economics, Richards assembled model kitchens that were open to the public, initiated academic programs of study, coordinated conferences on home management, and acted as a general spokesperson for the new discipline she had created. These annual conferences began to solidify the key concepts surrounding professionalism, home economics, and home management. They also united various members of the academic community who sought to add support to a growing women's movement. In 1908, Richards established the American Home Economics Association, of which she became president. She encouraged women's colleges to adopt the discipline of "domestic science," arguing that by understanding ideas related to home economics, women could further expand their knowledge of larger social and political issues.

As the first woman in America to gain acceptance to the Massachusetts Institute of Technology (MIT), and in fact the first woman to be admitted to any American scientific college, Richards played a crucial role in igniting interest in what would eventually become the feminist movement. While at MIT, she founded the Women's Laboratory and developed the school's first curriculum in the field of life sciences. In 1881, along with feminist academic Marion Talbot, Richards established the American Association of University Women in order to encourage future women graduates to pursue higher education.

industries and was one of two women awarded membership to the American Institute of Mining Engineers in 1879.

Richards recognized that not all women had the same kinds of professional contacts that she had, and if they were to succeed in science, they would need the same opportunities and tools as men. She established the science division of the Society to Encourage Studies at Home and later solicited funding for, and guided the production of, MIT's Women's Laboratory. It was a step in the right direction for women in science, but Richards's students were still not official MIT students. It was not until 1883, based on the success of the Women's Laboratory and thanks to Richards's influence, that MIT allowed women full status as students.

Once MIT officially decided to allow women to attend as full students, Richards was hired as a full professor. She was assigned to MIT's sanitary chemistry department in 1884, where she remained for the rest of her career. While there, she also continued her own studies and research into contamination, proposing simple ways for people to prevent contamination and the spread of disease. Even though physician Ignaz Semmelweis had been encouraging doctors to wash their hands since 1847, Richards was the first to suggest that public towels and drinking cups in public restrooms harbored infectious diseases. She also recognized that America's rapid industrialization had caused environmental problems. Richards was one of the first to propose that efficiency and ecology did not have to be mutually exclusive; indeed, she introduced the German term *Ökologie* (ecology) to the English-speaking world in 1892.

Working with chemist and MIT professor John M. Ordway, Richards also studied spontaneous combustion and fireproofing, eventually developing methods and materials for creating fire-resistant factories and thereby saving the lives of countless factory workers. Edward Atkinson, one of her coworkers on the fire-proofing project, appointed her the first woman science consultant to the Manufacturers Mutual Fire Insurance Company.

Drawing on her practical knowledge, Richards created a housekeeping school at the Boston-based Women's Educational and Industrial Union in 1899. The school taught Richards's specialized branch of ecology known as domestic sciences, which eventually became known as home economics. One of the main tenets of home economics involved more sanitary and efficient methods of food preparation and cooking.

Richards called her proposal for proper food preparation *euthenics*, from the Greek *euthenein*, meaning to thrive or flourish. Based on her conclusions, she published *Food Materials and Their Adulterations* in 1885, which resulted in the first Pure Food and Drug Act in Massachusetts. Richards completely remodeled her own home based on the principles of home economics, creating better heating and ventilation systems and even rerouting her plumbing to make it more efficient. She demonstrated her new methods of cooking at the 1893 Chicago World's Fair.

IMPACT

Richards's revolutionary ideas about applying science to everyday life inspired many of the modern conveniences taken for granted in the twenty-first century, including dry cleaning and school lunch programs, which rely heavily on the principles of euthenics. In *The Cost of Shelter* (1905), she outlined ways to make homes more efficient and cost effective, many of which involve reducing the size of homes. These ideas received their fair share of criticism, which stemmed mostly from the perceived status of elegantly designed homes and indentured servants at the time.

In 1908, Richards was elected the first president of the American Home Economics Association, which she had helped found. Even though she had received more than the requisite amount of education usually required for achieving a doctoral degree, it was not until 1910, when Smith College granted Richards an honorary doctorate, that she was so honored. She died a year later in Jamaica Plain, Massachusetts. In 1973, Vassar College established the Ellen Swallow Richards Professorship, and in 1993, she was inducted into the National Women's Hall of Fame.

Alex K. Rich

FURTHER READING

Bowden, Mary Ellen. *Chemical Achievers: The Human Face of the Chemical Sciences*. Philadelphia: Chemical Heritage Foundation, 1997. 156–58. Print. Discusses Richards as a notable chemist and includes information on her work applying scientific principles to home economics.

Clarke, Robert. *Ellen Swallow: The Woman Who Founded Ecology*. Chicago: Follett, 1973. Print. A biography of Richards that discusses her work related to environmentalism, water purity, and sanitary engineering.

Goldstein, Carolyn Goldstein. *Creating Consumers: Home Economics in Twentieth-Century America*. Chapel Hill: U of North Carolina P, 2012. Print. Presents information on the history of home economics and women consumers, noting Richards's role in creating the field of home economics and her work combining scientific research and social change.

Richardson, Barbara. "Ellen Swallow Richards: 'Humanistic Oekologist,' 'Applied Sociologist,' and the Founding of Sociology." *American Sociologist* 33.3 (2002): 27–57. Print. Discusses Richards as a feminist and reformer, describing her views on women's roles and her influence in areas such as women's labor, education, and social movements.

BERNHARD RIEMANN

German mathematician

Nineteenth-century German mathematician Bernhard Riemann built on the work of German mathematician Gottfried Leibniz and Swiss mathematician Leonhard Euler to define position mathematically, as a corollary to defining magnitude algebraically. Riemann's algebraic functions and Riemannian geometry laid the *foundations of the field of topology, central to physics, quantum theory, and general relativity.*

Born: September 17, 1826; Breselenz, German Confederation
Died: July 20, 1866; Selasca, Italy

Primary field: Mathematics
Specialty: Geometry

EARLY LIFE

Georg Friedrich Bernhard Riemann was born on September 17, 1826 in the Hanoverian village of Breselenz (now Jameln, Germany). His father, a Lutheran pastor, had two sons and four daughters with Riemann's mother, Charlotte Ebell. When Riemann was young, his mother and several other members of his family contracted tuberculosis and died. Bernhard started studying arithmetic around the age of six and quickly became a prodigy. He was homeschooled and began developing his own mathematical problems. At age ten, Riemann's father arranged for a tutor to instruct his son in more advanced math and geometry.

At fourteen, Riemann left home for the first time to live with his grandmother in Hanover, where he attended school for two years. At sixteen, his grandmother died, and Riemann moved to Lüneburg to continue his secondary education.

Riemann's father wanted him to become a preacher, and Bernhard studied Hebrew in Lüneburg. An outstanding student of mathematics, he was excused from regular math classes and invited to read from the instructor's library. He read mathematician Adrien-Marie Legendre's 859-page *Theory of Numbers* in six days. He mastered Legendre's work and became interested in prime numbers. The so-called Riemann's hypothesis, a problem he developed later and that mathematicians have yet to solve, stems from Legendre's work concerning how many prime numbers exist. Bernhard also studied Euler's calculus. At nineteen, he went to study theology and philology at the University of Göttingen. His passion for numbers drew him to mathematical lectures in equation theory, definite integrals, terrestrial magnetism, and Carl Friedrich Gauss's least squares. Bernhard eventually gained his father's permission to forego becoming a preacher to study mathematics in Berlin.

LIFE'S WORK

For two years in Berlin, Riemann studied modern mathematics. After attending lectures by mathematician Gustav Lejeune Dirichlet, he became interested in analysis and number theory. Riemann also studied modern geometry, including elliptic functions. He developed the idea that elliptic functions could be derived using complex variables. This spawned one of his most outstanding contributions to mathematical history, an analytic function of a complex variable.

In his early twenties, Riemann returned to Göttingen to study philosophy. At Göttingen, Riemann worked with physicist Wilhelm Weber, a student of mathematician Carl Friedrich. Riemann became Weber's lab assistant in experimental physics. In 1851, Riemann, at the age of twenty-five, submitted his dissertation to Gauss with the title "Foundations for a general theory of functions of one complex variable." The dissertation revolutionized elliptic functions and algebraic geometry and laid the foundations for modern holomorphic functions, the system of topology, Abelian integrals, and Riemann manifolds. Biographers have since theorized that Riemann was seeking some kind of unified field theory. Riemann's work was not officially proved accurate until mathematician David Hilbert examined his work in 1900.

In 1853, Riemann's interest in physics, first stimulated by Weber, once again flowered. In December 1853, he prepared papers on gravity, light, magnetism, and electricity and applied for his Habilitationsschrift (a required lecture and paper for academic advancement in Germany). Success in one's Habilitationsschrift would gain a scholar permission to lecture at the university for no pay. Although Riemann hoped his work in physics would be accepted, Gauss encouraged Riemann to write on the foundations of geometry instead. Riemann had to start afresh, and his progress was slowed by health problems. It was spring before his work was ready. Riemann's probationary work included a lecture given June 10, 1854. This paper, "On the hypotheses which lie at the foundations of geometry," matched algebra with geometric proofs and made possible the application of geometry to physics. Gauss approved of this Riemann earned a lectureship. In later decades, physicist Albert Einstein would recognize in Riemann's work the material he was looking for to explain a universe of curvature.

From 1855 to 1859, Riemann and Dirichlet collaborated on Abelian functions, hypergeometric series, and differential equations. During this time, Riemann had a nervous breakdown and took a vacation in the mountains. Richard Dedekind, a fellow mathematician and good friend of his, joined him. Riemann recovered and his theory on Abelian functions was published in 1857. That same year, he gained the title of assistant professor. Although the position resulted in more earnings for Riemann, he continued to struggle financially.

Dirichlet died May 5, 1859. The government made Riemann his successor, partly due to Dirichlet's constant support and partly to Riemann's own growing reputation. He was granted an apartment, and other

The Riemann Manifold

German mathematician Carl Friedrich Gauss, hired by the king of Prussia to survey his entire kingdom, developed a way to measure the distance of a curve from within that curve. This work influenced Bernhard Riemann and inspired one of his most interesting contributions to topology, the Riemann manifold.

Topology developed in the later nineteenth century and became a major mathematical field in the twentieth century. It is the study of those properties of geometric configurations that are not affected by twisting, stretching, etc. The planes of the real world can be measured with integrals and derivatives in two, three, and four dimensions. In 1854, Riemann presented a theory that allowed these old techniques to expand into n (limitless) dimensions if the planes were very small. Working under Gauss, who had proved from the simple physical world of the surveyor that he could measure a valley without climbing outside onto the mountain, Riemann too went beyond the usual dimensions. He took the mathematics of such measurements into infinite dimensions represented by the variable n. The result is an infinite variety of manifolds that can be measured in terms of distance, and in which angles can be determined, all without reference to a space outside the manifold. This is of utmost importance, since humans cannot go outside three, or at most four, dimensions. It simplifies measurements for mathematicians, since they need not add extra dimensions in the abstract (which complicates things) to study a given surface.

Algebraically, the Riemann manifold is a structure of points that has the nature of a curve, or a one-dimensional complex shape, or a field extending according to R to the nth power to a finite limit. The usefulness of Riemann manifolds is that they enable professional geometers to measure with a Riemannian metric and calculus, geometric features of complex structures. Mathematicians can calculate distance and angle, if the manifolds are differentiable. Some are not. Riemannian manifolds also apply to Einstein's general relativity as a method for calculating changes to spaces over distances due to gravitational fields. Higher-dimension manifolds are also important in quantum physics and come up both in field theory and gravitation. Spacetime with its four dimensions, symmetry groups of multi-dimensions, and gauge fields are all basic to the study of field theory and gravitation. These can be studied in terms developed by Riemann in his work on the Riemann manifold.

European mathematicians started to recognize his contributions. Riemann traveled to Paris in 1860 and began his memoir. In this, he developed quadratic differential forms, which are basic to relativity theory. Later, Einstein's 1916 publication on general relativity scrutinized Riemann's ideas. Now well paid, Riemann married one of his sisters' friends, Elise Koch, in July 1862. He was thirty-six. Two months later, he began suffering from pleurisy, a symptom of tuberculosis and pneumonia.

Riemann convalesced in Italy, and for the rest of his life travelled between home and southern Italy, seeking a full recovery that never came. His daughter, Ida, was born in Pisa, 1863. Early in 1866, Riemann was named a foreign member of the Berlin Academy. In March 1866, he became a member of the French Academy of Sciences, and in June, he was elected to the Royal Society of London. He worked when his strength allowed him to until his last day, studying the mechanics of the inner ear's workings. Riemann died July 20, 1866 in Selasca, Lake Maggiore. He was buried in the village of Boganzola.

IMPACT

Non-Euclidian geometry, relatively new in the nineteenth century, was not immediately accepted in academic communities during Riemann's era. Riemann observed that the Cartesian plane, comparable to a piece of paper, was not truly flat. When observed in minute detail, the Cartesian plane is a jumble of complex planes, and Riemann was fascinated with the mathematics of these tiny spaces. This was a revolutionary contrast to Euclid, and many academics became angry when Riemann challenged time-treasured theories. Riemann's theories were called curious and absurd. However, they changed existing knowledge of geometry and space from flat and limited to infinite and point-crammed, making more knowledge of these spaces and geometries accessible to geometers. Riemann's definition of curvature presaged Einstein's theory of relativity.

Much more productive research has been done in the wake of almost everything Riemann developed. His flair was for making connections among things that seemed disparate at the time, but which now are taken for granted. For example, before Riemann, math and physics were distinctly separate fields, with empirical research heavy on the physics side, and the possibility of pure research tempting on the other. Today, the two fields are deeply interlinked. Riemann's scope of genius was fostered no doubt by his wide-ranging studies in mathematics, philosophy, physics, electricity, gravity, the human ear, theology, and language. His so-called Riemann surfaces are widely considered the most productive and influential of his scientific contributions.

Amanda R. Jones

FURTHER READING

Jost, Jürgen. *Riemann Geometry and Geometric Analysis*. 5th ed. Berlin: Springer, 2008. Print. Presents Riemannian geometry from the vantage point of Einstein's theory of general relativity. Includes a discussion of quantum field theory.

Knoebel, Arthur, et al. *Mathematical Masterpieces: Further Chronicles by the Explorers*. New York: Springer, 2007. Print. Reviews mathematical histories of discrete/continuous algorithms, curvature, and number history. Each section contains reproductions of primary documents and concludes with problems to solve.

Odifreddi, Piergiorgio. *The Mathematical Century: The 30 Greatest Problems of the Last 100 Years*. Trans. Arturo Sangalli. Princeton: Princeton UP, 2004. Print. Presents a review of the work of mathematician David Hilbert, whose work utilizes Riemannian geometry.

OLE CHRISTENSEN RØMER

Danish astronomer

Seventeenth-century Danish astronomer and mathematician Ole Christensen Rømer was the first scientist to demonstrate that light was not instantaneous and the first scientist to attempt to measure its speed. In addition to his work as a teacher, observatory builder, and instrument maker, he served two kings of Denmark in a number of important and influential posts.

Born: September 25, 1644; Aarhus (Århus), Denmark
Died: September 19, 1710; Copenhagen, Denmark
Primary field: Astronomy
Specialties: Observational astronomy; theoretical astronomy

EARLY LIFE

Ole Christensen Rømer was born on September 25, 1644 in Aarhus (also known as Århus), Denmark, a large, ancient city and major port. He was the son of successful shipping merchant Christen Pedersen and his wife Anna Olufsdatter Storm Pedersen, the daughter of a local politician. Weary of being mistaken for other men in the area named Christen, Pedersen changed the family surname to Rømer to indicate his origin: Rømø, one of the Wadden Sea islands off the southwest coast of Denmark.

A bright and curious child, Rømer was educated through the equivalent of high school in Aarhus. At the age of eighteen, he was enrolled at the University of Copenhagen to study mathematics with a concentration on astronomy. He continued with his education following his father's death in 1663.

At the university, Rømer took courses from brothers Thomas Bartholin, a mathematician and physician, and Rasmus Bartholin, professor of geometry and medicine. Rasmus observed and wrote about the great comet of 1664–65, visible for weeks, an object that was later blamed for the Great Plague of London (1665–66) and the Great Fire of London (1666). Rasmus, whom King Frederick III had selected to publish the papers of Danish astronomer Tycho Brahe, was much taken with Rømer's keen mind, and in 1664 brought him into the Bartholin home to help with the task. The project consumed more than six years, during which time Rømer earned a bachelor's degree at the university and fell in love with Rasmus's daughter, Anne Marie.

LIFE'S WORK

In 1671, while double-checking the calculations in Brahe's manuscripts, Rømer and Bartholin traveled to Hven Island to visit the site of Brahe's observatory, Uraniborg, which had been demolished in 1601. There they met and worked with Bartholin correspondent Jean-Felix Picard, a French priest and astronomer who was conducting his own research related to the late Dane's observations.

Picard, impressed by Rømer's enthusiasm and talent for astronomy, offered the young man a position at the brand-new Royal Observatory in Paris (opened in 1671).

Rømer's Proposition: The Speed of Light Has a Finite Limit

In the seventeenth century, the two-thousand-year-old Aristotelian view of the nature of light was still generally accepted. Light was considered an instantaneous phenomenon of infinite speed. Though scientists throughout millennia had occasionally suggested that light might not be immediate, until the invention of the telescope in the early 1600s, it was impossible to closely observe, time, and measure the movements of distant objects—a capability that was key to the examination of the properties of light.

By the 1670s, when Ole Christensen Rømer began working at the Royal Observatory in Paris, telescopes had been considerably strengthened and improved. Some of the improvements came courtesy of Rømer himself, whose refinements increased the accuracy of their measurements and enhanced the value of astronomical observations. As part of his duties working under observatory director Giovanni Cassini, Rømer was tasked with studying the orbit of Io, the innermost of the four moons of Jupiter that Galileo discovered in 1610, and the fourth-largest satellite in the solar system. The observations were recorded in tables that Cassini published, which served as an aid to navigators and cartographers in calculating longitude by predicting when Io's eclipses would be visible from given latitudes.

For four solid years, Rømer faithfully watched and timed Io moving around Jupiter. During that time, he observed that it took about 42 hours for the moon to circle the planet. Each orbit, Jupiter eclipsed Io. Rømer timed and recorded the periods of hundreds of eclipses. Over the months, he noted that the intervals between Io's eclipses gradually decreased as Earth moved toward Jupiter, and increased as Earth moved away from the giant planet. Rømer attributed the 22-minute difference between the shortest and longest intervals to the changing distances between Earth and Jupiter, and concluded from the discrepancy that light must have a finite speed. The farther it had to travel, the longer it took for light to reach Earth. Rømer published his findings in 1676. His discovery stirred considerable debate and inspired contemporaries like astronomers and physicists Christiaan Huygens and Isaac Newton to explore the properties and characteristics of light.

Rømer attempted to calculate the actual speed of light. However, hampered by imprecise information about the orbits of Jupiter and Earth, and a lack of standardization in terrestrial measurements, his estimates of light speed were about one-third too slow. Rømer, having begun the investigation, subsequently turned to other matters. Within a decade, Newton suggested that, based on Rømer's findings, it would take about eight minutes for light from the sun to reach Earth (the accepted modern figure is eight minutes and nineteen seconds). By the early seventeenth century, other astronomers had zeroed in on light's actual speed. Advanced technology in the twentieth century ultimately fixed the speed of light at 186,282 miles per second—a fundamental concept essential to astronomy, physics, communication, computer science and space exploration.

The opportunity was too good to pass up, so Rømer accepted. He was immediately inducted into the new French Academy of Sciences (founded by "the Sun King," Louis XIV in 1666), and in 1672 he relocated to Paris.

In France, under the patronage of long-reigning Louis XIV, Rømer worked alongside Picard as an assistant to Italian-born astronomer Giovanni Cassini, designer and director of the Royal Observatory. Rømer was kept busy with a number of projects. He served as astronomy tutor to the king's eldest son and heir apparent, eleven-year-old Louis (called the Dauphin, or dolphin, from an ancient coat-of-arms insignia). With Picard, Rømer worked to solve hydraulic problems associated with the renovation and expansion of the fountain systems in the garden of the Versailles palace. One of his major tasks, under the auspices of the French Academy of Sciences, was to conduct astronomical observations throughout the country. It was while making these observations in the mid-1670s that Rømer first measured the speed of light. After publishing his findings, Rømer came to the attention of King Christian V of Denmark, who reserved a professorship for Rømer.

Rømer did not leave France until 1681. Upon his arrival in Denmark, he was finally able to marry Anne Marie Bartholin. The same year, under the patronage of King Christian V, he was appointed professor of astronomy and mathematics at the University of Copenhagen. He was also named astronomer royal, in which capacity he became director of the Rundtarnen (Round Tower) in Copenhagen, one of the oldest state-supported observatories in Europe. Rømer refurbished the observatory and installed several new astronomical instruments at the facility, some of his own invention.

Christian V relied increasingly upon Rømer in technical matters. After Christian's death in a hunting accident in 1699, his successor, Frederick IV, continued the astronomer's sponsorship. Rømer, as a favored court official, served in a variety of advisory roles to both kings and was rewarded accordingly. He was named master of the mint, royal harbor surveyor, and inspector of naval architecture. He was also named the king's authority on ballistics, and he was put in charge of a highway commission.

Rømer gained political power as well. In 1688, he was named a member of the Privy Council. Five years later, he served as a judicial magistrate. In 1694, he was appointed top tax assessor. By 1705, he had been elected as a senator and as mayor of Copenhagen, and in 1706 he held a post as head of the state council. A true dynamo as a public servant, Rømer was seen everywhere during Copenhagen's rapid expansion in the late seventeenth and early eighteenth centuries. He plotted new paved streets and avenues, planned and installed city lighting (inventing an oil lamp in the process), improved sewage systems, and made provisions for more reliable water supplies and drainage. Rømer also served as a police prefect and fire marshal.

Despite all his civil duties, Rømer did not neglect his scientific work. He devised a number of new instruments and made improvements to other devices. In 1704, he built the Tusculum, or Tusculanum, observatory near Vridsløsemagle, his summer home, and filled it with the most accurate astronomical instruments of the day. Rømer continued to research particular problems—such as measuring the parallax of stars and the length of Earth's orbit around the sun—until his death a week before his sixty-sixth birthday.

IMPACT

A multitalented scientist, Rømer delved into civil engineering, hydraulics, and cartography. He was also skilled at designing instruments related to his principal specialty, astronomy. Some of Rømer's innovations still exist, while others have been lost.

Rømer's solution to the problem of bringing water to the palace gardens of Versailles allows for the magnificent fountains to continue astonishing visitors to this day. As a Danish court official, he instituted the Gregorian calendar (introduced in 1582) on March 1, 1700, making Denmark one of the first non-Catholic countries

to adopt the solar part of the new calendar (the lunar portion was not accepted until 1776). To simplify commercial trade, he reformed and standardized the Danish system of weights and measures, anticipating the metric system that would become commonplace in Europe in the early nineteenth century. Rømer created a new thermometer based on the fixed freezing and boiling points of water, which inspired his correspondent Daniel Gabriel Fahrenheit to devise the temperature scale that bears his name.

Models of some of Rømer's astronomy-specific instruments can still be seen in museums throughout the world. Among these are a planetarium showing the planets orbiting the sun, and an eclipsarium to calculate the orbit and eclipses of the moon; both were first built in Paris in the late 1670s by royal clockmaker Isaac Thuret, who used Rømer's designs. Another invention, the transit telescope, which measures angular distances from the zenith of stars passing the meridian, has long been adopted in astronomy. Rømer's alt-azimuth mount, which rotates an instrument about vertical and horizontal axes, has been adapted for multiple modern purposes: telescopes, cameras, solar panels, and artillery.

The bulk of Rømer's written work was destroyed in the Great Copenhagen Fire of 1728, which consumed much of the city and damaged the Round Tower observatory. Only a few pages of notes concerning his planetary observations were preserved. These papers assisted nineteenth-century German astronomer Johann Gottfried Galle in discovering the planet Neptune.

Jack Ewing

FURTHER READING

Christianson, John Robert. *On Tycho's Island: Tycho Brahe and his Assistants, 1570–1601.* Cambridge: Cambridge UP, 2009. Print. Illustrated study of the work of the Danish astronomer and alchemist Tycho Brahe who inspired others, like his assistant Johannes Kepler and his compatriot Ole Rømer, to continue and expand upon his groundbreaking research.

Osborne, Richard. *The Universe: Explained, Condensed, and Exploded.* Edison, New Jersey: Chartwell, 2009. Print. Illustrated overview of the cosmos. Incorporates the history of observation and exploration while touching upon such astronomical concepts as the origin of the universe, the nature of time and the character of space.

Taton, Reni, and Curtis Wilson, eds. *Planetary Astronomy from the Renaissance to the Rise of Astrophysics:*

Part A, Tycho Brahe to Newton. Cambridge: Cambridge UP, 2003. Print. Multivolume project that covers the entire scope of investigation of the solar system from earliest times to the present, with emphasis on individuals like Ole Rømer who helped advance the science of astronomy.

WILHELM CONRAD RÖNTGEN

German physicist

Wilhelm Conrad Röntgen made important contributions to several areas of physics but is best known for his revolutionary discovery of X-rays and his investigations of their properties.

Born: March 27, 1845; Lennep, Prussia (now Remscheid, Germany)
Died: February 10, 1923; Munich, Germany
Also known as: Wilhelm Conrad Roentgen
Primary field: Physics
Specialty: Atomic and molecular physics

EARLY LIFE

Wilhelm Conrad Röntgen was the only child of Friedrich Conrad Röntgen, a German textile manufacturer and merchant, and Charlotte Constanza Frowein, who came from a Dutch merchant family. When he was three, his family moved to Apeldoorn, his mother's hometown in Holland. There, he attended primary public school and later became a student at Kostschool, a private boarding school. In 1862, Röntgen went to Utrecht, where he entered a secondary technical school, from which he was later expelled for refusing to inform on a fellow student who had drawn an unflattering caricature of a teacher. Although he attended some classes at the University of Utrecht, he was unable to become a formal student because he lacked a secondary school diploma. He resolved his academic problems by passing the difficult entrance examination of the recently established Federal Institute of Technology (or Polytechnic) in Zurich, Switzerland.

In November 1865, Röntgen began his education as a mechanical engineer. Over the next three years, he studied various technical courses but found his greatest fulfillment in a physics course taught by Rudolf Clausius, a distinguished scientist who helped found modern thermodynamics. Röntgen eventually passed his final examinations with excellent grades and received his diploma on August 6, 1869.

Röntgen remained in Zurich after graduation to work in the laboratory of August Kundt, a Polytechnic physics professor who had befriended him. Röntgen studied different gases to see if they all expanded uniformly with increases in temperature, as predicted by Gay-Lussac's law, and discovered that some had expanded to greater volumes than the law predicted. Less than a year later, he submitted his dissertation, "Studies on Gases," to the University of Zurich, which granted him a doctorate on June 22, 1869. While working in Zurich, Röntgen met his future wife, Anna Bertha Ludwig. In 1871, when Kundt accepted a position at the University of Würzburg, Röntgen accompanied him as his assistant, and the following year he married Bertha.

LIFE'S WORK

Röntgen's lack of a secondary school diploma again hindered his academic advancement at Würzburg, so he and his wife subsequently moved, with Kundt, to the Kaiser Wilhelm University in Strasbourg. Based on the success of his scientific investigations with Kundt, he received an offer of a full professorship from the Agricultural Academy in Hohenheim, Württemberg, in 1875. However, he was unhappy with that institution's experimental facilities and returned to Strasbourg a year and a half later as an assistant professor in theoretical physics.

Röntgen wrote a series of papers on the properties of gases that exhibited his growing skills as an experimental physicist, and in 1879, he was offered the chair of physics at the University of Giessen. During the ensuing nine years, he did important work on crystals, their generation of electricity when subjected to heat (pyroelectricity), and their generation of electricity when subjected to mechanical stress (piezoelectricity). His greatest discovery, however, was his confirmation of a prediction made by Scottish physicist James Clerk Maxwell that a magnetic field would be generated within dielectrics such as glass plates when they are moved back and forth between two electrically charged plates. Dutch physicist Hendrik Antoon Lorentz named this effect, which Röntgen detected with a sensitive device, the "roentgen current." Röntgen later considered this discovery as an important step in his work on X-rays.

Recognition of Röntgen's accomplishments in physics brought him offers from other universities. In 1888, he turned down the chair of physics at the University of Utrecht but accepted the University of Würzburg's proposal to occupy Kundt's former position. During his first six years at Würzburg, he published seventeen papers on such topics as the properties of solids and liquids. His fame as a physicist and respect for his political sagacity led to his election in 1894 to the rectorship of the university. One year later, he left his position as rector and took up a new field of scientific research.

Philipp Lenard, a Hungarian German physicist, had been studying cathode rays by means of an apparatus he constructed that allowed what some called "Lenard rays" to enter the air beyond the apparatus. Röntgen became interested in exploring these rays, and on November 8, 1895, he wrapped a cathode-ray tube with black paper to observe the narrow beam of rays from the tube. By chance, he noticed that a screen coated with barium platinocyanide and located some distance from the tube glowed with a brilliant fluorescence. This puzzled him, because cathode rays had an effective range of only a few centimeters. He therefore suspected that he might have come upon a previously unknown kind of radiation, which he termed "X-rays." Over the next several weeks, Röntgen experimented with the position of the screen and blocking the beam of rays with materials of various kinds and thicknesses, leading him to many

---

Röntgen Discovers X-Rays

In 1895, Wilhelm Conrad Röntgen was experimenting with cathode-ray tubes. A cathode-ray tube is a glass tube with two electrodes lodged within—a cathode, which receives a negative charge of electricity, and an anode, which receives the positive charge. (In Röntgen's time, the cathode was not heated as in later practice.) By passing a large current at high voltage through the tube, many interesting electrical effects could be observed. These differed depending on whether the tube was evacuated or filled with different gases.

Röntgen designed an experiment to verify and extend the observations of his fellow German physicists Heinrich Hertz and Philipp Lenard. They had discovered that the tubes could have an external electrical effect within a few centimeters of the tube's outer wall. In other words, the air had become ionized.

To further analyze the external effects of the electrical discharge, Röntgen used a very heavy, empty cathode-ray tube covered with thick cardboard to make it completely light-tight and further protected with an external layer of tin foil. Window curtains completely darkened the room. A very high voltage generated by an induction coil was applied to the tube. No light leaked through and Röntgen was about to prepare for the planned experiment when he noticed a glimmer of light coming from the barium platinocyanide screen with which the experiment was to have been performed. This fluorescent screen was on his workbench, about a meter from the glass tube. He performed the experiment repeatedly, each time moving the screen farther and farther from the tube. Even at a distance of two meters, the screen glowed.

Röntgen realized that some sort of ray was being emitted from the tube, and he began to investigate its nature. He set the screen up at different angles to the tube and directed the invisible beam through paper, wood, and sheets of aluminum, copper, silver, gold, and platinum of varying thicknesses, finding that the rays penetrated all the materials he used with the exception of a sheet of lead. Intrigued by the blocking power of the lead, he tried again, holding a small disk of lead between his finger and thumb. When the apparatus was energized, he was astonished to find the outline of his fingers and more startled to observe that he could see the outline of his finger bones.

Over the following weeks, he experimented to ensure that his observations were not in error. Through these experiments, he discovered that X-rays travel in straight lines, are unaffected by magnets or electrically charged plates, and can ionize gases. Unlike light rays, X-rays can neither be reflected from a mirror nor refracted in a prism. Like light rays, they can blacken photographic plates, which Röntgen used to record the first X-ray images, including one famously revealing the bones of his wife's hand.

Röntgen communicated his discovery to the scientific community by letter and by the publication of his famous paper, "On a New Kind of Ray: A Preliminary Communication," on December 28, 1895. He later received many honors for his work, the most significant being the very first Nobel Prize in Physics in 1901.

further discoveries about the nature of X-rays—among them the fact that they pass unimpeded through all materials except lead and platinum.

On December 28, 1895, when Röntgen announced his discoveries to the world, both scientists and the public were fascinated by the mysterious rays that could even reveal the skeletons inside living humans. Physicians in Europe and America quickly put them to medical use in diagnosing broken bones and foreign objects in human bodies. Röntgen knew that his rays had commercial potential, but out of altruism, he refused to patent his discovery.

Kaiser Wilhelm II of Germany was the first dignitary to honor Röntgen with an award, on January 14, 1896. The kaiser's award was following by many others, culminating in Röntgen's reception of the first Nobel Prize in Physics in 1901. By that time, he had accepted a distinguished position as professor of experimental physics and head of the physical institute at the University of Munich, where he would remain for the next twenty years. During that period, he witnessed the use of X-rays by physicians to treat skin diseases and cancer and by physicists to study atomic arrangements in crystals. His own work centered on crystals, their electrical conductivity, and the influence of radiation on them. Röntgen also faced claims that other scientists had observed the effects of X-rays before him. However, although Lenard may have observed fluorescence near a Crookes tube, he never investigated this observation in the way Röntgen later did.

Although Röntgen received many honors on the occasion of his seventieth birthday in 1915, the privations brought on by World War I had a negative influence on his scientific work. His wife died in 1919 after a long illness. Furthermore, he, like most Germans, was affected by postwar political turmoil, ruinous inflation, and food shortages. His own health began to fail, and other physicists took over his work. Röntgen died in Munich during the morning of February 10, 1923, from an intestinal cancer.

IMPACT

The medical applications of X-rays were quickly recognized, but the impact of X-rays on physics and chemistry proved to be even more momentous. For example, Henry Becquerel's investigation of X-rays led directly to his discovery of radioactivity. In 1912, Max von Laue suggested that X-rays may be diffracted by crystals, and scientists soon discovered that diffracted rays allowed them to determine the three-dimensional structures of many crystals. English physicist Henry Moseley

dis-covered characteristic X-rays emitted by each of the chemical elements, leading to a deeper understanding of the periodic table. So significant were these and other discoveries that some scholars called Röntgen's discovery of X-rays the event that initiated a second scientific revolution, because it ushered in the modern physics of the twentieth century, just as the discoveries of Galileo Galilei, Johannes Kepler, and Isaac Newton had forged the new science of the seventeenth century.

With the passage of time, the practical uses of X-rays multiplied. So many medical applications were developed that an entirely new medical specialty, radiology, was created, and new technologies such as computerized axial tomography (CAT) rely on high-resolution X-ray pictures to study the human brain. In industry, engineers use X-rays to study stresses in various materials and the strengths of welds, while computer technicians use them to etch integrated circuits. Scholarship has benefitted as well, with archaeologists using X-rays to study mummies and other ancient artifacts without harming the objects and astronomers studying the X-rays emanating from different parts of the universe to better understand stars, pulsars, and black holes. They even play a role in ensuring passenger safety at airports and seaports, helping workers to inspect luggage and cargo for dangerous items. These examples do not exhaust the significant applications that continue to be discovered over a century after Röntgen first found and characterized these powerful rays.

Robert J. Paradowski

FURTHER READING

Baigrie, Brian S. "Shadow Pictures." *Scientific Revolutions: Primary Texts in the History of Science*. Upper Saddle River: Pearson, 2004. Print. A chapter containing an English translation of Röntgen's "On a New Type of Rays" preceded by a helpful historical introduction.

Nitski, W. Robert. *The Life of Wilhelm Conrad Röntgen, Discoverer of the X-Ray*. Tucson: U of Arizona P, 1971. Print. A popular biography concentrating on Röntgen's research before, during, and after the discovery of X-rays. Chronology, bibliography, and index, with English translations of Röntgen's three most famous papers.

Thomsen, Volker. "Atomic Perspectives: Wilhelm Conrad Röntgen and the Discovery of X-Rays." *Spectroscopy* 23.7 (2008): 30–34. Print. Provides historical context for and details of Röntgen's most famous discovery. Includes diagrams and historical photographs.

F. SHERWOOD ROWLAND

American chemist

*F. Sherwood Rowland was a key figure in global
political efforts to control and reverse the pollution
of Earth's atmosphere by chlorofluorocarbon (CFC)
gases. He found that in addition to depleting ozone,
CFCs also contribute to the greenhouse effect, leading
to global warming and climate change.*

Born: June 28, 1927; Delaware, Ohio
Died: March 10, 2012; Newport Beach, California
Also known as: Frank Sherwood Rowland
Primary field: Chemistry
Specialties: Physical chemistry; radiochemistry; atmospheric sciences

EARLY LIFE

Frank Sherwood Rowland was born on June 28, 1927, in
Delaware, Ohio, the second of three sons born to Sidney
Archie Rowland and Margaret Lois Drake. His father, a
mathematics professor and chair of the mathematics department at Ohio Wesleyan University, also served for
two terms as the mayor of Delaware in the mid-1930s.
Rowland's mother, a University of Chicago graduate,
taught high school in Indiana before marrying.

Rowland skipped fourth grade because of accelerated progress and entered high school at the age of
twelve, graduating a few weeks short of his sixteenth
birthday. During several summer vacations, he had his
first experiences with systematic data collection when
his high school science teacher went on vacation and
recruited Rowland to substitute for him as a volunteer
at the local weather station, collecting information on
temperatures and precipitation.

In the early years of World War II, when Rowland was
too young to serve in the military, he attended Ohio Wesleyan University, where he played basketball and baseball
and earned four varsity letters. In 1945, he enlisted in the
US Navy and served for fourteen months as a specialist
third class. Two years after he left the Navy, in 1948, he
received his bachelor's degree from Ohio Wesleyan.

After graduating, Rowland attended the University
of Chicago and worked with Willard F. Libby, who had
recently developed the carbon-14 (radiocarbon) dating
technique for which he would receive the 1960 Nobel
Prize in Chemistry. Rowland received a master's degree from Chicago in 1951. He focused on radiochemistry and wrote his PhD dissertation in 1952 on the
chemical state of cyclotron-produced bromine atoms.

He combined his academic work with sports, playing
on university teams and the Oshawa semiprofessional
baseball club in Canada. In 1952, Rowland married Joan
Lundberg, also a Chicago graduate; they would have
two children, a daughter and a son.

LIFE'S WORK

The Rowlands moved to Princeton University in the
fall of 1952, after Rowland was hired as a chemistry
instructor. Four years later, he was appointed assistant
professor at the University of Kansas; in time, he advanced to the rank of full professor. His research at
that time was focused on the chemistry of radioactive
atoms.

In 1964, Rowland accepted the position of founding chair of the chemistry department at the University
of California, Irvine (UCI), which was scheduled to enroll its first students the following year. He advanced to
an endowed chair at UCI, becoming the Donald Bren
Research Professor of Chemistry and Earth Systems
Science. When Rowland retired in 1970 as chair of the
department, he looked for a field of research that would
mesh with his growing interest in chemical problems
in the environment. His work after "retirement" would
be his legacy.

While attending a workshop sponsored by the US
Atomic Energy Commission (AEC) in 1972, Rowland
became intrigued by data collected by researchers on a
ship traveling from Great Britain to Antarctica. The scientists' data showed the concentration of human-made
chlorofluorocarbon (CFC) molecules in the atmosphere
along that route. Rowland knew that the CFC molecules
would not remain inert forever. The following year, he
requested and received funding from the AEC to study
what happens to atmospheric CFCs.

Late in 1973, Mario J. Molina, a recent PhD graduate of the University of California, Berkeley, joined
Rowland's research group as a postdoctoral fellow. Molina elected to concentrate on CFC issues with Rowland. Their investigations showed a potentially grave
environmental threat involving the depletion of the
Earth's stratospheric ozone layer. They documented that
the CFC compounds found in aerosol sprays, air conditioners, refrigerators, and other household items, as well
as emissions from factories and automobiles, have been
destroying the ozone layer that blocks the sun's ultraviolet rays. In humans, ultraviolet radiation

---

Reactions to F. Sherwood Rowland's Research

Though the findings reported by F. Sherwood Rowland and Mario Molina in the June 1974 issue of *Nature* were dire, both the scientific community and the public at large were slow to respond. According to Rowland and Molina's original findings, one single chlorine atom, a byproduct of consumer goods that contain chlorofluorocarbon (CFC) molecules, has the capacity to deplete more than one hundred thousand ozone atoms in the Earth's stratosphere. That single atom could remain in the atmosphere for nearly a century. With these numbers in mind, Rowland feared that the Earth's demise was imminent.

The eventual banning of CFCs and widespread awareness of climate change and global warming were due to the diligence of Rowland himself, who endured years of backlash for his work. Trade journals at the height of the Cold War accused Rowland of working for the Soviet Union's KGB security agency, and in 1975, the American chemical company DuPont ran a full-page advertisement in the New York Times saying that Rowland was trying to "hypothesize" them out of existence. Rowland also found himself ostracized by fellow scientists, at least until his findings were verified by British researchers in 1985.

That Rowland pursued a ban on CFCs was a testament to the seriousness with which he viewed his work. Reportedly, he was not sure if he would be able to convince others of the importance of the ban. The study of climate change did not yet exist in the 1970s, much less the suggestion that humans could be responsible for said climate change, which accounted for the chilly reception Rowland received from the scientific community at large. The link from humans to climate felt to many like too large a leap. Still, Rowland never wavered in his conclusions. He firmly believed that he was personally responsible for more than publishing papers. He advocated for action when it was called for, asking at a White House roundtable on climate change in 1997, "If not us, who? If not now, when?"

Even after Rowland was celebrated for his work, he continued to speak out against the dangers of greenhouse gases. He devoted the last years of his life to researching the 2010 Deepwater Horizon oil spill in the Gulf of Mexico when he observed harmful air pollution rising from the spill. This time, he received a quicker response; NASA launched an intense research effort shortly after his findings were reported.

---

causes various health problems, including skin cancer, cataracts, sunburn, and excessive aging and wrinkling of the skin.

By late 1974, after Rowland and Molina published their results in the journal *Nature* in June 1974, there was strong public concern about ozone depletion and controversy over whether humans were responsible for it. Legislative hearings and heavy media coverage followed. In the United States, a ban on the nonessential use of CFCs in aerosol sprays was announced on March 17, 1978, by the US Consumer Product Safety Commission, the Environmental Protection Agency, and the Food and Drug Administration. In May 1985, British researchers published a paper announcing the discovery of an "ozone hole" above Antarctica, leading to more intense research on a global scale.

Over his long career, Rowland produced more than 420 scientific publications on atmospheric chemistry, radiochemistry, and chemical kinetics. He and his team continued to work on the problems of global atmospheric pollution, paying special attention to the growth in concentration of greenhouse gases such as carbon dioxide. Through emission and absorption of infrared radiation, these gases trap heat in the Earth's atmosphere. This leads to what is called the greenhouse effect, which causes the Earth to warm.

In 1995, Rowland, Molina, and Dutch atmospheric scientist Paul J. Crutzen were awarded the Nobel Prize in Chemistry for their research into the depletion of the Earth's ozone. Rowland also received a variety of other honors for his work, including honorary doctorates and awards from universities in the United States and abroad; he was awarded the Tyler Prize for Environmental Achievement (1983), the Charles A. Dana Award for Pioneering Achievements in Health (1987), the Japan Prize in Environmental Science and Technology (1989), the Peter Debye Award in Physical Chemistry from the American Chemical Society (1993), and the Roger Revelle Medal of the American Geophysical Union (1994), among others. He was added to the Global 500 Roll of Honor of the United Nations Environmental Program in 1988.

Rowland served from 1991 to 1994 as president-elect, president, and then chair of the board of the American Association for the Advancement of Science. He then served as the foreign secretary of the National Academy of Sciences from 1994 to 2003. He died on

March 10, 2012, at the age of eighty-four.

IMPACT

Rowland's collaborative work on atmospheric altera-
tion by CFCs alerted the world to stratospheric ozone
depletion and the dangers it poses to the environment,
to humans, and to plant and animal life. In 1987, the
United Nations Environmental Program responded by
forming an initiative that led to the Montreal Protocol
on Substances that Deplete the Ozone Layer, signatories
of which agreed to reduce their respective nations' CFC
production by 50 percent by 2000. Subsequent amend-
ments to the protocol banned the production of CFCs
in developed countries, which were responsible for virtually all emissions. The developing world was given
until 2010 to control CFC emissions.

The Nobel committee's press release that announced
the awarding of the Nobel Prize in 1995 to Rowland, Molina, and Crutzen summed up the importance of their work:
"By explaining the chemical mechanisms that affect the
thickness of the ozone layer, the three researchers have
contributed to our salvation from a global environmental problem that could have catastrophic consequences."

Global warming and climate change have since become
critical concerns, and they remain major topics among
politicians, scientists, activists, business leaders, and the
global community in general.

Gilbert Geis

FURTHER READING

Attwood, George K., and Jeffrey A. Joens. "Ozone Depletion and Ozone Holes." *Ecology Basics*. Vol. 2. Pasadena: Salem, 2004. 457–64. Print. An article on ozone
depletion caused mainly by CFCs in the stratosphere.

Parson, Edward A. *Protecting the Ozone Layer: Science
and Strategy*. New York: Oxford UP, 2003. Print.
A history of the international efforts to protect the
ozone layer since the 1970s.

Randall, David. *Atmosphere, Clouds, and Climate*.
Princeton: Princeton UP, 2012. Print. Describes the
science behind atmospheric processes and the atmosphere's effect on climate change.

Rowland, F. Sherwood. "Stratospheric Ozone Depletion." *Annual Review of Physical Chemistry* 42
(1991): 731–68. Print. Rowland's findings regarding the pollution of Earth's atmosphere.

HENRY NORRIS RUSSELL

American astrophysicist

*Henry Norris Russell was among the first astrophysical
theorists in the United States. Seeking to explain his
observations and to understand the physics of stars,
he incorporated theory into the descriptive science of
astronomy. He is best known for his work in developing
the Hertzsprung-Russell (H-R) diagram, a major tool
used to understand the composition and evolution of
stars.*

Born: October 25, 1877; Oyster Bay, New York
Died: February 18, 1957; Princeton, New Jersey
Primary fields: Astronomy; physics
Specialties: Astrophysics; theoretical astronomy

EARLY LIFE

Henry Norris Russell was born the first son of Presbyte-
rian pastor Alexander Gatherer Russell and Eliza Hoxie
Norris Russell, in Oyster Bay, New York. Raised in a
strict Christian home, Russell was profoundly affected
by his religious upbringing and remained deeply faith-
ful his entire life. In 1890, Russell entered the Princeton

Preparatory School and stayed with his maternal aunt,
Ada Louise Norris, in Princeton, New Jersey, during the
school year. He would return to Oyster Bay during the
summer months. Russell proved to be an excellent student.

In 1893, just one month before his sixteenth birthday, Russell entered the College of New Jersey (now
Princeton University). In 1897, he graduated with highest honors. He continued his studies and received his
PhD in 1900. His doctoral work led to the development
of methods to study binary star orbits. However, health
problems forced Russell to interrupt his work for the
rest of that year.

By 1902, Russell had traveled to Cambridge University in England to study and do research. He returned
to Princeton in 1905 to accept a faculty position, living
again with his aunt Ada. He soon met Lucy May Cole,
and they were married on November 24, 1908. The couple, who lived with Ada, would have three daughters and
a son. Ada died in 1914, leaving her home to her nephew,
and he lived there for most of the rest of his life.

LIFE'S WORK

Throughout his career, Russell worked on a wide range of areas in astronomy, studying geophysics, the stars, planets, nebulas, and the moon. He did not study much of the galaxies, however. Russell's earliest work on binary stars provided new ways to compute parallaxes, which are important in determining stellar distances. His studies of eclipsing binary stars allowed him to determine the sizes of stars, and he determined new ways to estimate the masses of binary star systems. His work, always careful and painstakingly accurate, set a new standard of precision for researchers.

Russell discovered several critical important relationships among stars. By knowing the distances of stars and their apparent magnitudes (how bright the stars appear in the sky), he could determine the absolute magnitudes of stars (how luminous a star is in actuality). He observed a definite pattern between the luminosity of a star and its color. The color of a star is related to its temperature, and almost all of the very hot, blue stars are also very bright. However, only some of the cool, red stars are bright as well. Most of the cooler stars are dim. This observation led him to propose that cool stars could be separated into two groups. Those in the brighter group, he reasoned, must also be much larger than the dimmer group.

Unknown to Russell, Danish astronomer Ejnar Hertzsprung had been working on very similar studies. When Russell was told of Hertzsprung's studies, he immediately embraced Hertzsprung's work and even adopted his terms "giant" and "dwarf" for these two groups of stars. Most of this data was in tabular form until Russell produced a plot of absolute magnitudes versus spectral types in 1913. This plot was presented at meetings of the Royal Astronomical Society and the American Astronomical Society. Astronomers immediately recognized how such a graphical representation of the data could be used to understand stars better. American astronomers began to refer to the plot as the Russell diagram, but by the 1930s, astronomers worldwide began to call it the Hertzsprung-Russell (H-R) diagram, noting Hertzsprung's contributions as well.

In his quest to understand stars, Russell spent much of his career working on a theory of stellar evolution. He observed that most stars appear to lie along a strip that runs diagonally across the absolute magnitude versus spectral type plot from the upper left to the lower right. However, some stars seem to lie along a strip leading from the upper left to the upper right on the diagram; this strip became known as the main sequence. The stars in the upper right of the strip, Russell reasoned, are Hertzsprung's giant stars, while stars on the main sequence are dwarf stars. Russell eventually settled upon a model in which stars begin as giants and then become smaller and hotter until they appear on the upper-left portion of the main sequence. Then, he hypothesized that the stars move down along the main sequence, becoming cooler and dimmer.

Though many aspects of this model turned out to be incorrect, astronomers have found that stars do indeed begin in the upper right of the H-R diagram and move onto the main sequence. However, they do not move along the main sequence. Rather, when they begin to die, they again move off the main sequence to the upper right portion of the diagram.

Eager to help in the war effort during World War I, Russell became affiliated with George Ellery Hale's National Research Council. He initially worked on a project to improve artillery parallax and ranging. Later, he worked on aircraft navigation systems. After the war, he returned to his job as a Princeton professor.

To determine the chemical composition of stars, Russell worked with stellar spectroscopy. Like most astronomers of his day, he believed that the sun and stars are composed of materials similar to those that compose the Earth. Because different stars showed different spectral lines, Russell believed they had different compositions. However, Cecilia Payne, in doing research for her PhD, concluded that the sun and all stars essentially have the same composition, almost entirely hydrogen and helium, which turned out to be a controversial finding. Russell strongly disagreed with Payne's theory because those elements are very rare on Earth. Under his influence, Payne backed down from her theory and even declared her work flawed. However, when Russell, who was more interested in truth than in being right, was presented later with undeniable evidence that Payne's conclusions were correct, he became a wholehearted supporter of her theory that stars were composed mostly of hydrogen and helium.

IMPACT

Russell's most enduring legacy was his work in determining relationships between the luminosity and temperature of stars. His plot of absolute magnitude versus spectral type became the basis of all future graphical depictions diagramming that data. The H-R diagram was critical to the development of a theory of stellar evolution and has become one of the most important and useful tools for stellar astronomers.

Russell Announces His Theory of Stellar Evolution

When Henry Norris Russell first presented his diagram plotting stellar brightness and density versus spectral type, color, and temperature (now known as the Hertzsprung-Russell or H-R diagram) in 1913, he also offered his interpretation of the diagram in terms of stellar evolution. Most stars fall either on a diagonal band stretching across the diagram (the "main sequence") or on a horizontal strip across the top (the "giant sequence"). On the main sequence, stars vary in brightness and color, ranging from bright blue to dim red. On the giant sequence, stars vary in color but have a fairly constant brightness. Russell explained the two sequences in terms of the ages of stars in each sequence. He asserted that a star's evolution is driven by gravity alone and that a star begins its life cool, red, dim, and diffuse, and grows increasingly dense, bright, and hot (with an associated color change) as it contracts. Once it has contracted so far that gravity can condense it no further, it begins to cool, becoming dimmer and redder.

Russell hypothesized that the large red stars at one end of the giant sequence are the youngest, very diffuse, and just beginning to collapse. As a star collapses, he postulated, it becomes denser and changes colors as it crosses the giant sequence, eventually brightening and leaving the giant sequence for the main sequence. At its hottest point, which Russell believed to be the midpoint of its life, the star is at the top of the main sequence among the brightest and bluest stars. As it then begins to cool and become denser, it slides down the main sequence from being a hot blue star to being a yellow star like the sun and finally to being a dim red star, very dense and near the end of its life. Thus, there are two sorts of red stars, young and old, distinguishable by their spectra, as Danish physicist Ejnar Hertzsprung had previously demonstrated.

Russell's concise, straightforward scheme of stellar evolution neatly fit the known data and accommodated the accepted explanation for why stars shine and how they form, exist, and die. The later discovery that nuclear fusion, rather than gravitational collapse, powers stars for most of their lifetimes brought about drastic revisions in Russell's scheme. Nonetheless, his explanation of how the H-R diagram reveals the evolution of stars laid the groundwork for later research. He even suggested that a type of energy release related to radioactivity could counteract the gravitational pull inward and give a star a longer lifetime than it would have otherwise.

Today, it is believed that while a star forms because a cloud of material collapses under the influence of gravity, conditions eventually become hot enough in the center of the forming star that nuclear fusion begins to occur. The star then lives out most of its life cycle in one spot on the H-R diagram, its gravitational pull inward balanced by the energy released in nuclear fusion. Gravity becomes important again at the end of the star's lifetime, when its fate is determined by the mass it contains. Astronomers' current understanding of such phenomena as white dwarfs, neutron stars, and black holes—the end products of evolution for various masses of stars—would not be possible without the foundational interrelationships between density, brightness, temperature, and spectral type that the H-R diagram presents.

Russell also was instrumental in bringing theoretical physics into astronomy. Until his time, astronomy, particularly in the Americas, amounted to cataloging and describing what one observed through research. Russell, however, sought to explain observations and to understand the physics of stars.

In addition to his professional contributions, Russell brought astronomy to those outside the field. He wrote a monthly column for *Scientific American* magazine and eventually became an associate editor of astronomy for the magazine. In addition, he coauthored a textbook, lectured to students, and gave several public talks on the topic of science and religion. Finally, Russell was one of the last astronomers to work as a generalist in the field, focusing his work on a wide range of topics. Later astronomers would tend to become specialists in certain subfields of astronomy.

Raymond D. Benge, Jr.

FURTHER READING

DeVorkin, David H. *Henry Norris Russell: Dean of American Astronomers*. Princeton: Princeton UP, 2000. Print. A well-researched and thorough biography of Henry Norris Russell. Includes an extensive bibliography.

Gregersen, Erik, ed. "Henry Norris Russell." *The Universe: A Historical Survey of Beliefs, Theories, and Laws*. New York: Britannica Educational, 2010. 78–82. Print. Contains a brief biography of Russell, focusing primarily on the development of his most lasting legacy, the Hertzsprung-Russell diagram.

Talcott, Richard. "Making Sense of Stars." *Astronomy* 34.4 (2006): 53–56. Print. A very short and easy to understand explanation of the Hertzsprung-Russell diagram and how it is used. Includes diagram examples.

ERNEST RUTHERFORD

British physicist

British physicist Ernest Rutherford is known as the father of nuclear physics. His experiments with radiation, description of the structure of the atom, and initial success at artificially splitting the atom laid the foundation for nuclear weapons and power generation.

Born: August 30, 1871; Nelson, New Zealand
Died: October 19, 1937; Cambridge, England
Primary field: Physics
Specialties: Atomic and molecular physics; nuclear physics; radiochemistry

EARLY LIFE

Ernest Rutherford was born on August 30, 1871, in Nelson, New Zealand, one of twelve children. His grandfather moved to rural New Zealand from Scotland in 1843, and Rutherford's father, James Rutherford, worked as a wheelwright and farmer. His mother, Martha Thompson, was a school teacher and emigrated from England in 1855.

Rutherford attended rural primary schools before his admission to Nelson College (a secondary school) in 1887. He excelled academically, and won a scholarship to Canterbury College at the University of New Zealand in 1889. He earned his bachelor's degree in 1892. He continued on a mathematics scholarship and earned a master's degree in 1893. His university work was primarily concentrated in research on magnetism and electrical technology.

In 1894 Rutherford won an 1851 Exhibition Science Scholarship and was accepted as a graduate research student at Trinity College at the University of Cambridge to work in the Cavendish Laboratory with physics professor J. J. Thomson, who would be credited with the discovery of the electron in 1897.

LIFE'S WORK

Rutherford began working in the field of radiation and studied the conductivity of gases that were ionized by bombardment with X-rays. In 1896, he began conducting similar experiments using radiation from uranium. He noted two distinct types of rays: one consisting of positively-charged particles that did not penetrate matter, and another of negatively-charged particles (later shown to be high-speed electrons) that easily penetrated matter. He would later name these alpha and beta rays. These experiments marked the beginning of Rutherford's lifelong study of radioactivity and atomic particles.

Rutherford received his research degree from Cambridge in 1897. The next year, he accepted the position of the Macdonald Chair of Physics at McGill University in Montreal, Canada. There, he studied the radioactive decay of thorium. About three times as common but significantly less radioactive than uranium, its decay produces an isotope of radon (then called thoron). Radon was the last of the noble (inert) gases to be isolated. During his time in Montreal, Rutherford married Mary Georgina Newton in 1900. They would have one daughter, Eileen.

In working with radon, Rutherford noted that radiation dissipated in geometrical progression with time. In 1905, he would extend this predictable "half-life" principal to use radium to date rocks, a process later extensively used with carbon-14 to date biological material. These experiments provided the first accurate formulation and proof of the process by which radioactive elements break down at the atomic level as heavy atoms release radiation and create new, slightly lighter atoms. For example, radium becomes lead-206, and carbon-14 decays to become nitrogen-14.

Rutherford documented his work in numerous published research papers, and was elected to England's Royal Society in 1903. He published the book *Radioactivity* in 1904. His Silliman Lectures at Yale University were collected in the 1906 work *Radioactive Transformations*.

In 1907, Rutherford took a position as the Langworthy Professor of Physics at the University of Manchester in England. In 1908 he received the Nobel Prize in Chemistry for his "investigations into the disintegration of the elements, and the chemistry of radioactive substances." Beginning in the year after winning the Nobel, Rutherford entered a period in which he made many of his most significant discoveries. Working with German physicist Hans Geiger, he conducted further experiments in bombarding elements with radiation. By that time, Rutherford had named alpha particles and recognized that they were ionized helium atoms, stripped of their electrons. He began measuring the scattering of alpha particles when shot through thin sheets of metal.

In 1906, J. J. Thomson had extended his discovery of the electron to propose a new theory of the structure of the atom. In what was termed the "plum pudding model," he conjectured that the atom contained numerous electrons ("plums") spread throughout a positively-charged "pudding."

However, in Rutherford's experiments, the scattering of alpha particles was not uniform as predicted by

Ernest Rutherford Discovers the Nucleus of the Atom

On April 29, 1897, J. J. Thomson announced that he had discovered tiny subatomic particles, which he called "corpuscles"—electrons, as they were later renamed—that were much smaller than the atom. Thomson's discovery confirmed not only that atoms existed but also that they were probably made up of even smaller particles. According to Thomson's theory, the atom was made up of a positively charged interior of great volume, compared with the tiny negatively charged electron enclosed within it. Thomson described the aggregate as analogous to plum pudding, with electrons (corpuscles) being the plums suspended in the surrounding material.

In 1907, Ernest Rutherford had been experimenting with the particles that appeared to emanate from the radioactive atom. These efforts had been narrowed to a series of experiments that he hoped would finally identify these particles and their nature. Assisting him were Hans Geiger and Ernest Marsden.

Rutherford and his assistants learned from Thomson that the electron was a piece of the atom and that it was considerably lighter and smaller than the whole atom. They also knew its charge was negative, so that whatever was left of the atom had to be much heavier and have a net positive charge. Yet the particles that were emitted by the radioactive material Rutherford was examining (called alpha particles) were much heavier than electrons but still smaller than a whole atom. The question that perplexed Rutherford was whether, like the electron, these were also a part of the atom.

The theory behind Rutherford's experiments was that an alpha particle from the radioactive element would race down a glass tube from its source and strike the atoms in a gold foil target. If the atoms were made up of Thomson's plum pudding, then as the massive alpha particle struck the electrons, they would be deflected only slightly or not at all. By measuring where the tiny blips of light struck the gold foil, Rutherford could calculate the angle of deflection and indirectly determine the mass of whatever the alpha particle had struck on its way down the tube. He reasoned that the deflections of the larger alpha particles striking tiny electrons would be minimal, but that if, by the most bizarre of circumstances, one of these particles should encounter a series of electrons on its way through an atom, the deflection might register as much as 45 degrees.

The experiments began in 1910 with Geiger assisting Marsden, counting the almost invisible flashes of light on the fluorescent screen through a magnifying lens in a completely blackened laboratory. They immediately found that one out of about eight thousand alpha particles was deflected at an angle, varying from greater than 45 to 180 degrees.

It was obvious to Rutherford that plum pudding could never account for such wild deflections. One plausible explanation, which he eventually accepted, was that the atom contained a pinpoint nucleus that occupied only a minuscule portion of the total volume of the atom but, at the same time, itself contained nearly all the atom's mass. The electrons, he supposed, distantly orbited the densely packed core. On March 7, 1912, Rutherford presented his theory at the Manchester Literary and Philosophical Society.

Rutherford had the correct idea of the nucleus. Electrons do not orbit in the classical sense, however; they exist in a quantum state, as Niels Bohr would later prove. By 1913, Rutherford's vision would be replaced by Bohr's quantum view. Quantum mechanics would join with Albert Einstein's work on relativity to reorder physics and redefine the nature of all matter and energy.

Thomson's model. In 1909, using very thin gold leaf, Rutherford, Geiger, and research assistant Ernest Marsden noted that some particles actually bounced backwards. It was impossible that electrons would cause such deflection, due to their small electrical force.

By 1911, Rutherford deduced that the only likely explanation for a force great enough to cause this scattering was that the positive charge in the atom is contained in a very small area, rather than being spread out. He was able to mathematically deduce by the degree of scattering that this positive nucleus must be extremely compact. Although not yet complete, this was the beginning of the first accurate model of the atom.

In 1912, another of Thomson's former students, Niels Bohr, helped Rutherford refine his model of the atom by applying quantum theory to describe how electrons generally remain in stable orbits around the nucleus. Although this refinement is credited to Bohr, this theory is often referred to as the Rutherford-Bohr model of the atom. With H. G. Moseley, Rutherford extended his use of radiation to determine the atomic number (equal to the number of protons) of various elements.

In 1919, Rutherford announced that in experiments begun two years earlier, he had artificially "split" the atom by bombarding normally stable nitrogen with alpha particles to create fast protons (hydrogen) and an isotope of oxygen. Shortly after this discovery, he accepted an offer to succeed Thomson as the Cavendish Professor of Physics at the University of Cambridge.

Over the next two decades, Rutherford either directly or indirectly set into motion many of the pivotal discoveries of nuclear physics. In 1920, he predicted the existence of the neutron, an uncharged particle just slightly heavier than the proton. Because of the difficulty in physically detecting an uncharged particle, it was not until that 1932 that Rutherford's student at Cambridge, James Chadwick, would prove its existence.

After successfully lobbying the British government for funding in 1929, Rutherford oversaw John Cockcroft and Ernest T. S. Walton's development of one of the first high-energy particle accelerators, a linear accelerator used to bombard elements with artificially accelerated protons. The cyclotron, a circular accelerator, was developed about the same time in the United States by Ernest Lawrence.

Along with Chadwick and Charles Drummond Ellis, Rutherford published *Radiation from Radioactive Substances* in 1930. Later works by Rutherford include *The Artificial Transmutation of the Elements* (1933) and *The Newer Alchemy* (1937).

IMPACT

The first nuclear fusion reaction was created at Rutherford's Cambridge lab, as announced in 1934 by Marcus Oliphant and Paul Harteck. They bombarded concentrated heavy water (deuterium) with deuterons to produce tritium and helium. This process would lead to the creation of the hydrogen bomb, first detonated in 1952.

Although Enrico Fermi had unknowingly created atomic fission as early as 1934, fission was first detected in 1938 by Otto Hahn, one of Rutherford's former students at McGill University. Hahn's work was the precursor to the Manhattan Project, the atomic weapons program in the United States during World War II. Commercial fission power plants were introduced by the mid-1950s.

Rutherford himself anticipated neither the rapid development of nuclear weaponry nor nuclear power, as he was accustomed to the low-level radiation typified by the natural decay of heavy elements. It was not until physicist Leó Szilárd and others perfected means of instigating fission chain reactions that the vast energy of heavy elements could be released almost in an instant, instead of over millions of years.

J. Robert Oppenheimer, scientific director of the Manhattan Project, was one of Rutherford's students at Cambridge. Students and research associates of Rutherford to win the Nobel Prize include James Chadwick, John Cockcroft, Ernest T. S. Walton, Patrick M. S. Blackett, G. P. Thomson (J. J. Thomson's son), Edward V. Appleton, Francis W. Aston, and Cecil Powell.

In 1931, Rutherford was granted peerage as First Baron Rutherford of Nelson, New Zealand, and Cambridge, and became a member of the House of Lords, making his popular title Lord Rutherford. He died on October 19, 1937, at the age of sixty-six, due to complications from a hernia. His ashes are interred in Westminster Abbey in London.

John Pearson

FURTHER READING

Heilbron, John L. *Ernest Rutherford and the Explosion of Atoms*. New York: Oxford UP, 2003. Print. A biography of Rutherford that discusses his research and contributions to the field of physics, including his work with radioactivity and his discovery of atomic structure.

Reeves, Richard. *A Force of Nature: The Frontier Genius of Ernest Rutherford*. New York: Norton, 2008. Print. Discusses Rutherford's life and the influence of his scientific work on history and politics. Contains information on his discovery of atomic structure.

Roberts, John. "Ernest Rutherford: Father of Nuclear Physics." *Nuclear Future* 7.4 (2011): 28–31. Print. Presents information on the atomic nucleus and nuclear physics related to nuclear decay, nuclear magnetic resonance, radiocarbon dating, and fission.

Walker, Phil. "The Atomic Nucleus." *New Scientist* 1 Oct. 2011: i–viii. Print. Describes Rutherford's influence on the field of science as related to atomic theory and nuclear physics.

JOHANNES ROBERT RYDBERG

Swedish physicist

Johannes Robert Rydberg was a Swedish physicist best known for his studies on the spectral analysis of chemicals. He discovered formulas for predicting spectral lines of chemicals and metals before atomic structure was properly understood. The Rydberg constant is named for him.

Born: November 8, 1854; Halmstad, Sweden
Died: December 28, 1919; Lund, Sweden
Also known as: Janne Robert Rydberg
Primary field: Physics
Specialties: Atomic and molecular physics; physical chemistry

EARLY LIFE

Johannes Robert Rydberg was born on November 8, 1854, to Sven Rydberg, a merchant who died just four years later, and Maria Anderson. He studied in his hometown of Halmstad for his primary and secondary education, graduating in 1873. That same year, he enrolled at the University of Lund, where he would study and then teach until his death in 1919. He began by studying pure mathematics, earning his bachelor's degree in 1875 and his doctorate in 1879. Afterward, he became more interested in physics, and in 1882, he was given the post of assistant lecturer in physics at Lund. His career rose steadily until he was awarded a full permanent professorship of physics in 1901. His appointment came after being denied tenure in favor of another physicist who was a personal friend of King Oscar II of Sweden.

In 1882, Rydberg published his first physics paper on the subject of friction. Early in his physics career, he became interested in the subject that would make him famous—the newly developed periodic table of elements. The modern periodic table is based on the design of Russian chemist Dmitry Ivanovich Mendeleyev (1834–1907), who published his version in 1869. As chemistry became more sophisticated, chemists were beginning to determine the difference between elements, which are made of only one kind of atom, and compounds, which are made of two or more elements in different ratios. Mendeleyev's periodic table grouped the elements by atomic weight, or, as it is now known, number of protons. Protons had yet to be discovered, however, and this grouping was not perfectly understood. Rydberg's later work would help define the properties of elements and their position on the periodic table.

LIFE'S WORK

Rydberg began his work in physics soon after the discovery that different chemicals emit unique spectral lines when burned by flames or electricity. When a chemical burns, it emits light; when that light passes through a prism, it fractures into a spectrum, or rainbow, and the width of the different colored lines can be measured. The chemical composition of stars can be determined this way because stars are simply burning balls of chemicals. When a star's light passes through a prism (or its modern equivalent), it produces spectral lines that can be analyzed to discover which chemicals exist in that star and in what quantities. Chemists found that the same chemical will produce the same spectrum every time, and so they knew that the atoms of the chemical must somehow relate to the spectrum of light produced by the chemical. The connection, however, was not understood.

Rydberg began studying the spectra of elements around 1884. He was determined to quantify and decipher the spectral data that had been collected by other chemists and find what patterns may emerge. He hoped that his research would help him piece together a model of atomic structure, and although he died before he was successful, later scientists based atomic models on his work.

His first step toward finding a mathematical model for the spectra was to assign whole numbers to the spectral lines, starting with one for the shortest wavelength. He called it the *wave number* and defined it as the number of waves per centimeter of any given color. His solid mathematics background made him uniquely qualified to attempt to quantify physical data, and through trial and error, Rydberg developed his equations for predicting spectral lines, presenting them in 1887. (It is unclear whether he was aware of the work of fellow mathematician Johann Jakob Balmer at this time and, if so, to what extent Balmer's calculations influenced his own.) Rydberg's conclusions were published by the Royal Swedish Academy of Scientists in 1890.

Rydberg was correct in assuming that there must be a periodic relationship between the forces drawing atoms together and their atomic weights. After all, the periodic table arranges elements in order of increasing weight, and no elements fall halfway between two adjoining elements; they increase in whole numbers when measured correctly. It is now known that the atomic weight is the weight of the protons in an element, that protons only exist as whole units, and that all protons are the same size and weight.

Rydberg's equations did not yield exact results, only very good approximations. Although they worked

fairly well, neither he nor any other chemist or physicist could explain the physical laws behind them. The true internal structure of the atom remained a mystery, but Rydberg's formulas would eventually prove useful in its discovery by Danish physicist Niels Bohr in 1913.

Rydberg married Lydia E. M. Carlsson in 1886, and the couple had two daughters and one son. He remained at Lund for the rest of his life. After a stroke in 1911, Rydberg had to curtail some of his teaching duties. In 1915, his failing health forced him to quit active teaching altogether.

In 1919, Rydberg was elected a foreign member of London's Royal Society, although he was never elected to the Royal Swedish Academy of Sciences. He was nominated for a Nobel Prize in 1917 but did not win. He was nominated again for the 1920 award, but the Nobel committee would not grant awards posthumously, and Rydberg died of a brain hemorrhage in Lund on December 28, 1919.

Johannes Robert Rydberg Discovers the Rydberg Constant

The Rydberg constant (R_∞) is an invaluable product of Swedish physicist Johannes Robert Rydberg's spectral formulas. As Rydberg was constructing his formulas, he decided to use wave number instead of wavelength. Wavelength measures the distance between peaks of a wave of energy or a photon, while wave number is the number of waves in one centimeter. Wave number is reciprocal to the wavelength—the longer the wavelength, the smaller the wave number—and Rydberg found it easier to use for his calculations. The equation that Rydberg derived used a number that turned out to be a constant.

If a hydrogen atom is in its ground state, meaning it has no net charge and its electrons are in their lowest possible orbits, the Rydberg constant is the smallest amount of energy needed to ionize a hydrogen atom—that is, excite the atom to its next highest state. Hydrogen is the smallest, lightest atom, consisting of only one proton and one electron. Hydrogen tends to either lose its one electron or gain another, since the lowest electron orbit more readily holds zero or two electrons. The Rydberg constant is the wave number of the lowest-energy photon capable of ionizing a hydrogen atom.

Danish physicist Niels Bohr would later prove that the Rydberg constant can be calculated using other known constants such as Planck's constant, the speed of light,

and the mass of an electron, further validating it. The Rydberg (Ry) energy unit represents the energy of the Rydberg constant photon. These findings would help scientists determine the spectra of other, similar atoms as well.

Rydberg used his formulas in an attempt to create his own periodic table, which he arranged in a spiral instead of in horizontal rows. His table was essentially correct, except that he left holes for two elements he believed to be between hydrogen and helium because he incorrectly thought helium's atomic number was four instead of two. Rydberg called his missing elements *nebulium* and *coronium*. Both of these hypothetical elements were later shown to be related to interactions of other elements, not elements in their own right.

The Rydberg constant is of great importance in atomic spectroscopy, and Rydberg's formulas would have a lasting influence on electrodynamics, the area of quantum mechanics that describes the interactions of light and matter. Until 2010, the Rydberg constant was considered the most accurately measured constant. In 2010, when researchers at the Paul Scherrer Institut in Switzerland made the most accurate measurements of a proton to date, they found that it has a smaller radius than previously thought, meaning that either the Rydberg constant or the theory of quantum electrodynamics would have to be adjusted.

IMPACT

Rydberg's equations hinted at the true nature of atoms, later uncovered completely by Niels Bohr. Using the suggestion of physical structure glimpsed from Rydberg's equations, and with help from the theories of Max Planck and Ernest Rutherford, Bohr presented an atomic model that is still considered valid. He grouped the positively charged protons and neutral neutrons at the center of the atom, with negatively charged electrons moving in defined orbits around the nucleus. The simplest model of an atom resembles a solar system, with the protons and neutrons as the much larger sun at the center and the tiny electrons orbiting like planets. In reality, electrons can move in three dimensions at a set distance from the nucleus, forming orbiting electron clouds, or electron shells, with different energy states. If an atom picks up energy, the electrons can jump to outer shells farther from the nucleus and jump back down again to release the energy. The release of energy caused by an electron jumping down to a closer orbit is what causes the spectrum of light released by burning chemicals.

In 1954, the Lund University Physics Department held the Rydberg Centennial Conference on Atomic Spectroscopy in honor of the hundredth anniversary of Rydberg's birth. Niels Bohr was among the distinguished speakers.

Mary Parker

FURTHER READING

Martinson, I., and L. J. Curtis. "Janne Rydberg—His Life and Work." *Nuclear Instruments and Methods in Physics Research Section B* 235.1 (2005):17–22. Print. A detailed biographical article of Johannes Rydberg and his work in spectral analysis.

Parker, Barry R. *Quantum Legacy: The Discovery that Changed the Universe*. New York: Prometheus, 2002. Print. Discusses the use of the Rydberg constant and the physicists who built upon Rydberg's ideas.

Rigden, John S. *Hydrogen: The Essential Element*. Cambridge: Harvard UP, 2003. 197–210. Print. Includes a chapter devoted to the discovery of the Rydberg constant and its later applications in physics.

Thomsen, Volker. "Atomic Perspectives: The Spectral Lines of Hydrogen." *Spectroscopy* 23.11 (2008): 29–32. Print. Traces the evolution of quantum theory from Johann Balmer through Niels Bohr, placing Rydberg's contributions in historical context. Includes tables, figures, and mathematical equations.

Florence R. Sabin

American anatomist

Eminent anatomist Florence R. Sabin did important research into brain development and the lymphatic system. She also worked in immunology, especially focusing on tuberculosis. She was the first woman to graduate from the Johns Hopkins School of Medicine, as well as the school's first female faculty member and first female full professor.

Born: November 9, 1871; Central City, Colorado
Died: October 3, 1953; Denver, Colorado
Primary field: Biology
Specialty: Anatomy

Early Life

Florence Rena Sabin was born in Central City, Colorado, on November 9, 1871. She was the second daughter of mining engineer George Kimball Sabin and schoolteacher Serena Miner. Her paternal grandfather was a doctor. Sabin and her family moved to Denver when she was four. When she was seven, her mother died of puerperal fever. She and her sister, Mary, attended Wolfe Hall, an Episcopalian boarding school in Denver, for a year before moving to Chicago. Once in Chicago, the family lived with George's brother Albert Sabin.

In Illinois, Sabin and her sister attended a private school for two years, spending their summer vacations with their paternal grandparents in Saxtons River, Vermont. The sisters attended the Vermont Academy boarding school. Although Sabin had planned to be a pianist, she had always been strong in math and science, and she decided while in high school to focus on academics instead. Upon graduation, she and her sister were expected to attend college, and both went to Smith College in Massachusetts.

At Smith College, Sabin majored in zoology. During her junior year, she developed a strong interest in the study of biology. After receiving her bachelor of science from Smith College in 1893, she taught high school math at Wolfe Hall for two years to earn the money for her first year of medical school at Johns Hopkins. After teaching at Wolfe Hall, she became an assistant in the Smith College biology department. The summer before entering Johns Hopkins, she worked at the Marine Biological Laboratory in Woods Hole, Massachusetts.

Life's Work

In 1896, Florence Sabin entered Johns Hopkins School of Medicine. The medical school had just started accepting female students, and as part of the third coed class of medical students, Sabin was one of fourteen women in her class of forty-five. It was not long before her aptitude caught the attention of anatomist Franklin P. Mall, a prominent scientist at Hopkins. He became her mentor, and their professional relationship would span many years.

Mall encouraged Sabin to do research. At his suggestion, she developed the first three-dimensional model of the medulla and midbrain from serial microscopic sections of a newborn baby's nervous system. This research became the basis of Sabin's *An Atlas of the Medulla and Midbrain* (1901), which became a widely used textbook. The second project suggested by Mall was a study of the embryological development of the lymphatic system.

Florence R. Sabin's Work with the Origins of the Lymphatic System

During her tenure at Johns Hopkins School of Medicine, Florence R. Sabin conducted research on the lymphatic system. *Lymph* is a clear or white fluid made up of bacteria-fighting white blood cells and chyle, a fluid of proteins and fats from the intestines; the lymphatic system includes the lymph nodes, ducts, and vessels, as well as organs such as the adenoids, spleen, thymus, and tonsils. Together, the system helps the body fight off infections.

Sabin hoped her research would settle the existing controversy about how the lymphatic system developed. Most researchers were convinced that the vessels making up the lymphatic system were formed independently of the veins in the circulatory system. Sabin, however, believed that the lymphatic vessels formed from the veins themselves. She was not convinced that the existing studies, done on pig embryos, were indicative of the early development of structures. To prove her hypothesis, Sabin decided to work with younger pig embryos instead of the older ones that previous researchers had used; this way, she could see the actual development of the system as it happened, rather than after the fact. She also used a method called supravital staining, which is the staining of living cells with non-toxic dyes that allows observers to view vital processes as they take place.

To study the lymphatic system development in pig embryos, Sabin injected dyes into the lymphatic vessels. As the embryos developed, the dye allowed her to see the lymphatic vessels actually budding from the veins, thus proving her hypothesis and disproving the earlier theory that the vessels developed independently before attaching to the veins.

Sabin published her results in a number of papers, as well as a chapter in the *Manual of Human Embryology* (1910–12), edited by Franz Keibel and Franklin P. Mall. The research Sabin conducted using supravital staining led her to study monocytes, the cells involved in the body's immune responses. In particular, she studied the body's immune response to the tuberculosis bacillus.

In 1900, upon graduation from the Johns Hopkins School of Medicine, Sabin had an internship at Johns Hopkins Hospital, during which she decided she preferred research and teaching to the actual practice of medicine. Attaining a teaching position as a woman would prove to be difficult, however.

Following her internship year, Sabin received a fellowship from the Baltimore Association for the Advancement of University Education for Women that allowed her to continue the research she had started under Mall. A paper she subsequently wrote on the origin of the lymphatic system received the Naples Table Association's prize for scientific research by women—one thousand dollars, a considerable sum at the time. Sabin was the first recipient of the prize, which also resulted in a research position at the Stazione Zoologica (Zoological Station) in Naples, Italy. She spent a year in Naples, then returned to her research at Johns Hopkins.

When Sabin was appointed assistant instructor in the Department of Anatomy at Johns Hopkins in 1902, she became the first woman faculty member at the university. She was made an associate professor in 1905. After Mall's death in 1917, the school initially selected Lewis Weed, one of Sabin's former students, to chair the anatomy department; threatened by protests on the part of Sabin's friends, however, Johns Hopkins reconsidered and hired Sabin as a professor of histology, making her the first woman to become a full professor at the school.

While a professor at Johns Hopkins, Sabin did groundbreaking work on the origins of the lymphatic system. Her work included studies demonstrating that the structures of the lymphatic system are formed from embryonic veins and not from other tissues. As part of her research, she used a method of staining cells that facilitated the study of living cells.

By the early 1920s, Sabin was anxious to devote more of her time and effort to research. She became the first woman to head the Department of Cellular Studies at the Rockefeller Institute for Medical Research in 1925. From her arrival at the institute in 1925 until her departure thirteen years later, Sabin led research on the mechanisms of tuberculosis, and her team made major strides in furthering understanding of the disease. Between 1930 and 1934, she wrote a biography of Franklin Mall, the man who had acted as her mentor at Johns Hopkins.

Upon retiring from the Rockefeller Institute in 1938, Sabin moved back to Colorado. She lived with her sister and corresponded regularly with her research colleagues. She also attended conferences and served on the boards of many organizations. In 1944, Sabin chaired the Health Committee of Colorado's Post–War

Planning Committee at the behest of Governor John Vivian. As chair, she investigated health services in the state and, finding them deficient in funding, staffing, and legislative support, became a passionate advocate for health-service reform. She drafted a number of bills that became known as the Sabin Program. Although she worked hard to ensure the success of her program, only four of its six bills were passed in 1947.

Following her time as chair of the Health Committee, Sabin served as chair of the Interim Board of Health and Hospitals of Denver until 1951. Next, she served as manager of the Denver Department of Health and Charities, where she launched an initiative to improve sanitation in the city. The initiative included enforcing existing health regulations for restaurants and food suppliers, as well as testing for tuberculosis and syphilis.

IMPACT

Florence Sabin was a remarkable woman whose life was made up of many significant firsts. She was not only the first woman to hold faculty and other important positions at prestigious institutions but also the first researcher to prove new theories on the development of the lymphatic system. It was Sabin who devised a new technique to observe living cells. Her "hanging drop" technique allowed her to observe the formation of stem cells and their eventual function as red and white blood cells in living chick embryos. She was also the first person to see a heart beat in a chick embryo. With her new staining techniques, it was possible to tell the various blood cell types apart for the first time.

In addition, Sabin's work with tuberculosis brought her acknowledgement from the National Tuberculosis Association, along with a grant to support her work. Her testing program reduced the incidence of tuberculosis in Denver from 54.7 per 100,000 people to 27 and the frequency of syphilis from 700 per 100,000 people to a mere 60, both large gains in the area of public health.

Sabin was well known during her lifetime and received a number of honors and awards, including some that had never been given to a woman before. She was the first female president of the American Association of Anatomists (1924) and the first woman to be elected to the National Academy of Sciences (1925). Among her other honors are the Trudeau Medal of the National Tuberculosis Association (1945) for her early work on the disease and the Lasker Foundation's Public Service Award (1951) for her public health work in Colorado. The medical school of the University of Colorado dedicated a new biological sciences building in her honor in 1951. In 1959, she was honored with a statue in the National Statuary Hall of the US Capitol.

Gina Hagler

FURTHER READING

Bluemel, Elinor. *Florence Sabin: Colorado Woman of the Century*. Boulder: U of Colorado P, 1959. Print. A biography of Sabin, written by a physician's wife and librarian who knew Sabin personally. Includes a bibliography.

Morantz-Sanchez, Regina. *Sympathy and Science: Women Physicians in American Medicine*. Chapel Hill: U of North Carolina P, 2000. Print. A study of women in medicine that discusses Sabin at some length. Originally published in 1985 and reprinted with a new preface.

Sabin, Florence R. *The Origin and Development of the Lymphatic System*. 1913. Cornell U Lib., 2009. Print. A reprint of Sabin's 1913 book on the lymphatic system.

---, and Henry M. Knower. *An Atlas of the Medulla and Midbrain*. Charleston: Nabu, 2010. Print. A reprint of Sabin's 1901 work on the brain development of newborns, which became a popular and widely used textbook at the time of initial publication.

CARL SAGAN

American astrophysicist

One of the best-known scientists of the twentieth century, Carl Sagan had the unique ability to conduct significant astronomical and planetary research and make science interesting and accessible to the public. He inspired the catch phrase "billions and billions of stars" after his memorable description of the universe and its objects in his television series Cosmos.

Born: November 9, 1934; Brooklyn, New York
Died: December 20, 1996; Seattle, Washington
Primary fields: Astronomy; physics
Specialty: Astrophysics

EARLY LIFE

Born in Brooklyn, New York, Carl Edward Sagan knew from an early age that he wanted to be an astronomer

Sagan Brings Science to the Masses

The writings for which American astronomer Carl Sagan became famous were not his scholarly essays, but his works of popular science. His first major book, *Dragons of Eden: Speculation on Human Intelligence*, was published in 1977. The book, which concerns the development of the human brain throughout history, was widely acclaimed, spending several months on the best-seller list of the *New York Times* and winning the Pulitzer Prize for general nonfiction in 1978. This work brought Sagan to the public's attention as a popularizer of science.

Sagan wrote several other books, including *Broca's Brain: Reflections on the Romance of Science* (1979), before his television series, *Cosmos*, was aired on public television. *Cosmos*, a thirteen-part documentary, became Sagan's most famous work. Dismayed by the relative lack of media attention given to the various National Aeronautics and Space Administration (NASA) projects, Sagan conceived of the idea of a regular television series about the solar system, the universe, and the potential existence of intelligent life beyond Earth. Although the project employed well over one hundred people, including Sagan's wife as cowriter, Sagan himself narrated the series and, rather unusually, appeared on camera most of the time. The series, which was filmed at locations all over the world, took three years to produce and was aired in 1980. *Cosmos* won three Emmy Awards and a Peabody Award, and some 500 million viewers in sixty different countries watched the series. In addition, an accompanying book by the same title, also published in 1980, became the best-selling nonfiction science book in US history up until that time.

Sagan wrote and cowrote numerous other books, including *Comet* (1985) and *Shadows of Forgotten Ancestors* (1992). Among his most notable works is *Contact* (1985), his first and only science-fiction novel. Because of his enormous popularity, Sagan was paid an advance of two million dollars for the book, an unprecedented amount for a first novel. *Contact*, a story about the first message from an extraterrestrial race, received mixed but generally positive reviews. Sagan had originally intended *Contact* to be produced as a motion picture, but after many delays, he decided to turn it into a novel first. A film version starring Academy Award–winning actor Jodie Foster was finally released in 1997. Unfortunately, although Sagan worked on the film production up until the time of his death, he did not live to see its actual release.

when he grew up. Fascinated by the notion that the stars are like the Earth's sun but merely farther away, he read about astronomy and other sciences on his own. He also supplemented his reading with science-fiction magazines, which he carefully evaluated for their scientific accuracy.

Even while avidly pursuing these interests, Sagan did not yet know that it was possible to make a living as an astronomer. While attending high school in Rahway, New Jersey, where his family had moved at the end of World War II, Sagan learned that it was indeed possible to pursue astronomy as a career, not merely as a hobby. With support from his parents, Sagan began studying physics at the University of Chicago in 1951 at the age of sixteen.

The University of Chicago, which had several Nobel Prize–winning scientists on its faculty, was an ideal environment for Sagan. He learned that other scientific fields such as biology and chemistry were also relevant to his interests, which had expanded to include the origin of life. He even organized a series of science lectures on campus, foreshadowing his later success as a popularizer of science.

Sagan went on to pursue a doctoral degree in astronomy and astrophysics under Dutch astronomer Gerard Kuiper at the University of Chicago campus in Williams Bay, Wisconsin. Before receiving his doctorate in 1960, Sagan met and married biologist Lynn Alexander, with whom he later had a son. Sagan held academic posts at various institutions, including Harvard University, before accepting a permanent professorship at Cornell University in 1968, where he remained until his death.

From the beginning of his academic career, Sagan proved to be an energetic researcher and writer, publishing numerous papers and articles over the years. In 1966, he wrote a nontechnical educational book on planets that was published as part of a Time-Life science book series. In the same year, he coauthored *Intelligent Life in the Universe* with Soviet scientist I. S. Shklovskii, an unusual collaboration in light of the Cold War hostilities between the two nations at that time. Sagan also conducted significant research on such topics as the greenhouse effect on Venus and the composition of the atmosphere of Titan, one of Saturn's moons.

LIFE'S WORK

By the late 1960s, Sagan was fairly well known in the scientific world as an expert on the possibility of extraterrestrial life. In fact, when Arthur C. Clarke and Stanley Kubrick began working on the film *2001: A Space Odyssey* (1968), they consulted with Sagan about what the alien creatures in the film should look like. Ultimately, they followed Sagan's advice and decided not to show the aliens.

Sagan's entry into the public's view, however, did not occur until 1972, when he made a brief appearance on *The Tonight Show*, hosted by Johnny Carson, to promote a book of his essays titled *Cosmic Connection* (1972). Carson liked Sagan enough to invite him back a few weeks later, at which time the scientist spoke about one of his favorite topics, the history of the universe. Viewers were so enthralled with Sagan's knowledge and charisma that he became a regular guest on *The Tonight Show*. Never before had a practicing scientist become so widely known to the American public.

After his success on *The Tonight Show*, Sagan realized that the public could find science fascinating if it were presented to them correctly, and that he had a talent for doing so without abandoning the actual research itself. The dual nature of Sagan's contributions is illustrated by the fact that he simultaneously served as editor in chief of *Icarus*, a highly technical scientific journal, and wrote several articles for *Parade*, a Sunday magazine supplement with national distribution.

In the meantime, Sagan and his first wife had divorced, and Sagan married artist Linda Salzman, with whom he had two sons. In the early 1970s, Sagan and Salzman worked together with the National Aeronautics and Space Administration (NASA) on the Pioneer project. Pioneer 10 was a NASA spacecraft designed to explore the outer solar system in general and the planet Jupiter in particular before becoming the first human-made object to leave the solar system. Inspired by the possibility of alien life, Sagan suggested that a message from humankind be placed aboard the spacecraft in case it ever encountered an alien race in the distant future. With NASA agreement, Sagan designed the message, which was placed on a gold anodized aluminum plate on the spacecraft. The basic message employed mathematic and scientific concepts that Sagan believed constituted a "universal language" that any intelligent race could understand. Salzman contributed a drawing of two nude human figures.

Sagan's interstellar message received much public attention, and, in spite of some negative reactions to the nude figures, most people supported the idea of sending a message to the stars. In fact, the project received enough support that it was repeated on the Pioneer 11 spacecraft as well as on the two Voyager spacecraft launched

in 1977. Ironically, Sagan ultimately collaborated with his third wife, Ann Druyan, on the Voyager message; Druyan's brain waves were recorded on a gold-plated phonograph record, along with greetings in dozens of languages, that was included on the Voyager spacecraft. Sagan and Druyan married in 1981, one month after his divorce from Salzman became final, and they remained married until the scientist's death in 1996. Sagan and Druyan had a daughter and a son.

Even during the busiest periods of his life, Sagan did not neglect his writing. In 1977, he published *The Dragons of Eden: Speculation on Human Intelligence*. *Cosmos*, a book based on his popular television series of the same name, was published in 1980. Five years later, Sagan published *Contact*, his first and only science-fiction novel, which was later adapted for film.

Sagan also took on another role: public policy activist and adviser. After studying the effect of massive dust storms on Mars, Sagan began to calculate how vast amounts of dust could affect the Earth's climate. In 1983, a controversial television film, *The Day After*, gave a fictional account of the effects of nuclear war. Immediately after the show, a panel of scientists, including Sagan, discussed these effects, and Sagan voiced his opinion that a "nuclear winter," brought about by debris from nuclear bombs blocking the sunlight, could completely devastate the Earth's climate and possibly cause the extinction of humankind. While many scientists disagreed with Sagan's belief that the effects would be so devastating, enough people paid attention to the theory that it prompted some historians to claim that Sagan played a significant role in nuclear disarmament and the end of the Cold War.

In 1995, Sagan was diagnosed with myelodysplasia, a rare bone-marrow disorder that can lead to leukemia. Several bone-marrow transplants extended his life, but on December 20, 1996, he died of pneumonia, a complication of the disease.

IMPACT

Sagan was simultaneously a scientist and a media celebrity whose enormous popularity both helped and hurt his career. Although almost all scientists recognize that public awareness and support are essential to scientific research, scientists have historically been skeptical of any colleague who receives a large amount of media attention. From his early college days when he organized public science lectures at the University of Chicago, Sagan was seen by some as calling too much attention to himself. In a commentary titled "Kinship with the Stars" in *Discover* in 1997, Jared Diamond asserted that Sagan was ultimately rejected for membership in the National Academy of Sciences, despite having been provisionally approved, because of his fame. The same scientists who continually bemoaned the public's lack of interest in science felt that Sagan could not possibly be a serious scientist because he spent too much time in the public eye. Eventually the academy recognized its mistake and awarded Sagan its highest honor, the Public Welfare Medal in 1994. However, their earlier rejection of Sagan may have made young scientists wary of jeopardizing their scientific careers by becoming involved in public education.

In spite of the negative attitudes directed toward him by other scientists, Sagan was very successful in the wide variety of activities he pursued. He has been credited with inspiring many young people to choose science as a career path.

Amy Sisson

FURTHER READING

Davidson, Keay. *Carl Sagan: A Life*. New York: Wiley, 2000. Print. Presents a well-researched account of the life and career of the scientist, whom the author describes as a true visionary.

Head, Tom, ed. *Conversations with Carl Sagan*. Jackson: UP of Mississippi, 2006. Print. Contains sixteen interviews with Sagan conducted over a twenty-six-year period, in which Sagan discusses topics related to science, religion, and life.

Sagan, Carl. *Cosmos*. 1980. New York: Random, 2002. Print. The companion to Sagan's world-renowned television series. Contains numerous color photographs and illustrations, an introduction that discusses the origin and development of the television series, and an extensive list for further reading.

ABDUS SALAM

Pakistani physicist

Twentieth-century theoretical physicist Muhammad Abdus Salam became the first Muslim scientist to win a Nobel Prize in 1979 for his codevelopment of a theory unifying electromagnetic and weak nuclear forces. Salam was also involved in Pakistan's efforts to build a nuclear bomb.

Born: January 29, 1926; Santokdas, British India (now Pakistan)
Died: November 21, 1996; Oxford, England
Also known as: Muhammad Abdus Salam; Mohammad Abdus Salam
Primary field: Physics
Specialties: Theoretical physics; electromagnetism; nuclear physics

EARLY LIFE

Abdus Salam was born in the village of Santokdas in British India on January 29, 1926. Although his father was a teacher living in the Punjabi town of Jhang, his mother followed tradition and went to Santokdas, where her own father was posted, to give birth to her first child, Abdus Salam. He would have six brothers and two sisters.

The name Abdus Salam is single phrase meaning "servant of God (Allah), who is peace." Despite his objections, Westerners commonly used Salam as his last name. It was not until 1974 that Abdus Salam chose the first name of Muhammad.

Abdus Salam grew up in a devout Ahmadi Muslim family who encouraged learning. At age fourteen, Abdus Salam received the highest score recorded for the entrance examination of the University of the Punjab in Lahore. He was awarded a scholarship to attend that university's Government College.

He published his first paper in 1943 as an undergraduate, proposing solutions for mathematical problems set by Indian mathematician Srinivasa Ramanujan (1887–1920). In 1944, Abdus Salam earned his bachelor of arts degree in mathematics from Government College. Two years later, he received his master of arts in mathematics there.

In 1946, Abdus Salam received a scholarship to attend St. John's College at Cambridge University in England. From there, in 1949, Abdus Salam graduated with a bachelor of arts in mathematics and physics with highest honors in both majors.

Entering the PhD program, Abdus Salam discovered he had neither patience with nor enjoyment in physics experiments and moved to theoretical physics. In 1950, Abdus Salam received the Smith's Prize from Cambridge University for his predoctoral work.

Abdus Salam published his PhD thesis, featuring work in quantum electrodynamics, in 1951. He returned home to the newly formed nation of Pakistan to teach mathematics at Government College. In 1952, he was awarded his PhD in theoretical physics from Cambridge.

LIFE'S WORK

In Pakistan, Abdus Salam was made head of the Mathematics Department at the University of the Punjab in 1952. His administrative and teaching duties left him almost no time for research. Feeling isolated as a scientist and under threat of violence as an Ahmadi, Abdus Salam left Pakistan in 1954. He became a lecturer at St. John's College.

In 1956, Abdus Salam discovered neutrino parity violation. However, doubts raised by Austrian theoretical physicist Wolfgang Pauli led Abdus Salam to delay publication of his theory until 1957. By then, he had been scooped by Chinese American theoretical physicists Chen Ning Franklin Yang and Tsung-Dao Lee.

Abdus Salam began to develop a mathematical solution to unify both electromagnetic force and weak nuclear force, two of the four fundamental forces known to physics in the 1950s. In 1957, he was appointed professor of applied mathematics at the Imperial College of Science and Technology in London. Two years later, he was elected a fellow of the Royal Society of London. In 1960, he became professor of theoretical physics at Imperial College.

In addition to his professorship in London, Abdus Salam became chief scientific adviser to Pakistan's president, Ayub Khan, in 1961. There, Abdus Salam was instrumental in invigorating work at the Pakistan Atomic Energy Commission (PAEC) and was a founder of Pakistan's Space and Upper Atmosphere Research Commission (SUPARCO) on September 16, 1961.

At Imperial College, Abdus Salam worked on his theory to unify the two physical forces. He began an exchange with two American theoretical physicists, Sheldon Lee Glashow and Steven Weinberg, who were pursuing the same idea in the United States. In 1963, Abdus Salam published his theories about the vector meson, a subatomic particle.

In 1964, Abdus Salam founded the International Centre for Theoretical Physics (ICTP) in Trieste, Italy. With this, he realized his dream to create an institution where international theoretical physicists, particularly from developing countries, could meet and engage in intellectual interchange. Abdus Salam served as director from 1964 to 1993 and as president from 1994 to 1996.

Abdus Salam served as Pakistan's delegate to the International Atomic Energy Agency (IAEA) from 1963 to 1964. At this time, he was also instrumental in convincing the United States to provide Pakistan with a small uranium nuclear research reactor. It went live under Abdus Salam's supervision in Nilore, near Islamabad, Pakistan, in 1965.

By 1966, Abdus Salam had combined his own theory for the unification of the electromagnetic with the weak nuclear force with that Glashow had developed. In 1967, Abdus Salam completed the mathematical proof of their electroweak theory, which was published in 1968.

After the December 1971 war between India and Pakistan, which Pakistan lost, Abdus Salam attended the secret Multan meeting held by Pakistani president Zulfikar Ali Bhutto on January 20, 1972, to discuss nuclear arms for Pakistan. There, it was decided to build a Pakistani atomic bomb. To further this end, Abdus Salam founded the Theoretical Physics Group of the PAEC in 1972.

Back in England, Abdus Salam began collaboration with Indian-born American theoretical physicist Jogesh Chandra Pati. Together, they pursued the quest to develop a grand unified theory combining all four known fundamental forces in physics. In 1974, they published their Pati–Salam model. The model proposes a theory that adds an additional fourth "color" to describe different quarks, with this fourth color representing leptons.

In March 1974, Abdus Salam and Pakistani nuclear engineer Munir Ahmad Khan established the secret organization known as the Wah Group of Scientists, whose duty was to build an atomic bomb for Pakistan. On September 7, 1974, the Pakistani parliament declared that the Ahmadi sect was non-Muslim. In response, Abdus Salam took the first name Muhammad and grew out his beard to show his allegiance to Islam.

In England, Abdus Salam looked into theories for the possible existence of supersymmetry in particle physics. In 1978, he received the Royal Medal of the Royal Society. He also accompanied a secret Pakistani science mission to China to establish nuclear cooperation.

In 1979, Abdus Salam, Glashow, and Weinberg received the Nobel Prize in Physics. It was awarded for their joint and independent contributions to establish a theory that unified the electromagnetic and weak nuclear force.

Throughout the 1980s, Abdus Salam combined his research in theoretical physics with strong advocacy to establish research institutions for theoretical scientists

Abdus Salam, Sheldon Glashow, and Steven Weinberg Develop Electroweak Theory

By the early twentieth century, physicists knew of four fundamental forces: gravity, electromagnetism, and the strong and the weak nuclear forces. It became a desire to look for theories that would unify two or more of these forces. Yet in 1956, these four forces were still being studied separately.

Once Abdus Salam returned to England in 1954, he attempted unification of the weak nuclear force and electromagnetism. In 1956, Abdus Salam discovered a parity violation for weak nuclear force interaction. However, he was discouraged by the objection of Wolfgang Pauli and did not publish his discovery until one year later. By this time, two American physicists had published their own discovery of this fact.

Since this parity violation linked the weak nuclear force to electromagnetic interactions, Abdus Salam intensified his efforts. In 1958, he began work with British Australian physicist John Clive Ward and cooperated with American theoretical physicist Steven Weinberg on the issue. This was a remarkable scientific cooperation, soon amended by contact with American theoretical physicist Sheldon Glashow. The scientists relied on postal mail, meetings at professional conferences, and visits, such as Weinberg's yearlong stay at Imperial College in 1961–62, to conduct their intellectual interchanges.

A major breakthrough came in 1961 when Abdus Salam, Ward, and Glashow independently realized that there existed both an electromagnetic and a neutral current to enable parity conservation for the electromagnetic force and parity violation for the weak nuclear force. That year, Abdus Salam and Weinberg also provided proof for spontaneous symmetry breaking in the weak nuclear force, which had been proposed by British theoretical physicist Jeffrey Goldstone. In 1963, Abdus Salam and Weinberg incorporated the Higgs mechanism in their developing unification theory.

Finally, in 1966, Abdus Salam and Glashow combined their theories. In 1967, Abdus Salam provided the mathematical proof, just as Steven Weinberg arrived at this theory as well. In 1968, Abdus Salam and Glashow published their results. Their theory became known as electroweak theory.

It took several years until electroweak theory was proved by an experiment at the Geneva laboratory of the European Organization for Nuclear Research (CERN). When nuclei were hit by a beam of neutrinos, the neutral current predicted by Abdus Salam, Glashow, and Weinberg was measured. A second proof came in 1978 from an experiment at the Stanford Linear Accelerator (SLAC), where asymmetries caused by electromagnetic and weak interference were observed.

The Nobel Prize in Physics for 1979 recognized the mutual scientific achievement of Abdus Salam, Glashow, and Weinberg in developing electroweak theory. Their theory has been considered a major part of the Standard Model of particle physics, which integrates electromagnetic, weak nuclear, and strong nuclear forces.

from developing countries. In 1983, Abdus Salam established the Third World Academy of Sciences in Trieste. This was followed by his creation of the Third World Network of Scientific Organizations, also in Trieste, in 1988.

The onset of progressive supranuclear palsy, a degenerative neural condition, forced Abdus Salam to relinquish directorship of the ICTP in Trieste in 1994. He also exchanged his professorship at Imperial College for the position of senior research fellow.

Abdus Salam kept his private life confidential. With his first wife, whom he married before returning to England in 1954, he had three daughters and one son. With his second wife, British biochemist Louise Napier Johnson, he had a son and a daughter. Abdus Salam died on November 21, 1996, in Oxford, of Parkinson's disease. He was buried alongside his parents in Rabwah, Pakistan.

IMPACT

Throughout his scientific career, Abdus Salam focused on theoretical physics and issues in nuclear physics. He was also a tireless advocate and creator of influential international institutes fostering scientific interchange among scientists, particularly theoretical physicists, in developing countries.

For his achievements in theoretical physics, Abdus Salam received many honors. Outstanding among them is the 1979 Nobel Prize in Physics he shared with Sheldon Glashow and Steven Weinberg. In his successful professional life, he received honorary doctorates from over forty universities.

Abdus Salam's creation and long stewardship of the ICTP was recognized in 1997, when it was renamed the Abdus Salam International Centre for Theoretical Physics. To date, about five thousand scientists have attended this center every year. Since its inception in 1964, more than half of the 125,000 scientists who spent research time at the center have come from developing countries, demonstrating the success of Abdus Salam's dedication to bring such scientists out of often-isolated professional lives.

Abdus Salam's contributions to Pakistan's creation of nuclear weapons has been controversial. He saw this development as necessary counterweight to the existing nuclear weapons of India.

Pakistan's official rejection of his Ahmadi faith as being non-Muslim deeply hurt Abdus Salam. Even though he left the country in protest in 1974, he continued to feel loyalty for his native land, which he expressed by fostering the work of Pakistani scientists abroad. He also supported them in the international scientific community, especially at the ICTP and its later associated institutions. Sadly, his grave in Pakistan has been repeatedly vandalized by those who begrudge his Ahmadi faith.

R. C. Lutz

FURTHER READING

Duff, Michael, ed. *Proceedings of the Salam + 50 Conference*. July 7, 2007, Imperial College London. London: Imperial College, 2008. Print. Conference held in honor of the fiftieth anniversary of Abdus Salam's appointment at the college. Introduces Abdus Salam's ideas in theoretical physics, recollects his colleagues' scientific work with him, and emphasizes his humanitarian role. Section on his personal life includes essays by his daughter and his grandson.

Ellis, John, et al., eds. *The Abdus Salam Memorial Meeting*. November 1997, Abdus Salam International Centre for Theoretical Physics. Singapore: World Scientific, 1999. Print. A collection of scientific articles covering such cutting-edge theories as superstrings. Conference commemorated the tenth anniversary of the death of Abdus Salam.

Fraser, Gordon. *Cosmic Anger: Abdus Salam—The First Muslim Nobel Scientist*. Oxford: Oxford UP, 2012. Print. Perceptive and sympathetic biography of Abdus Salam, focusing on his scientific achievements and his struggle with Pakistani authorities, especially in light of religious discrimination against his Ahmadi faith. Portrays Abdus Salam as deeply committed to ending the isolation of scientists in developing countries.

FREDERICK SANGER

British biochemist

Twentieth-century biochemist Frederick Sanger was awarded the Nobel Prize in Chemistry in 1958 for his discovery of the structure of the insulin molecule and again in 1980 for his invention of a technique for determining the sequence of DNA.

Born: August 13, 1918; Rendcomb, England
Primary field: Chemistry
Specialties: Biochemistry; molecular biology; genetics

EARLY LIFE

Frederick Sanger was born on August 13, 1918, in Rendcomb, England, to a Quaker family. He was the son of a physician, also named Frederick Sanger, and his wife Cicely, heiress to a cotton-manufacturing business. Sanger attended St. John's College at the University of Cambridge, where he obtained a bachelor's degree in natural sciences in 1939. After his undergraduate degree he received first class examination scores in advanced biochemistry. He stayed on at Cambridge to begin his PhD in biochemistry.

In keeping with his Quaker tradition, Sanger was a conscientious objector during World War II. Instead of joining the military he worked in the laboratory of Albert Neuberger, where he studied the metabolism of the amino acid lysine. Sanger was awarded his PhD in 1943, after which he won a Beit Memorial Fellowship for Medical Research. This income enabled him to work in the laboratory of A. C. Chibnall at Cambridge. Chibnall, whose research group had been working with insulin, suggested that Sanger explore the structure of the molecule.

LIFE'S WORK

Insulin is a hormone manufactured in the pancreas. It brings glucose (sugar) from the blood into cells, where it is used for energy. Because some diabetics require injections of insulin, a purified form of bovine insulin was available to Sanger for his research.

All proteins are made of amino acids linked together in a specific order. There are twenty common amino acids. Just as the letters of the alphabet can be rearranged to make infinite words, these twenty amino acids form many different proteins. When Sanger began his work, scientists knew proteins were made of amino acids, but they had not yet discovered that the amino acids in each protein were arranged in a specific sequence.

Sanger used the chemical dinitrophenol to bind to one amino acid at a time in the insulin molecule, removing each amino acid from the rest of the chain. He identified the individual amino acids using paper chromatography, a technique for identifying components in liquids. In paper chromatography a solvent is drawn up by filter paper and amino acids dissolved in the solvent will move different distances up the paper. Some amino acids are more strongly attracted to the paper and others to the solvent. When the paper dries, the amino acid leaves a smear behind. Sanger examined these smears to identify each amino acid.

The process was slow, and it took until 1955 to determine the whole sequence. Sanger discovered that the insulin molecule is actually made of two separate chains of amino acids, or polypeptides, linked together. Insulin was the first protein ever to be sequenced, but the work was important in other ways too. Since scientists knew that DNA (deoxyribonucleic acid) coded for proteins, the fact that proteins were ordered molecules meant that DNA must have a sequence that is important too. It was later discovered that the sequence of nitrogenous bases in a gene determines the sequence of amino acids in a protein. In this way, DNA carries heritable traits from one generation to the next.

In 1958, Sanger earned the Nobel Prize in Chemistry for his sequencing work on insulin. Diabetics have benefited from his research because it enabled pure human insulin to be produced using techniques of genetic engineering. Before this advancement, people with diabetes had to rely on insulin purified from animals. Animal insulin was not as effective, and sometimes caused allergic reactions.

Sanger was appointed to the Medical Research Council at Cambridge in 1951. By 1962 the council moved to a new location in the Laboratory of Molecular Biology, also at Cambridge, and Sanger was promoted to head of the Division of Protein Chemistry there. Sanger was surrounded by colleagues who were interested in DNA, and he began working on a method to rsequence the DNA molecule.

Nucleotides are the building block molecules that make up DNA. Each nucleotide includes one of four nitrogenous bases: adenine (A), thymine (T), guanine (G), or cytosine (C). The sequence of these bases codes for the sequence of amino acids in a protein. Sanger developed a technique to read the sequence of bases in DNA—a technique based on DNA's ability to replicate itself. The double helical DNA molecule looks like a spiral staircase in which the "stairs" are made of pairs of bases bound together, A with T and C with G. Because of this precise pairing, each strand can serve as a template to synthesize a new strand.

During synthesis of a growing strand, the new nucleotide to be added binds to an oxygen atom on the last nucleotide in line. Sanger came up with the idea of using dideoxynucleotides, which are nucleotides with no oxygen, to bind on to. When these get incorporated into a growing strand, no new nucleotides can bind, and the chain is terminated. The reaction mixture includes normal nucleotides as well, so it produces a mixture of different-length pieces of DNA. They get separated on a slab of gel, leaving a pattern that looks like the bar code on a price tag. That bar code reveals the bases in the DNA sequence.

Sanger and his research group eventually sequenced the genome (all the DNA) of the bacteriophage phi-X 174. A bacteriophage is a virus that attacks bacteria. Bacteriophages are convenient to study because they can grow in petri dishes with bacteria, and because they cannot infect people. This particular virus had a genome of 5,375 nucleotides, which is small compared to genomes other organisms. Sanger won the 1980 Nobel Prize in Chemistry for developing the technique and sequencing the genome of bacteriophage phi-X 174. This was the first intact genome ever to be sequenced from any organism. Sanger shared the prize with Paul Berg and Walter Gilbert.

More ambitious sequencing efforts followed, including the first sequencing of the genome of human mitochondria. Mitochondria are subcellular organelles that provide humans with energy. Now comparisons of mitochondrial DNA from different populations are revealing paths of migration taken by ancient peoples as they spread out of Africa.

IMPACT

The sequencing of bacteriophage λ (lambda) was Sanger's largest effort, at over 48,000 nucleotides. DNA sequencing was a tremendous achievement because it allows us to compare a gene with its protein product. Some inherited diseases are due to mutations in a gene for a crucial protein. Sanger's work laid the foundation for curing inherited diseases using genetic engineering.

For example, some children are born with SCIDS (severe combined immunodeficiency syndrome), an inherited defect in the immune system that prevents them

Frederick Sanger Determines the Structure of Insulin

Proteins are large molecules that contain carbon, hydrogen, oxygen, nitrogen, and sulfur. They transport molecules, provide support and protection, and control chemical reactions. By the early 1940s, it was well established that proteins were made of some twenty different amino acids, but little was known about their arrangement and order. Determining the building plan for these complicated molecules was one of the greatest research problems of the twentieth century.

In 1943, Frederick Sanger began a twelve-year study that established the unique amino acid sequence of insulin—the hormone needed for the treatment of diabetes. Working with fellow British biochemist A. C. Chibnall, Sanger showed that the building blocks of proteins have a definite, specified order. Sanger developed strategies and techniques for uncovering this sequence that have been applied to many other proteins.

First, Sanger determined how many chains there were on the insulin molecule. The first amino acid in any chain has a free amino end. Sanger attached a colored dye, fluorodinitrobenzene (FDNB), to the insulin molecule. The dyed insulin was then broken into individual amino acids. Sanger found that the dye had reacted with two different amino acids. Therefore, he concluded that insulin had two chains. Sanger separated the two chains by oxidizing (combining with oxygen) the sulfurs that joined them.

When a protein is treated with strong acid, it comes apart into its individual amino acids. Sanger, however, gently treated each insulin chain with a weaker acid solution. The chain came apart but broke into bigger pieces of three, four, or five amino acids. Sanger separated these fragments and used his dye to find the identity of the first amino acid in each piece. He also determined the amino acid composition of each small piece and began to put the pieces together.

Besides using the acid solution that broke the chain in various places, Sanger also used digestive enzymes—chymotrypsin and trypsin—to cut the amino acid chains in specific places. The order of the chain was determined by overlapping the various fragments.

Once Sanger had successfully found the order of the two chains of the insulin molecule, he had to figure out how they were joined. The smaller chain, the amino acid with a sulfur group, had four cysteines (crystalline amino acids derived from cystine). The larger chain had two cysteines. Therefore, there were several different ways in which the chains could be linked.

By 1955, Sanger had determined the amino acid sequence of the 21-unit A chain and the 30-unit B chain of bovine insulin. He also found that insulin from other animals differed very slightly in its composition. He showed that these two chains were linked by sulfur bridges joining the cysteines at position 7 in both chains. A second disulfide bridge linked position 20 of the first chain with 19 of the second. This landmark work provided conclusive evidence that a protein had a very specific sequence of amino acids.

Frederick Sanger's work in determining the sequence of the amino acid units in insulin established conclusively that proteins have a definite order in the arrangement of their amino acids. This finding suggested to other scientists that there must be a genetic code that provides the information for the amino acid sequence. For his work Sanger was awarded the 1958 Nobel Prize in Chemistry.

from fighting off disease. These children once had to be kept in sterile plastic chambers just to stay alive. Using Sanger's sequencing method, researchers identified the "misspelling" in the DNA sequence. Experimental genetic engineering has corrected the problem for some children with SCIDS, who are now freed from confinement and living normal lives.

An automated version of the Sanger method was also used in the international Human Genome Project. The sequencing of the entire genome from a volunteer was recently completed and the sequence is still being analyzed. Questions about the ethical implications of the technology have also been raised, and continue to be discussed.

Frederick Sanger retired in 1983. The Sanger Centre was established in his honor in 1992, funded by the Wellcome Trust. Located in Cambridge, England, it is primarily focused on investigating genomes, with an eye toward health and medical applications of the work. The Sanger Centre was one of the sequencing centers involved in the Human Genome Project.

Courtney Farrell

FURTHER READING

García-Sancho, Miguel. "A New Insight into Sanger's Development of Sequencing: From Proteins to DNA, 1943–1977." *Journal of the History of Biology* 43.2 (2010): 265–323. Print. Discusses Sanger's scientific career related to his research on RNA and DNA sequencing, genomics, and bioinformatics and biomedicine.

Manchester, Keith. "Protein Sequencing Fifty Years Ago: Fred Sanger and the Amino Acid Sequence of Insulin." *South African Journal of Science* 101.7–8

(2005): 327–30. Print. Presents information on Sanger's work with the amino acid and protein sequencing and his study of the molecular structure of insulin.

Sanger, Frederick, and Margaret Dowding. *Selected Papers of Frederick Sanger: With Commentaries*. Singapore: World Scientific, 1996. Print. Includes publications from Sanger's research on RNA and DNA sequencing, amino acids, and insulin, as well as Sanger's reflections on his papers and why they were included in the collection.

MATTHIAS JAKOB SCHLEIDEN

German biologist

Nineteenth-century biologist Matthias Jakob Schleiden contributed to the concept of cell theory through his observations that plants are composed of cells, and that such cells represent the fundamental structure of plants.

Born: April 5, 1804; Free Imperial City of Hamburg (now Hamburg, Germany)
Died: June 23, 1881; Frankfurt am Main, Germany
Primary field: Biology
Specialty: Cellular biology

EARLY LIFE

Matthias Jakob Schleiden was born April 5, 1804 in Hamburg, to Andreas Benedikt Schleiden and Eleanore Bergeest Schleiden. His father was a prominent physician trained at the University of Jena. His younger brother, Karl Heinrich Schleiden, later became a prominent theologian after training in Jena. Schleiden's earliest interests were in the field of botany.

Schleiden entered the university at Heidelberg in 1824, where he began studying law. After graduating in 1827, he returned to Hamburg and established a law practice in that city. It is known that Schleiden attempted unsuccessfully to die by suicide in 1831 after suffering for a time from severe depression. When he recovered, he decided to pursue his true interest, the study of medicine, and he enrolled in the University of Göttingen. Schleiden studied with German chemist Friedrich Stromeyer. Among his classmates were Robert Bunsen, a pioneer in photochemistry, and philosopher Jakob Fries. Fries believed in a mechanistic approach to nature, a worldview that Schleiden espoused much of his life.

Schleiden's interest in the sciences was in informed Fries' *Mathematical Philosophy of Nature* (1822). Like English physicist Isaac Newton, Fries argued that an understanding of nature required an analytical approach. Schleiden concluded that to understand nature he would have to immerse himself in mathematics, and he began working with German mathematician Carl Friedrich Gauss. Schleiden spent his final two years at Göttingen working with Gauss, who helped expand his understanding of the subject.

After graduating with a medical degree in 1834, Schleiden accepted a position in the laboratory of physiologist Johannes Müller at the Humboldt University in Berlin.

LIFE'S WORK

Müller's interest was primarily the study of optics. As a student, he had observed the function of the optic nerve and its response to light. Müller was considered among the founders of the scientific method developed in Germany, and his 1833 physiology textbook, *Handbuch der Physiologie des Menschen* (Handbook of human physiology) influenced generations of physiologists. Schleiden worked with Müller developing his cell theory of plants—namely, that they were composed of individual cells carrying out the specific functions of the plant.

Among Müller's students was Theodor Schwann, who extended Schleiden's cell theory to include the cellular structure of animals as well. Both Schleiden and Schwann, however, mistakenly believed cell reproduction resulted from the initial formation of a cytoblast (nucleus) around which the cell substance would crystallize.

Schleiden published his observations on plants, "Beiträge zur Phytogenesis" (Contributions to plant origins)," in 1838. Schleiden began the work by disparaging many of his forerunners in the field. Indeed, his contemporaries often described him as being arrogant. This view is supported by Schleiden's descriptions of the work of prominent biologists, such as that of French biologist François-Vincent Raspail, as not being worthy of study. In his article, Schleiden presented his model of cell origins involving the cytoblast. To his credit, Schleiden did pay tribute to earlier work by Robert Brown in his description of the nucleus—the organelle that Schleiden renamed the "cytoblast" in his article.

In 1839, Schleiden received a PhD in botany from the University of Jena, where he subsequently accepted a position as an assistant professor. He continued his study of plants, publishing *Principles of Scientific Botany* in 1842, which encompassed his earlier work with Müller and his work at Jena. Schleiden also attempted to incorporate his views on plant evolution into the book.

Although Schleiden's research interests were within the discipline of botany, and he was in charge of the botanical gardens at the university, he preferred thinking of himself as one who studied the anatomy and physiology of plants. To Schleiden, a botanist was little more than a plant librarian, chiefly interested in naming, collecting, and classifying plants.

Schleiden remained at the University of Jena some twenty years, eventually being promoted to vice president and dean. In 1850, he began to lecture on anthropology. Perhaps due to overwork, or perhaps the result of the same psychological issues that had plagued him in his youth, Schleiden again suffered increasingly from depression. His work on cell origins had also come under attack, most notably by physiologist Robert Remak. Remak's work dealt primarily with the replication of embryonic cells in the chicken, and his conclusion that replication was through a process of binary fission was at odds with that of Schwann's (and by extension Schleiden's) description of cytoplasmic crystallization.

Schleiden's Observation of Plant Cells Becomes Component of Cell Theory

The first observation of cells dated to the 1660s when the English philosopher Robert Hooke observed slices of cork with the newly developed instrument the microscope. Hooke termed the porous spaces he observed "cells," since they resembled the cells in which monks studied. A contemporary of Hooke's, Nehemiah Grew, made similar observations on plants, even producing drawings to depict what he observed. However, both Hooke and Grew missed the significance of what they were observing.

Schleiden carried out most of his studies on plants in the mid-1830s, following his collaboration with Johannes Müller. His interest focused on the origins of cells from embryonic tissue. Schleiden already understood the basic function of cells in the plant, that the cell maintains an independent function or life of its own as well as playing an integral role in the tissue of which it is part. What was not immediately clear was the origin of the plant cell.

Centrally located within the cell was the nucleus, first described by Franz Bauer in the 1790s and given its modern name (nucleus) by Robert Brown in 1933. Schleiden likewise observed the plant nucleus, but renamed it as a "cytoblast," reflecting his belief that its function is in the generation of the cell. Schleiden published his hypothesis on the mechanism by which the cell is generated in the paper "Beiträge zur Phytogenesis" (Contributions to plant origins) in 1838. Schleiden's view was that once the cytoblast has matured, a thin vesicle forms on its surface, from which the cell grows out. Eventually the contents of the cell split, producing more cells. Although his observations were crucial to the development of cellular biology, Schleiden's interpretation of his research was incorrect. He had been observing endosperm, cells that are fused in what is termed a syncytium during an initial period of cellular growth. To the naturalist—the term "scientist" had not yet been coined—of the early 1830s, Schleiden's interpretations were reasonable. Nevertheless, the conclusion he reached by 1838, namely, that plants are composed of cells, proved to be correct.

Schleiden continued his work with further observations in higher plants, observing once again their cellular makeup and concluding that all aspects of plant physiology had their origins in the individual cells. Schleiden's other contribution to what evolved into cell theory was his refutation of the idea of spontaneous generation, that organisms spontaneously formed from inanimate material in the environment. Schleiden believed, correctly, that all plants, including algae and lichens, arose from preexisting cells.

In 1862, Schleiden resigned from his position at Jena, and after a brief sojourn to Dresden, accepted a post as professor of botany and anthropology at a university in present-day Estonia. This was likely in part the result of Schleiden's relationship with Fries. Schleiden had been increasingly including concepts of physical anthropology into his lectures at Jena, often with the mechanistic view of nature originally described by Fries in 1822. Schleiden was also an early advocate of English naturalist Charles Darwin's work and was in agreement with Darwin's views on natural selection being central to the process of evolution.

Schleiden remained in Dorpat through 1864, resigning as his lectures came into increasing conflict with the Russian church. After his retirement, he lived in several towns throughout Germany, including Dresden, Darmstadt, and Wiesbaden. He died on June 23, 1881, while residing in Frankfurt am Main, Germany, in the middle of work on a treatise describing the role of the horse in civilization.

IMPACT

Schleiden's hypothesis that plants were composed of cells, and that plant functions were carried out by the cells of which they were composed, was part of what became known as cell theory. His colleague in Müller's laboratory, Theodor Schwann, came to similar conclusions in his studies of animal cells. Schleiden and Schwann were as commonly linked in biology as James Watson and Francis Crick were in their discovery of DNA structure over a century later.

It was for his observation of cells in plants that Schleiden received acclaim. However, his belief that cells arose from what he termed the cytoblast, in which vesicles gradually formed around the nucleus as the cell matured, served only to confuse scientists attempting to study cell division. Further, Schleiden's model was shortly afterwards adapted by Schwann for his own hypothesis explaining the replication of animal cells—the cytoblast around which the rest of the cell assembles.

The first evidence that neither model was correct came about several years later when Austrian botanist Franz Unger and Swiss botanist Karl von Nageli each correctly described the process of cell division in plants.

Richard Adler

FURTHER READING

Alberts, Bruce, et al. *Essential Cell Biology*. New York: Garland Science, 2009. Print. College-level introduction to the cell. Highlighted with numerous photographs, the book provides a thorough description of cell structure and function in both plants and animals.
Harris, Henry. *The Birth of the Cell*. New Haven, CT: Yale UP, 1999. Print. Presents a history of cell biology with an emphasis on the personalities of those who developed its history.
---. *The Cells of the Body: A History of Somatic Cell Genetics*. Cold Spring Harbor: Cold Spring Harbor Lab P, 1995. Print. Provides a history of cytogenetics and the role played by individuals who coined the modern terms common in cell biology.

MAARTEN SCHMIDT

Dutch American astronomer

Astronomer Maarten Schmidt measured the distance and luminosity of quasars, some of the oldest and most distant objects in the universe. He then led the study of radio sources, gamma rays, and X-rays generated by galaxies and other cosmological matter.

Born: December 28, 1929; Groningen, Netherlands
Primary field: Astronomy
Specialties: Observational astronomy, astrophysics, cosmology

EARLY LIFE

Maarten Schmidt was born on December 28, 1929, in Groningen, in the northern part of the Netherlands. His

father, a civil servant, worked as a government accountant and later as chief accountant in The Hague. Schmidt became interested in science at an early age and built a chemistry laboratory at his home. During five years of German occupation during World War II—and subsequent city blackouts that made more stars visible—he became fascinated with astronomy. An uncle who was an amateur astronomer helped the teenaged Schmidt build his first telescope.

Schmidt graduated from high school after the war. In 1946, he entered Groningen University to major in science, with concentrations in mathematics, physics, and astronomy. He graduated with a bachelor's degree in 1949 and was called into military service, serving for several months in-country. He then enrolled at the University of Leiden for postgraduate study. Schmidt became an assistant to astronomer Jan Hendrik Oort, examining the brightness of comets to help support Oort's theory that there is a band of comets circling our solar system (later called the Oort cloud). In 1950 and 1951, Schmidt accompanied a university expedition to a point on the equator in Kenya where he spent a year measuring declinations of stars. Declination, similar to latitude, is a way to determine the location of stars.

Returning to the Netherlands, Schmidt continued his research into the Milky Way: He measured star distances and densities and plotted the spiral structure of the galaxy. In 1954, he met teacher and fiber artist Cornelia Tom; he married her the following year. They had three daughters: Elizabeth, Marijke, and Anne.

After earning his PhD in 1956, Schmidt gained a two-year Carnegie Institution fellowship to study star clusters at Mount Wilson Observatory near Pasadena, California. Afterward, he returned home briefly to work at the Leiden Observatory before accepting an offer in 1959 to teach at the California Institute of Technology (Caltech) in Pasadena.

LIFE'S WORK

After arriving at Caltech, Schmidt conducted research into the mass and distribution of matter in galaxies. In 1959, he developed the Schmidt star formation law, which holds that the rate of star formation is proportional to the surface density of a galactic gas cloud.

In the early 1960s, Schmidt began a series of observations using the two-hundred-inch telescope at Palomar. He initially focused his studies on the Andromeda Galaxy, the spiral galaxy closest to the Milky Way at about 2.6 million light-years distance from Earth. Schmidt paid particular attention to astronomical radio sources, or sources that emit radio wavelength signals. He studied the spectra and redshifts of radio galaxies and in 1963 concentrated on a radio source known as 3C 273, in the constellation Virgo. Schmidt determined that the object, though of relatively small size—about the diameter of the solar system—is highly energetic. The brightest of its kind, brighter than galaxies containing billions of stars, 3C 273 has a luminosity one thousand times the luminosity of the Milky Way Galaxy. Schmidt found that 3C 273, which emits a strong radio signal, exhibits a large redshift of 0.158. This indicates that it is receding from Earth at a speed of about thirty thousand miles per second. This also means that 3C 273 is located about 2.5 billion light-years from Earth.

The radio source 3C 273 and others like it were soon called quasi-stellar radio sources, or quasi-stellar objects (QSOs), shortened to "quasars" by 1964. The identification of 3C 273 and other quasars, some of the most ancient and most distant objects in the known cosmos—3C 273, as the brightest quasar, is the closest known quasar to Earth—landed Schmidt's portrait on the cover of *TIME* magazine on March 11, 1966. The existence of quasars also launched a flurry of astronomical activity that has continued since then, aimed at searching for other extraterrestrial objects that give clues to the age, dimensions, and character of the universe.

Meanwhile, Schmidt throughout the 1960s continued to study the evolution and distribution of quasars; he concluded that they were more abundant when the universe was young. His findings helped reinforce the theory of an expanding universe—a result of the "big bang"—and undercut the competing static or steady-state theory of the universe. Schmidt coauthored *Galactic Structure* with Dutch astronomer Adriaan Blaauw in 1965, and published the definitive work at the time on quasars, *Quasi-Stellar Objects*, in 1969.

A full professor of astronomy at Caltech from 1965, Schmidt served as head of the department from 1972 to 1975. He then led Caltech's division of physics, mathematics, and astronomy for three years. Between 1978 and 1980, Schmidt was the last director of the Hale Observatories (the University of Chicago's Yerkes Observatory in Wisconsin, the Carnegie Institution's Mount Wilson Observatory in Los Angeles, and Caltech's Palomar Observatory in San Diego County) before Mount Wilson withdrew from the group. Schmidt served from 1984 to 1986 as president of the American Astronomical Society, and from 1992 to 1995 was chairman of the board of the Association of Universities for Research in Astronomy (AURA).

Schmidt lent his expertise to the planning of the Very Long Baseline Array (VLBA), a series of ten radio telescopes spread across more than five thousand miles between Hawaii and the US Virgin Islands. Constructed between 1986 and 1993, the multipurpose VLBA monitors terrestrial wind patterns and tectonic movements; maps and tracks galaxies; measures distances to stellar objects; assists in spacecraft navigation; watches for potentially deadly near-Earth asteroids; and searches for black holes, quasars, pulsars, and other distant objects.

Schmidt later was a member of teams investigating stellar gamma ray and X-ray sources via the Keck Observatory in Hawaii. He also worked on the German

Schmidt Identifies Quasars

Between 1960 and 1963, radio astronomy, which detects objects in space by intercepting the radio signals that these objects emit, was faced with a puzzle: Astronomers had detected radio waves from an unidentifiable source. Whereas most previously studied radio sources were either peculiar galaxies or nearby gas clouds, this new type of source seemed to have no such identity. They were given numbers referring to their positions in space, and would later be called quasi-stellar objects, or quasars. Diameters were measured for these objects in 1960 by British astronomer Cyril Hazard and his colleagues.

American astronomers Allan Rex Sandage and Thomas A. Matthews studied photographs of the mysterious radio sources in September 1960. They noticed that the photograph of the area at the position of 3C 48 included what appeared to be a star-like object with a peculiar feature: a faint wisp of light seemed to be pointing at it. Sandage obtained a spectrum of this stellar object and measured its colors. The spectrum resembled nothing that had been seen before. Instead of a bright continuum of light of different colors with various dark lines, which a star would typically display, the spectrum of 3C 48 showed a weak continuum with broad, fuzzy lines. None of these lines corresponded with any elements that were known to be contained in stars. The only thing the colors indicated was that 3C 48 is a very hot object.

In 1962, Hazard's team measured the position of 3C 273 by using Earth's moon as a locator. When they compared the radio position of 3C 273 with optical photographs showing the part of the sky the radio waves were coming from, the astronomers found that the radio position corresponded exactly with what looked like a bright star. The apparent brightness of this "star" was measured at approximately six hundred times fainter than the naked-eye limit—what can be seen without a telescope—which would later be understood as a result of its distance from Earth.

When the identification of 3C 273 was announced, Maarten Schmidt decided to obtain a photograph and a spectrum of the quasi-stellar object. The photograph showed a bright stellar object with a faint wispy structure to one side, "pointing" toward the other object. The spectrum looked much like that of 3C 48, but with the broad emission lines in entirely different places. Schmidt realized that the object's spectral lines would make sense if they were normal lines of common elements, but redshifted greatly to longer than usual wavelengths. In redshift, a source of light that is moving rapidly away from an observer will have all of its light wavelengths shifted to redder, longer wavelengths, by an amount that depends upon its velocity. By identifying four of the lines as being caused by hydrogen gas—the most common element in the universe—Schmidt found that the object 3C 273 must be moving away from Earth at about thirty thousand miles per second. Comparing this information with the rate of speed at which the universe is believed to be expanding, it was possible to measure the distance to 3C 273: about 2.5 billion light-years.

Aerospace Röntgen satellite project (ROSAT), operational from 1990 to 1999, and the 37,000-pound Compton Gamma Ray Observatory (CGRO), in orbit around Earth from 1991 to 2000. In the late 1990s, Schmidt retired to become professor emeritus at Caltech. Since then, he has continued to observe objects in the universe.

Schmidt has often been honored for his work. The American Astronomical Society awarded him the Helen B. Warner Prize in 1964 and the Henry Norris Russell Lectureship in 1978. He received the Gold Medal from the Royal Astronomical Society in 1980, the James Craig Watson Medal from the National Academy of Sciences in 1991, and the Bruce Medal from the Astronomical Society of the Pacific in 1992. In 2008, Schmidt received the Norwegian Kavli Prize in Astrophysics: a gold medal and a cash award of one million dollars.

IMPACT

Though Schmidt did not discover the first-known quasi-stellar objects—British radio astronomer Cyril Hazard found the mysterious 3C 273 in 1962, and other objects that were later identified as quasars had been discovered in the late 1950s—he was the first to analyze a quasi-stellar radio source and to calculate its distance, velocity away from Earth, and luminosity. Schmidt's findings, which led to the term "quasar," gave astronomers a glimpse of light produced in the early stages of universe formation and provided new information about the evolution of galaxies.

More than 1,500 quasars have been found. From subsequent studies, astronomers have reached several conclusions about quasars: They are a type of extragalactic galaxy with an intensely energetic core; they are associated with massive black holes; some emit radiation far into space, but most are radio quiet; and some of them are receding at almost the speed of light. Additionally, some quasars, called blazars, are extremely variable. Other quasars may be paired or grouped. Radio-loud quasars are useful in locating distant galaxies and other objects with high redshift. The interest in quasars, spurred by Schmidt's findings, led to the discovery of the first pulsar, or pulsating neutron star, in 1967, and ultimately to the discovery of the first extrasolar planets in 1992.

Jack Ewing

FURTHER READING

Kidger, Mark R. *Cosmological Enigmas: Pulsars, Quasars, and Other Deep-Space Questions*. Baltimore: Johns Hopkins UP, 2007. Print. A mix of fact and speculation about distant objects like quasars, which provide clues to the origin, age, dimensions, and character of the universe.

Melia, Fulvio. *Cracking the Einstein Code: Relativity and the Birth of Black Hole Physics*. Chicago: U of Chicago P, 2009. Print. An examination of Einstein's theory of relativity as applied to the expanding universe and the concept of time. Incorporates the discoveries and hypotheses of scientists like Stephen Hawking and Maarten Schmidt.

Overbye, Dennis. *Lonely Hearts of the Cosmos: The Story of the Scientific Quest for the Secret of the Universe*. Boston: Back Bay, 1999. Print. A history of astronomical observation and discoveries that shaped modern concepts of the universe, much of it conducted via the Mount Palomar telescope, as told through an examination of the personalities of scientists like Schmidt.

ERWIN SCHRÖDINGER

Austrian physicist

Erwin Schrödinger invented wave mechanics in 1926, for which he received the Nobel Prize in Physics in 1933, and he helped develop the formal equations that are central to quantum mechanics. His pioneering work on the relationship between physics and living systems influenced the growth of molecular biology.

Born: August 12, 1887; Vienna, Austria-Hungary (now Austria)
Died: January 4, 1961; Alpbach, Austria
Primary fields: Physics; mathematics
Specialties: Theoretical physics; quantum mechanics

EARLY LIFE

Erwin Schrödinger was the only child of a well-to-do and highly intellectual Viennese family. With the exception of a brief stay at a public elementary school in Innsbruck, he was educated by a tutor. At the age of eleven, he commenced a program of studies in the classics and in mathematics and physics at a Viennese Gymnasium, a liberal arts high school.

Schrödinger entered the University of Vienna in 1906. The following year, he began to attend lectures in theoretical physics. In 1910, he received his doctorate and assumed a position as assistant to Franz Exner at the university's Second Physics Institute, where he remained until the outbreak of World War I. During this period, Schrödinger published papers on a range of subjects, including magnetism, radioactivity, X-rays, and Brownian motion.

Following an undistinguished service in the military, brief appointments at Jena, Stuttgart, and Breslau culminated with Schrödinger's appointment in 1921 to the chair of theoretical physics in Zurich, a position formerly held by Albert Einstein. Prior to his stay in Jena, he had married Annemarie Bertel on June 6, 1920. During this period, his papers touched on a number of subjects, including general relativity, probability theory, dielectric phenomena, three- and four-color theories of vision, and atomic theory in particular. The papers that secured his reputation were composed in a half-year's flourish of creativity before he left Zurich. It was there in 1926 that Schrödinger invented wave mechanics and published what is known as the Schrödinger wave equation, laying the foundation of modern quantum mechanics.

LIFE'S WORK

Schrödinger's invention of wave mechanics represented an attempt to overcome some difficulties generated by Niels Bohr's theory of the hydrogen atom. In particular, attempts to construct a theory of a stable system of more than two particles (such as the helium atom, with a nucleus and two electrons) had failed. Drawing inspiration from Louis de Broglie's suggestion that a particle is merely a wave crest on a background of waves, Schrödinger used the mathematics of waves in a way that attempted to eliminate quantum jumps, or the notion that electrons move instantaneously from one level to another. He sought to represent this quantum transition as the passage of energy from one vibrational form into another, instead. The transition of an electron from one energy state to another, Schrödinger believed, was akin to the change in the vibration of a violin string from one note to another. These results were announced by Schrödinger in four seminal papers published in the journal *Annalen der Physik* (Annals of physics) in 1926, the first of which contains his famous wave equation.

Schrödinger's wave mechanics was eagerly embraced by numerous scientists who had been puzzled by the emerging atomic theory and regarded the model of a wave as furnishing a realistic account of microprocesses. It was also criticized on a number of counts: It was not clear how a wave could make a Geiger counter click as though a single particle were being recorded or how blackbody radiation was to be explained in terms of Schrödinger's waves. A further wrinkle arose when Carl Eckart and Paul A. M. Dirac showed that Werner Heisenberg's equations (which were based on the supposition that electrons are particles) were equivalent to Schrödinger's theory that electrons are waves.

Bohr suggested that both models, particle and wave physics, are valid and complementary descriptions of the world—that in some cases, it is appropriate to utilize the particle concept and, in others, it is better to use the wave concept. Max Born's suggestion that Schrödinger's wave function expressed the probability of finding a particle at a given point in space supported Bohr's resolution to the controversy. The location of a particle cannot be ascertained with certainty, but the wave function enables one to work out the probability that the particle will be found in a certain place. Finally, Heisenberg suggested in 1926 that scientists cannot measure both the position and the momentum of an electron at the same time. The more one knows about its position, the less one knows about its momentum, and vice versa.

These developments were largely accepted by the time Schrödinger succeeded Max Planck in 1927 as the renowned chair of theoretical physics at the University of Berlin. There, Schrödinger enjoyed a fruitful period amid the intellectual companionship of other prominent physicists until Nazi leader Adolf Hitler assumed power in 1933, the same year that Schrödinger and Dirac received the Nobel Prize in Physics. Schrödinger's

background ensured that his position was secure. His opposition to the Nazi regime, however, induced him to give up his post. Schrödinger settled in Oxford for a brief, unproductive period, but in 1936, he succumbed to homesickness and accepted a position in Graz, Austria. He was abruptly dismissed in 1938, and he fled Austria when Hitler's forces invaded later the same year.

During 1935, Schrödinger had published a paper that criticized the probabilistic laws of quantum theory. In quantum mechanics, a radioactive atom might decay and emit an electron, or it might not. Schrödinger was upset by the absurdity of this implication and framed a famous thought experiment designed to expose it. In this experiment, he envisioned a box that contains a radioactive source, a device for detecting radioactive particles, a live cat, and a container of poison. The detector is switched on long enough that there is a fifty-fifty chance that one of the atoms in the radioactive material will decay and that the detector will record the presence of a particle. If the detector does record such an event, the poison container is broken and the cat dies. If not, the cat lives.

In the world of ordinary experience, there is a fifty-fifty chance that the cat will be killed. Without examining the contents of the box, it is safe to assert that the cat is either dead or alive. In the world of quantum physics, neither possibility is real unless it is first observed. The atomic decay has neither occurred nor not occurred. Since the fate of the feline is tied to the state of the radioactive material, one cannot say that the cat is dead or alive until the inside of the box is examined. This implication, Schrödinger declared, reveals the absurdity of quantum mechanics. It is one thing to conceive of an elementary particle such as an electron being neither here nor there, but quite another to conceive of a concrete thing such as a cat in this indeterminate state.

In 1939, Eamon de Valera arranged for Schrödinger to serve as the first director of the school of theoretical physics at the Dublin Institute for Advanced Studies. During this fruitful period of his career, Schrödinger published many works on the application and statistical interpretation of wave mechanics and on problems concerning the relationship between general relativity and wave mechanics. As a senior professor, Schrödinger gave lectures from time to time. Four of his books, *What Is Life?* (1944), *Science and Humanism: Physics in Our Time* (1951), *Nature and the Greeks* (1954), and *Mind and Matter* (1958), were written for these lecture series. The most famous of these lectures was "What

Schrödinger Proposes the Wave-Mechanical Theory of the Atom

In the 1910s, Niels Bohr had theorized that the electrons in an atom orbit the nucleus only at certain distances, or energy levels, much as planets orbit the sun. These levels are determined by a constant discovered by Max Planck, which relates to units, or quanta, of light.

Louis de Broglie expanded on this work, hypothesizing that if light can have some of the properties of particles, matter may have some of the properties of waves. He especially sought to find exact positions of the electrons in an atom by treating them as if they moved in the same wavelike patterns as those of light. In 1923, de Broglie suggested that the energy levels Bohr had found were simply certain numbers multiplied by Planck's constant. However, he could not find enough supporting evidence, and no means had been found to predict where an electron would go in any particular atom.

Erwin Schrödinger became fascinated by Bohr's and de Broglie's theories but found them flawed. Both prior theories assumed that the light waves associated with certain atoms (their "spectra") came from electromagnetic waves radiating from the atoms. Schrödinger believed that the energy levels found by the earlier theories resulted from "standing waves"—waves overlapping each other so exactly that no other radiation can escape—rather than of continuously radiating energy. Radiation could be detected only when electrons moved from one energy level to another, while the overlap of their paths did not form a standing wave.

Schrödinger developed a complicated equation, now known as the Schrödinger wave equation, to predict where an electron would be at a certain time. He presented this equation, along with its development, support, and consequences, in a series of papers published in 1926. It was quickly shown that the values found by calculating Schrödinger's wave equation for certain numbers corresponded exactly to Bohr's energy levels, as well as to other key data.

Meanwhile, Werner Heisenberg was using much of the same data to develop a "matrix-mechanical" view of the atom based entirely on experimental evidence. Heisenberg and Schrödinger published their discoveries within one year of each other, and it was soon shown that the same results could be generated with Schrödinger's wave equation that Heisenberg had with his matrices. The combination of these two theories gave a firm basis for a complete theory of quantum mechanics.

For his work, Schrödinger received the Nobel Prize in Physics in 1933. His wave equation gave rise to a new branch of physics, became the basis for virtually all subsequent developments in chemistry, and had a great impact on many other areas of science, including astronomy and biology. In chemistry, Schrödinger's equation has been used to explain bond energies and bond lengths between the atoms in a molecule, and it continues to suggest other properties of chemical bonds. The field of molecular biology developed from the introduction of quantum mechanical theories into chemistry. In astronomy, quantum theory has affected research into the composition and structure of stars and the rate at which they generate energy, among other areas of research.

Is Life?" presented in 1944 to a large and enthusiastic audience. The thesis of these lectures is that quantum physics is required for understanding biological replication. Although his theme was controversial, it aroused much interest among many promising young physicists, including Francis Crick, and encouraged them to turn to biology.

In 1956, illness curtailed Schrödinger's productivity. His friend Hans Thirring arranged for him to become professor emeritus of theoretical physics at the University of Vienna. He died in 1961 after a prolonged illness.

IMPACT

Schrödinger is primarily known for inventing wave mechanics and the equation that bears his name, but his legacy is much greater. His collected papers include important contributions to virtually every branch of physics, and he constantly encouraged physicists to examine the foundations of their discipline and its relationship to other scientific endeavors. As a philosopher, he was worried about the problems of knowers in a world governed by probabilistic laws.

While his interests knew no bounds, Schrödinger was somewhat narrow in his outlook on questions of physics. His conservativeness was not surprising, given that he was already a senior member of the scientific community steeped in traditional concepts and theories when he made his most important contributions during the mid-1920s. Indeed, Schrödinger resisted the innovations of indeterminacy and the instantaneous jumping of electrons from one state to another. His most important contribution, the articulation of wave mechanics, attempted to describe atomic structures in terms of waves, an established model in the scientific community. Schrödinger furnished scientists with invaluable tools for problem solving, but his wave mechanics represented a return to nineteenth-century ideas.

Brian S. Baigrie

FURTHER READING

Gribbon, John. *In Search of Schrödinger's Cat: Quantum Physics and Reality*. 1984. London: Transworld, 2012. Print. Argues that Schrödinger's wave mechanics attempted to restore nineteenth-century concepts, an assessment first made by some of Schrödinger's contemporaries, such as Born. Provides a historical backdrop for the development of the central concepts of quantum mechanics.

Schrödinger, Erwin. *What Is Life? The Physical Aspect of the Living Cell*. 1944. Cambridge: Cambridge UP, 2003. Print. Influenced an entire generation of scientists, including Francis Crick, who helped to unravel the structure of the living molecule.

Wallace, Dorothy, and Joseph J. BelBruno. *The Bell That Rings Light: A Primer in Quantum Mechanics and Chemical Bonding*. Hackensack: World Scientific, 2006. Print. Investigates the intersections of quantum mechanics and chemistry, with discussion of Schrödinger's scientific discoveries.

THEODOR SCHWANN

German biologist

Nineteenth-century biologist Theodor Schwann contributed to the development of cell theory through his observations of the notochord in animals. He also helped to uncover the role played by pepsin in digestions, and discovered the cell covering on nerves, now called Schwann cells.

Born: December 7, 1810; Neuss, Kingdom of Prussia (now Germany)
Died: January 11, 1882; Cologne, Germany
Primary field: Biology
Specialty: Cellular biology

EARLY LIFE

Theodor Ambrose Hubert Schwann was born on December 7, 1810 in Neuss, a town in what was then the Kingdom of Prussia and is now simply part of Germany. He was the third of ten children. Both his father and grandfather were goldsmiths. Schwann's father also operated a printing press. During his early life, Schwann was an introvert. He inherited his father's mechanical abilities, and constructed crude microscopes and electrical devices to conduct rudimentary science work.

Schwann was raised in a strict Catholic family and culture. After graduating from the local Jesuit high school, where he excelled in physics and mathematics, Schwann enrolled at the Jesuit College of the Three Crowns in Cologne in 1826. Schwann's family hoped he would follow in the footsteps of his elder brother, Peter, who joined the clergy and became a professor of theology at Frauenberg. However, after enrolling in a philosophy class in 1829 at the University of Bonn, Schwann decided he would pursue a career in medicine. It was at Bonn that Schwann also met the physiologist Johannes Müller, who played an influential role later in Schwann's professional life. Müller introduced Schwann to scientific research and provided the opportunity for him to study spinal nerves and the process of blood coagulation.

In 1831, Schwann enrolled at the University of Würzburg and began studying medicine. At Würzburg, Schwann studied with bone surgeon Cajetan von Textor and pathologist Johann Lukas Schönlein.

In 1832, the July Revolution swept through much of Europe, including the German states, and many of the teachers at Würzburg, including Textor, were dismissed, or opted to relocate to safer environments. Schwann left Würzburg to enroll at the Friedrich Wilhelms University in Berlin. Coincidently, Müller was offered a position as Chair and Professor of Anatomy and Physiology at the university, providing Schwann with a mentor to direct his medical studies. In 1834 Schwann completed his doctoral thesis, "De necessitate æris atmosphærici ad evolutionem pulli in ovo incubato" (The requirement for atmospheric air for development of the chick embryo), and received his medical degree.

LIFE'S WORK

Müller arranged for Schwann's appointment as an aid at the university's anatomical museum in 1834. Schwann replaced anatomist Jacob Henle as Müller's assistant at the museum in 1840.

799

Schwann carried some of his most important scientific work during the first four years of his appointment as a museum aid, including his role in applying cell theory to animals. Schwann described these events late in his career, during a celebration of his professorship at Liege. He had a dinner discussion with the plant anatomist Matthias Schleiden, who described his observations of the nuclei found in plant cells. Schwann noted to Schleiden that he had observed similar structures in animal notochords and was curious whether they played a similar role in the gill cartilage of *Rana esculenta* (frogs). After showing the images to Schleiden back in the laboratory, Schwann decided to investigate the role played by nuclei in cell formation.

Schwann was interested in testing for the presence of a "life force." In an era in which spontaneous generation had yet to be disproven, some scientists attributed the existence of all cell metabolic properties to such a force. Schwann attempted to address the question by demonstrating the role of specific physiological processes to account for events that take place within cells.

Among his first discoveries was his identification of an enzyme involved in digestion. Schwann termed the enzyme pepsin, named for "pepsis," an early term meaning digestion. He also demonstrated the role of microscopic agents in both putrefaction and fermentation, disproving any role of spontaneous generation.

Schwann's application of what modern scientists would call the scientific method was particularly instructive in refuting the concept of a "life force" as a factor in spontaneous generation. In the 1760s, Italian biologist Lazzaro Spallanzani demonstrated that heated infusions did not decay. Schwann replicated Spallanzani's work but also measured the oxygen content of the heated air, showing the level was identical to regular air, and that the heated air would still allow survival of a frog. Schwann's idea was premature, however, and it was not until a generation later that French microbiologist Louis Pasteur proved his theory correct.

The foundation of cell theory as applied to plants and animals is attributed to the work of Schleiden and Schwann. However, their views regarding the role of

Schwann Applies Cell Theory to Animal Cells

The first observation of cells is attributed to English philosopher Robert Hooke, who in the 1660s reported their presence for his monograph *Micrographia* (1665) while investigating pores on slices of cork and wood. The term "cell" was coined because of the pores' resemblance to chambers in which monks lived. English anatomist Nehemiah Grew and Italian physician Marcello Malphigi concurrently made similar observations. However, neither the origin of cells—termed "vesicles" by Malphigi and "bladders" by Grew—nor their function was established at the time.

Schwann's development of "cell theory," a designation he coined, was the direct result of conversations he had with plant biologist Matthias Schleiden, also an associate of Johannes Müller. By the mid-1830s, Schleiden had established the role of cells in plant structure. Schwann meanwhile had been studying physiology in animals, including metabolic processes and putrefaction. As Schwann related decades later, he and Schleiden were having dinner together one day in October 1837, during which Schleiden described his work with plants and plant nuclei. Schwann realized the similarity between Schleiden's description of plant cells and his own observations of cells in the notochord of frogs and invited Schleiden back to his laboratory to

demonstrate. Schwann had also observed a similarity between cartilage and the structure of plant cells.

Schwann spent the next several years in further study of cell structures in a variety of animal tissues. The work culminated with his publication *Mikroskopische Untersuchungen über die Übereinstimmung in der Struktur und dem Wachstum der Thiere und Pflanzen* (Microscopic Research into the Accordance in the Structure and Growth of Animals and Plants, 1839). The work was divided into three sections. The first portion was a description of the *chorda dorsalis* (notochord) in frogs, as well as his comparison of cartilage with plant cell structure. His observations included descriptions of a white substance that surrounded the nerve fibers, cells that became known as "Schwann cells." The second portion of the treatise compared the differentiation patterns of various cells in the organism, while the third portion consisted of a philosophical argument. It argued that the cell and its functions, rather than being guided by a supernatural power, behave as other elements found in nature. While portions of his thesis, including the crystallization of amorphous material around a nucleus during cell reproduction, would later be proven incorrect, Schwann's merging of structure and function became the basis for the work of others in cell research.

the nucleus, or cytoblast as it was then known, were inaccurate. Schleiden and Schwann theorized that cells were generated from an amorphous material referred to as the "cytoblastem." Further, their theory proposed that the nucleus formed within the cytoblastem, with the remainder of the cell crystallizing around the structure. Schwann's first major publication, *Microscopical Researches into the Accordance in the Structure and Growth of Animals and Plants* (1839), was the outcome of this work. However, this view of the cell was later shown to be inaccurate through the work of Polish physiologist Robert Remak and German pathologist Rudolf Virchow in the 1840s and 1850s.

Schwann took a position as professor of anatomy at the Catholic University of Louvain in Belgium in 1838. He spent the next nine years in Louvain, working primarily as a lecturer. In his scientific work, he worked to further the idea that microscopic organisms are the basis for decay. Schwann also demonstrated the critical role of bile in digestion, concluding that interference with bile secretion by means of a biliary fistula can have lethal effects on the organism.

In 1848, Schwann's colleague, physiologist Joseph Spring, persuaded him to accept an offer at the University of Liege. Schwann replaced Spring as chair of the anatomy department in 1853. His career in laboratory research was largely complete by the time he moved to Liege. Nevertheless, he remained interested in the development of mechanical devices, a skill he retained from his youth. Among his inventions in Liege was an industrial device used to remove water from mines.

In 1858, Schwann was appointed to professorships in physiology, general anatomy, and physiology. As he aged, he gradually retired, teaching only physiology by the 1870s as an emeritus professor. During Christmas 1881, he suffered a stroke while visiting his family in Cologne and died early in January 1882.

IMPACT

Schwann's contribution to cell theory in animals mirrored the accomplishments of Schleiden in plant biology. While helping to refute the theory of spontaneous generation, Schwann also established the origins of cell and tissue structures in animals, demonstrating their development from preexisting cells. In Schwann's view, the cell served a structural purpose but was also the source of metabolic processes for the organism.

Schwann's use of microscopy for analysis of tissues and cells established the field of modern histology. His methods of investigation, including applications of the scientific method, served as a model for the scientific work of others. Virchow, considered the father of cellular pathology, was among those who built on Schwann's work by demonstrating the role of the cell in the establishment of disease processes, while at the same time refuting Schwann's views on the origin of cells from cytoblasts. In addition to his accomplishments in cell biology, Schwann's investigation of digestive processes helped lay the foundation of metabolic research.

Richard Adler

FURTHER READING

Alberts, Bruce, et al. *Essential Cell Biology*. New York: Garland Science, 2009. Print. College-level introduction to the cell. Highlighted with numerous photographs, the book provides a thorough description of cell structure and function in both plants and animals.

Pollard, Thomas, et al. *Cell Biology*. Philadelphia: Saunders, 2007. Print. Intermediate-level college textbook on cell structure and function. Emphasis is placed on cell processes.

Schwann, Theodor. *Microscopical Researches into the Accordance in the Structure and Growth of Animals and Plants*. Charleston: Nabu, 2010. Print. Reproduction of Schwann's original paper on cell biology.

KARL SCHWARZSCHILD

German astrophysicist

Karl Schwarzschild developed a new use for photography as a tool for measuring the brightness of stars, particularly variable objects. He was the first to develop a solution for Albert Einstein's general relativity field equations, dealing with gravity around a star of such intensity that it becomes a black hole.

Born: October 9, 1873; Frankfurt am Main, Germany
Died: May 11, 1916; Potsdam, Germany
Primary fields: Astronomy; physics
Specialties: Observational astronomy; theoretical astronomy; astrophysics

EARLY LIFE

Karl Schwarzschild was the eldest of six children. His father, a prosperous businessman in Frankfurt, encouraged his early interest in science, particularly astronomy. He was the first of his family to be interested in science; indeed, he wrote and published his first two astronomical papers, on the topic of double-star orbits, when he was only sixteen. While in school, he was introduced to J. Epstein, a mathematician with a private observatory. From Epstein's son, Schwarzschild learned to make and use a telescope and studied advanced mathematics and celestial mechanics. After local education at the primary and secondary level, he spent two years at the University of Strasbourg and then two more years at the University of Munich. He received his doctorate from that university in 1896, graduating *summa cum laude*. His doctoral thesis was on the application of the theory of stable configurations in rotating bodies, developed by Henri Poincaré, to investigations of tidal deformation in satellites and the validity of Pierre-Simon Laplace's theory for the origin of the solar system. He also invented a multislit interferometer for measuring the separation of double stars.

LIFE'S WORK

Schwarzschild was interested in observational astronomy. In the early 1890s, he developed the use of photography (later called photographic photometry) to measure the apparent magnitude of stars using a photographic plate to substitute for the human eye at the telescope. Using his new method of measuring the image densities on the plates, he was able to establish the magnitude of 367 stars; he used those results to secure a teaching position at the University of Munich. In all, he worked on thirty-five hundred stellar objects of magnitude greater than 7.5, at the same time showing conclusively that there was a vast difference between visual (with the unaided eye) and photographic magnitude or brightness, a difference later known as the star's color index. His results also led him to suggest that periodic variable stars behaved as they did, going through a regular cycle of maximum and minimum brightness, because of periodic temperature changes. In turn, this hypothesis led to further work on Cepheid variables by English astronomer Arthur Eddington.

From 1896 to 1899, Schwarzschild worked as an assistant at the Kuffner Observatory in Vienna. After some time spent lecturing and writing, he received an associate professorship in 1901 from the University of Göttingen. A year later, he became a professor of astronomy there as well as the director of its observatory. In 1909, he succeeded Hermann Vogel as the director of the Astrophysical Observatory in Potsdam.

Schwarzschild worked extensively in theoretical astronomy and in subjects as diverse as orbital mechanics, the curvature of space throughout the known universe, stellar energy production, and the surface structures of the sun. In 1900, he suggested that the geometry of space did not necessarily have to conform to Euclidean geometry, in which two parallel lines are forever parallel and the sum of interior angles of a triangle is always 180 degrees. Light rays from a star hitting the Earth's orbit at two widely separated points form an overextended triangle. By measuring the interior angles of such a hypothetical structure, he attempted to determine the curvature of space, since he knew that, if the angles added up to more or less than 180 degrees, he would be dealing with non-Euclidean space. He concluded, from his experimental results, that if space were curved, it had an extremely large radius of curvature, so large as to be unnoticeable in as small a region as the solar system.

In 1906, Schwarzschild worked diligently on a paper showing that a star should not be considered as a simple gas held together by its own gravity. Thermodynamic properties, particularly concerning the transfer of heat inside the stellar surface by both convection and radiation, had to be present. To deal effectively with this situation, he invented the concept of radiative equilibrium in astrophysics, a balance of the energy flowing inward and outward to help maintain the star's stability. He showed mathematically how radiative processes would be important in conveying heat in stellar atmospheres and how energy could be transferred at and near the sun's surface. Many of his ideas were stimulated by his observation of the total solar eclipse in 1905, an event he photographed with a newly devised instrument, one forming spectrograms from an objective prism at the eyepiece of the telescope. This instrument allowed him to derive information on the chemical composition of various areas at differing depths in the sun's atmosphere.

Among the topics to which he contributed was the field of stellar statistics, which studies large numbers of stars and their associated data. The methods and techniques he developed are now standard in graduate stellar astronomy courses. He designed, as a new tool for analysis, a spectrographic objective that provided a reliable means of determining a star's radial velocity, the speed and direction in which it is moving. Many new contributions to geometric optics stemmed from this fertile period.

Schwarzschild Predicts the Existence of Black Holes

In 1915, Albert Einstein published his general theory of relativity, in which he discussed a "space-time continuum" that included four dimensions: length, width, height, and time. This revolutionary concept stood in opposition to Isaac Newton's universal law of gravitation. According to Newton, gravity is an attractive force acting between all particles of matter in the universe. Einstein, however, believed that gravity is a consequence of local space-time being distorted by the presence of a large mass, such as a star or planet.

When general relativity was first proposed, the mathematics of its equations was thought to be incomprehensible. The first person to find an exact solution to its equations was Karl Schwarzschild. In 1916, when Schwarzschild was working on his solution, he was serving in the German armed forces in Russia, where he contracted a fatal disease. Shortly after his return home, he completed his work and sent a copy to Einstein. Within a few months, Schwarzschild died.

Schwarzschild had sought to determine what would happen if gravity around a spherical body became infinitely powerful. The result, the "Schwarzschild solution, describes a black hole," an object so dense that even light could not escape from it. Difficulties in interpreting the Schwarzschild solution, however, cast some doubt upon its validity until the 1960s, when its true significance was recognized thanks to further studies on stellar structure and evolution.

The formation of a black hole is believed to be the final stage in the decay of a massive star. The exact sequence of events depends entirely on the star's mass. After losing much of its outer material in the supernova stage, the star's core begins to collapse. If its mass is 1.4 solar masses or smaller, the star ends up as a "white dwarf," in which the pressure exerted by the electrons prevents total collapse. If the stellar mass is between 1.4 and 3.1 times the mass of the sun, gravity is so intense that electrons and protons combine to form neutrons, resulting in a "neutron star."

If the star's mass is greater than 3.1 solar masses, even neutrons cannot counteract the force of gravity, and the star collapses farther, with its surface gravity becoming ever greater. Consequently, the velocity needed to escape this gravitational body increases. After the escape velocity reaches the velocity of light, further collapse results in a black hole. The distance at which the escape velocity equals the velocity of light is the "Schwarzschild radius," or event horizon, beyond which events cannot be determined.

The diameter of the Schwarzschild radius depends on the core's mass. For example, a decayed stellar core with twenty solar masses has an event horizon with a sixty-kilometer radius. Within this boundary, however, the remains of the star continue collapsing to a point of infinite pressure, infinite density, and infinite curvature of space-time known as the "Schwarzschild singularity."

It is now recognized that the Schwarzschild solution describes a static black hole, a type of black hole that has mass but does not rotate or have electric charge. Variations on Schwarzschild's work have produced such theoretical objects as rotating black holes, black holes with electrical charge, and those with both charge and rotation. Although astrophysicists have identified several objects that may be black holes, only further research will determine whether the Schwarzschild solution describes a real object or is only an exercise in theoretical mathematics.

Schwarzschild volunteered for military service in 1914, at the start of World War I, first manning a weather station in Belgium, then transferring to France for the job of calculating the trajectories for long-range cannon shells. Craving action, he managed to transfer again, to Russia. While in Russia in 1916, he heard of Albert Einstein's new general theory of relativity. As a result, Schwarzschild wrote two papers on the theory, both published that year.

Schwarzschild provided a solution—the first to be found—to the complex partial differential equations fundamental to the theory's mathematical basis. He solved the Einstein equation for the exterior space-time of a spherical nonrotating body, thereby predicting the formation of black holes. The theoretical study of black holes and the continuing search for them has become an important field in modern astronomy, particularly since they can be used to solve some of the most fundamental problems of stellar, galactic, and cosmological astronomy.

While in Russia, Schwarzschild contracted pemphigus, an incurable metabolic disease of the skin. He was disabled and living solely at home in 1916 when he died. For his service in the war effort, he was awarded an Iron Cross. In 1960, he was honored by the Berlin

Academy, which named him the greatest German astronomer of the preceding century.

IMPACT

As an astronomer and theoretician, Schwarzschild achieved many great things in his chosen field, despite his short life. His practical skill was demonstrated in the innovative instruments he designed and built, including astrophotographic tools, spectral analysis instruments, and designs in geometrical optics. With his exceptional mathematical ability, he contributed greatly to theoretical astronomy in subjects including celestial mechanics, stellar physics, solar dynamics, thermodynamics of stellar interiors, and applications of the theory of relativity, all of which remain important fields of research in modern astronomy.

Schwarzschild attached great importance to lecturing and writing on popular astronomy. He attempted to make difficult subjects in physics and astronomy more lucid, presenting pictures with words that the average nonscientist could understand. He was equally at home with his scientific associates, ready to discuss and extend any conjecture or idea. As a theoretical astrophysicist, he was one of the great promoters of Niels Bohr's 1913 theory of atomic spectra, a theory that he believed would solve most of the analytic problems of stellar spectral analysis. While on his deathbed, Schwarzschild finished a famous paper on that subject, in which he developed the rules of quantization. That work, developed

independently by Arnold Sommerfeld, provided for the theory of the Stark effect and the quantum theory of molecular structure.

Among those whom Schwarzschild inspired was his son Martin Schwarzschild (1912–97), who later followed in his footsteps. The younger Schwarzschild later contributed his own great work in astronomy, primarily on the theory of stellar structure and evolutionary dynamics.

Arthur L. Alt

FURTHER READING

Kaufmann, William J., III. *Black Holes and Warped Spacetime*. San Francisco: Freeman, 1979. Print. Discusses the general theory of relativity and its consequences, particularly in terms of star deaths. Extensive section on the Schwarzschild radius and its importance in forming black holes, altering the space around the star. Written for general readers, with a comprehensive nonmathematical treatment.

Melia, Fulvio. *The Edge of Infinity: Supermassive Black Holes in the Universe*. New York: Cambridge UP, 2003. Print. Includes information about Schwarzschild's discoveries.

Talcott, Richard. "What Makes a Black Hole Tick?" *Astronomy* 33.10 (2005): 80–81. Print. A series of diagrams explaining the composition of black holes for nonspecialists.

CLAUDE SHANNON

American mathematician and computer scientist

Twentieth-century American mathematician and computer scientist Claude Shannon is often called "the father of information theory" in recognition of his pioneering work in the field of networked electronic communications and his application of Boolean logic to computer design. He is also credited with the creation of digital computers and their binary circuit design.

Born: April 30, 1916; Petoskey, Michigan
Died: February 24, 2001; Medford, Massachusetts
Primary fields: Computer science; mathematics
Specialties: Information theory; logic; mechanics; mathematical analysis

EARLY LIFE

Claude Elwood Shannon was born on April 30, 1916, in Petoskey, Michigan, the son of Claude Shannon Sr. and the former Mabel Wolf. Shannon is a distant cousin of American inventor Thomas Edison. His father's family was among the first European settlers of New Jersey; his mother was the child of German immigrants. Shannon's father worked as a businessman, attorney, and probate judge. His mother was a language teacher who served as the principal of Gaylord High School in Gaylord, Michigan, the town in which he spent his first sixteen years.

As a student, Shannon excelled in science and mathematics. At home, he loved to work on mechanical devices, building a radio-controlled model boat, model planes, and a telegraph that connected to his friend's home half of a mile away.

In 1932, at age sixteen, Shannon enrolled at the University of Michigan, where his sister Catherine had recently earned a graduate degree in mathematics. He began studying the work of nineteenth-century British mathematician and logician George Boole, who established logic as a field of mathematics and created what is now known as Boolean algebra. In 1936, Shannon graduated from the University of Michigan with two undergraduate degrees, one in mathematics, and the other in electrical engineering.

In the fall of 1936, he enrolled at the Massachusetts Institute of Technology (MIT) as a graduate student and took a part-time position as a research assistant in the electrical engineering department. At MIT, Shannon began working with a differential analyzer designed by engineer and MIT professor Vannevar Bush. The analog computer was then the most advanced calculating machine ever devised. While working on the analyzer's intricate relay circuits, Shannon began to theorize that a simpler relay and switching circuit system could be designed.

LIFE'S WORK

A relay is composed of three parts: a spring, a moveable electrical contact, and an electromagnet. While relays are relatively simple devises, the relay circuits that controlled the functioning of early analog computers were not. As a research assistant, Shannon considered these complex and improvised relays to be inefficient. He and his fellow assistants spent more time keeping them in good working order than running computations through the analyzer. During the summer of 1937, as he worked at Bell Laboratories in New York City, he realized that far more effective relays could be made by using Boolean algebra, because the algebra employed a simple, two-value (or binary) system. By manipulating just two symbols, 1 and 0 (with the 1 representing "on" and the 0 representing "off"), electrical switching circuits could be made effective and logical, instead of in the ad-hoc way in which these relays were then being assembled.

Shannon elaborated on these trailblazing ideas in his 1937 master's thesis, "A Symbolic Analysis of Relay and Switching Circuits," which helped lay the foundation for the development of digital computers and digital switching circuits. While the paper's central focus was how binary systems could improve the complicated switching circuits then needed by the Bell Telephone Company, fellow engineers and mathematicians quickly understood the broader implications of Shannon's work.

Bush was among the first people to recognize the importance of Shannon's work. In addition to suggesting that Shannon switch from MIT's electrical engineering department to the mathematics department, he urged

Claude Shannon and the Creation of the Digital Age

Thanks to the work of Claude Shannon, information has become a tangible commodity. Without his pioneering work, we would not have the kind of easy access to information we enjoy in the information age. His work also heralds an age yet to come—when computers will act with an intelligence that mirrors our own.

In 1937, Shannon demonstrated how Boolean algebra could improve computer circuit designs by shifting them away from analog ad-hoc development and toward a digital system employing binary circuits that could switch circuits on and off as needed. This two-symbol logic, developed by George Boole, also created an opportunity to improve computer software as well by breaking it down into the same pattern of 1s and 0s.

In 1948, Shannon established the field of information theory. For the first time, people had a scientific method by which to study the communications process. Through this work, Shannon proposed that information could be broken down into "bits" per second and transmitted over a given channel, so long as the information in bits does not exceed the channel's capacity. Information theory is considered his most important contribution to science and engineering, as it remains the foundation for computer design by establishing limits on such things as storing information and compressing data, and also has applications in a broad range of scientific fields.

Shannon's work in the 1950s in the still-emerging field of artificial intelligence highlights how far ahead of his time he was. His computer chess programs, as well as his mechanical mouse, Theseus, demonstrated that computers could be learning devises with the ability to progress past their initial programming through interaction with humans (i.e., by playing chess with them), or through outside stimuli (i.e., a flexible, changeable maze). While this work has yet to reach fulfillment in a computer capable of true artificial intelligence, it does show that machines can mimic human behavior.

him to look at the genetic research then being conducted at the Carnegie Institution in Cold Spring Harbor, New York. Shannon, like Bush, quickly understood that Boolean algebra could also help organize genetic information. After spending the summer of 1939 in Cold Spring Harbor, Shannon wrote his doctoral thesis, "An Algebra for Theoretical Genetics." In 1940, he earned a doctorate in mathematics and a master's in electrical engineering from MIT.

Following his graduation from MIT, Shannon began working as a research fellow at the Institute for Advanced Study in 1940. He then returned to Bell Laboratories in the spring of 1941. By year's end, the United States had entered the Second World War and Bell, like all other major US companies, turned its attentions to the war effort. During the war, Shannon worked on secrecy systems aimed at preventing enemy forces from neutralizing or countering US weapons systems. Through this work, Shannon became a skilled cryptographer. He also helped to develop fire control systems for anti-aircraft use, and anti-aircraft directors, devices that pinpointed enemy planes or rockets and then calculated the aim of counter missiles.

Shannon's wartime work helped shape the development of information theory in what has been called his masterpiece, *A Mathematical Theory of Communication*. In this seminal work, first published in 1948, Shannon demonstrated a practical way to transmit messages electronically without their being garbled. In order to do this, Shannon had to define information. He eschewed the idea that information must be conceived of something specific having to do with its content, like letters, numbers, or video. Instead, he held that information need be nothing more than the easily transmitted 1s and 0s of Boolean algebra. The ideas he developed in *A Mathematical Theory of Communication* serve as the building blocks of digital computing. Shannon's ideas have also been applied in fields such as biology, for example, so that scientists now think of strands of DNA as pieces of information that form the collective whole of a given organism.

In 1956, Shannon joined the faculty at MIT, where he served until 1978. During this period, he conducted work at MIT's Research Laboratory of Electronics. Shannon built numerous devices, including a motorized pogo stick, a rocket-powered Frisbee, and a box he called the "Ultimate Machine," consisting of a single switch on a box. When the switch was flipped on, a hand popped out of the box, turned the switch off and slid back into the box. In 1950, he developed one of the first computer chess programs, which he used to challenge chess champion Mikhail Botvinnik in 1965. (Shannon's computer was defeated by Botvinnik in forty-two moves. In 1950, Shannon created one of the world's first artificial intelligence (AI) devices, an electronic mouse he called Theseus, which used relay circuits to wind its way through a flexible maze. The mouse was able to learn how to get through the reshaped maze because it was programmed to first find a familiar location and then look for a way out. Shannon's 1953 paper, "Computers and Automata," is considered a primary document in the AI field.

In 1949, Shannon married Mary Elizabeth ("Betty") Moore, a numerical analyst he met while working at Bell Labs. The couple had four children together. During his lifetime, Shannon received numerous awards for his work, including the engineering award known as the Alfred Nobel Prize (1940), the National Medal of Science (1966), and the Kyoto Prize for Basic Sciences (1985). He was also a member of a number of several scientific associations, including the National Academy of Sciences.

Shannon died on February 24, 2001 in Medford, Massachusetts.

IMPACT

Although Shannon is not as famous as Albert Einstein, his contributions to digital computing and information theory are as fundamental to these fields as Einstein's general theory of relativity has been to physics.

By developing new ways to employ Boolean logic's binary system of 1s and 0s, Shannon helped create a streamlined and logical architecture for both computer hardware and software. Every modern digital device—computers, cell phones, DVDs, and GPS systems—employs this two-symbol logic in order to work properly. The circuits (or hardware) within these devises transmit information in this binary way, just as the information (or software) functions through a system of 1s and 0s.

Shannon's establishment of information theory fundamentally revolutionized the way science conceives of information. Prior to Shannon, information was thought of as words on a page, notes in a piece of music, pictures on a television screen. Shannon revealed that information could be simplified and transformed into a stream of 1s and 0s in order to be communicated and processed electronically. He even described the white spaces between words as the twenty-seventh letter of the alphabet because, as specific bits of information, they reduce confusion in written language. Shannon's work has had far-ranging applications in biology, literature, psychology, and phonetics.

Christopher Mari

FURTHER READING

Gleick, James. *The Information: A History, a Theory, a Flood*. New York: Pantheon, 2011. Print. Discusses how the concept of what information is has evolved with the development of communications technology, profiling Shannon along with a number of innovators, including Charles Babbage, who invented the first mechanical computer.

Nahin, Paul J. *The Logician and the Engineer: How George Boole and Claude Shannon Created the Information Age*. Princeton: Princeton UP, 2012. Print. Examines the lives of George Boole, the nineteenth-century British mathematician and logician, and Shannon, who used Boole's logic to develop information theory and modern digital computing.

Poundstone, William. *Fortune's Formula: The Untold Story of the Scientific Betting System that Beat the Casinos and Wall Street*. New York: Hill, 2005. Print. Describes how Shannon and fellow scientists Ed Thorpe and John Kelly (who developed the "Kelly criterion" of investing), employed information theory to betting and stock market investments to amass personal fortunes.

CAROLYN SHOEMAKER

American astronomer

Twentieth-century American astronomer Carolyn Shoemaker has discovered more than thirty comets, including Shoemaker-Levy 9, which struck Jupiter in 1994. Over the course of her career, Shoemaker discovered more than eight hundred asteroids and thirty-two comets. Her work in astronomy began when she started working as a field assistant for her husband, geologist Eugene Shoemaker.

Born: June 24, 1929; Gallup, New Mexico
Primary field: Astronomy
Specialty: Observational astronomy

EARLY LIFE

Carolyn Spellman Shoemaker was born in Gallup, New Mexico in 1929. Her father, Leonard, was a rancher who later opened a clothing store. Her mother, Hazel Arthur, worked as a school teacher before marrying. Shoemaker was the family's second child. Her older brother was named Richard. The family moved to Chico, California, shortly after Carolyn's birth.

After high school, Shoemaker enrolled at California State University in Chico, where she earned both a bachelor's degree and a master's degree in history and political science, as well as credentials to teach at the high school level. Uncertain about her career path, she became a seventh-grade teacher. However, Shoemaker did not enjoy the experience and left teaching after one year.

In 1950, at her brother's wedding, she met Eugene ("Gene") Shoemaker, who had been her brother's roommate at the California Institute of Technology (Caltech) and was serving as the best man at his wedding. They corresponded during her year of teaching and were married on August 18, 1951. Shortly after their wedding, Shoemaker began accompanying her husband during his field work in geology, searching for new sources of uranium.

The Shoemakers had three children, and Shoemaker became a full-time mother. She and the children accompanied Gene during summer field work. He was a natural teacher and explained much about his work to his wife and children.

LIFE'S WORK

In 1963, after several moves, the family relocated to Flagstaff, Arizona, where the US Geological Survey had established a training center for astronauts in preparation for the Apollo moon launch. Lowell Observatory had agreed to offer its Clark Telescope to obtain images for a lunar landing site. Also located at the observatory was the US Air Force Aeronautical Chart and Information Center, which was beginning to prepare lunar maps for the National Aeronautics and Space Administration (NASA). During this time, both Shoemakers earned their airplane pilot license.

The family moved to California when Gene accepted a position at Caltech, his alma mater. It was there, while watching the Project Voyager images of flying past Jupiter in real time, that Shoemaker became captivated by planetary science.

After her children had grown, she began assisting with the Palomar Planet-Crossing Asteroid Survey, which Gene and Eleanor Helin had begun at Caltech in 1973, in order to search for asteroids approaching Earth. She found it easy to use the stereomicroscope that her husband and Helin had designed specifically for use with the Palomar telescope. Realizing her skill at finding asteroids, Gene Shoemaker relied on his wife to scan images taken by the Palomar machine.

Shoemaker was fifty-one years old before she officially embarked on a career in astronomy. In 1980, the US Geological Survey Center offered her a position as a visiting scientist. Nine years later, she became a research professor of astronomy at Northern Arizona University. Along with her husband, she was also on the staff of the Lowell Observatory in Flagstaff, Arizona.

For twelve years, beginning in 1984, the Shoemakers traveled annually to the Australian Outback to study crater impacts. They used Landsat images taken from space to identify land features. After four years of work, they had increased the known number of craters in Australia from ten to eighteen. They used their observations of more than twenty craters to hypothesize about the surface of the moon.

The Shoemakers began the Palomar Asteroid and Comet Survey (PACS) in 1983, utilizing a 0.46-meter Schmidt telescope. Along with Canadian astronomer David Levy, they usually spent one week each month in California, northeast of San Diego, where the Palomar Observatory was located. The team divided duties: Gene readied the film, while Levy set the camera's focus and moved the telescope into position. Shoemaker's task was to look through the stereomicroscope at images in pairs taken at different times, to see if she could spot movement. During that time, the team took more than three hundred photographs. It was at Palomar in 1993 that the trio, who by then had been working together for a decade, first saw the Shoemaker-Levy 9 comet.

Shoemaker identified thirty-two comets and over eight hundred asteroids with her husband, with a discovery rate of one comet found for every one hundred hours of examining photographs. A typical night of searching typically lasted thirteen hours. As an ardent observer of the night sky, Shoemaker reset her body clock to stay up all night and sleep during the day.

In 1988, she and her husband were jointly awarded the Rittenhouse Medal by the Rittenhouse Astronomical Society. In 1990, Northern Arizona University of Flagstaff awarded Shoemaker an honorary doctoral

---

The Discovery of Periodic Comet Shoemaker-Levy 9

The night of March 23, 1993 was cloudy in southern California, where the Palomar Observatory is located. Carolyn and Gene Shoemaker and Canadian astronomer David Levy were spending one week each month taking photographs of the night sky. They took one photograph every hour. The year had not been good for observing. In January, they had just one clear night, while February brought only one clear hour. Gene Shoemaker believed that trying to capture anything on film that March night would be a waste of time and money.

Carolyn Shoemaker used a stereo microscope that her husband had helped develop to examine the photos. As she was studying the films two days after that cloudy night, she noticed a smear near the planet Jupiter. She described it as looking like a squashed comet. Unlike most comets, it did not have a bright core at the center or a single tail appended to that core. Rather, this image showed an elongated core with several tails.

Later, Shoemaker realized she was seeing a comet that Jupiter's gravity had captured around 1929, bringing its orbit around the planet, rather than around the sun as is usual for comets, and thus technically making it a moon. In July 1992, some twenty months before being photographed, the comet had come within 120,000 kilometers of Jupiter. The force of Jupiter's tides was shredding the comet into fragments strung out like pearls on a necklace, as another astronomer described it. Each "pearl" became its own comet. The team had discovered the ninth of these comets and named it Periodic Comet Shoemaker-Levy 9.

As more data was received and studied, scientists realized that the comet would not survive the next orbit around Jupiter. By May 1993, the Smithsonian Astrophysical Observatory's Brian G. Marsden predicted that the comet would smash into the planet. A group of astronomers at the Space Telescope Science Institute in Baltimore, Maryland, watched for six days, beginning on July 16, 1994, as the comet fragments began exploding in Jupiter's upper atmosphere, producing fireballs that left the planet's bands scarred for several weeks. Using the *Galileo* space probe on its way to Jupiter following its 1989 launch, and the Hubble Space Telescope, scientists observed the collision, which left craters the size of Earth on Jupiter's surface.

Gene Shoemaker had long wanted to observe a meteorite or comet crashing, although he expected the event to occur on Earth. Because of his wife's diligent observation, he was able to achieve this dream.

degree in science. Five years later, she and her husband received the Scientists of the Year Award. In 1996, the National Aeronautics and Space Administration presented Shoemaker with the Exceptional Scientific Achievement Medal.

In 1997, the Shoemakers were in a serious head-on car crash en route to Goat Paddock Crater in Australia. Although Shoemaker recovered from extensive injuries and later returned to her career, her husband Gene was killed.

Impact

Prior to the Jupiter event in the summer of 1994, scientists had not taken seriously the idea that a comet or other astral body might actually strike Earth. The comet collision on Jupiter changed that opinion. As a consequence, the US Air Force began searching for asteroids at the White Sands Missile Range in New Mexico. More than nineteen thousand asteroids were discovered within less than a year. An asteroid one-kilometer-long or more could cause significant damage to Earth; twenty-six of the nineteen thousand asteroids observed in 1994 were at least that size. Astronomers have since charted an estimated 50 percent of the Near Earth Objects (NEOs), which include satellites and space debris, as well as tools and cameras that astronauts have dropped. In addition, using photographs from orbit and from air, scientists have identified more than 150 craters on Earth as probable sites of comet impact. Scientists are considering the possibility that ancient comet impacts created the chains of craters observed on icy moons.

The National Aeronautics and Space Administration (NASA) used images of the Shoemaker-Levy 9 impact as part of its Small Bodies—Big Impacts curriculum in 2011. The photographs, taken by the *Galileo*

probe and the Hubble Space Telescope, are the only ones existing of a comet crashing into a planet.

Through her diligent searching of the night sky photographs, Shoemaker has encouraged further exploration. The fact that she received no formal training as a scientist has encouraged others with an interest in astronomy or other fields of science. In 2006, she was present at the dedication of the Shoemaker Open Sky Planetarium. Through her public speaking and articles, Shoemaker continues to inspire a love of astronomy.

Judy A. Johnson

Further Reading

Armstrong, Mabel. *Women Astronomers: Reaching for the Stars.* Marcola: Stone Pine, 2008. Print. Includes a section on Shoemaker, highlighting her contributions to astronomy. Illustrations, index, references are also appended.

Ferris, Timothy. *Seeing in the Dark: How Amateur Astronomers are Discovering the Wonders of the Universe.* New York: Simon, 2002. Print. Contains interviews with well-known amateur astronomers, including David Levy. Illustrations, bibliography, index, star maps, and glossary.

Levy, David H. *David Levy's Guide to Observing and Discovering Comets.* Cambridge: Cambridge UP, 2003. Print. Levy recounts his own experiences as an amateur astronomer, including working with the Shoemakers and discovering Shoemaker-Levy 9. Includes photographs, appendix, and an index.

Minard, Anne. *Pluto and Beyond: A Story of Discovery, Adversity, and Ongoing Exploration.* Flagstaff, AZ: Northland, 2007. Print. Shoemaker wrote the foreword to this work, which includes information about astronomy, particularly the work at Flagstaff's Lowell Observatory, as well as a bibliography.

Eugene M. Shoemaker

American geologist and planetary scientist

Twentieth-century geologist and planetary scientist Eugene Shoemaker pioneered the field of astrogeology, the study of the geological makeup of celestial bodies. In the 1960s, he was involved with the first unmanned missions to the moon and provided geological training to Apollo astronauts. He and his wife discovered numerous comets and asteroids during their careers,

including the Shoemaker-Levy 9 comet that collided with Jupiter in 1994.

Born: April 28, 1928; Los Angeles, California
Died: July 18, 1997; Alice Springs, Australia
Also known as: Gene Shoemaker
Primary fields: Astronomy; Earth sciences
Specialties: Geology; astrophysics

EARLY LIFE

Eugene Merle Shoemaker was born on April 28, 1928 in Los Angeles, California. A gifted student, he graduated from the California Institute of Technology (Caltech) in Pasadena at age nineteen. A year later, he earned his master's degree there, after completing his thesis on a study of Precambrian metamorphic rocks.

Also in 1948, Shoemaker began his lifelong involvement with the US Geological Survey (USGS). While conducting his first fieldwork for the USGS, looking for deposits of uranium in Utah and Colorado, he became fascinated with the idea of space exploration. As he read of experiments the US government was then doing with seized German V-2 rockets, Shoemaker was inspired to explore the possibility of a manned moon mission.

Shoemaker theorized that the moon's craters were formed by the impact of asteroids and volcanic eruptions. In 1952, he traveled to Meteor Crater in Arizona. The 4,000-foot-wide depression was among the most recent meteor impact craters on Earth. As he made the first comprehensive geological analysis of the crater, he became convinced that it—like the larger craters on the moon—had been formed by the impact of an asteroid. His analysis of Meteor Crater also helped solve a scientific riddle. If a meteor had formed the crater, why had no such object ever been found? Shoemaker concluded that a 150-ton iron meteorite had crashed in Arizona 50,000 years ago and was instantly vaporized in an explosion equal to the force of a 20-megaton nuclear bomb.

Shoemaker earned his second master's degree at Princeton University in 1954 and his doctorate in 1960, for which he wrote a thesis on his work at Meteor Crater. In 1951, he married the former Carolyn Spellman, with whom he had three children.

LIFE'S WORK

As a geologist, Shoemaker looked at the ways in which violent explosions shaped their impact sites. With the USGS, he studied volcanic processes, observing that uranium was often located in the eroded vents of ancient volcanoes. He also surveyed the craters left after the test detonations of nuclear weapons under Yucca Flat in Nevada. He soon realized the characteristics of craters made by nuclear detonations were similar to the ones he had observed at Meteor Crater. While researching the mechanics of meteor and nuclear impact craters, he and geologist Edward Chao discovered coesite, or shocked quartz. This type of silica forms under tremendous

pressure and is ejected in a ring pattern following a violent impact.

In 1961, Shoemaker got his chance to do pioneering work in the field of astrogeology when he was tapped to head the Astrogeology Research Program of the USGS at Flagstaff, Arizona. This was the same year that President John F. Kennedy committed the National Aeronautics and Space Administration (NASA) to mounting a manned moon mission by the end of the decade. As head of the program at Flagstaff, Shoemaker was involved with the unmanned *Ranger* and *Surveyor* missions to the moon. He also helped train the astronauts in geological science. Shoemaker wanted to become the first geologist on the moon—despite the fact that NASA was considering only trained pilots, and not scientists, as astronauts. In 1963, he was diagnosed with Addison's disease, an adrenal gland disorder. The diagnosis disqualified him from becoming an astronaut.

In 1964, Shoemaker and his staff at USGS used telescope images to draft the first geological lunar map, as well as outline geologic time on the moon. For this work, Shoemaker is credited with laying the foundations of lunar geology as a scientific discipline.

In 1969, Shoemaker became a professor of geology at Caltech, where he served as Chair of its Division of Geology and Planetary Sciences for three years. He began to study comets and asteroids that crossed Earth's orbit. He became convinced that an impact from one of these celestial bodies could wipe out most life on Earth. Many scientists theorize that a comparable event ended the age of the dinosaurs 65 million years ago. Shoemaker advocated that astronomers systematically track these objects and develop an "early-warning system" in order to prevent a calamity from occurring. Shoemaker, along with Eleanor Helin, provided a plan to track the Apollo asteroids, some of which formed the impact craters on Earth and the moon. The search program was operational by 1973.

Shoemaker studied and tracked celestial objects with the 18-inch-diameter telescope at the Palomar Observatory outside San Diego, California. Beginning in 1980, his wife Carolyn worked alongside him, studying images made from the films taken at the Palomar Observatory. Three years later, the Shoemakers discovered their first comet together. In all, the discovery of over thirty comets and over one thousand asteroids would eventually be credited to this trailblazing team.

The couple's most famous discovery occurred in March 1993. Along with their colleague, Canadian

Shoemaker Brings Geological Principles to Outer Space

Geology is the branch of science devoted to the study of the rocks of which the planet Earth is composed. Geologists seek to understand the history of Earth, its plate tectonics, and how prior atmospheric events influenced the evolution of life. Eugene Shoemaker was the first geologist to apply geology to the stars in order to learn about other planets and celestial bodies. His pioneering work in the field of astrogeology began with his close study of the moon in the 1960s. Throughout his career, he studied the entire solar system—every planet and numerous asteroids and comets—and used what he learned to flesh out humankind's understanding of how it began and evolved.

Shoemaker's trailblazing research into the effect of impacts on Earth and other celestial bodies revealed that neither Earth's solar system, nor any other, is a closed system. In addition to bringing minerals and other materials to their impact sites, Shoemaker helped to uncover the fact that meteorites can reshape the surface of a planet or even bring about the extinction of life. Through his work at Meteor Crater and at impact sites around the globe, Shoemaker helped his fellow scientists see the importance of impact as a critical component of the geological process on Earth, and by extension, other worlds.

Shoemaker's longtime survey of asteroids and comets was also infused with geological principles. He and his wife tracked and documented the trajectories and characteristics of near-Earth asteroids and comets, as well as in their significant discovery of Periodic Comet Shoemaker-Levy in 1993. That comet and its subsequent crash into Jupiter broadly expanded existing knowledge of comet impacts on planets in general and highlighted the specific importance of Jupiter's massive gravitational pull in keeping pieces of space debris out of the inner solar system. The event also seemed to confirm what Shoemaker and other researchers had been saying for some time—that the impact of a comet or asteroid on Earth is possible, and that efforts should be undertaken to prevent a calamitous collision event.

---

astronomer David H. Levy, the Shoemakers found an extraordinary comet in the outer solar system, which had come within sixteen thousand miles of Jupiter. At the time of its discovery, the Shoemaker-Levy 9 comet had been ripped apart by Jupiter's terrific gravitational pull, and its fragments began being pulled inexorably toward Jupiter. Astronomers across the world watched in amazement for four days beginning on July 16, 1994, as twenty fragments from the comet fell into Jupiter's atmosphere, resulting in tremendous fireballs.

Although Shoemaker retired from his professorship at Caltech in 1985 and from the USGS in 1993, he continued to work at the Lowell Observatory in Flagstaff, traveling around the world to study impact craters. On July 18, 1997, during an expedition to Alice Springs in the Northwest Territory of Australia, Shoemaker was killed in an auto accident. His wife was severely injured in the crash but survived to continue working in astronomy. In July 1999, some of Shoemaker's cremated remains were sealed in a small capsule designed by planetary scientist Carolyn C. Porco and sent to the moon aboard the unmanned *Lunar Prospector* spacecraft.

IMPACT

Shoemaker is credited with creating the discipline of astrogeology, or planetary science. Prior to his lifetime, such work was considered part of astronomy as a whole. His application of geological fundamentals to the study of celestial bodies revolutionized the way scientists map planets, moons, asteroids, and comets. His work influenced the *Apollo* missions and continues to have an impact on the work of unmanned probes sent deep into the solar system by scientists to learn how the planets evolved and how their geology played a part in that evolution.

Shoemaker's fieldwork at Meteor Crater and other impact sites highlighted the importance of celestial impacts on the development of Earth's geology. Shoemaker also helped to popularize the theory of a meteor event leading to the extinction of the dinosaurs.

Yet Shoemaker's most significant contribution to science is also his most famous: his codiscovery of the Shoemaker-Levy comet, which provided astronomers with a key opportunity to learn about both a comet's dynamics and the planetary science of Jupiter. For the first time, scientists witnessed two celestial bodies colliding in Earth's solar system. Shoemaker-Levy's collision led many astronomers to theorize that Jupiter may act as a kind of "cosmic vacuum cleaner" for the inner solar system and protect Earth from more frequent meteor impacts like the one that wiped out the dinosaurs.

Shoemaker received numerous awards throughout his career. Among his most notable are the Wetherill Medal from the Franklin Institute in 1965, the Gilbert Award from the Geological Society of America in 1983, and the Kuiper Prize from the American Astronomical Society in 1984. In 1980, he became a member of the National Academy of Sciences. In 1992, President George H. W. Bush presented him with the National Medal of Science, the nation's highest scientific honor.

Christopher Mari

FURTHER READING

Chaikin, Andrew. *A Man on the Moon: The Voyages of the* Apollo *Astronauts*. New York: Penguin, 2007. Print. Presents a comprehensive overview of the *Apollo* missions that sent US astronauts to the moon in the late 1960s and early 1970s. Provides information about the missions themselves, reviewing biographical information about Shoemaker and describing his contributions to the US space program.

Faure, Gunter, and Teresa M. Mensing. *Introduction to Planetary Science: The Geological Perspective*. Dordrecht: Springer, 2007. Print. Provides an analysis of Earth's solar system and demonstrates how Shoemaker helped scientists to better understand it. Includes numerous recent photos, including images taken by the Cassini-Huygens probe and the Hubble Telescope.

Levy, David H. *Shoemaker by Levy: The Man Who Made an Impact*. Princeton: Princeton UP, 2000. Print. Full-length biography of Shoemaker, delineating his contributions to planetary science throughout his long career.

GEORGE D. SNELL

American immunologist

George Snell discovered the presence of histocompatibility antigens on the surface of cells, and provided a molecular explanation for rejection of tissue transplants. His work contributed to understanding the role played by these proteins in immune cell interactions.

Born: December 19, 1903; Bradford, Massachusetts
Died: June 6, 1996; Bar Harbor, Maine
Primary field: Biology
Specialties: Genetics, biochemistry, cellular biology

EARLY LIFE

George David Snell was born December 19, 1903, in Bradford, Massachusetts. He was the youngest of three children of Cullen and Kathlee Snell. In addition to his full-time job at a local YMCA, Snell's father was also an amateur inventor. When Snell was four years old, his family moved to Brookline, where he completed his public school education. As a young student, Snell showed an early interest in mathematics and the sciences.

In 1922, Snell enrolled at Dartmouth College in New Hampshire. He became interested in genetics after enrolling in a course taught by Professor John Gerould, whose worked focused on the study of genetics and physiology of butterflies. After graduation from Dartmouth in 1926, Snell began graduate studies at Harvard University. At Harvard, he studied with biologist William Ernest Castle, who was among the first to study Mendelian inheritance in mammals. Snell spent summers working at Woods Hole, Massachusetts, where he studied the genetics of *Habrobracon*, the parasitic wasp.

Snell earned his PhD in 1930. His thesis work addressed gene linkage in mice. Because inbred strains of mice had yet to be developed, Snell relied on mutations for his linkage studies, which included characteristics such as hairless, short-eared, and dwarf individuals in animals brought by amateur breeders. Ultimately, he was able to describe over twenty-five such characteristics.

LIFE'S WORK

Following his graduation, Snell spent a year as an instructor at Brown University before accepting a postdoctoral position at the University of Texas, where he worked with botanist Hermann Muller. Muller had discovered the ability of irradiation to induce mutations in fruit flies. He later earned a Nobel Prize for this work. Between 1933 and 1946, Snell built upon Muller's work, demonstrating that irradiation could induce analogous mutations in mice.

In 1933, Snell moved to the University of Washington in Seattle. In 1935, he moved to the Jackson Laboratory in Bar Harbor, Maine, to resume his work studying mutations in mice. Geneticist Clarence Cook Little,

Snell Discovers Histocompatibility Antigens on Surface of Tissues

Beginning early in the twentieth century, scientists began undertaking serious attempts at tissue transplantation. However, these attempts were rarely successful. Attempts to graft tissue on burn patients during World War II resulted in frequent rejections and infections. Scientists observed that subsequent attempts using the same donor resulted in a significantly more rapid rejection. This suggested that rejection was an immune phenomenon. Snell became interested in the immunological role in transplantation rejection after he arrived at the Jackson Laboratory in 1935. At the time, Snell was working on a text dealing with mammalian genetics. Clarence Little, founder and director of the laboratory, wrote a chapter on the subject of tumor transplantation, which piqued Snell's interest and changed the direction of his research.

Two of the challenges Snell faced were the large number of immune genes already described in the mouse; and that understanding the function of individual genes required strains of mice that differed at only a single locus (the position of a gene sequence on a chromosome). Snell solved the problem through repeated "backcrossing" between two strains of mice—crossing progeny with a parent. Eventually, he produced what he called "congenic" mice, mouse strains that differed at only one locus.

During the late 1930s, immunologist Peter Gorer had observed that when tumors were transplanted into mice their immune system not only rejected the tumor, but produced antibody proteins against the antigens on tumor tissues. Gorer referred to the target protein on the tumor cells as "antigen II". Such antibodies in the mouse serum were the likely cause of the more rapid rejection upon subsequent exposure to the tissue. In 1946, Gorer joined Snell to test his antisera on the tissues of the congenic mice Snell had bred. They found certain congenic mice produced antigen II while others did not, the difference resulting from different alleles at the site of the gene locus that encoded the antigen.

In 1948, Snell published his work describing his methods for producing the congenic strains of mice he had bred. In describing the collaborative work he carried out with Gorer, Snell proposed calling the genes that encoded antigen II, the basis for tumor rejection by Gorer's antisera, "histocompatibility genes," or H genes. The first of the genes Snell described was called the H-2 locus, noting the role of antigen II in its discovery. Further experiments measuring recombination rates within the H region revealed at least two separate but linked genes were involved, and were termed H-2K and H-2D genes.

As Snell located and studied additional histocompatibility genes, it became clear their significance was not always equivalent. Some histocompatibility gene differences led to rapid rejection, while others seemed to have no role in tumor rejection. Similar results were found when skin grafts were studied instead of tumor transplantation. Snell interpreted these results by concluding some loci encoded "major" histocompatibility genes, while others encoded "minor" such genes. When genetic mapping established the locus on the mouse chromosomes where each of these genes was located, they were found to be linked within the same region of chromosome 17. The region was subsequently named the "major histocompatibility complex," or MHC.

a former student of Castle's, had founded the Jackson Laboratory in 1929, and he appointed Snell the facility's mammalian geneticist.

Snell was well acquainted with the challenge inherent in the study of mouse genetics. In 1935, only some twenty-five breeds of mutant mice were available, reflecting the low rate of natural mutations. Snell spent five years in Maine studying radiation-induced mutations in mice. During that time, he met and married Rhoda Carson at Bar Harbor, and the couple had three sons. In 1943, Snell edited the first book that summarized the work accomplished at Jackson Laboratory: *The Biology of the Laboratory Mouse*, which became a classic work in the field of genetics.

By the early 1940s, the focus of Snell's work shifted to transplantation rejection. He began his work by studying the inability of mice to accept transplants of tumors from other mice. Little had previously demonstrated that tissue compatibility genes, which regulated incompatibility, acted in a dominant/recessive Mendelian manner. Snell's first goal was to determine whether these genes could be better observed using visible markers. By 1945, he had a number of such markers; once Snell determined the visible marker was linked to a specific histocompatibility gene, he had a simpler means to observe mutations in those genes. By backcrossing his mice—crossing with a parent numerous times—Snell was also able to breed strains of mice differing at only a single gene locus within the region that regulated transplant rejection.

Pathologist Peter Gorer, who had been studying the immune response to tumors transplanted among mice, joined Snell in this work. Gorer had described a protein on the surface of these cells, termed "antigen II," which was key to understanding the ability of incompatible mice to produce antibodies and reject such tissue (an antigen is any substance that triggers the production of antibodies). Snell demonstrated antigen II was a tissue antigen, which he named the histocompatibility antigen (H-2). Despite a fire in 1947 that devastated the inbred mouse colony, Snell was able to produce a number of congenic mouse strains used in identifying various loci within the histocompatibility region.

In 1952, Snell was appointed staff scientific director at the Jackson Laboratory. He continued to study the relationship between the major histocompatibility complex (MHC), as the region in the mouse chromosome encoding the histocompatibility genes came to be called, and rejection of cancer cells. Snell retired from the Jackson Laboratory in 1968, though he continued his writing on mouse genetics as well as his evolving views on the subject of ethics. He presented his ideas on ethics in the 1988 book *Search for a Rational Ethic.* Snell received the 1980 Nobel Prize in Physiology or Medicine in recognition of his work on histocompatibility. He died June 6, 1996.

IMPACT

Snell's investigation of histocompatibility genes in the mouse was directly applicable to similar studies carried out in humans. Since the recognition of an ever-growing number of gene products within the MHC could be identified on the surface of white blood cells, the human counterparts became known as human leukocyte antigens (HLA). Snell recognized the primary function of the genes within the MHC was not in transplant rejection, but rather in

regulation of the immune response itself. By the 1980s, an "alphabet soup" of gene loci were identified in the mouse H-2 region, as well as in the equivalent human HLA region. The immune genes were grouped largely into two primary classes designated class I and class II. The class I antigens define the concept of "self" for the immune system, functioning in the immune recognition of cells infected with internal parasites, such as viruses, that were also the basis for transplant rejection. Scientists have identified a large number of variations within each member of the class. Class II antigens are involved in regulating the immune response, including the cell-cell interactions, which take place in the initiation of that response.

During his later years, Snell followed the growing recognition of the enormous complexity inherent in the immune complex genes. What he had proved to be true in mice was shown to be equivalent in humans and has since been demonstrated in nearly all vertebrates.

Richard Adler

FURTHER READING

Abbas, Abdul, and Andrew Lichtman. *Basic Immunology: Functions and Disorders of the Immune System*, 3rd ed. Philadelphia: Saunders, 2011. Print. Presents a general overview of immunology. Includes explanations and diagrams discussing the relationship of the histocompatibility complex and immune function.

Eisen, Eugene, ed. *The Mouse in Animal Genetics and Breeding Research.* Hackensack: Imperial College, 2005. Print. Discusses the role of the mouse in the history and application of mammalian genetics. Snell's work in the field is reviewed.

Wilkes, David S. *Immunobiology of Organ Transplantation.* New York: Springer, 2004. Print. Presents detailed discussion of transplantation immunology at the cellular and molecular levels.

FREDERICK SODDY

English chemist

Frederick Soddy received a Nobel Prize in Chemistry for revolutionizing the understanding of the nature of radioactive particles, specifically by proposing the existence of isotopes—atoms of the same chemical element that have the same atomic number but different radioactive properties and atomic weights. His theory *ran counter to the long-held assumption that all atoms of a particular element were identical in size and atomic weight.*

Born: September 2, 1877; Eastbourne, England
Died: September 22, 1956; Brighton, England

Primary field: Chemistry
Specialty: Atomic and molecular physics

EARLY LIFE

Born in Eastbourne, a resort town along the coast of the English Channel, Frederick Soddy was the youngest of seven children. His mother, Hanna Green, died before he was two years old; his father, Benjamin Soddy, a successful corn and seed merchant, was instrumental in his early development. Soddy's father taught him about economic realities and social classes, the restrictions placed on those with a rural background or lacking education, and the importance of technology in achieving social and economic advancement. Soddy, however, showed an early aptitude not for economics but for hard sciences.

At Eastbourne College, a prestigious boarding school in Sussex, Soddy, at age seventeen, coauthored with the school's science headmaster a groundbreaking paper on chemical reactions involving carbon dioxide. Buoyed by this success and determined to pursue a career in theoretical chemistry, but concerned about his own readiness for the rigors of university study, Soddy enrolled in a year of preparatory studies at University College of Wales at Aberystwyth. He then secured a science scholarship to Merton College, Oxford.

Soddy began his study at Merton in 1896. Although socially awkward, he distinguished himself for his thoroughness and his probing intellect. He passed the chemistry examination in 1898 and achieved a first-class rating in the School of Natural Sciences. For the next two years, Soddy remained at Oxford, but he grew restless over the university's lack of advanced chemistry research facilities. In 1900, he decided to pursue a position in chemistry at the richly endowed McGill University in Montreal, Canada.

At McGill, Soddy worked in first-rate facilities under the direction of one of the early century's most promising theoretical chemists, Ernest Rutherford, whose pioneering work was in the new field of radioactivity. Over the next two years, Soddy and Rutherford published a series of highly regarded papers theorizing

---

Frederick Soddy, Forefather of Ecological Economics

When Frederick Soddy abandoned scientific research in favor of economics in his later years, he was viewed as a man squandering his potential for greatness. His economic theories and prescriptions for monetary policy, which were based on the laws that govern physics, were dismissed as quackery. It was not until many years after Soddy's death that his writings, which include *Money versus Man* (1933), *Wealth, Virtual Wealth and Debt: The Solution of the Economic Paradox* (1926), *The Role of Money* (1934), and *Money as Something for Nothing: The Gold "Standard" Snare* (1935), were rediscovered and viewed in a more favorable light.

Soddy arranged his economic theories in accordance with the laws of thermodynamics. For example, the first two laws of thermodynamics, which address the conservation of energy, forbid perpetual motion. Using the common metaphor of the economy as a machine, Soddy challenged the notion of the economy as a machine capable of generating an infinite amount of wealth. He asserted that wealth is tangible, as evidenced by the goods that we buy with our money. The dollars in our pockets are not real wealth, Soddy claimed, but are simply symbols that represent our claim on the economy's ability to generate wealth now. Conversely, debt is a claim on the economy's ability to generate wealth in the future. When these two concepts are not properly balanced, problems occur in the economy. When claims on present wealth surpass the actual ability of the economy to generate wealth, crises occur.

Soddy outlined five separate points to address the problems he saw as inherent in the system. Of these five points, the first four are now common practice. He called for floating international exchange rates, proposed abandoning the gold standard, advised that federal surpluses and deficits be used as tools of policy to counter cyclical trends in the economy, and called for a bureau of economic statistics as well as a consumer price index. His last proposal has not been implemented but is prescient in the wake of the 2008 financial crisis: Soddy admonished banks to end the practice of creating money and debt out of nothing, a direct contradiction to the leveraged-debt products hawked by banks before the 2008 recession.

Soddy's writings are now considered the antecedents of the modern study of ecological economics, which views economics through the "living system" lens of a larger ecosystem. Ecological economists advocate for sustainability of the environment as well as of tangible wealth. Much like Soddy, present-day ecological economists hope to apply years of scientific advancements to human (and human-nature) interactions.

about the phenomena of nuclear decay and the disintegration of highly unstable radioactive elements into other radioactive elements.

LIFE'S WORK

Upon returning to England in 1902, Soddy went to work at University College, London with Sir William Ramsay, a Nobel Prize winner who had studied the gaseous products of radioactive decay and had first discovered the noble gases. As Soddy began what would become his defining work, scientists wanted to determine the chemical identification of the elements produced in radioactive decay. They had begun to identify a mystifying variety of apparently new elements produced by such processes, which challenged the systematic premise of the periodic table, an ingenious arrangement devised barely fifty years earlier in which physical and chemical qualities in elements were conceived as functions of their atomic weight. Researchers wanted to know whether these apparently new elements actually were new, and, if they were, how they would fit in the limited spaces available in the periodic table. Together, Soddy and Ramsay demonstrated that the radioactive decay of radium bromide produces helium. Although Ramsay's international credibility was subsequently undermined by his public endorsement of an eccentric scheme to extract gold from seawater, Soddy avoided such distractions and accepted a post at the University of Glasgow in Scotland in 1904.

During the next ten years at Glasgow, Soddy developed his revolutionary radioactive displacement law, which drew on his experimental work showing that uranium decays into radium. Soddy's pioneering work first describes the transformations that occur when a decaying radioactive element loses either its alpha or beta particles, then theorizes that the loss of an alpha particle by an element with an even number on the periodic table causes a dramatic but predictable shift in that element's atomic weight (a decrease of four) and its atomic number (a decrease of two). Thus, alpha decay creates an element that would be two places to the left in the standard periodic table. Beta emission revealed a similarly predictable shift to one place higher. What were being created by radioactive decay were not new elements but rather variations of elements already charted.

Soddy's results led to a radical premise, which he published in 1913: two or more elements might be identical chemically and occupy the same space in the periodic table but still differ in their atomic weight. He would receive the Nobel Prize in Chemistry in 1921 for this revolutionary work. Soddy described the elements being produced as *isotopes*, a coinage of Scottish doctor and family friend Margaret Todd; the term draws from the Greek and means "the same place."

In 1914, Soddy left Glasgow to accept the chair in chemistry at the University of Aberdeen, where he continued his work, specifically in the extraction of lead from the radioactive ore thorite. During World War I, he assisted in research work to extract ethylene, a potent anesthetic, from coal gas. After the war, Soddy accepted an endowed chair in chemistry at Oxford, where it was anticipated he would lead Oxford's efforts to develop a research facility with an international reach. That was not to be, however. Soddy was distant and prickly with his students, quarreled with faculty, found the administration unimaginative, and quickly alienated the facility from significant funding.

Soddy then turned from research work to studies in social and economic philosophy, working on an ambitious agenda for improving humanity by the unconditional embrace of technology. Boldly, he applied the quantum principles of energy and elemental transformation to the flow and distribution of money, drawing on arguments he had heard years before from his wealthy father. After he took early retirement from Oxford in 1936 at age fifty-nine, shortly after the death of his beloved wife, Soddy emerged as a vigorous proponent of sweeping iconoclastic political, economic, and social reforms. Indeed, after World War II, Soddy, like many other scientists, became alarmed by atomic bombs and the contributions his earlier work had inadvertently made to their development. He also was keenly aware that his work had helped H. G. Wells write his 1914 science-fiction classic *World Set Free*, which first described atomic-powered bombs. Soddy began to advocate for the banning of nuclear weapons and the use of nuclear energy for peaceful purposes only.

Soddy died on September 22, 1956, in Brighton, England. He is remembered not only for his groundbreaking theoretical work but also for his considerable body of economic writings and his unflagging dedication to social activism.

IMPACT

Positioned historically at the threshold of what would become the atomic age, and then the nuclear age, Soddy belongs to the generation that first clarified in the spirit of scientific investigation the bewildering implications of the new field of radioactivity and charted for the first time the eccentric patterns of a subatomic world. Long after his hypothesis describing isotopes had become a scientific commonplace, Soddy, much like his far-better-known contemporaries such as Bertrand Russell, Linus Pauling, J. Robert Oppenheimer, and Albert Einstein, found his public voice amid the anxieties of the post–Hiroshima and Nagasaki nuclear era. In his mind, problems such as economic inequity and political strife could be solved by the application of scientific principles of order and design and the embrace of the promise, rather than the horrors, of technology. With visionary energy and a moral compassion that derived from his profound appreciation of the symmetry and purposeful organization of the subatomic world, Soddy extended the reach of twentieth-century science by applying its most complex principles as metaphors for compassionate social and political evolution.

Joseph Dewey

FURTHER READING

Brown, G. I. *Invisible Rays: A History of Radioactivity.* Phoenix Mills: Sutton, 2002. Print. A concise introduction to the science behind Soddy's hypotheses, beginning more than two centuries before his work.

Malley, Marjorie C. *Radioactivity: A History of a Mysterious Science.* New York: Oxford UP, 2011. Print. Includes a section on Rutherford and Soddy's collaboration within the context of the larger history of radioactivity.

Merricks, Linda. *The World Made New: Frederick Soddy, Science, Politics, and Environment.* New York: Oxford UP, 1996. Print. A biography that includes an analysis of Soddy's second career in economic and political philosophy and clarifies his understanding of the role of scientists in a postwar world.

MARY SOMERVILLE

Scottish scientist and writer

After preparing a celebrated translation and explanation of Pierre-Simon Laplace's Traité de mécanique céleste, *Somerville became a central figure in British and American scientific networks, and her widely read books helped define the disciplines within the physical sciences.*

Born: December 26, 1780; Jedburgh, Scotland
Died: November 29, 1872; Naples, Italy
Also known as: Mary Fairfax, Mary Fairfax Somerville, Mary Greig
Primary field: Earth sciences
Specialty: Geophysics

EARLY LIFE

Mary Somerville was born Mary Fairfax, the fifth of seven children. Her mother, Margaret Charters, was the second wife of her father, William George Fairfax, a British admiral who fought with James Wolfe at Quebec during the Seven Years' War of 1756–63. Although Somerville attended boarding school for one year at the age of ten, her parents believed that women should develop domestic skills and not pursue formal education. When she was a teenager, however, she became intrigued by mathematics problems she found in a women's magazine and began to teach herself. An uncle encouraged her, and she was able to obtain John

Bonnycastle's *An Introduction to Algebra* (1782) and Euclid's *Elements of Geometry* when she was fifteen.

In 1804, Somerville married her cousin Samuel Greig, a captain in the Russian navy who was stationed in London, where Somerville gave birth to two sons, in 1805 and 1806. She was unable to continue her studies during that period, but after Greig died in 1807, she returned to Jedburgh and pursued more education. She was assisted by professors from the nearby University of Edinburgh, such as John Playfair and John Leslie. She also became a friend of Henry Brougham and other founders of the *Edinburgh Review*, with whom she shared Whig political views. Her most significant mentor was William Wallace, who became the professor of mathematics at Edinburgh after Playfair died in 1819. Somerville read French mathematics and astronomy under Wallace's tutelage and studied Greek and botany. She also gained support from her second husband, William Somerville, a first cousin whom she married in 1812 and with whom she would have four children. A surgeon and fellow of the Royal Society, William studied geology and mineralogy with her.

In 1814 and 1815, two of Somerville's children died. In 1816, William moved the family to London, where he took up a position as principal inspector for the Army Medical Board. After his job was lost to government budget cuts in 1817, he worked only occasionally. He and Somerville spent their free time visiting

---

Somerville Writes *Physical Geography*

Somerville's most popular work was a book called *Physical Geography* (1848). Inspired by the work of naturalist Alexander von Humboldt, the book broadened the day's definition of "geography" to include animal, vegetable, and even human life. In the years before his death, Humboldt had attempted to set down all that was known about the physical universe in a multivolume work called Cosmos (1845). Both Humboldt and Somerville were interested in humans' role in obtaining a larger picture of the universe, but it was Somerville who sought to draw scientific connections among the physical sciences; a deeply religious woman, Somerville believed that the ability to demonstrate these connections was proof of a higher power.

Among the observations Somerville makes in *Physical Geography* is the work of the earthworm in improving soil. She also cites the symbiotic relationship between plants and animals in the creation of oxygen. Somerville is very specific about humans' role as a part of nature as a whole and concludes that a divine Providence is responsible for these intricate interactions. This view of people in relation to nature (she writes that humans are a part of the "living landscape") differed significantly from the predominant Victorian view that humans were superior to all creatures and in complete control of their environment. *Physical Geography* provides a detailed analysis of the Earth's physical environment but also reveals the context within which nineteenth-century scientists viewed their work. The nineteenth century saw significant advancements in the physical sciences, namely astronomy, geography, geology, and meteorology. There was a feeling among intellectuals and scientists (and religion played no small part) that humankind was on the verge of a new epoch of discovery.

Somerville concludes *Physical Geography* with an eye toward the future. While she worries about the deterioration of the living landscape (she frets about the possible extinction of lions, tigers, and elephants in particular), she writes of her excitement at the prospect of harnessing the power of nature to improve technology. Despite the controversies caused by its publication, *Physical Geography* was used in classrooms for more than fifty years after Somerville's death and is considered to have been the first textbook in physical geography.

---

mathematicians Jean-Baptiste Biot, François Arago, Pierre-Simon Laplace, and other scholars in Paris. In 1819, William was appointed director of the Royal Military Hospital in Chelsea, where he remained until 1836.

LIFE'S WORK

Although Somerville believed too much study was responsible for her ten-year-old daughter Margaret's death in 1823, she continued her own studies and prepared her first scientific paper, which was on the relationship between sunlight and magnetism. William communicated it to the *Philosophical Transactions of the Royal Society* in 1826. Though Somerville's conclusions in that paper proved to be incorrect, her friends encouraged her to continue with public presentations.

In 1827, British statesman Henry Brougham asked Somerville to translate Laplace's *Traité de mécanique céleste* (5 vols., 1798–1827), a treatise demonstrating that the solar system was self regulating, as had been predicted by physicist Isaac Newton's gravitational theory. After consulting with Augustus de Morgan and Charles Babbage, she added to her translation a "preliminary dissertation" that explained the mathematics readers needed to understand Laplace's ideas. Her introduction also set Laplace's work in historical context and presented some of her own mathematical work. Her translation, with her commentary, was published as *The Mechanism of the Heavens* in 1831. The book was immediately pirated in the United States; translated into French, German, and Italian; and adopted as a textbook at the University of Cambridge in 1837.

In 1834, Somerville followed this work with the two-volume *On the Connexion of the Physical Sciences*. This book's explanation of interconnections among astronomy, physics, magnetism, meteorology, and physical geography secured her fame as an expositor. English physicist David Brewster praised her book's argument—although he was unsure women would read it—and Scottish physicist James Clerk Maxwell later described it as a seminal work of the nineteenth century. During that same year, Somerville was elected to honorary memberships in the Royal Irish Academy and the Société de Physique et d'Histoire Naturelle of Geneva. In 1835, she was elected an honorary member of the Royal Astronomical Society. To encourage others to synthesize and explain science, British prime minister Robert Peel awarded her an annual pension of two hundred pounds—an amount increased to three hundred pounds in 1837. Meanwhile, ten editions of *On the Connexion of the Physical Sciences* appeared during the first four decades after its original publication.

Somerville's husband William was frequently ill, and the couple had substantial financial obligations to their relatives. The family resided in Italy, where the cost of living was much lower, almost continuously after 1838. In 1836, Somerville wrote a paper for the French Academy of Science that was delivered by Arago. Her 1845 paper for the Royal Society was delivered by astronomer John Herschel.

Through these years, Somerville maintained her scientific friendships, which also included geologist Charles Lyell and naturalist Alexander von Humboldt. In 1848, she published *Physical Geography*. This book covered the same subject as a book by Humboldt but was organized differently. Her division of geography into physical regions, rather than nations, and her description of the inhabitants of Earth, sea, and air made the book a popular text. She also relied on Lyell's uniformitarian geology and assigned a central role to solar energy. Although her acceptance of the theory of an old Earth led to denunciations from the House of Commons and the Church of England, *Physical Geography* went through seven editions.

Despite the controversy her book raised, Somerville continued to receive honors. In 1857, she was elected to the American Geographical and Statistical Society, and the Italian Geographical Society likewise made her a member in 1870. Meanwhile, she made significant revisions in some of her books as they were republished, but she never incorporated Charles Darwin's theory of evolution by natural selection into *Physical Geography*.

Somerville supported woman suffrage and signed a petition in 1862 that urged the University of London to permit women to sit for degrees. She finished her last book, *On Molecular and Microscopic Science*, in 1869. During that same year, she was elected to the American Philosophical Society and presented with the Royal Geographical Society's Victoria Gold Medal and the Victor Emmanuel Gold Medal of the Geographical Society of Florence. She received at least twenty-five awards in all.

Somerville's last decades were marked by the deaths of her husband in 1860 and her only surviving son, Woronzow Greig, in 1865. Although her daughters outlived her, they never married. Somerville died in Florence, Italy, on November 29, 1872. After her death,

an island in the Arctic Ocean was named for her in recognition of her interest in polar exploration, and Oxford University's Somerville College was named after her when it opened in 1879.

IMPACT

Somerville was viewed as the leading woman scientist of her era. She was part of a generation that was conversant across all the bodies of scientific knowledge then extant. Male intellectuals treated her as an equal; they praised her publications and accepted her definitions of the physical sciences. Because no clear boundaries between professional and amateur scientists then existed, Somerville was able to study independently and participate in scientific culture alongside premier scientists, just as men did who learned science informally. Indeed, both provincial and foreign scientists considered it essential to call on her when they visited Europe after 1830.

Like most of her peers, Mary Somerville believed that women were incapable of making truly original discoveries. Although male scientists appreciated her work, they offered her only honorary memberships in their learned societies. Curiously, gender-based perceptions of Somerville reversed during her lifetime. After she died in 1872, women eulogized her as a scientific pioneer, while men developed a sentimental view of her as a symbolic curiosity. Later scholars have wrestled with interpreting the meaning of her roles and contributions to the history of science.

Amy Ackerberg-Hastings

FURTHER READING

Chapman, Allan. *Mary Somerville and the World of Science*. Bath: Canopus, 2004. Print. A brief but lively introduction to Somerville's life that summarizes her background and writings, putting them into the wider context of nineteenth-century science.

Patterson, Elizabeth Chambers. *Mary Somerville and the Cultivation of Science*. Boston: Martinus, 1983. Print. Patterson cataloged Somerville's manuscripts and produced the most thorough account of her life's work and influences.

Somerville, Martha. *Personal Recollections, From Early Life to Old Age, of Mary Somerville*. 1874. Whitefish: Kessinger, 2008. Print. Somerville's autobiography, published posthumously and edited by her daughter to omit scientific details and people deemed uninteresting.

LAZZARO SPALLANZANI

Italian physiologist

Spallanzani conducted important studies in bodily regeneration and fertilization. He also challenged the theory of spontaneous generation—the idea that microbial life-forms could arise from decaying matter—helping to overturn an assumption that had dominated science and popular imagination for centuries.

Born: January 12, 1729; Scandiano, Italy
Died: February 11, 1799; Pavia, Italy
Primary field: Biology
Specialties: Physiology, microbiology

EARLY LIFE

Lazzaro Spallanzani was born on January 12, 1729, in Scandiano, Italy. Following a Jesuit education in the classics and philosophy, he studied law at the University of Bologna, where he also attended physics and mathematics lectures delivered by his cousin, Laura Bassi.

A mother of twelve and one of the first women to become a professor in Europe, Bassi instilled in young Spallanzani a love of science. She likely influenced Spallanzani's spirit of skeptical and critical inquiry as well. Bassi was an early proponent of the physics of English scientist Sir Isaac Newton, who envisioned nature as subservient to natural laws, not divine whim. As Bassi's embrace of Newton's controversial ideas defied conventional wisdom, Spallanzani would follow suit with his own bold rejection of the theory of spontaneous generation.

With Bassi's behind-the-scenes support, Spallanzani earned his father's blessing to pursue a doctorate in philosophy. In 1754 or 1755, Spallanzani, then in his mid-twenties, secured his first university appointment as a professor of logic, metaphysics, and Greek. Academic work would dominate the rest of his professional life, even after he was ordained as a priest a few years later. Spallanzani fielded offers from several universities before accepting a chair at the University of Modena in the early 1760s.

During the six years he spent in Modena, Spallanzani's reputation grew. He turned down a number of offers before being personally persuaded by the Habsburg empress Maria Teresa to accept, in 1769, the chair of natural history and curatorship of the museum of natural history at the University of Pavia. He retained both positions for the next thirty years.

LIFE'S WORK

The theory of abiogenesis, or spontaneous generation, had prevailed from ancient times until 1668, when Italian physician Francesco Redi proved, in a series of controlled experiments, that the presence of maggots on rotting meat was the product of fly eggs and not the meat itself. Yet belief in the capacity of life-forms to generate spontaneously—encouraged by the invention of the microscope, which unveiled a teeming world of microorganisms that seemed to originate out of nowhere—remained strong in Spallanzani's day.

In 1761, Spallanzani encountered the work of two of the leading proponents of abiogenesis, Georges-Louis Leclerc, Comte de Buffon, and the English priest John Tuberville Needham. It was common knowledge that, with time, water in which organic matter was left to decay would be swarming with microscopic life, and that boiling the water would kill off these life-forms. In a series of experiments, Needham boiled his solutions before transferring them to sealed containers. When microscopic examination revealed the eventual presence of cellular life despite boiling and sealing, Needham claimed to have produced definitive proof that microscopic life-forms can arise spontaneously.

Spallanzani, however, remained skeptical and set out to duplicate Needham's experiments. Unlike Needham, Spallanzani took pains to control the factors that might permit the survival of existing microorganisms or the entrance of new ones from the surrounding air. His rigorous methods exposed critical flaws in Needham's work; Spallanzani's experiments showed that not boiling the solution for a sufficient time period and failing to draw off the air before sealing the containers compromised the conditions from which Needham's creatures allegedly generated. When Spallanzani boiled hermetically sealed flasks for one hour, the flask contents remained permanently free of microorganisms, thus discrediting the possibility of abiogenesis.

Spallanzani's results, which he published in the late 1760s, laid the groundwork for Louis Pasteur's work on sterilization techniques, which would greatly reduce food-borne illnesses and human suffering in the nineteenth century. To acknowledge his legacy, Pasteur ordered that a portrait of Spallanzani be hung in his institute in Paris.

Having debunked the notion of abiogenesis, Spallanzani turned his attention to the mysteries of how

Spallanzani Disproves the Theory of Spontaneous Generation

Lazzaro Spallanzani's most famous findings concerned the spontaneous generation of microorganisms. Thinkers such as John Needham upheld that living things appeared from nonliving matter via spontaneous generation. By the mid-eighteenth century, the idea of animal and plant origination from nonliving matter already had been rejected by scientists, but some still believed that microbes could generate in this way. Microbes, according to Spallanzani's contemporaries, can arise spontaneously from food without the influence of outside factors. Spallanzani, however, believed that microbes should also have parents, because *omne vivum ex vivo* (a Latin phrase meaning "all life is from life"), and so began experiments to determine the origination of microbes.

In a paper published in the late 1760s, Spallanzani showed that food, when placed in glass vessels immediately sealed by fusing the glass, did not generate microbes. He suggested that microbes (or the parents of the microbes that he tried to find) came to the food from the air and could be killed by exposure to heat—a process now referred to as sterilization. However, critics of Spallanzani's work, especially Needham and French scientist Georges-Louis Leclerc, Comte de Buffon, responded by arguing that heat destroyed the "vital force" that was required for spontaneous generation to take place. Thus, the question of spontaneous generation was not resolved in Spallanzani's lifetime. Nevertheless, Spallanzani laid the foundation for canning, an airtight process of food preservation that was invented by French chef Nicolas Appert in 1810. Later, Appert built a factory to produce canned food. In his office, he featured a large portrait of Spallanzani; he even named his dog Lazzaro.

In the nineteenth century, with the experiments of French scientist Louis Pasteur, the idea of spontaneous generation was finally conclusively defeated. Pasteur repeated Spallanzani's experiments in a special flask with a curved neck, which allowed the free access of fresh air but not dust particles carrying germs. Heating the flask according to Spallanzani's method, Pasteur proved that microbial life flourished in instances of exposure to germ-carrying particles, but that samples within the flask could remain sterile and free of microbial growth when isolated.

organic matter is actually created. He began by investigating the processes by which certain species regenerate amputated body parts. After carefully observing how certain worms, salamanders, and frogs managed to regrow feet, limbs, jaws, and heads (as his experiments on more than seven hundred decapitated snails demonstrated), Spallanzani established the principle known as Spallanzani's law. This principle states that the degree of an organism's regenerative power exists in proportion to the organism's age, with a younger creature enjoying a greater capacity than an older one.

Spallanzani's interest in reproduction led him to experiments in which he explored the process of egg fertilization in mammals. He erroneously held to the ancient notion that an embryo preexisted in ova as a tiny yet complete version of the creature that would eventually grow to full size. He did gain enough understanding of the conception process, however, to bring about the first recorded animal birth (of a dog) as a result of artificial insemination.

Spallanzani also contributed greatly to an understanding of how digestion works. He attached strings to samples of food that he then fed to various animals. Withdrawing the sample, he recovered from animal digestive tracts samples enclosed in perforated containers, and in this way Spallanzani demonstrated that digestion is a chemical process. To show that human digestion, too, depended on the dissolving action of what he named "gastric juice," Spallanzani produced his own samples of such fluids for his experiments, repeatedly inducing himself to vomit on an empty stomach.

Spallanzani made important discoveries about other physiological processes as well. He was the first to establish the existence of connective tissues between veins and arteries in warm-blooded animals. He explained the role of heartbeats in creating arterial pressure and, thus, a pulse. He also studied the carbon dioxide and oxygen production of plants, the phosphorescent actions of fireflies and electric rays, the migratory patterns of swallows, and the ability of bats to navigate by echolocation.

Spallanzani did not limit his meticulous observations of the natural world to the animal kingdom. Throughout his career, he undertook numerous scientific expeditions throughout Europe to acquire geological, fossil, and animal specimens for his museum. Those expeditions gave Spallanzani occasion to speculate upon the many natural phenomena he witnessed. He wrote about the origins of mountain springs, the nature of waterspouts and whirlpools, and the physics underlying a stone's skipping across the surface of a lake.

In 1788, Spallanzani traveled to the Kingdom of the Two Sicilies (now Italy) during a period of lively geological activity in a quest to add to his museum's collection. His risky explorations of three volcanoes led to a new understanding of eruption dynamics. Although he inhaled toxic volcanic fumes in the process, Spallanzani was able to measure lava-flow rates, identify minerals and gases, and record observations that would lay the foundation for the science of volcanology.

Toward the end of his life, Spallanzani, a vigorous climber and hiker, began to experience health problems, including chronic bladder infections. He had just turned seventy when, on February 11, 1799, he died in Pavia after slipping in and out of a uremic coma. He is said to have willed his bladder to the university museum as an anatomical exhibit.

IMPACT

In a remarkable life that spanned much of the eighteenth century, Italian natural philosopher Lazzaro Spallanzani studied the world around him in a manner that presaged the modern scientific method. He applied his extraordinary powers of observation and rational analysis to phenomena in physics, geology, and meteorology, though he was primarily interested in biological questions. The discoveries he made about the digestive, circulatory, and reproductive processes would make lasting contributions to the field of medicine. Spallanzani is also considered a founder of the disciplines of microbiology and volcanology.

Although the chronology of Spallanzani's legacy belongs to the era of natural philosophy, his tendency to think outside of the constraints of traditional assumptions and his scrupulous experimental methods were ahead of his time. In his insistence on repeating experiments multiple times and his attention to variables, Spallanzani displayed an advanced scientific rigor. Evidence of the distinctly modern character of Spallanzani's method can be found in his many scientific insights, the validity and usefulness of which have survived into the present day.

Beverly Ballaro

FURTHER READING

Dinsmore, Charles E. "Animal Regeneration: From Fact to Concept." *BioScience* 45.7 (July/August 1995): 484–92. Print. Discusses key concepts regarding animal regeneration. Describes the research contributions of Abraham Trembley, Charles Bonnet, and Spallanzani.

Harris, Henry. *Things Come to Life: Spontaneous Generation Revisited*. New York: Oxford UP, 2002. Print. Reexamines the historical context and legacy of the theory of spontaneous generation, and the controversy surrounding its challenge in the seventeenth and eighteenth centuries.

Sutherland, Mary E. "Lazzaro Spallanzani." *Embryo Project Encyclopedia*. Arizona State Univ., 2007. Web. 10 July 2012. Biographical sketch of Lazzaro. Part of a larger project devoted to investigating the history of embryo research.

HANS SPEMANN

German biologist

In a career that spanned the late nineteenth and early twentieth century, German biologist Hans Spemann taught zoology and comparative anatomy for forty years and conducted influential research at several German universities. In the course of transplantation experiments, he was the first scientist to create a clone. Spemann received the Nobel Prize in Physiology or Medicine for his discovery of the principle of embryonic induction.

Born: June 27, 1869; Stuttgart, Germany
Died: September 9, 1941; Freiburg, Germany
Primary field: Biology
Specialties: Zoology; anatomy

EARLY LIFE

Hans Spemann was born on June 27, 1869 in Stuttgart, Germany. The son of prominent publisher Johann Wilhelm Spemann and his wife Lisinka Hoffman Spemann, he was raised in a wealthy family. After graduating from the local gymnasium, Hans worked for his father for one year and served a mandatory year of military service. Spemann then enrolled in a medical studies program at the University of Heidelberg, where he worked with anatomist Karl Gegenbaur, who inspired his interest in zoology. After earning his bachelor's degree in medicine in 1892, Spemann married Klara Binder. The couple had three sons and one daughter. Not long after his marriage,

Spemann enrolled at the University of Munich for additional clinical training and laboratory work.

In 1894, Spemann relocated to the University of Würzburg to begin teaching zoology, where he took graduate courses at the university's Zoological Institute under such professors as cytologist Theodor Boveri, physiologist and cell biologist Otto Bütschli, plant physiologist Julius Sachs, and physicist Wilhelm Röntgen, a Nobel laureate. In 1895, Spemann earned his PhD in anatomical studies with concentrations in zoology, botany, and physics. His dissertation focused on the cell lineage of nematodes. The following year, Spemann was stricken with tuberculosis.

LIFE'S WORK

Following his recovery, Spemann returned with new purpose to Würzburg to continue his duties as a lecturer. Shortly after the turn of the century, he began a period of intense laboratory research and experimentation on the embryos of salamanders, newts, and frogs, concentrating on the division and transplantation of the cells of fertilized eggs. He published his first paper related to his studies in 1901.

In 1908, Spemann became professor of zoology and comparative anatomy at the University of Rostock, one of the oldest and largest institutions of higher education in northern Europe. He continued his work experimenting with amphibian embryos, investigating embryological induction in the development of particular tissues.

Between 1914 and 1919, Spemann served as chair of the department of experimental embryology and developmental mechanics at the Kaiser Wilhelm Institute (KWI) for Biology. From 1915 to 1918, Spemann served as codirector of the institute with geneticist Carl Correns.

In 1919, Spemann moved to Freiburg, a city on the French border. As a zoology professor at the University of Freiburg, Spemann set up a Department of Embryology (later renamed the Spemann Graduate School of Biology and Medicine). At Freiburg, Spemann and his colleagues and students carried out numerous experiments in transplantation. The department attracted many students who would become well-known scientists in Germany or abroad, including embryologist Viktor Hamburger and biologist Johannes Holtfreter.

Spemann's doctoral student, Hilde Mangold, conducted work of particular importance. She carried out a series of experiments that Spemann designed, adroitly using microsurgery tools and techniques that Spemann pioneered. During 1921 and 1922, in support of her advanced degree, Mangold performed nearly five hundred transplanted grafts that demonstrated the "organizer effect" (later called embryonic induction), a key principle in the cell division of fertilized eggs. In 1924, Mangold and Spemann coauthored a paper entitled "Induction of Embryonic Primordia by Implantation of Organizers from Different Species."

The paper served as the primary basis for the awarding of the 1935 Nobel Prize in Physiology or Medicine to Spemann. Mangold died of injuries she sustained after a gasoline heater in her home exploded. The Nobel Prize committee does not give awards posthumously, and Mangold was never formally recognized for her contributions, though Spemann always fully credited her important work in public and in his papers.

Spemann retired from his teaching work soon after winning the Nobel Prize, the first embryologist so honored. In 1938, he published a book—*Embryonic Development and Induction*—detailing his earlier experiments. The book also discusses an experiment involving the replacement of one egg nucleus with another nucleus, a concept that laid the foundation for nuclear-transfer cloning in the early 1950s. Spemann died in 1941 at age seventy-two.

IMPACT

Throughout his career, Spemann was preoccupied with the practical and theoretical aspects of experimental embryology, which was a brand-new field of research when he began his career in the late nineteenth century.

Much of Spemann's work involved the manual division of the microscopic cells of fertilized eggs taken from such animals as newts, salamanders, and frogs in order to observe what happens when cells are split at various places and at different stages of development. To do so, Spemann had to invent the tools necessary to perform such experiments. He created needle-like knives from extruded glass to cut the embryos, and made miniscule pipettes to suck up fragments of cells. He also formed almost invisible glass rods with blunt ends to make small impressions in wax to hold embryos in place and built infinitesimal bridges made of glass to support delicate transplanted tissues. Always innovative, Spemann even used fine hairs from his infant daughter's head to make tiny loops and nooses with which to divide cells.

Spemann spent his entire career exploring the subject of cell development and evolution. In the process, he established many of the principles and techniques of modern embryology and set the stage for the science of cloning.

Jack Ewing

The Organizer Effect and Embryonic Induction

From the beginning of his scientific career, Hans Spemann was consumed with understanding the process of a living organism's development. All animals grow from a single fertilized cell that divides repeatedly, meanwhile evolving into cells with vastly different purposes. Spemann wondered how the cells of complicated creatures knew to organize into particular structures such as eyes, mouths, internal organs, skin, or limbs. What controlled such organization, and where was this control centered?

To answer such fundamental questions, Spemann performed numerous experiments that were significant in advancing the study of embryology and in increasing knowledge about evolution.

Like many scientists, Spemann began by imitating previous research to observe firsthand the results of his experiments. Beginning at the end of the nineteenth century, he duplicated the efforts of such researchers as zoologist Oscar Hertwig and physiologist Amadeo Herlitzka in exploring the germ plasm theory of evolutionary biologist August Weismann. Spemann at first experimented with newt eggs, using his daughter's baby-fine hair to divide individual fertilized cells. Some divisions produced two-headed newts, while others resulted in fully developed twins.

In later experiments, Spemann focused upon the development of eyes in frogs: he transplanted optical cells to the bellies of frogs—where the cells formed into a lens—only to discover that eyes also formed normally in the amphibian's head. Spemann called this remarkable result "double assurance" for the built-in multiple protections of an organism that provide several potential paths toward carrying out the hereditary task of successful development. Spemann's research helped spur later studies of regenerative biology, a process of renewal or restoration (such as the re-growth of a missing starfish arm or a gecko's lost tail) that can occur in many species, including humans.

In 1909, young American embryologist and cell biologist Ethel Nicholson Browne (later Mrs. Harvey) had conducted groundbreaking research on a small tubular freshwater animal with tentacles known as the hydra. She cut off a piece of tissue from a hydra's mouth, grafted it to another hydra, and watched as a new hydra grew to maturity at that spot.

From the mid-1910s onward, Spemann expanded upon Browne's studies. He used microsurgery to transplant the outer germ cell layer (known as the neuroectoderm) of an amphibian embryo in its early or gastrula stage to its belly skin. In test after test, the grafted tissue became indistinguishable from other belly skin: its hereditary function had changed to adapt to the new condition. This indicated that a cell's purpose is not always fixed in early developmental stages. However, transplants performed later in development retained their original form at the new site.

In an attempt to understand when the destiny of a cell was determined, Spemann devised a series of tests in the early 1920s for his talented student Hilde Pröscholdt Mangold to perform, using embryos from dark- and light-colored species of newts so that results could be easily seen. Mangold patiently repeated experiments, transplanting tissue from the top lip of the embryonic blastopore (mouth opening) of one species to the belly of the second species. The tests demonstrated that the new graft induced changes in the host embryo, causing it to organize its tissues at the transplantation site and to initiate the development of a second embryo, complete with brain, internal organs, and skin of a different color. Thanks to Mangold's painstaking work, Spemann had discovered the origin and operating principles of what he called the "organizer effect," now known as embryonic induction.

FURTHER READING

Rheinberger, Hans-Jörg. *An Epistemology of the Concrete: Twentieth-Century Histories of Life*. Durham: Duke UP Books, 2010. Print. Examines the lives, work, and ultimate impact of twentieth-century experimental biologists and life scientists, including Spemann.

Shubin, Neil. *Your Inner Fish: A Journey into the 3.5 Billion-Year History of the Human Body*. New York: Vintage, 2009. Print. Illustrated work incorporating Spemann's experiments in embryological development into an interesting discussion of animal evolution in general and human evolution in particular.

Slack, Jonathan M. W. *Essential Developmental Biology*. Hoboken: Wiley-Blackwell, 2005. Print. Explains the processes involved in the development of an embryo on molecular and cellular levels, from fertilization to maturity; contains many full-color drawings, a glossary, and a bibliography.

JOHANNES STARK

German physicist

Stark's detection of the Doppler effect in a terrestrially generated light source led to his discovery that a strong electric field will split the spectral lines of chemical elements. Stark's experiments provided confirmation of Albert Einstein's special theory of relativity and evidence for the controversial quantum theories of Max Planck.

Born: April 15, 1874; Schickenhof, Kingdom of
   Bavaria (now Germany)
Died: June 21, 1957; Traunstein, West Germany (now
   Germany)
Primary field: Physics
Specialty: Atomic and molecular physics

EARLY LIFE

Johannes Stark was born in the German town of Schickenhof. His father was a landed proprietor. The young Stark demonstrated early scholarly promise and eventually attended the gymnasiums (German secondary schools) of Bayreuth and Regensburg before entering the University of Munich in 1894. After studying chemistry, crystallography, mathematics, and physics courses for three years, he received his doctorate for a dissertation entitled "Untersuchung über Russ" (Investigations into lampblack, 1897). Stark successfully completed the state examinations required for teaching higher mathematics in 1897 and assumed the post of assistant to Eugen von Lommel of the Physical Institute at the University of Munich in October of that year. Shortly thereafter, he married Luise Uepler.

In 1900, Stark became a privatdozent (unpaid lecturer) at the University of Göttingen—the beginning of a tumultuous career in higher education that lasted until 1922. Stark did not work well with his coworkers or superiors, which led to frequent moves from one university to another. In 1906, he received an appointment at a technical institute in Hannover, where he aroused the dislike of his immediate superior, Julens Precht, who eventually had Stark transferred to Greifswald in 1907 and Aachen in 1909. In 1917, Stark returned to Greifswald as a full professor. Two years later, he took a similar position at the University of Würzburg, where he remained until 1922.

LIFE'S WORK

Stark's productive career spanned approximately the years 1902 to 1928. After 1920, he became increasingly involved in what might be called the racial politics of German science, a matter in which he had already become bitterly embroiled in earlier years.

Stark's first and most important published work, *Die Elektrizität in Gasen* (Electricity in gases, 1902), involved electrical conduction in gases. Stark's discoveries were based on the Doppler effect. As early as 1842, Austrian physicist Christian Johann Doppler predicted that a luminous object moving toward a stationary observer would appear to be a different color than the color the same object would appear to be if it were moving away from the observer. Doppler theorized that all stars emit neutral or white light and that their apparent colors are caused by their relative velocities toward or away from Earth.

It was not possible to detect the Doppler effect with any sources of light generated on Earth until the twentieth century, because no earthly light source could attain sufficient velocity. In his 1902 book, Stark correctly predicted that the Doppler effect might be observed in canal rays. German physicist Eugen Goldstein discovered in 1886 that by placing the cathode in a cathode ray tube so that it divided the tube into two equal parts, and by piercing the cathode with a number of holes, one could observe many brightly colored rays traveling in straight lines and entering the space behind the cathode through the holes. Goldstein named these rays *Kanalstrahlen*, or canal rays.

A number of twentieth-century physicists investigated canal rays, but it fell to Stark to demonstrate the Doppler effect in canal rays in an ingenious experiment that revealed the effect in the hydrogen lines. Stark proposed his experiment as proof of Albert Einstein's 1906 theory of special relativity. Stark had founded, in 1904, the *Jahrbuch der Radioaktivität und Elektronik* (Yearbook of radioactivity and electronics), a scientific journal that he edited until 1913. In 1907, he became the first editor to request an article from Einstein concerning relativity. In 1907, he even proposed that his experiments furnished proof of Max Planck's quantum theories.

He remained a champion of relativity and quantum theory until 1913, when his animosity toward Jews increased due to personal rivalries and professional jealousy; he then denounced quantum theory and the special theory of relativity and held to his criticism of these theories until his death. Despite his racism, Stark was

Stark Reveals the Effects of Electricity on Light Spectra

Johannes Stark's affiliation with the Third Reich places an inconvenient burden on his place in the history of physics. Nevertheless, as a young researcher at the University of Göttingen, Stark made important discoveries in the field of atomic physics, particularly in his discovery of what later came to be known as the Stark effect.

Physicists of the time understood that molecular fields made up of disproportionate levels of electrons would have varying energy rates, depending on whether their imbalance occurred to the right or left of an electric field. It was also established that electric fields pull certain facets of molecules in equally opposing directions. But by applying an external electronic field and splitting this spectrum, Stark proved that light could be polarized, perpendicular to a preestablished spectrum. He noted that this is the result of the interaction between charged particles and hybrid orbitals present within electric fields. Using canal rays, he observed that the Doppler effect that applies to light applies to atoms as well. The discovery netted Stark the Nobel Prize for Physics in 1919, over a decade before the emergence of the Third Reich.

While Stark sabotaged his own reputation and scientific career by aligning with the new Nazi regime in Germany, his work was documented extensively and thus was able to be continued by future generations of physicists after the war. Later studies reexamined the Stark effect and led to the investigation of the effects of external electric fields on light absorption. These efforts would set the groundwork for what would become known as the quantum-confined Stark effect, or QCSE—effects to the optical spectrum in quantum wells caused by external electrical fields.

The Stark effect and the experiments it influenced were crucial to physicists in their development of such technologies as semiconductors, which are the basis for modern electronics and span a wide variety of industries, from defense, medicine, manufacturing, and computing, to communications and information technology. Knowledge of the Stark effect has also been crucial for the development and widespread implementation of fiber-optic communication and applications. These systems permit the transmission of both light and data communication across great distances. Fiber-optic applications have been widely utilized in contemporary sensory systems and laser technology.

accorded many honors. He was awarded the Baumgartner Prize by the Vienna Academy of Sciences in 1910, and in 1914 he won both the Vahlbruch Prize of the Göttingen Academy of Sciences and the Matteucci Medal of the Rome Academy. In 1919, he was honored with the Nobel Prize in Physics. Of all the recipients of the Nobel Prize, Stark was undoubtedly the most ignored by the world media and the international scientific community. In 1922, he resigned his university post in protest of what he perceived to be the growing Jewish dominance of German academic life and retired to pursue private research.

His last important scientific work, *Atomstruktur und Atombindung* (Atomic structure and atomic bonding), appeared in 1928. The book confirmed the anti-Semitic stand that had made him unpopular with many of his colleagues and had forced his retirement. Stark would almost certainly have remained in an obscure retirement after 1922 had circumstances not brought Adolf Hitler to power in 1933.

The Nazis brought Stark out of retirement and appointed him president of the Physikalisch-Technische Reichsanstalt (Physical-Technical Institute) on April 1, 1933. This position gave him considerable influence over appointments to academic positions in German universities and over the allocation of research funds. His enemies within the academy nevertheless prevented his election as president of the German Physics Association that year and prevented his gaining membership in the prestigious Prussian Academy the next. In June 1934, however, the Nazis appointed Stark president of the German Research Association. His two presidencies and the concurrent passage of the Nuremberg Laws allowed Stark to exercise enormous influence on the course of physics research and teaching in Germany. The Nuremberg Laws established that only "Aryans" were citizens of the Reich, and that a noncitizen could not hold a government post. Since professors were government employees, the laws gave Stark legal authority to purge the German universities of most Jewish professors. A few "non-Aryans" were able to keep their jobs, because of stipulations in the laws that noncitizen government employees who served honorably during World War I or whose fathers had died in that war could retain their posts.

After the outbreak of widespread anti-Semitic violence in Germany on the *Kristallnacht* in 1938, Stark was able to retire the remaining Jewish professors, supposedly for their own protection. He was never able to remove all of his opponents from their positions, but he did much to prevent the acceptance of theories presented by Jewish scientists.

Several influential German physicists were so opposed to Stark's attacks against other scientists that Stark was obliged to retire from public life in 1939. In 1947, Stark stood trial before a Denazification court for his activities in the Third Reich and his attacks on Jewish academics. The court found him guilty and sentenced him to four years in a labor camp. Stark served the entire term despite his advanced years. He died in Traunstein on June 21, 1957.

IMPACT

Stark's scientific accomplishments have been overshadowed by the ignominy of his affiliation with the Nazi government. During his early years, he exerted a considerable and positive influence on physics, although later in his life his influence was far greater and far more negative. From 1900 to 1913, he was still in the vanguard of the new physics. His championing of the theories of Einstein, Planck, and others was important to their international acceptance. His own experiments did much to validate the theoretical work of those who laid the foundations of modern physics. Even though the Stark effect is considered of comparatively little practical value by modern physicists in the analyses of complex spectra or atomic structure, it still represents a milestone in atomic research.

Unfortunately, Stark is best remembered not for his scientific accomplishments but rather for his political activities. He will be remembered most vividly as a victim of the ideology that swept his country and the world into tragedy.

Paul Madden

FURTHER READING

Hoffman, Dieter. "Between Autonomy and Accommodation: The German Physical Society during the Third Reich." *Physics in Perspective* 7.3 (Sept. 2005): 293–329. Print. Sketches the history of the German Physical Society from its founding in 1845 through the 1930s. Reviews the influence of Nazism on the society.

---, and Mark Walker. "The German Physical Society under National Socialism." *Physics Today* 57.12 (Dec. 2004): 52–8. Print. Offers a history of the society, including Stark's role in the organization during Hitler's regime.

Matteo, Leone, Alessandro Paoletti, and Nadia Robotti. "A Simultaneous Discovery: The Case of Johannes Stark and Antonio Lo Surdo." *Physics in Perspective* 6.3 (Sept. 2004): 271–94. Print. Describes how both scientists simultaneously discovered that hydrogen spectral lines split into components by an external electric field. A technical article, best for advanced students.

ERNEST HENRY STARLING

British physiologist

Starling discovered the mechanisms that regulate the output of the heart and the flow of lymphatic fluid and discovered the role of hormones in the control of organ function.

Born: April 17, 1866; London, England
Died: May 2, 1927; near Kingston Harbor, Jamaica
Primary field: Biology
Specialty: Physiology

EARLY LIFE

Ernest Henry Starling was born in London and was reared there by his mother and a Canadian governess. His father was the Clerk of the Crown in Bombay, India, and returned to Great Britain on leave only once every three years. Despite the infrequent contact between father and son, the elder Starling is said to have influenced his son toward a career in medicine. Starling's choice of a career in physiology was an extremely unlikely one in the educational setting of late nineteenth-century Great Britain. Education for everyone up to the age of ten became compulsory in 1876; any training beyond that age was mainly in the classics, with little emphasis on modern languages and even less on natural science. At age thirteen, he enrolled in King's College School and studied divinity, Greek, Latin, French, ancient history, English, and mathematics. He distinguished himself in university entrance examinations and entered Guy's Hospital Medical School in 1882.

Starling's outstanding examination scores set him apart from his classmates and brought him to the attention of Leonard Charles Wooldridge, the demonstrator in physiology and later physician in chief at the hospital. Wooldridge introduced Starling to German experimental physiology and arranged for his protégé to spend a summer in Heidelberg studying under Wilhelm Kühne. The exciting discoveries of the German physiologists persuaded Starling to concentrate on physiology rather than opt for a medical practice. At the end of his clinical training in 1889, Starling accepted Wooldridge's former position as demonstrator and began to lay the groundwork for modern cardiovascular physiology. Several years later, Starling joined William Maddock Bayliss at University College. It would prove to be a fruitful partnership. Starling was a forceful visionary, innovative and impatient, while Bayliss was deliberate, cautious, methodical, and kind. Together they would collaborate on some of the most important discoveries in the field of physiology.

LIFE'S WORK

Starling's first publication with Bayliss, written while he was still at Guy's Hospital, described the earliest successful attempt to record a mammalian electrocardiogram and showed that contraction began at the base of the heart and proceeded to the apex. This study disproved the then-accepted hypothesis that all parts of the heart contracted simultaneously.

Starling next became interested in the formation of lymphatic fluid and the physical processes of secretion and absorption of this fluid in the cavities of the body. After four years of work with Bayliss, Starling showed that pressure inside a capillary determined the rate at which lymph seeped into the tissues, and that protein colloid determined the reabsorption of the lymphatic fluid from the tissues back into the capillary by osmotic pressure. Once this theory was established, Starling developed a model for heart failure in which the failing heart, unable to maintain arterial and capillary pressure, allows lymphatic fluid to enter the circulation under the influence of unopposed osmotic pressures. This model accounted for the dilated heart associated with heart failure, and Starling studied the significance of this dilation in his later work.

In 1897, a new physiology laboratory opened at Guy's Hospital, but these new facilities were not sufficient inducements for Starling to leave University College; in 1899, Starling accepted the Jodrell Chair of Physiology at University College. In the same year, he was elected a Fellow of the Royal Society, at the age of thirty-three.

Starling and Bayliss next worked on intestinal function and in 1902 concentrated on pancreatic secretion. Injecting acid into a segment of jejunum (the middle part of the small intestine), completely isolated except for its blood supply, resulted in copious pancreatic secretion. In the absence of any other connection between jejunum and pancreas, the unknown messenger had to be carried through the blood; the chemical messenger was named secretin. To describe such chemical messengers, Starling coined the word *hormone* in 1905. He noted that the pancreas produced a hormone that regulated the ability of tissue cells to utilize glucose.

As chair of physiology, Starling undertook very little active research between 1904 and 1909. Instead, during this time he successfully sought funding for a new physiology building at University College and took elocution lessons to improve his public speaking, for he was frequently called to address large audiences. Starling was now in a position to modify the empirical, practical nature of British medical education. In 1903, his idea of a curriculum emphasizing basic science and a medical school with its own hospital for teaching and research was published in the *British Medical Journal*.

This publication marked Starling's appearance as a thinker outside the laboratory, and in this role he became an effective public opponent of the antivivisection movement a few years later. In 1903, Stephen Coleridge, the leader of the antivivisectionists, publicly accused Starling and Bayliss of dissecting a dog without first anesthetizing it, a criminal offense. Bayliss failed to obtain a retraction from Coleridge and filed suit against him. As the dog had indeed been anesthetized, the jury awarded two thousand pounds and costs to Bayliss. This award was used to set up a research fund at University College.

As a result of these agitations, in 1906 Parliament set up a royal commission to investigate Coleridge's criticisms of the 1876 act; Starling chaired a committee to select witnesses from the scientific community on behalf of scientific investigation. Starling himself testified before the commission. As a result of Starling's efforts, the commission almost completely rejected the charges of the antivivisectionists.

Starling's second great productive period, leading to his formulation of the "law of the heart," began in 1911. World War I interrupted this work, however. Starling served in the Royal Army Medical Corps after being dissuaded from enlisting as an infantryman. In 1917, he resigned his commission and returned to London.

The Frank-Starling Law of the Heart

In 1911, Ernest Henry Starling sought to identify the mechanism that controls cardiac function. Starling and his associates used an isolated heart-lung preparation. They showed that within certain limits the output of the isolated heart is independent of arterial resistance and proportional to venous inflow. In 1914, Starling demonstrated that beyond these limits cardiac output falls, despite further increases in venous inflow to the heart. His first plots of ventricular function curves appeared in 1914. These discoveries were made at a time when many doubted that cardiac output rose during exercise, and when no one had thought of focusing on venous inflow as the prime determinant of the output of the heart.

In 1918, using information recorded by Italian physiologist Dario Maestrini several years earlier, Starling accurately theorized that the length of cardiac muscle fibers in the heart directly controls its transition from resting to active states. He came to understand that the elastic properties of the cardiac muscle were essential in providing a balance between the amount of blood traveling to the heart and the amount of blood exiting the heart. The law of the heart states that the more the elastic cardiac tissue is stretched, the farther back it retreats—similar to the behavior of a simple elastic band. This relationship is essential in examining how the heart operates. Starling observed that three factors contribute to the amount of stretch contained in the elastic tissue of the heart. The most significant factor is the amount of blood left in the cardiac ventricles (one of the heart's two chambers that collects and releases blood to the body) directly after they contract and relax. The more blood there is for the heart to pump, the more powerful the ventricular contraction, and therefore, the more broad the stretch of the muscle fibers. The next contributing factor is the amount of time it takes for blood to fill the ventricular chamber. If the heart is beating quickly, there exists a less substantial filling time, and as a result, a less extensive stretching of the cardiac muscles. The last factor relates to the venous return, the flow of blood back to the heart from other areas of the body. The rate of the return of blood to the heart should be commensurate with the heart's filling time in order for the heart to function properly.

The law of the heart is named after Starling as well as German physiologist Otto Frank, who had also researched heart contractions. Frank conducted his research independently and well before Starling's investigation, but both are given credit for the discovery of the law.

Starling left his professorship at University College in 1922 and became the Fullerton Research Professor of the Royal Society. At this time a new anatomy building and an extension to the physiology department were built at University College, and he saw his efforts to develop the medical school move closer to fruition.

In the next two years, Starling worked on renal function, showing that the glomerulus (a network of capillaries in the kidney) is in fact a simple filter and that the renal tubule actively secretes some substances into the urine while reabsorbing others. Discouraged about his health, in 1927 Starling took a cruise to the West Indies and died unexpectedly onboard ship near Kingston, Jamaica.

IMPACT

Ernest Henry Starling was responsible for numerous important physiological discoveries, including the Starling equation (regarding the way fluids move within the human body), peristalsis (the contraction of smooth muscles in the body), hormones, and many others. The law of the heart is perhaps Starling's greatest contribution to clinical medicine, for it dictates the principles of the diagnosis and treatment of heart failure.

Moreover, he criticized a system and a society in which ignorance was prized, amateurism valued, muddling through was a virtue, and practical knowledge of the natural world was denigrated. His life's work was a forceful statement of the opposite principle, for, based on reason and knowledge of natural phenomena, he made discoveries that were to prevent or relieve immeasurable human suffering.

James A. Cowan

FURTHER READING

Chapman, Carleton B. "Ernest Henry Starling: The Clinician's Physiologist." *Annals of Internal Medicine* 57. 2 (1962): 1–43. Print. An account of Starling's life that sets his accomplishments against the background of early twentieth-century British society. Clearly describes the details of experiments, and includes a complete chronological annotated bibliography.

"Ernest Henry Starling (1866–1927): The Clinician's Physiologist." *Journal of the American Medical Association* 214 (1970): 1699–1701. Print. An overview of Starling's life and work, including a brief section on his impact on medical education.

Fye, W. Bruce. "Ernest Henry Starling: His Law and Its Growing Significance in the Practice of Medicine."

Circulation 68 (1983): 1145–47. Print. Shows how Starling's basic scientific discoveries have become increasingly important to clinical medicine.

Henderson, John. *A Life of Ernest Starling*. New York: Oxford UP, 2005. Print. A biography exploring the personal, clinical, and political aspects of Starling's life, as well as his scientific discoveries.

NICOLAUS STENO

Danish anatomist and geologist

Considered by many to be the founder of geology, Nicolaus Steno provided scientific explanations for the existence of fossils, stratification, and the constancy of crystal angles. As an anatomist, he made important discoveries regarding glands, muscles, the heart, and the brain.

Born: January 11, 1638; Copenhagen, Denmark
Died: December 5, 1686; Schwerin, Holy Roman Empire (now in Germany)
Also known as: Niccolo Stenone; Nicholas Stenonis; Nicolas Stenon; Niels Steensen; Niels Stensen
Primary fields: Earth sciences; biology
Specialties: Geology; anatomy; paleontology

EARLY LIFE

While the Thirty Years' War (1618–48) was convulsing Europe, Niels Stensen, who later latinized his name to Nicolaus Steno, was born on the first day of 1638 according to the Julian calendar, though it was January 11 according to the Catholic Gregorian calendar. His Lutheran father, Sten Pedersen, was a successful goldsmith who counted the king as one of his customers. His mother, Anne Nielsdatter, had, like her husband, been previously married and widowed.

Because of a severe illness, Steno was homebound until he was six years old. His full recovery was followed by the sudden death of his father. His mother remarried, but her new husband died within a year, and Steno's half sister and her husband took over his care. He attended a Lutheran academy, where he was taught Latin and chemistry.

Steno pursued his education at a difficult time in Denmark. When he was sixteen, a plague caused the deaths of one-third of Copenhagen's population, and throughout most of his time at the University of Copenhagen, the city was under siege by the Swedes.

Nevertheless, the young medical student was able to learn anatomy from Thomas Bartholin and absorb the new ideas of such scientists as Galileo and René Descartes. Because of the chaotic situation in Copenhagen, however, Steno was unable to get his degree. In the fall of 1659, carrying a letter of introduction from Bartholin, he traveled throughout Germany for several months before arriving in Amsterdam in the Dutch Republic in spring of 1660. Here, and then three months later in Leiden, he continued his medical education and began his research.

LIFE'S WORK

In Amsterdam, while studying with the anatomist Gerhard Blasius, Steno made his first important discovery. While dissecting a sheep's head, he found an oral cavity that proved to be a source of saliva. This duct of the parotid gland became known as Steno's duct or Stensen's duct (*ductus stenonianus*). After Steno matriculated into the University of Leiden, he performed other dissections, some of which resulted in new discoveries. One such discovery was the tear-producing glands of the eyes. In 1663, he published *Nova musculorum & cordis fabrica* (*New Structure of the Muscles and Heart*, 1994), based on his finding that the heart is a muscle, which contradicted ancient authorities who saw the heart as the "home of the soul." The following year, he published a book summarizing his anatomical experiments on glands, *De musculis et glandulis observationum specimen* (Specimen of observations on muscles and glands).

The death of Steno's stepfather in 1663 occasioned his return to Copenhagen, but when he was denied a position at the university, he left for Paris. In 1664, still in Paris, he received his medical degree in absentia from the University of Leiden. Melchisedec Thévenot, a wealthy government official, supported Steno's work

Nicolaus Steno Introduces the Principles of Stratigraphy

In his 1669 work, *Prodromus to a Dissertation Concerning Solids Naturally Contained within Solids*, Nicolaus Steno, sometimes called the "father of stratigraphy," describes three of the fundamental principles of what became the science of stratigraphy. Stratigraphy is a branch of geology that deals with sedimentary and layered volcanic rocks, specifically their formation, layering, and relationships to each other.

In addition to discussing organic remains preserved in sedimentary layers of rock, *Prodromus* also provides a theoretical basis for the nascent field of stratigraphy. First, Steno reiterates his principle of superposition, which states that lower strata in the geologic column are older than upper strata, barring extensive deformation from structural causes. This principle rests on the assumption that all sedimentary rocks and minerals were once sediment grains suspended in water, and therefore fluid. During the deposition of lower layers, sediment that would later form upper layers would thus still be in fluid form.

Steno then introduces the principles of original horizontality and lateral continuity. Original horizontality means that strata are originally deposited horizontally due to the force of gravity. While there are some exceptions—strata may occasionally be deposited on a slight gradient, or drape over a textured surface—this principle is generally accurate and useful for many types of geological analysis. Assuming that most strata were originally deposited horizontally allows for structural analysis of deformations such as folded anticlines and synclines or tilted strata.

The second principle, that of lateral continuity, states that a stratum originates as a single continuous layer that extends in all directions until limited by factors such as the depositional basin and sediment type. Layers may thin out at the edges due to lesser sediment availability. Thus, similar rocks separated by a topographic feature such as a valley, or even an ocean, can be assumed to have been originally continuous. This principle is useful for interpretation of structural features such as faults, where previously continuous layers become discontinuous, and also for global-scale analysis of continental movements. One line of evidence used in the early twentieth century by Alfred Wegener in developing his hypothesis of continental drift, which eventually became the theory of plate tectonics, was that margins of different continents have extremely similar strata containing similar species of fossils.

Steno recognized that certain geological events could create apparent geological exceptions to his principles, including cave formation and collapse, as well as uplift. Later geologists came to recognize that although events such as folding, faulting, tilting, and intrusive magmatic activity can cause anomalies in the stratigraphic record, they leave evidence in the layers that allows for interpretation of the geologic history. Stratigraphy forms a necessary foundation for the science of geology and understanding of the Earth's history, and it also has crucial economic applications in fields such as oil and natural gas exploration and exploitation.

on muscles and the brain. An invitation to become court physician to the grand duke Ferdinand II de' Medici in Florence, Tuscany (now in Italy), led him away from France in 1665.

For his first two years in Florence, Steno worked at the Hospital of Santa Maria Novella on muscles, brain anatomy, and embryology. Using a microscope, he observed muscles as bundles of geometric units, each subdivided into fibrils. In 1667, he published a book called *Elementorum myologiae specimen* (*Specimen of Elements of Myology*, 1994) on his geometric description of muscles, explaining muscle contraction as an aggregation of the tensile forces in each unit.

It was also during this time in Italy that Steno converted from Lutheranism to Catholicism. In 1669, he

published his discourse on the anatomy of the brain, in which he criticized René Descartes's writings on the nature of humanity and the soul. For example, Descartes believed the soul to be connected to the body through the pineal gland in the brain, but Steno pointed out that animals other than humans have pineal glands. During the late 1660s, he also conducted embryological research, helping to establish that females of viviparous, as well as oviparous, species produce eggs. His discoveries in embryology were published in the 1670s.

Many scholars consider Steno's work in geology, paleontology, and crystallography to be his most significant. His studies in geology and paleontology began in the fall of 1667 when he dissected the head of a great white shark that had been clubbed to death on the coast of Leghorn (Livorno) in Tuscany. Steno was particularly impressed by the number and structure of the shark's teeth. In his report to Duke Ferdinand, he noted the similarities between the shark's teeth and the "tongue stones" (*glossopetrae*) common in Tuscany and elsewhere. He proposed that these tongue stones were fossilized shark's teeth. This piqued his curiosity about other fossils, such as seashells found on mountains, and for the next eighteen months he traveled throughout Tuscany, making observations of rock layers, collecting fossils, and visiting quarries, caves, mines, and private geological collections.

The result of Steno's studies was his greatest work, *De solido intra solidum naturaliter contento dissertationis prodromus* (1669; *The Prodromus to a Dissertation Concerning Solids Naturally Contained within Solids*, 1671), better known as the *Prodromus*. The book was meant to be the prelude to a much larger geological treatise, which he never wrote; still, the observations, ideas, and theories it contained were important breakthroughs, including the first modern form of paleontology, the first description of the Earth's geology as one that changes over time, the founding principles of a new branch of geology called stratigraphy, and a section on crystallography.

While Steno was writing the *Prodromus*, he received an invitation from the Danish king, Frederick III, to serve in his court. Before reaching Copenhagen, however, he learned that the king had died. He also received word that his patron, Ferdinand, was gravely ill, and by the time he returned to Florence, the grand duke was dead. The new grand duke, Cosimo III de' Medici, was more interested in religion than science, but because he admired Steno's piety, he gave him a villa on the Arno River in which to pursue his geological studies.

Two years after his return to Florence, Steno's geological research was once again interrupted by a summons to Denmark, which Steno reluctantly accepted. In the winter of 1673 in Copenhagen, he gave his final public lecture on science before returning to Italy to become a priest. He later became a bishop in Hanover, from where he served Catholics in Germany, Denmark, and Norway.

When the Catholic duke Friedrich died and was succeeded by his Lutheran brother, Ernst August, Steno moved to Munster, where he instituted many reforms. His high standards created enemies, however, so he moved to Hamburg, where his extreme asceticism and emphasis on poverty drew criticism as well as admiration. After two years in Hamburg, Steno spent the remainder of his life in Schwerin, about seventy-five miles east. His harsh ascetic practices weakened his failing health, and he died on the morning of December 5, 1686, after his final confession. Following Steno's death, Cosimo III had his remains transferred to Florence, where they were laid to rest in San Lorenzo Basilica.

Impact

Historians of medicine have praised Steno's skills as an anatomist, but his most important achievements were in geology. Steno's principles of original horizontality and superposition marked the beginning of stratigraphy, while his recognition of fossils as remnants of ancient organisms helped elucidate the history of fossil-bearing rocks.

Critics have pointed out that despite introducing the chronological study of the Earth's history, Steno had a weak understanding of the massive length of geological time. Because he was influenced by the prevailing theological analysis of biblical chronology, Steno thought that the world was only several thousand years old. However, unlike Galileo, he did not suffer persecution for his scientific ideas, and church censors found nothing problematic with his *Prodromus*. He himself saw no contradiction between his scientific and religious work.

Robert J. Paradowski

Further Reading

Cutler, Alan. *The Seashell on the Mountaintop: How Nicolaus Steno Solved an Ancient Mystery and Created a Science of the Earth*. New York: Penguin, 2004. Print. Includes a biography of Steno and an analysis of his contributions to geology. Illustrations, index.

Kermit, Hans. *Niels Stensen, 1638–1686: The Scientist Who Was Beatified*. Leominster: Gracewing, 2003. Print. Presents a biography of Steno as a religious leader. Illustrations, bibliography, index.

Kuznetsov, V. "Nicolaus Steno and Sessions of the International Geological Congress." *Lithology and Mineral Resources* 40.5 (2005): 483–86. Print. Discusses Steno's contributions to geology during the late 1600s and the implications for lithology.

Miniati, Stefano. *Nicholas Steno's Challenge for Truth: Reconciling Science and Faith*. Milan: Franco Angeli, 2009. Print. Analyzes the interactions between Steno's scientific and religious pursuits as they influenced his spiritual evolution.

Oldroyd, David R. *Thinking about the Earth: A History of Ideas in Geology*. Cambridge: Harvard UP, 1996. Print. A comprehensive overview of the history of Earth sciences that analyzes Steno's work as a significant part of this history.

YELLAPRAGADA SUBBAROW

Indian biochemist

During the 1930s, Yellapragada SubbaRow determined the roles of phosphocreatine and adenosine triphosphate as the energy "currency" in cells. Later, he helped explain the role of the vitamin folic acid in cell metabolism. He and pathologist Sidney Farber devised a way to apply the folic acid antagonist methotrexate in the treatment of cancer.

Born: January 12, 1895; Bhimavaram, India
Died: August 9, 1948; Pearl River, New York
Also known as: Yellapragada Subbarao
Primary field: Biochemistry
Specialties: Biochemistry; chemistry

EARLY LIFE

Yellapragada SubbaRow was born January 12, 1895, the fourth of seven children to Jagannadham and Venkamma SubbaRow, in Bhimavaram in the West Godavari district of Andhra Pradesh in what was then British India. His father, a member of the sect of Niyogi Brahmins, had served with the government as a member of the revenue service until forced to retire because of illness. As a result, the SubbaRow household was poor.

At the age of fourteen, SubbaRow ran away from home, but was returned by men sent to look for him by his mother. Following the death of his father, SubbaRow completed his secondary education at the Hindu High School in Madras. After twice failing the entrance examinations, he enrolled at Madras Presidency College.

As a college student, SubbaRow was undecided about his career direction. During this era, Mahatma Gandhi was protesting the British presence in India, calling for a boycott of British goods. In solidarity with the movement speaking out against British rule in India, SubbaRow began wearing only traditional khadi dress, and entered the Ramakrishna Mission, a service organization. SubbaRow's colleagues at the mission encouraged him to enroll in Madras Medical College. SubbaRow decided that the practice of medicine was a good way to serve humanity.

After enrolling in medical school, SubbaRow also married Seshagiri Rao, who grandfather had offered to help fund his work in medical school. SubbaRow planned to continue his studies at the Harvard School of Tropical Medicine, financed by a scholarship established by his older brother Purushottam.

After the deaths of two of his brothers from the tropical disease sprue, he opted instead to become a lecturer in physiology at Ayurvedic College in Madras. Having acquired funding help from his father-in-law, SubbaRow enrolled at Harvard Medical School in the fall of 1923.

LIFE'S WORK

After arriving in Boston, SubbaRow took a job as a custodian at Peter Bent Brigham Hospital. As a medical student, he began learning research techniques in tropical medicine. Completing the program in June 1924, SubbaRow joined Harvard's Department of Biochemistry, where he began working with biochemist Cyrus Fiske. Their first project involved the development of a procedure for measuring the level of phosphorus in a solution. At this time, most chemical quantization consisted of the application of a method of chemical analysis called colorimetry. Otto Folin, chair of the Department of Biochemistry, had developed such methods for measurement of proteins or sugars in solution. SubbaRow and Fiske developed a similar method for analysis of phosphorus. By December of 1924, they had refined the procedure enough to be able to present it to the American Society of Biological Chemists. The Fiske-SubbaRow method was subsequently included in biochemistry textbooks, and SubbaRow and his colleagues used it to explain a part of sugar metabolism: the mechanism by which energy is produced during the conversion of glycogen to lactic acid. The work ultimately led to the discovery of phosphocreatine and adenosine triphosphate (ATP) as sources of energy for muscle.

As an alien working at Harvard during the Depression years, SubbaRow's chances for promotion were limited. Nonetheless, he continued his research, working on isolating extracts from liver that could be used to treat pernicious anemia. Credit for discovering the role played by vitamin B_{12} subsequently went to medical researchers George Minot and William Murphy, though at least one pharmaceutical company, Lederle Laboratories in Pearl River, New York, was aware of SubbaRow's contributions. Harvard recognized SubbaRow's work by promoting him to associate professor.

In May 1940, SubbaRow joined Lederle as associate director of research, overseeing the development of vitamins and antibacterial compounds such as penicillin. The first antibiotic that SubbaRow's unit discovered was aureomycin, the first of the tetracycline-like class of antibiotics. SubbaRow also began an investigation into the cause of tropical sprue, the disease that had killed his two brothers. He discovered that a newly recognized vitamin, folic acid, was effective in reversing certain forms of the disease, and he developed procedures for large-scale synthesis of the vitamin. The synthesis of folic acid came to the attention of Dr. Sidney Farber at Children's Hospital in Boston, who theorized that the vitamin might be of use in treating certain forms of leukemia. Farber's idea proved wrong; folic acid actually increased the rate at which leukemic cells proliferated. However, SubbaRow and his colleagues had also synthesized modified forms of folic acid—folic acid analogs—which did prove effective in treating leukemia. One of these, methotrexate, became a standard method of treatment in an antileukemic "cocktail."

SubbaRow died on August 9, 1948. He was fifty-five years old.

IMPACT

SubbaRow's research improved understanding of the role played by phosphocreatine and ATP as sources of energy within muscle tissue. The Fiske-SubbaRow

---

SubbaRow Develops Folic Acid Analog as Treatment for Leukemia

Cancer in general, and leukemia in particular, were considered largely incurable into the 1940s, and treatment, at least for solid tumors, consisted primarily of surgery. However, the discovery that nitrogen mustard, originally developed as a means for gas warfare during World War I, could suppress growth of lymphatic and other bone-marrow-derived cells, presented new research opportunities to scientists. In 1942, pharmacologist Alfred Gilman and physician Louis Goodman observed that treatment of lymphomas with mustard derivatives produced short-term regression of certain lymphomas, opening a door for application of chemotherapy in treatment of cancers.

In a fortuitous manner, Yellapragada SubbaRow was able to apply the same concept of chemotherapy to treatment of leukemia. Lucy Wills, an English physician, and George Minot, a 1934 Nobel laureate, discovered that the vitamin folic acid contributed to maturation of bone marrow cells. Sidney Farber, a physician at Boston's Children's Hospital, tested the effect of folic acid on children with leukemia. He observed that rather than treating the disease, folic acid actually enhanced the growth of leukemic cells. Farber reasoned that if folic acid enhanced the growth of cells, a folic acid antagonist might have the opposite effect, inhibiting leukemic cell growth.

Working with Brian Hutchings and Doris Seeger at Lederle Laboratories, SubbaRow began testing various methods of synthetically producing folic acid. They discovered that growing yeast under fermentative conditions produced a slight variation in the structure of folic acid. Preliminary trials of the substance, termed teropterin, showed it was capable of causing regression in certain cases of breast cancer. Farber hoped to test the effects of teropterin on leukemia in children. During the summer of 1947, Farber and Richard Lewisohn tested teropterin on a number of children with leukemia as well as at least one adult with an extensive case of throat and nasal cancer: George Herman "Babe" Ruth. The drug provided some evidence for short-term remission and regression of the cancers, but fell far short of a cure. But Lewisohn was sufficiently satisfied with the results of treatment on Ruth's tumor that he presented the work at the International Cancer Research Congress in St. Louis that September. Nevertheless, Ruth's cancer continued to progress, and the baseball great died the following August.

Farber was satisfied that the principle underlying folic acid antagonists was sound, and requested SubbaRow continue to synthesize other forms of antifolate drugs. In December 1947 SubbaRow and Dr. Harriet Kiltie provided Farber with a newer version of a folic acid antagonist, aminopterin. Aminopterin proved more effective than teropterin, producing remission that lasted several months in leukemic children. However, the drug was significantly more toxic, which rendered its long term use problematic. SubbaRow continued to synthesize other modified forms of folic acid antagonists, and in 1948 developed methotrexate (amethopterin), an aminopterin derivative. The drug proved significantly more effective than aminopterin, and exhibited little of the toxicity associated with the precursor drug. Methotrexate has continued into the twenty-first century as one of many forms of chemotherapy for cancers and leukemias, as well as a treatment for certain autoimmune diseases.

method of phosphorus estimation became the standard colorimetric method of analysis for generations of biochemists. SubbaRow's application of this procedure was critical. While investigating the process by which muscle glycogen was converted to lactic acid, Fiske and SubbaRow discovered the presence of the intermediate phosphocreatine. Further analysis demonstrated that hydrolysis of phosphocreatine released a phosphate molecule that in turn became linked to adenosine, ultimately creating the "energy currency" used by muscles and cells in general, ATP. While it would remain for another generation of scientists to explain precisely how ATP was used, SubbaRow's discovery laid the groundwork for those future studies.

SubbaRow's other major contribution during his tenure at Lederle was his development of the first effective drugs for treatment of certain forms of childhood leukemia. The first of the antileukemic drugs, the folic acid antagonist teropterin, proved to exhibit only limited success, despite the publicity associated with its brief effectiveness in treating baseball great Babe Ruth. However, the derivatives aminopterin and amethopterin (methotrexate) proved more effective in treating

a variety of cancers. SubbaRow's relatively early death came as a shock to his colleagues. Nevertheless, his role in the development of the first generation of chemotherapeutic drugs contributed to the belief that cancer could one day be cured.

Richard Adler

FURTHER READING

Mukherjee, Siddhartha. *The Emperor of All Maladies: A Biography of Cancer*. New York: Simon, 2010. Print. Historical discussion of cancer from the descriptions in ancient Egypt to present-day treatments. Reviews the development of chemotherapy as a form of treatment.

Olson, James. *Making Cancer History: Disease and Discovery at the University of Texas M.D. Anderson Cancer Center*. Baltimore: Johns Hopkins UP, 2009. Print. Discusses the history and development of chemotherapy. Reviews the work of Sidney Farber and the use of methotrexate.

Skeel, Roland T. *Handbook of Cancer Chemotherapy*. 8th ed. Baltimore: Lippincott, 2011. Print. Reference work for oncologists. Detailed review of known tumors and chemotherapy treatments.

JAMES B. SUMNER

American biochemist

Sumner crystallized the enzyme urease in 1926, the first successful example of such a chemical process. Subsequently, he was able to demonstrate that urease is a protein, providing the first evidence that enzymes are members of that organic category.

Born: November 19, 1887; Canton, Massachusetts
Died: August 12, 1955; Buffalo, New York
Primary field: Chemistry
Specialties: Biochemistry; physical chemistry

EARLY LIFE

James Batcheller Sumner was born November 19, 1887, the son of Charles and Elizabeth Kelly Sumner, textile manufacturers and members of a wealthy New England family. Several relatives were widely known for their cultural pursuits: Charles's brother Frederick was a noted violinist, and his mother's uncle James Batcheller was known as the "walking encyclopedia of Marblehead." Sumner's education began at the Eliot Grammar School and was continued at the Roxbury Latin School,

both historical private schools with roots in the seventeenth century. Sumner's education was briefly interrupted after a hunting accident resulting in the loss of his left arm below the elbow. Sumner had been left-handed, but he taught himself to use his right hand. Despite the loss of an arm, James continued to excel in sports, even becoming an expert in tennis.

Sumner entered Harvard College in 1906 with the intent of studying electrical engineering; however, interactions with several of Harvard's most prominent chemists, in addition to discussions with his uncle Frederick, resulted in Sumner's interests changing to chemistry, in which he received a degree in 1910. During this period, Sumner produced his first published article in the *Journal of the American Chemical Society* in 1910.

Sumner's first job after college was working for his uncle Frederick at the Sumner Knitted Padding Company, a manufacturer of padding for tables and chairs. But after a few months he accepted an offer to teach at Mount Allison College in New Brunswick, Canada, as a

Sumner Crystallizes the Enzyme Urease, Demonstrates Protein Structure

The ability of urease (the enzyme that enables the hydrolysis of the organic compound urea) to decompose the substrate urea had been known since the 1870s, when bacterial extracts were demonstrated to produce an active "ferment" that acted on urea. Other than developing methods for the assay of the ferment and urea, however, little was known of urease's chemical nature.

Sumner became interested in the characterization of urease following a lecture by Harvard professor and biochemist Lawrence Joseph Henderson. Henderson had been trained in physiology, and in his lecture he expressed the belief that enzymes could not be characterized given the state of research at the time, in the early twentieth century. The purification of enzymes had been an aspiration of early twentieth-century scientists for many years. Sumner decided to disprove Henderson through the characterization of urease found in the jack bean (*Canavalia*). The choice was not an accident; the jack bean had been shown to contain significant levels of urease and thus appeared as an ideal source.

Sumner had to address significant difficulties in his early work. Isolation proved more difficult than expected, a challenge compounded by the lack of proper laboratory equipment in his laboratory at Cornell University. Sumner's first success was the isolation from the jack bean of three globular proteins, which he named concanavalin A, concanavalin B, and canavalin. Sumner later observed that concanavalin A was a hemagglutinin, a protein that agglutinated, or adhered, blood cells. In the 1960s, the protein was also found to be a mitogen, a molecule that stimulates the growth of lymphocytes.

In 1922, following a sabbatical leave, Sumner attempted again to isolate and characterize the jack bean urease. Several years of work in testing various solvents and precipitation methods finally resulted, by 1926, in a crystalline precipitate that demonstrated urease activity. The publication of Sumner's research largely resulted in skepticism in the scientific community. Criticisms largely centered on scientists' inability to repeat Sumner's work and on skepticism that the enzyme was a form of colloid rather than a protein. Richard Willstätter, a 1915 Nobel laureate in chemistry, argued that the enzymatic activity was associated with a carrier. His hypothesis was finally rejected, however, when Sumner's colleagues demonstrated the protein nature of other enzymes.

In July 1929, Sumner went on a sabbatical leave, this time to Stockholm, Sweden, where he again demonstrated his procedure for the isolation and crystallization of urease from the jack bean. Since urease activity in his sample correlated with protein concentration, and since enzymes such as trypsin or pepsin that degrade protein also diminished the level of urease activity, Sumner finally was able to convince most of his rivals that urease was a protein. When antiurease prepared in rabbits was added to the urease sample, the result was a precipitate that contained urease activity. These results further supported Sumner's contention that urease is a protein.

---

professor of science. He taught two courses in chemistry and one course in physiology. This was followed by an assistantship in chemistry at Worcester Polytechnic Institute in Massachusetts.

In 1912, Sumner entered the medical school at Harvard to study biochemistry. His thesis advisor, Swedish American chemist Otto Folin, initially discouraged Sumner because of the loss of his arm, but Sumner was determined to become a chemist and overcame Folin's reluctance. Sumner graduated with a master's degree in 1913 and a PhD in biochemistry in 1914. His second professional publication, a description of the role of the liver in urea production, was published in the *Journal of Biological Chemistry*.

LIFE'S WORK

Following graduation from Harvard, Sumner took a vacation in Europe, during which he received an appointment offer as assistant professor of biochemistry at Cornell Medical College. He would remain with Cornell University for his entire professional career, a time period spanning some forty years.

Sumner's appointment included both teaching and research responsibilities. His first courses included lectures and laboratories in biochemistry taught to medical students, as well as a similar course for home economics students. Sumner's research opportunities were limited, given the lack of proper laboratory equipment and facilities, as well as his having only one graduate assistant.

His interest in the purification of enzymes came almost by default. Given the limitations of the laboratory, Sumner decided to attempt a long shot—the isolation and purification of an enzyme. Since his previous graduate work involved the study of urease, an enzyme that promotes hydrolysis in the organic compound known as urea, studying this enzyme was the logical choice. Beginning in 1917 and throughout his long tenure at Cornell, Sumner's work in characterizing urease would be the primary focus of most of his research. In 1920, Sumner was offered a Belgian American fellowship to work with biochemist Jean Effront at the medical school of the University of Brussels. Effront was a major figure in enzyme research but discouraged Sumner from attempting to purify urease, as he considered the project too difficult. Instead, Sumner decided to work with Edgard Zunz, a professor of pharmacology, who studied blood coagulation.

Since the jack bean contained large quantities of urease, Sumner chose the bushy American plant as the source for the enzyme. However, the task proved more difficult than Sumner initially had expected. Though he was able to isolate several globular proteins from the jack bean, it was only after testing a wide variety of solvents and washing procedures that he was able to precipitate pure crystals of the urease enzyme. In the summer of 1926, Sumner published his work in the *Journal of Biological Chemistry*.

Despite producing many papers on the same subject over the next five years—several of which were written with David B. Hand, who later became prominent in the area of food technology—few biochemists accepted Sumner's idea that urease was a protein, and others insisted that the enzyme carrier was what had crystallized. It was only after John Northrop and Moses Kunitz at the Rockefeller Institute crystallized pepsin, trypsin, and chymotrypsin in a similar fashion that other biochemists acknowledged that the isolation and crystallization of enzymes, though difficult, could be accomplished. In 1929, following the first publications of his urease purification, Sumner was promoted to professor of biochemistry in the medical school.

Sumner continued his research on jack bean proteins even after the purification of urease. In 1936, he reported that concanavalin A, one of the proteins he had previously identified in the jack bean, was capable of agglutinating red blood cells. Several publications, in 1937 and 1938, reported the crystallization and characterization of another enzyme from the jack bean, catalase, which breaks down the substrate peroxide in the cell. Ironically, catalase is a nonprotein enzyme, but by the late 1930s the protein nature of most enzymes was accepted. In total, Sumner isolated and characterized over a dozen enzymes over the course of his scientific career. In 1946, Sumner, along with Northrop and Wendell M. Stanley, was awarded the Nobel Prize in Chemistry for his work in the purification of enzymes.

In 1947, he became the director of the enzyme chemistry laboratory at Cornell. In 1955, Sumner began preparations for retirement. He agreed to move temporarily to Belo Horizonte, Brazil, where he would help to establish an enzyme laboratory at the University of Minas Gerais School of Medicine.

While Sumner's professional career included the authoring of several textbooks of biochemistry, primarily addressing the structure and functions of enzymes, he also contributed to the popular culture of the time. He was an expert cook, often surprising his students with questions about cooking that applied chemical principles. He was fluent in several languages, learning Portuguese while planning his move to Brazil.

During the summer of 1955, he was diagnosed with terminal cancer. He died on August 12, 1955. He was survived by his third wife, the former Mary Beyer, whom he married in 1943, and five children.

IMPACT

The immediate impact of Sumner's work was the recognition that enzymes can occupy a class of organic molecules called proteins. In the aftermath of Sumner's 1926 publication on the crystallization of urease, many biochemists refused to acknowledge that enzymes were proteins. The widespread skepticism resulted in part from the scientific community's inability to reproduce Sumner's experimental procedure; scientists had been trying unsuccessfully for years to crystallize enzymes. One German scientist reportedly expressed dismay that Sumner could isolate an enzyme when so many "great German chemists" had failed.

Once Sumner's procedures were published, other scientists were able to carry out the crystallization of additional enzymes. In 1930, Northrop reported first the crystallization of pepsin and, later, trypsin.

Richard Adler

FURTHER READING

Lesk, Arthur. *Introduction to Protein Science: Architecture, Function, and Genomics*. New York: Oxford UP, 2010. Print. Describes protein makeup and functions at both the macro and molecular levels, as well as more recent applications of protein expression in the cell.

Tanford, Charles, and Jaqueline Reynolds. *Nature's Robots: A History of Proteins*. New York: Oxford UP, 2001. Print. Discusses the history behind the discovery and understanding of proteins and Sumner's role in demonstrating the proteins as enzymes. Covers the controversies associated with his work.

Whitford, David. *Proteins: Structure and Function*. Hoboken: Wiley, 2005. Print. Moderately detailed discussion of amino acid and protein structure and functions. Includes the theory of protein crystallization, including references to Sumner's work.

IVAN SUTHERLAND

American computer scientist

Computer scientist Ivan Sutherland pioneered advances in artificial intelligence, simulation programming, and advanced circuitry. His work with computer graphics led to the development of the graphical user interface.

Born: May 16, 1938; Hastings, Nebraska
Primary field: Computer science
Specialty: Graphics

EARLY LIFE

Ivan Edward Sutherland was born on May 16, 1938, in Hastings, Nebraska. He grew up in a home in which education and intellectual curiosity were highly prized. His father held a PhD in civil engineering, and his mother was a teacher. The family eventually moved to New York, where Sutherland attended Scarsdale High School. While in high school, Sutherland had access to Simon, an early computer that was loaned to his family by inventor Edmund Berkeley. The computer could perform only rudimentary functions such as limited addition of numbers up to fifteen. Sutherland wrote an extensive program for Simon that enabled the machine to perform simple division in addition to its preprogrammed skills.

After graduating from high school in 1955, Sutherland received a full scholarship to study at the Carnegie Institute of Technology, later renamed Carnegie Mellon University. While completing his degree, Sutherland published articles in magazines such as *Computers and Automation*, and he also participated in the college's Reserve Officers' Training Corps (ROTC) program. He received his bachelor's degree in electrical engineering in 1959 and then moved to California to attend the California Institute of Technology (Caltech), from which he earned his master's degree in electrical engineering the following year. Sutherland earned his doctorate in the

same area of study from the Massachusetts Institute of Technology (MIT) in 1964.

While at MIT, Sutherland worked with some of the United States' leading computer scientists, including Claude Shannon and Marvin Minsky. Shannon supervised Sutherland's thesis, "Sketchpad: A Man-Machine Graphical Communication System." Sutherland created the computer program Sketchpad, which represented a significant advance in computer graphics technology, as it enabled the user to create images on a screen using a light pen. Prior to this discovery, those who worked on computers needed to type in commands to produce graphics. Sutherland bypassed this complex and time-consuming process with his simple yet revolutionary design, which had a lasting influence on the development of computer-aided design technology and on computer graphics and interfaces as a whole.

LIFE'S WORK

Sutherland joined the US Army after earning his doctorate to fulfill his commitment to the ROTC. From 1963 to 1965, he held the rank of lieutenant and served at the National Security Agency and the Advanced Research Projects Agency supervised by the Department of Defense. During this period, he worked extensively on computer timesharing, an innovation that enabled multiple users to interact with a computer at the same time. He was also granted a considerable sum of money to advance the United States' computer prowess as the nation sought to gain the upper hand in the technological Cold War against the Soviet Union, an effort that took on additional significance following the successful launch of the Soviet satellite Sputnik in 1957.

After completing his military duties, Sutherland found employment at Harvard University as a professor of electrical engineering. In 1968, he relocated to the University of Utah, taking the position of professor of

Sutherland Invents Sketchpad

While pursuing his doctorate in electrical engineering at the Massachusetts Institute of Technology (MIT) in the early 1960s, Ivan Sutherland sought to create a system of communicating with a computer using drawing rather than textual commands. At that time, computer technology was limited by a number of factors, including available memory and methods of entering commands, and the uses of computers were limited as well. Sutherland had begun to experiment with increasing the capabilities of computers as a teenager, and he recognized that further innovation was possible in this area. Under the supervision of his thesis adviser, Donner Professor of Science Claude Shannon, Sutherland created the computer program Sketchpad, which would prove to be a groundbreaking contribution to computer technology.

At MIT, Sutherland had access to the TX-2 computer, a sixty-four-kilobyte machine that by the standards of the day was far in advance of other systems. Sutherland's program took advantage of the TX-2's advanced technology and allowed him to draw lines using a graphical user interface. To draw a line or shape using Sketchpad, the user pointed a light pen, a device invented at MIT in the previous decade, at the computer screen. The pen was connected to a system of buttons and knobs that allowed the user to switch between specific functions, such as draw or copy, and to manipulate the magnification or orientation of the drawn images. Sketchpad also had the ability to store the structure of a drawing, allowing the user to reproduce and alter elements easily.

Sutherland explained the workings of his program in his thesis, "Sketchpad: A Man-machine Graphical Communication System." In addition to detailed discussion of his creation and use of the program, Sutherland included numerous drawings created using Sketchpad in the paper, providing concrete proof of the program's functionality. For this work, he earned his doctorate from MIT in 1963.

Sketchpad proved to be crucial to the development of computers over the course of the following decades. As a drawing program, it served as the precursor to computer-aided drafting and design technology, which in turn influenced the development of computer-generated animation. Sutherland's program helped to revolutionize the animation process and made possible the complex computer-generated movies and games that became common in the twenty-first century. However, Sketchpad was influential not only to computer-based art and design but also to computer technology as a whole. Sutherland's use of a light pen rather than text commands influenced the development of graphical interfaces that allowed users to interact with computers using a mouse, a light pen, or even their fingers. Graphical user interfaces made it possible for ordinary individuals to use computers without having to learn textual command languages and structures.

---

computer science. Under the leadership of David C. Evans, the Computer Science Department at the University of Utah became a major center of computer innovation. Also in 1968, Sutherland and Evans joined forces to form Evans and Sutherland, a firm responsible for significant innovation in computer graphics. Over the course of several decades, the company formulated methods of creating three-dimensional graphics and expanded the role of computers by making them effective simulators and design tools. By 1976, Sutherland had left his day-to-day role in the company to pursue new research opportunities, though he remained on its board of directors.

In 1976, Sutherland accepted the Fletcher Jones Professorship of Computer Science at Caltech, a post he held for four years. At Caltech, he shifted his attention away from graphics and toward the field of integrated circuit design. Sutherland made the subject a viable field of study at the university during his tenure while concurrently working to develop the school's computer science program. He also served as an adviser to the RAND Corporation, a research organization affiliated with the US military.

In 1980, Sutherland and computer scientist Robert Sproull established the consulting firm Sutherland, Sproull, and Associates, which was absorbed by the technology company Sun Microsystems in 1990. Sutherland remained with the firm after its acquisition by Sun, leading research in new technologies as a vice president and a fellow. From 2005 to 2008, he served as a visiting computer science professor at the University of California, Berkeley. He retired from Sun in 2009. Following his retirement, Sutherland and his wife, Marly Roncken, founded the Asynchronous Research Center (ARC) at Portland State University's Maseeh College of Engineering and Computer Science. Roncken became director of the ARC, while Sutherland took on the position of visiting scientist.

Sutherland has written numerous papers throughout his career and has filed more than fifty patents, many of which are related to computer graphics technology. He has received dozens of awards and citations for his contributions to the field of computer science, including the A. M. Turing Award in 1988 and the John von Neumann Medal in 1998. He was inducted into the National Academy of Engineering in 1973 and the National Academy of Sciences in 1978 and was named a fellow of the Computer History Museum in 2005.

IMPACT

Over the course of his career, Sutherland fundamentally altered the nature and function of the computer, particularly in the area of computer graphics. His research at the University of Utah and with the firm Evans and Sutherland helped usher in a new era of computer graphics and engineering, bringing significant computer advances to the defense industry and to a wide array of public and private interests. A number of leaders in the technology industry and related fields were students or colleagues of Sutherland; these include Edwin Catmull, a cofounder of Pixar Animation Studios, and John Warnock, a cofounder of the software company Adobe Systems.

Sutherland has become best known for his continuing effort to redefine the understanding of computers and what they can accomplish. In an era in which most computer researchers were limited to using simple binary codes, Sutherland sought to create functional systems that allowed humans to interact with computers on a more straightforward level. His creation of Sketchpad and his later work in graphics and displays greatly influenced the development of graphical user interfaces, one of the key factors leading to the widespread adoption of computers. Such interfaces enabled users to operate computers without the use of textual commands, making computers accessible to individuals unfamiliar with the devices' more technical workings. Sutherland has been recognized for his important contributions to the field of computer science by a number of industry organizations both in the United States and abroad.

Keith M. Finley

FURTHER READING

Blundell, Barry. *An Introduction to Computer Graphics and Creative 3-D Environments*. London: Springer, 2008. Print. Chronicles the development of computer graphics and discusses the effects of Sutherland's contributions on the field as a whole.

Norberg, Arthur L., and Judy E. O'Neill. *Transforming Computer Technology: Information Processing for the Pentagon, 1962–1986*. Baltimore: Johns Hopkins UP, 2000. Print. Examines the contributions of Sutherland and others working in the Defense Department's Advanced Research Projects Agency and calls attention to the creative environment that allowed Sutherland and his fellow inventors to make significant advances in computer technology.

Sutherland, Ivan, Robert F. Sproull, and David Harris. *Logical Effort: Designing Fast CMOS Circuits*. San Francisco: Morgan, 1999. Print. Explores Sutherland's efforts in the area of circuitry and effectively distills and summarizes the work that Sutherland and Sproull carried out while at Sun Microsystems.

JACK W. SZOSTAK

Canadian American biologist

Biologist Jack W. Szostak has led many groundbreaking investigations into the origins of life and genetic solutions to disease. His scientific contributions have earned him many honors, including the Nobel Prize for Physiology or Medicine in 2009.

Born: November 9, 1952; London, England
Primary field: Biology
Specialties: Genetics; biochemistry; molecular biology

EARLY LIFE

Jack William Szostak is the son of Bill and Vi Szostak. His father, an aeronautical engineer with the Royal Canadian Air Force, was studying at Imperial College when Jack was born in London, England. He was still an infant when his parents returned to Canada. Jack and his two sisters grew up in Germany and Canada as their father was transferred to different posts during a twenty-year career. Eventually, the family settled in Canada near Montreal, Quebec.

An excellent student, Szostak became interested in science at an early age, particularly chemistry and biology. As a boy, he had a basement lab, stocked with substances his mother brought home from the chemical company where she worked, and produced several spectacular explosions. In high school, he built a hydroponic garden. One summer, he worked at his mother's chemical-testing laboratory.

At the age of fifteen, Szostak graduated from Riverdale High School in the Pierrefonds-Roxboro section of Montreal. In 1968, he entered McGill University to begin his undergraduate education in cellular biology. Two years later, he joined the summer program at the Jackson Laboratory, a biomedical research institution in Bar Harbor, Maine. As part of the laboratory's mission to investigate genetics in order to prevent, treat, and cure human diseases, Szostak worked with mice, dissecting thyroid glands to analyze mutant hormones.

Upon returning to McGill, Szostak concentrated on plant biology with a focus on algae and published his first paper on peptide hormones. He graduated with a bachelor of science degree in 1972, then used a fellowship to enter Cornell University to study the DNA sequencing of genomes of yeasts, microscopic single-celled fungi. He earned his PhD in biochemistry in 1977 and stayed at Cornell for two additional years to conduct further genetic research.

LIFE'S WORK

In 1979, Szostak was appointed as a teacher of biological chemistry at Harvard Medical School and simultaneously became an independent researcher at the Dana-Farber Cancer Institute in Boston, Massachusetts. He continued to explore genetics, particularly the process of recombination, in which double-stranded DNA is broken and then repaired by combining it with other genetic material.

The following year, while attending a conference on nucleic acids, Szostak met Elizabeth Blackburn. A biological researcher at the University of California, San Francisco, Blackburn was conducting genetic experiments with freshwater protozoa that were similar in nature to Szostak's studies of yeasts. In subsequent discussions, Blackburn and Szostak focused on the function of telomeres, regions at the ends of DNA molecules that protect chromosomes from degrading. The two scientists decided to collaborate to test whether Blackburn's protozoa's telomeres would work with Szostak's yeasts.

Blackburn soon added former postdoctorate student Carol Greider, later a professor of molecular biology and genetics at Johns Hopkins University School of Medicine, to the collaborative team. In 1983, Szostak successfully became the first scientist to clone yeast telomeres. Meanwhile, Blackburn and Greider, applying the results of Szostak's research, were able to isolate and identify telomerase, the enzyme that creates telomeres in DNA.

The recombination and telomere breakthroughs attracted many postgraduate students to Szostak's lab and resulted in new opportunities. In 1984, when Szostak began teaching genetics at Harvard Medical School, he also accepted an appointment to the Department of Molecular Biology at Massachusetts General Hospital. By the late 1980s, when Szostak became a full professor of genetics at Harvard Medical School, his research team and Blackburn's had expanded knowledge of telomere genetics. Szostak's group produced mutated yeast cells that shortened telomeres and prematurely aged the cells; Blackburn's group experienced similar results in mutating protozoan telomerase RNA.

Having exhausted the possibilities of yeasts, Szostak began to gravitate toward the study of ribozymes, which are ribonucleic acid (RNA) molecules that were discovered during the 1980s. Ribozymes catalyze chemical reactions and are key components in the study of how life originated billions of years ago, as well as potential agents in the creation of genetic therapies to combat diseases.

In the early 1990s, Szostak's lab concentrated mainly on RNA. He developed a method of in vitro selection of biological molecules that would allow individual molecules to be screened for specific functions. Essentially an adaptation of the forces of natural selection, the test-tube technique allowed Szostak and his colleagues to evolve RNA aptamers (a term he coined), engineered acid-based molecules that bind to particular molecular targets like cells or tissues. Aptamers show great promise in their ability to zero in on specific diseases; in the early twenty-first century, the US Food and Drug Administration approved an aptamer-based drug for the treatment of age-related macular degeneration, a major cause of visual impairment.

Late in the 1990s, in addition to his other duties, Szostak joined the Howard Hughes Medical Institute, a private nonprofit organization headquartered in Chevy Chase, Maryland, that funds biological and medical research. Between 2000 and 2007, Szostak was also associated with the National Aeronautic and Space Administration (NASA) and was an active participant in the Astrobiology Institute in California. A principal investigator of the NASA's exobiology and evolutionary

Jack W. Szostak Helps Create the First Artificial Chromosome

Artificial chromosomes give biologists insight into the fundamental mechanisms by which cells replicate and play an important role in genetic-engineering technology. Soon after its invention in 1983 by Andrew W. Murray and Jack W. Szostak, the artificial chromosome proved to be of great value in the field of medicine.

Chromosomes are essentially carriers of genetic information—the code that is the blueprint for life. In higher organisms, the number and type of chromosomes in a cell's nucleus are characteristic of the species. The chromosome's job in a dividing cell is to replicate and then distribute one copy of itself into each new "daughter" cell. This process, which is referred to as either mitosis or meiosis, is of supreme importance to the continuation of life.

In 1953, biophysicists James D. Watson and Francis Crick discovered the structure of deoxyribonucleic acid (DNA), a double-helical form that would help to explain the mechanism behind cell division. During DNA replication, the chromosome unwinds to expose the thin threads of DNA. The two strands separate, and each acts as a template for the formation of a new complementary strand, thus forming two complete and identical chromosomes that can be distributed (or segregated) to each new cell.

In order to be a true working chromosome, an artificial chromosome must maintain the machinery necessary for replication and segregation. By the early 1980s, Murray and Szostak had recognized the possible advantages of using a simple, controlled model to study chromosome behavior. Since natural chromosomes are large and have poorly defined structures, it is almost impossible to study those elements essential for replication and segregation. Artificial chromosomes, on the other hand, are simple and have known components.

Before the synthesis of the first artificial chromosome, the chromosomal elements of replication and segregation had to be identified and harvested. The three elements thought to be required were the origin of replication, the site where the synthesis of new DNA begins; the centromere, a thinner segment that serves as the attachment site for the mitotic spindle; and the telomeres, which are located at both ends of the chromosome and are necessary to protect the terminal genes from degradation.

Once it was generated, Murray and Szostak's artificial chromosome was inserted into yeast cells to replicate. Yeast cells are relatively simple and well characterized but otherwise resemble cells of higher organisms. Although Murray and Szostak's first attempt resulted in a chromosome that failed to segregate properly, by September 1983, they had announced the successful creation of the first artificial chromosome.

One of the most exciting aspects of the artificial chromosome is its application to recombinant DNA technology, which involves creating novel genetic material by combining segments of DNA from various sources. For example, the artificial yeast chromosome can be used as a cloning vector. A segment of DNA containing a desired gene would be inserted into an artificial chromosome and then allowed to replicate in yeast until large amounts of the gene are produced.

Although amplifying DNA in this manner has been done before with bacterial plasmids as cloning vectors, the artificial yeast chromosome has the advantage of being able to hold larger segments of DNA, allowing scientists to clone large genes. This is of great importance, since the genes that cause diseases such as hemophilia and Duchenne muscular dystrophy are enormous. The most ambitious project to which the artificial yeast chromosome has been applied is the attempt to clone the entire human genome.

biology program, he contributed his expertise to studies of the origin, evolution, and distribution of life in the universe.

In the 2000s, Szostak's laboratory research began to center on the creation of protocells, which are replications of ancient inorganic matter that as a result of chemical processes organized into biological life, established a metabolism, became self-reproducing, and evolved into higher forms. In working to unravel the question of how life began, Szostak hopes ultimately to produce genetically generated and chemically based treatments of diseases to help preserve and prolong human life.

IMPACT

Since the early 1970s, Szostak has worked in tandem with his colleagues in attempting to understand the intricacies of genetics. His research in a number of related areas of molecular biology has far-ranging implications across several disciplines.

Szostak's collaboration with Elizabeth Blackburn and Carol Greider, which resulted in the discovery of the telomere-creating enzyme telomerase and earned the trio the 2009 Nobel Prize in Physiology or Medicine, offers tremendous promise for combating aging and degenerative diseases. Szostak's technique to develop aptamers has considerably shortened the evolutionary period of RNA molecules and simplified the screening process, opening the door for the genetic targeting of particular diseases. His contributions to NASA programs may pay dividends in the future, if humans ever explore other planets and strange new worlds beyond the solar system, and his investigations into the origins of life ultimately may reveal one of nature's longest-held secrets and could pave the way toward human immortality.

Szostak's recognitions for his innovative research include memberships in the National Science Foundation, the National Institutes of Health, the National Research Council, and the American Academy of Arts and Sciences. He was elected to the National Academy of Sciences in 1998 and to the New York Academy of Sciences in 1999. In addition to the Nobel Prize, he shared the 2006 Lasker Award with Elizabeth Blackburn and Carol Greider for their joint discovery of telomerase. Szostak has also been honored with the National Academy of Sciences Award in Molecular Biology (1984), the Genetics Society of America Medal (2000), and the Heineken Prize for Medicine (2008).

Jack Ewing

FURTHER READING

Atkins, John F., Raymond F. Gesteland, and Thomas R. Cech, eds. *RNA Worlds: From Life's Origins to Diversity in Gene Regulation*. Cold Spring Harbor: Cold Spring Harbor Lab, 2010. Print. A close look at the microscopic world of ribonucleic acid (RNA).

Kauffman, Stuart. *Investigations*. New York: Oxford UP, 2000. Print. An examination of the origins and basis of life. Includes discussion in chapter 2, "The Origins of Life," of Szostak's work with aptamers and his attempts to produce self-replicating RNA.

Szostak, Jack W. *The Origins of Life*. Cold Spring Harbor: Cold Spring Harbor Lab, 2010. Print. An illustrated discussion encapsulating Szostak's primary area of study: how prehistoric chemical reactions caused organic molecules to coalesce and replicate into what is known as life, and the possibility that similar reactions have or will occur in extraterrestrial settings.

Terence Tao

Australian American mathematician

Australian-born mathematician Terence Tao has made significant contributions to areas such as harmonic analysis and number theory. He is particularly known for his in-depth study of prime numbers.

Born: July 17, 1975; Adelaide, Australia
Primary field: Mathematics
Specialties: Calculus; mathematical analysis; number theory

Early Life

Terence Chi-Shen Tao was born in Adelaide, Australia, on July 17, 1975. His father, Billy Tao, was a pediatrician, and his mother, Grace, held a degree in mathematics and physics. He had two younger brothers. Tao excelled academically from an early age. He learned how to read by the age of two by watching the children's educational television show *Sesame Street*. He was also able to solve simple addition and subtraction problems, and he soon learned to type with one finger. By age three, he had progressed to the level of a six-year-old in math, writing, and reading.

Under the tutelage of his mother, Tao completed nearly all the elementary math curriculum by the age of five. A year later, he wrote his first computer program in BASIC, which he learned from reading a manual on the language. He entered high school in 1983, and during the subsequent years, he began to take classes in math, chemistry, and physics at Flinders University. Beginning at age ten, he competed in the International Mathematical Olympiad, and at thirteen, he became its youngest gold medalist. Tao earned his bachelor's degree in mathematics from Flinders in 1991 and completed his master's degree the following year. He went on to earn his PhD in mathematics from Princeton University in 1996, writing a thesis titled "Three Regularity Results in Harmonic Analysis."

Life's Work

Tao turned to teaching early, publishing his first math text, *Solving Mathematical Problems: A Personal Perspective* (1992), while still a teenager. After leaving Princeton, Tao accepted the position of Hendrick Assistant Professor at the University of California, Los Angeles (UCLA). He served as a visiting fellow and visiting professor at the University of New South Wales and was granted full professorship at UCLA in 2000. He also served as an honorary professor at the Australian National University. He married Laura Kim, an engineer, in 2002, and in 2007, he was appointed the James and Carol Collins Chair in the College of Letters and Science at UCLA.

While at UCLA, Tao received significant attention for his work in theoretical mathematics, particularly his work related to the Kakeya conjecture, a problem within the field of harmonic analysis. (Harmonic analysis uses equations from physics in an advanced type of calculus.) Along with two of his colleagues, Tao sought to determine the most space-efficient method of rotating an object in three dimensions. They ultimately developed an estimate of a certain geometric dimension's size in Euclidean space. Tao also completed significant work related to prime numbers (numbers greater than one that are only divisible by one and themselves) in collaboration with University of Cambridge professor Ben Green. Their findings became known as the Green–Tao theorem.

Although Tao primarily worked in areas related to calculus and differential equations, he also explored issues in related fields. Beginning in 2004, he and Emmanuel Candès, then a professor at the California Institute of Technology, sought to determine how to capture and reconstruct digital images in a more efficient way. At that time, digital cameras captured millions of pixels and then reduced the data to obtain an image. Tao and Candès created a new method based on a process known as compression sampling. This method soon came to be used by engineers seeking to create better magnetic resonance imaging (MRI) scanners, astronomical instruments, and one-pixel digital cameras. Tao and Candès also hold a patent on a method of correcting transmission errors with the use of linear programming. For their work in these areas, Tao and Candès were awarded the George Pólya Prize of the Society for Industrial and Applied Mathematics in 2010.

In 2006, Tao was one of four mathematicians to be awarded the Fields Medal, an award presented by the International Mathematical Union every four years. The award recognizes the achievements of mathematicians under the age of forty and has often been referred to as the Nobel Prize of mathematics. Tao was the first UCLA faculty member to receive the award. The citation noted Tao's four major areas of contributions: additive number theory, combinatorics, harmonic analysis, and partial differential equations. The award was presented in August 2006 in Madrid, Spain, at the International Congress of Mathematicians. Only a month later, Tao was awarded a MacArthur Fellowship, commonly known as a "genius" grant, which provides a $500,000 grant over a five-year period.

In 2009, Tao became a collaborator on a project known as Polymath, begun by mathematician Timothy Gowers of the University of Cambridge. Using a blog and a wiki-style website that allowed users to make contributions and changes, the project tested whether many people could solve a complex mathematical problem in collaboration. Although Gowers and Tao were

Tao Helps Reveal Prime Number Patterns

In 2004, while serving as a professor at the University of California, Los Angles, Terence Tao began to collaborate with University of Cambridge professor Ben Green on a significant study of prime numbers. Prime numbers are numbers greater than one that are divisible only by one and themselves: 2, 3, 5, 7, and so on. As early as c. 300 BCE, the ancient Greek mathematician Euclid proved that there is an infinite number of these prime numbers.

The question of prime number sequences has interested mathematicians since the late eighteenth century. They knew that the set of prime numbers contains sequences of equally spaced primes; for example, in a prime number sequence such as 5, 11, 17, the primes are separated by six. This sequence, consisting of three primes, can be referred to as a length 3 progression. Mathematicians soon began to wonder how long a sequence of equally spaced primes could be. By the time of Tao and Green's study, the longest prime number progression known was length 23, and each number in the sequence had sixteen digits. Tao and Green proposed that it is possible for a prime number progression to be of any finite length; that is, there is an infinite number of prime number progressions. If this is true, then there is a progression of length 100, and even one of length 1,000.

To reach this conclusion, Green and Tao studied Szemerédi's theorem, named for Hungarian mathematician Endre Szemerédi, who proved it in 1975. The theorem itself does not apply to prime numbers. However, Tao and Green took elements from the existing proofs of the theorem and modified them to create a theorem that could apply to prime numbers. They also relied on research about numbers known as "almost prime," which are more plentiful than prime numbers. An almost-prime number can be divided only by one, itself, and one prime number. Problems along the way led Tao and Green to use ergodic theory, which is a type of statistical analysis informed by physics.

Tao and Green described their findings, which became known as the Green–Tao theorem, in a paper titled "The Primes Contain Arbitrarily Long Arithmetic Progressions," which they posted online in 2004 and later published in *Annals of Mathematics* in 2008. The proof did not elucidate methods for finding these long sequences of prime numbers; however, it proved that they exist. In later papers, written independently or in collaboration with Green and other mathematicians, Tao refined his understanding of prime number progressions, expanding upon the Green–Tao theorem.

the moderators and main commenters, multiple people worked together on Polymath 1 with the stated goal of using combinatorics to find a simpler proof for the density Hales–Jewett (DHJ) theorem. Within six weeks, thirty-nine individuals worked together to write a new proof for the theorem. This fast pace was unprecedented in higher mathematics, and the success of the project led Tao and Gowers to create further Polymath projects over the following years.

Tao has published more than two hundred scientific papers and has collaborated with many different coauthors. Several of his books have been published by the American Mathematical Society. Tao maintains a popular blog in which he discusses his mathematical research and provides lecture notes, career advice, and other information related to mathematics. Many of his posts have been published in the collected volumes *Structure and Randomness* (2008) and *Poincaré's Legacies* (2009). Since 2002, Tao has served as an editor for a number of publications, including *The Journal of the American Mathematical Society*, *The American Journal of Mathematics*, *Dynamics of Partial Differential Equations*, and *Analysis and Partial Differential Equations*.

IMPACT

In recognition of his contributions to the field of mathematics, Tao was elected to the National Academy of Sciences in 2008 and the American Academy of Arts and Sciences in 2009. He was also named a corresponding member of the Australian Academy of Science and a fellow of the Royal Society. In addition to the Fields Medal, he has been awarded the King Faisal International Prize and the National Science Foundation (NSF) Alan T. Waterman award. Rarely given to mathematicians, the Waterman Award recognizes researchers under the age of thirty-five in any field of engineering or science that the NSF supports. In 2012, the Royal Swedish Academy of Sciences awarded Tao the Crafoord Prize, which is presented on a rotating basis among four different fields: astronomy and mathematics, biosciences, geosciences, and polyarthritis. Tao shared the prize with mathematician Jean Bourgain of Princeton University.

In addition to making a number of significant contributions in areas such as harmonic analysis, combinatorics, and partial differential equations, Tao has been particularly influential in his promotion of collaboration among mathematicians and his use of the Internet as a teaching tool. By sharing his lectures, articles, and general perspective on the field of mathematics online, Tao has broadened his own scholarship and that of others, both professional mathematicians and nonspecialists with an interest in math. His work with the Polymath project demonstrated that collaborative, Internet-based problem solving is both possible and effective. This style of collaboration has further served to allow people not working at the top levels of pure mathematics to contribute to developments in the field.

Judy A. Johnson

FURTHER READING

Mackenzie, Dana. "Primed for Success." *Smithsonian* 38 (2007): 74–75. Print. Discusses Tao's diverse areas of research and his success as a mathematician who crosses disciplines.

Nielsen, Michael. *Reinventing Discovery: The New Era of Networked Science*. Princeton: Princeton UP, 2012. Print. Discusses how the Internet and blogs have changed and generally improved scientific discovery and includes specific mention of Tao.

Szpiro, George G. *A Mathematical Medley: Fifty Easy Pieces on Mathematics*. Providence: American Mathematical Society, 2010. Print. Features a chapter on Tao and Green's work on prime numbers, providing a bit of the historical background to the problem.

Tao, Terence. *Solving Mathematical Problems: A Personal Perspective*. New York: Oxford UP, 2006. Print. Includes chapters on problem solving, number theory, algebra, and geometry and expresses Tao's personal perspective on the nature of mathematics and the ways in which problems can be solved.

---. *Structure and Randomness: Pages from Year One of a Mathematics Blog*. Providence: American Mathematical Society, 2008. Print. Collects Tao's blog entries from 2007, which include expository articles, lectures, and open problems and provide further insight into Tao's personality and personal understanding of mathematics.

Yates, Eleanor Lee. "They Call Him The 'Mozart Of Math.'" *Diverse: Issues in Higher Education* 23.24 (2007): 31. Print. Summarizes Tao's career and notes the growing international reputation he gained after receiving the Field Medal and the MacArthur Fellowship.

EDWARD TATUM

American biochemist

American biochemist and geneticist Edward Tatum, in collaboration with Stanford University colleague George Beadle, conducted experiments in which the bread mold Neurospora crassa was exposed to X-rays, resulting in mutant strains. In 1941, they published an important paper explaining their "one gene–one enzyme" hypothesis: the idea that genes encode enzymes that accelerate chemical reactions in cells. The hypothesis is considered the first significant concept in molecular biology.

Born: December 14, 1909; Boulder, Colorado
Died: November 5, 1975; New York, New York
Primary field: Biology
Specialties: Genetics; biochemistry; cellular biology

EARLY LIFE

Edward Lawrie Tatum was the eldest son of Mabel Webb Tatum and Arthur Lawrie Tatum, a chemistry and pharmacology professor who held both PhD and MD degrees. Tatum attended the Laboratory School at the University of Chicago for his undergraduate work but transferred to the University of Wisconsin in 1931, earning his BA, MS, and PhD degrees within three years. Tatum's thesis work included investigation into the role played by the B vitamin thiamine in bacterial metabolism. In 1934, he married June Alton with whom he would have two daughters, Margaret and Barbara.

In 1936, Tatum won a General Education Fellowship to study at the University of Utrecht, Holland. There he learned about concepts in microbial nutrition that would influence his later research. The following year, Tatum accepted a position as a research associate with George Beadle at Stanford University. They studied pigment production in *Drosophila* (fruit fly) larvae until 1941, when they decided the red bread mold *Neurospora crassa* was a better organism for their experiments.

LIFE'S WORK

We now know that DNA is genetic material that encodes all the proteins in the body. When Tatum and Beadle were beginning their research, however, this had yet to be conclusively proven, and they designed an experiment to determine if DNA encodes special proteins called enzymes. They thought—correctly, as it turned out—that different DNA sequences, or genes, probably encoded each enzyme.

When Tatum and Beadle were conducting their experiments, X-rays were already known to damage the long, delicate DNA molecule. Tatum reasoned that if DNA functioned as the blueprint for enzymes, then damaged DNA should produce damaged, and probably nonfunctional, enzymes. In 1941, Tatum and his team began the long process of irradiating thousands of cultures of *Neurospora* and screening them for mutations. Since X-rays cause random mutations, there was no way to choose which genes to target, so many cultures were needed. The goal was to find surviving cultures with mutations in genes for nutritional enzymes.

A few cultures out of thousands were successful. There were mutations in genes encoding enzymes used to synthesize essential nutrients. The mutated cultures were identified because they could only survive when supplemented with essential molecules like thiamine or choline.

The team's experiments demonstrated that enzymes are coded by DNA sequences called genes. In the same way that a blueprint details how a house is built, DNA encodes instructions for making proteins. What Tatum and Beadle didn't understand at the time was that DNA also encodes many other proteins besides enzymes.

In 1945, Tatum left Stanford University to teach at Yale University, where he collaborated with a brilliant young scientist named Joshua Lederberg. They adapted many of Tatum's *Neurospora* techniques to the study of bacteria, which resulted in the discovery of bacterial conjugation, which is the sharing of genetic information between a donor cell and a recipient. Since many bacteria reproduce by binary fission (splitting in half), they often produce offspring that are identical to the parent cell. Tatum and Lederberg proved that some bacteria can share genes in a process analogous to sexual reproduction.

Tatum's bacterial research used many of the same experimental design principles that proved useful in the *Neurospora* work. Like the *Neurospora* experiments, the bacterial research utilized strains of nutritional mutants that required supplementation to survive. In the first documented example of conjugation, two strains of bacteria with different mutations shared genes and repaired each other's deficiencies. It was later discovered that genes transferred by conjugation are carried on small circles of DNA called plasmids, which exist in addition to the larger circular chromosome found in most bacteria. Modern genetic engineering often makes use of plasmids to transfer genes from one organism to another.

In 1948, Tatum returned to Stanford as a professor of biology. He was especially interested in teaching the genetics of *Escherichia coli* (commonly called *E. coli*), a bacterium commonly used in laboratories. Tatum was promoted at Stanford, becoming chair of the biochemistry department in 1956. That same year, he and his first wife divorced. Within a year of his divorce, he married Viola Kantor.

In 1957, Tatum left Stanford again, this time for a professorship at the Rockefeller Institute for Medical Research in New York City (now Rockefeller University). The next year he and George Beadle were honored with half of the Nobel Prize in Physiology or Medicine for their groundbreaking research on the genetics of *Neurospora*. The other half of the prize went to Tatum's graduate student, Joshua Lederberg, for the discovery that bacteria are capable of mating and exchanging genes. In addition to the Nobel Prize, he was previously awarded the prestigious Remsen Award of the American Chemical Society in 1953.

After Kantor died in 1974, Tatum married his third wife, Elsie Berglund. Burglund survived Tatum, who was a heavy smoker, when he died from heart failure and complications of chronic emphysema on November 5, 1975.

IMPACT

The "one gene–one enzyme" hypothesis was a major discovery that explained how genetic traits are passed

---

Edward Tatum Proposes One Gene–One Enzyme Hypothesis

In 1937, Edward Tatum became a research associate in the Department of Biological Sciences at California's Stanford University and began his collaboration with geneticist George Beadle. Tatum and Beadle initially studied pigment production in the eye of the fruit-fly *Drosophila*, specifically studying production of the vermilion pigment. The difficulty was in understanding the significance of growth requirements that regulated the pathway for pigment production.

Beadle and Tatum decided to utilize a different organism for their investigation, one in which it was easier to produce and manipulate mutations: the bread mold *Neurospora crassa*. Tatum had already established that their strains required the vitamin biotin for growth; *Neurospora* was also better suited for genetic studies since its vegetative state contained only one copy of genes rather than the two in other organisms such as *Drosophila*. Geneticist Hermann Muller had demonstrated with fruit flies that mutants could be produced by exposing gametes to X-rays; Beadle and Tatum did the same with *Neurospora* spores, generating a large number of nutritional mutants (auxotrophs). Since Muller and others had shown that damage from X-rays takes place in the genetic material—not known to be DNA at the time of Beadle and Tatum's work—nutritional deficiency had to be the result of damage to individual genes.

By early 1941, Beadle and Tatum had developed three nutritional mutants with which they could work. Tatum's work with Beadle showed that *Neurospora* synthesized needed nutrients in a series of reactions that were catalyzed, or accelerated, by enzymes. The product of one reaction was fed into the next reaction in a chain that ended once the desired product was formed. By providing different nutrients to each mutant, they were able to determine which reaction was blocked in each strain. The pattern of transmission suggested the sites of mutations had to be located at specific loci on the *Neurospora* chromosomes. Their conclusion, which addressed the function of the gene, was that it controlled a specific chemical reaction. What was not immediately clear was the nature of the gene itself: Did the gene encode the catalyst (protein), or was the gene itself the catalyst, given the current belief that the genetic material in cells was protein. Even after Oswald Avery established DNA as the genetic material (1945), Tatum remained unsure of the nature of the gene itself. The phrase "one gene–one enzyme" was coined in 1948 by Norman Horowitz, a former postdoctoral student in Beadle's laboratory, while studying mutants that affect the pathway in arginine production, the gene (DNA) encodes an enzyme.

Scientists later determined that one gene actually encodes one polypeptide chain, a chain of amino acids strung together in a specific order, much like beads on a string. A functioning protein might be made up of only one chain or several chains entwined together. This discovery, plus the realization that there are many other proteins besides enzymes, led to the "one gene–one enzyme" hypothesis being renamed the "one gene–one polypeptide" hypothesis. Even that designation was later modified as it was determined to be an oversimplification.

---

from parent to child. It also laid the foundation for the field of genetic engineering. Scientists have used genetic engineering to help treat inherited diseases as well as to improve agriculture production. Other applications of the technology, such as cloning, have stimulated debate among ethicists.

One of the spin-offs of Tatum and Beadle's *Neurospora* work was the large-scale production of the infection-fighting antibiotic penicillin. (Penicillin is produced naturally by some species of fungus in order to kill off their bacterial competitors.) In 1944 during the US involvement in World War II, Tatum began working with the Office of Scientific Research and Development to mass-produce penicillin in order to treat the infected wounds that many soldiers were developing. Thousands of lives were saved as a result.

Tatum's bacterial conjugation research was significant because it proved that through conjugation, bacteria can pass on traits such as resistance to antibiotics. Conjugation can take place anywhere bacteria live, especially in hospital environments where many strains of bacteria intermingle. It may take years to develop an antibiotic, but once a single cell evolves to withstand it, that trait quickly spreads through the entire population of bacteria.

Courtney Farrell

FURTHER READING

Davis, Rowland H. *Neurospora: Contributions of a Model Organism.* New York: Oxford UP, 2000. Print. Explores the laboratory methods, physiology, development, and biochemistry of Neurospora and summarizes over seventy-five years of research. Tatum and Beadle's work is highlighted.

Gillham, Nicholas. *Genes, Chromosomes, and Disease: From Simple Traits, to Complex Traits, to Personalized Medicine.* Upper Saddle River: Pearson, 2011. Print. Provides an overview of medical genetics and discusses the social implications of genetics.

Horowitz, Norman H. "Neurospora and the Molecular Revolution." *Genetics* 151.1 (1999): 3–4. Print. Explains the impact of Neurospora research on molecular genetics.

Lederberg, Joshua. "Edward Lawrie Tatum." *Annual Review of Genetics* 13 (1979): 1–5. Print. Focuses on the life and work of biochemist Edward Tatum and covers his contributions to the foundation of biochemical genetics.

Raju, Tonse N. K. *The Nobel Chronicles: A Handbook of Nobel Prizes in Physiology or Medicine, 1901–2000.* Bloomington: 1st Books, 2002. Print. Profiles recipients of the Nobel Prize in Physiology or Medicine and describes their contributions to genetics.

HOWARD MARTIN TEMIN

American molecular biologist

Howard Temin discovered the presence of a reverse transcriptase enzyme in the capsid of ribonucleic acid (RNA) tumor viruses, providing an explanation for how their genome is copied into deoxyribonucleic acid (DNA). His work greatly influenced the development of treatments for deadly viruses.

Born: December 10, 1934; Philadelphia, Pennsylvania
Died: February 9, 1994; Madison, Wisconsin
Primary field: Biology
Specialties: Molecular biology; virology; biochemistry

EARLY LIFE

Howard Martin Temin was born December 10, 1934 in Philadelphia, Pennsylvania, the second of three sons in the family of Henry and Annette Lehmann Temin. Temin developed a love of history and science at a young age. He attended Charles W. Henry Elementary in Germantown, a suburb of Philadelphia. In 1951, he graduated

from Central High School, a school for advanced students in Philadelphia. Temin presented the valedictory address, during which he spoke of the challenges of the new atomic age.

Beginning in 1950, Temin attended the first of three summer sessions at Jackson Laboratory in Bar Harbor, Maine. His work included the study of gonadotropic hormones and their relationship to ovulation in rabbits. In 1953, he published his first scientific paper in the *Journal of Heredity* under the direction of biochemist Theodore Ingalls. The article discussed congenital abnormalities in mice.

In 1951, Temin enrolled at Swarthmore College, graduating with a degree in biology four years later. Temin demonstrated his independent streak by refusing to participate in graduation ceremonies following a dispute with faculty. Nevertheless, he was described in the class yearbook as a future giant in the field of molecular biology.

LIFE'S WORK

Temin entered graduate school at the California Institute of Technology (Caltech) in 1955, working with biologist Albert Tyler, a student of geneticist Thomas Hunt Morgan. Temin and Tyler studied the embryological development of fruit flies. Temin's colleagues at Caltech included biochemist John Cairns, geneticist Matthew Meselson and molecular biologist Frank Stahl, all of whom would subsequently leave significant imprints in of the field of genetics. In 1957, Temin joined the laboratory of virologist Renato Dulbecco. In the early 1950s, Dulbecco had published a method for quantitating poliovirus in monolayers of cells, based on the ability of the virus to produce foci of killing plaques on cells. Harry Rubin, a postdoctoral student, was attempting to develop an analogous method for the quantitation of a tumor virus, the Rous sarcoma virus (RSV), and Temin joined Rubin in this work. By 1958, Temin and Rubin published their first joint paper on the subject. They produced an assay test to determine the ability of RSV to transform normal cells into those with malignant properties, a procedure known as a focus assay.

Temin's and Rubin's research on the subject of RSV produced several scientific publications during the next year, including one of their observations that sensitivity of RSV to irradiation suggested a role for DNA in its replication cycle. Since the genome of RSV was RNA, Temin's interpretation was met with significant skepticism. In 1959, he suggested that given the radiation sensitivity of the virus, it likely replicated through a DNA intermediate, which integrated into the infected host genome. This argument was later termed the provirus hypothesis.

In 1959, Temin received his PhD from Caltech but remained there another year while pursuing further genetic studies of RSV. He became increasingly convinced that his provirus hypothesis was correct. The following year, he moved to the University of Wisconsin's McArdle Laboratory for Cancer Research, where he remained for the duration of his career.

In 1962, Temin married Rayna Greenberg. The couple had two daughters. During the next several years, Temin observed that inhibitors, which act at the level of DNA, would also inhibit the activity of RSV, while having no effect on growth of other RNA viruses. These results fit well with the provirus hypothesis.

At the time, viruses were not thought to incorporate enzymes within their structure. The idea that an enzyme could copy RNA into DNA was even more novel. In 1967, when biologist Joseph Kates demonstrated that poxvirus carried an enzyme for transcribing DNA into RNA as part of its structure. Other scientists began discovering similar results with other viruses. In addition, it was discovered that certain DNA transforming viruses did so through integration into host cell genomes.

In 1970, Satoshi Mizutani, a postdoctoral fellow in Temin's laboratory, developed an assay method for measuring the activity of an enzyme capable of transcribing RNA into DNA, an enzyme referred to as the reverse transcriptase. Temin announced the results at a cancer conference in Houston, Texas in May 1970. An article was published shortly afterwards in the journal *Nature*, along with an identical discovery reported by biologist David Baltimore using a murine (mouse) RNA tumor virus. The presence of the enzyme was subsequently reported in a large number of other RNA tumor viruses. In 1975, on his forty-first birthday, Temin was awarded the Nobel Prize in Physiology or Medicine.

Temin spent much of his career studying the genetics of avian tumor viruses such as RSV, now placed in the viral category of retroviruses—RNA viruses that utilize a DNA intermediate. Though internationally renowned for his work, he remained dedicated to the working in the laboratory. In 1992, he was diagnosed with cancer. Although his cancer proved fatal, Temin still managed to produce fifteen publications while battling the disease. He also applied for a patent for an AIDS vaccine. Late in his career, Temin received an honorary degree from his alma mater Swarthmore, as well as honorary degrees from numerous other universities.

Temin died on February 9, 1994, from a rare form of lung cancer, adenocarcinoma. Temin never smoked cigarettes and was a vociferous advocate of antismoking campaigns throughout his life.

IMPACT

Beginning with the work of pathologist Peyton Rous early in the twentieth century, it became apparent that the class of infectious agents known as RNA tumor viruses could transform normal cells into malignant ones. Temin's work in the 1960s suggested that these viruses replicate using a DNA intermediate. Since the cell was not known to encode an enzyme that copies RNA into DNA, Temin's hypothesis was initially ignored by the scientific establishment. Geneticist Francis Crick had posited in the 1950s that the flow of information in the cell went from DNA to RNA to protein, a flow known as the "central dogma of molecular biology." Temin's hypothesis seemed to contradict what had become the

Howard Temin Discovers Reverse Transcriptase

In 1955, Howard Temin enrolled in the graduate program at the California Institute of Technology where he became aware of the work carried out by Renato Dulbecco dealing with the Rous sarcoma virus (RSV). RSV, and even cell extracts containing RSV, had been demonstrated to induce breast tumors when inoculated into chickens as early as 1910, though the mechanism for how this occurred was unknown. Dulbecco had recently developed a method to count plaque polioviruses in laboratory dishes, and Temin joined Dulbecco's group, his doctoral thesis including an attempt to demonstrate an analogous procedure to measure RSV in chicken cells. Along with Harry Rubin, a postdoctoral fellow in Dulbecco's laboratory, Temin developed an infectious assay for RSV. However, instead of killing the infected cells, as was the situation with poliovirus, RSV transformed the chicken cells into a laboratory analogy of cancer cells. The infected cells grew into piles of foci that could be counted. Each infectious RSV particle produced a single focus, the cells of which exhibited characteristics shown also by cancer cells.

Temin's first clue that replication of RSV was unusual came from studies of the effects of X-rays or ultraviolet light on replication of the virus. Agents such as Newcastle's Disease Virus, which contained an RNA genome, replicated normally in cells previously irradiated (exposed to radiation) to prevent cell division. However when chicken cells were irradiated prior to infection by RSV, by then known to contain an RNA genome as well, the virus failed to replicate. When the cells were irradiated following RSV infection, viral replication was again partially sensitive. Temin attempted to explain these results by suggesting that both RSV and chicken cells shared a similar radiation target, the DNA. Since the RSV genome was RNA, the implication was that the virus required a DNA intermediate for replication. Temin proposed his provirus theory in 1959, at a time when no enzyme was known that could copy RNA into DNA.

After completion of his doctoral work in 1960, Temin moved to McArdle Laboratory at the University of Wisconsin, where he continued his studies of RSV replication. Further experiments supported his hypothesis that RSV replicates through a DNA intermediate, which integrates into the cell genome. For example, RSV replication was sensitive to agents such as the drug actinomycin D, which binds DNA and DNA analogs such as cytosine arabinoside. Meanwhile, other scientists had demonstrated the ability of viruses to incorporate enzymes into their physical structure, developing assay tests to measure such enzymes. Temin proceeded to study similar assay methods using purified RSV.

In 1970, Temin and a postdoctoral student, Satoshi Mizutani, finally developed an assay method that could measure the incorporation of nucleotides into DNA using an RNA template and RSV nucleocapsids as the source of enzyme. The enzyme, reverse transcriptase, was subsequently demonstrated to be present in numerous RNA tumor viruses. Temin published his work in the journal *Nature* in 1970, adjacent to a similar report by biologist David Baltimore who demonstrated the same enzyme in a mouse tumor virus.

consensus among biologists pertaining to Crick's hypothesis, despite the fact that Crick did not actually rule out the possibility of RNA to DNA transfer.

In 1970, Temin and Baltimore, working independently, demonstrated the presence of reverse transcriptase as part of the structure of viruses. The discovery explained how RNA tumor viruses could integrate into the host in a form known as a provirus. The existence of the reverse transcriptase was found to be integral to the replication of a larger class of viruses now called retroviruses.

Retrovirologists quickly attempted to apply Temin's work to explain how viruses might cause cancer. Their hypotheses regarding the provirus theory of cancer were subsequently shown to be premature, as it became increasingly that clear viruses were not associated with most human cancers. However, the reverse transcriptase was shown to play a major role in replication of other human retroviruses as well, most notably the human immunodeficiency virus (HIV). The first generation of anti-HIV drugs specifically targeted the viral reverse transcriptase. A cellular reverse transcriptase was also identified by molecular biologist Carol Greider in the 1980s as the enzyme that synthesizes telomeres on the tips of chromosomes. Temin's discovery opened the way for scientific acceptance of such an enzyme.

Richard Adler

851

FURTHER READING

Crotty, Shane. *Ahead of the Curve: David Baltimore's Life in Science*. Berkeley: U of California P, 2001. Print. Biography of Baltimore, codiscoverer of the reverse transcriptase. The role played by Temin in the discovery of reverse transcriptase is also highlighted.

Mukherjee, Siddhartha. *The Emperor of All Maladies: A Biography of Cancer*. New York: Scribner, 2010.

Print. Pulitzer Prize–winning book about cancer, from its earliest descriptions to modern discoveries and treatments. Temin's contributions are discussed.

Varmus, Harold. *The Art and Politics of Science*. New York: Norton, 2009. Print. Autobiography of one of the men who discovered the significance of cellular oncogenes. Discusses the role played by Temin and others in discovery and significance of the reverse transcriptase.

THEOPHRASTUS

Greek botanist

Theophrastus was an ancient Greek philosopher and scholar. Over the course of his long life, he wrote many treatises on logic, science, ethics, politics, and rhetoric. He is considered one of the founders of botany and taxonomy.

Born: c. 372 BCE; Eresus, Lesbos, Greece
Died: c. 287 BCE; probably Athens, Greece
Also known as: Tyrtamus
Primary field: Biology
Specialty: Botany

EARLY LIFE

Theophrastus was born in Eresus on the island of Lesbos around 372 BCE. According to ancient sources, his father gave him the name Tyrtamus, but he later won the nickname Theophrastus ("divinely speaking") because of his eloquence in philosophical arguments.

After his initial education on Lesbos, Theophrastus moved to Athens, where he became a student of Plato, the most influential of all Greek philosophers. After Plato's death around 347 BCE, it is thought that Theophrastus moved to Stagira, where Plato's disciple Aristotle had established a new school.

Theophrastus worked during the age known as the Hellenistic period, a time when Greek drama, science, and philosophy spread throughout the ancient world. Thus, Theophrastus was a major philosophical figure at a time when Greek philosophy was at the height of its influence.

LIFE'S WORK

In 335 BCE, Aristotle founded the Peripatetic ("wandering") school at the Lyceum in Athens. Theophrastus became one of the most famous of the students in this school. Guided by Aristotle, the Peripatetic school is famous for turning Greek philosophy away from the abstract ideas and theories espoused by Plato and moving it toward a direct and dogmatic study of the physical world. The school is seen as a predecessor to the seventeenth-century philosophy of empiricism, the belief that through testing and experimentation a philosopher can explain the physical world. Empiricism is the basis of the modern-day scientific method.

With Aristotle serving as headmaster, the philosophers of the Peripatetic school made inquiries into virtually all known areas of Greek thought. In science, they studied anatomy, astronomy, economics, embryology, geography, geology, botany, physics, and zoology. They also wrote philosophical tracts on aesthetics, ethics, politics, and rhetoric. The combined works of the Peripatetic school form an encyclopedia of Greek knowledge of the ancient world.

Theophrastus was known for his works on botany and wrote two famous treatises on plants and taxonomy. Although these works have been lost, other ancient writers refer to Theophrastus's works on metaphysics and aesthetics. It is also written that Theophrastus was favored by Aristotle, who in his will designated Theophrastus as the guardian of his estate and children. More important, upon his death in 322 BCE, Aristotle designated Theophrastus to succeed him as head of the Lyceum in Athens.

For the following thirty-five years, Theophrastus led the Lyceum. The school prospered under his guidance, reportedly enrolling more than two thousand students, but it began a long decline following Theophrastus's death. Theophrastus headquartered the school at his estate, where it continued to operate until 86 BCE, when it was destroyed during the Roman conquest of

Theophrastus Searches for First Principles

Theophrastus worked and studied closely with Aristotle; some scholars believe that a portion of Aristotle's *Ta meta ta physika* (n.d.; *Metaphysics*, 1801) was incorrectly attributed to Aristotle and was actually written by Theophrastus. This view is strengthened by Theophrastus's argument in his *Metaphysica* (n.d.; *On First Principles*, 2010). In the essay, he attempts to answer the fundamental metaphysical question: What is the nature of being and existence? He believes that there are "first principles," akin to Euclid's geometrical axioms, from which the nature of reality can be logically derived. Like the Euclidian axioms, these principles are not themselves susceptible of logical proof, but can be discerned or discovered by careful observation and analysis.

He begins by discussing what he calls "intelligibles"—things that can be grasped by the intellect. He rejects the idea that only "mathematicals" can be intelligible, for the figures and proportions of mathematical reasoning are human-created and have no independent or self-standing reality. Thus, they do not connect with the natural world. While they may have utility and validity, they are not sufficient for developing first principles rooted in reality. The first principles must account for "sensible" things, those that can be comprehended by the senses, not merely through intellectual analysis. Thus, for Aristotle and Theophrastus, the discovery of first principles lies in classifying objects and discovering their physical properties.

The two physical phenomena that interest Theophrastus are motion and life. Motion he sees as relating primarily to astronomy, to which he assigns an inclusive definition. One example he uses is that of the tides. They come in and drench everything and then recede, allowing things to dry out. To assign the tides to astronomy was a considerable insight in Theophrastus's time. However, he also remarks that the repetitive action of the tides is purposeless and thus may not be among the phenomena that should be investigated first.

He also sees apparently purposeless aspects of animals. He gives the examples of breasts in males, beards, and deer that grow enormous horns that cover their eyes and hamper them. Similar purposeless phenomena are found in plants.

From these observations he concludes that scientific investigation should begin with mathematics and with the search for some boundary in nature. He cites Democritus's notion that the atom is the indivisible particle of nature and suggests that it should be investigated. Once the boundaries are found, what exists would then be known. Inquiry could then begin to focus on how existing things, particularly plants and animals, relate to one another. This conclusion is consistent with Aristotle's *Metaphysics*.

Although Theophrastus and Aristotle were close collaborators, Theophrastus's reputation is overshadowed by Aristotle's. After Aristotle's death, Theophrastus became the leader of the Lyceum. The preservation of the Aristotelian tradition, and of Aristotle's ideas, may be laid at his door, and his own contributions are incorporated in the Aristotelian tradition.

Athens. By the time of his death around 287 BCE, Theophrastus was well-loved by his students and pupils, and reportedly the entire population of Athens attended his funeral.

Over the course of his long life, Theophrastus composed more than one hundred books that covered a wide variety of scientific, philosophical, historical, and psychological thought. However, few of these works have survived. His most complete surviving work is a multivolume botanical treatise, divided into two books: *Peri phytikon historion* (*Enquiry into Plants and Minor Works on Odours and Weather Signs*, 1916; commonly referred to as *The History of Plants*) and *Peri phytikon aition* (partial translation in *De Causis Plantarum*, 1976; commonly referred to as *On the Causes of Plants*).

Theophrastus was the first to undertake a systematic approach to botany. In his treatise, he discusses each plant in terms of description, classification, geographic distribution, mode of reproduction, and seed germination. Despite lacking modern-day terminology, Theophrastus distinguished two groups of flowering plants, as well as the differences between flowering plants and cone-bearing trees. His system continues to provide the basic principles for botanical studies.

In his botanical works, Theophrastus described more than five hundred species of plants that inhabited the Mediterranean. His classification system divided plants into four families: trees, shrubs, undershrubs, and herbs. He presented accurate theories on why some flowers bear petals and others do not. He classified the various locations of petals and ovaries on certain plants.

By studying plants over the course of their life cycles, Theophrastus described the ways in which specific plants and trees grow.

Theophrastus was the first scientist to record regeneration, the process by which a broken off root or branch can grow an entirely new plant. He also listed many plant species according to their common Greek names. In so doing, he was one of the first philosophers to attempt a system of taxonomy.

Theophrastus also introduced his own ethical views into his botanical tracts by declaring that the killing and eating of animals by humans is ethically wrong, because plants and vegetables provide sufficient nutrients for human survival. Therefore, Theophrastus is one of the first known vegetarians in human history.

There remain only fragments of his other scientific works, which include *Peri physikōn* (On physics) and *Peri lithōn* (*Theophrastus's History of Stones*, 1746). In *Peri physikōn*, Theophrastus writes the first known reference to pyroelectricity, a phenomenon in which certain minerals, when heated or cooled, sometimes generate an electric charge.

While not scientific, the only other important surviving work by Theophrastus is his *Charactēres ethikōi* (c. 319; *The Moral Characters of Theophrastus*, 1616). This book contains a series of brief descriptions in which Theophrastus ethically analyzes various types of people. Essentially, Theophrastus attempted to categorize people according to ethical characteristics, such as kindness or generosity, or cruelty, in a manner similar to his work with plants.

IMPACT

Though little of his work remains, Theophrastus was highly regarded by the ancients, with numerous references and citations to his philosophical work appearing in the work of later philosophers. However, because such a small number of Theophrastus's works survived, historical opinion is divided as to how much he influenced Western thought in areas other than botany.

Scientifically, Theophrastus is the most prominent botanist of the ancient era. His work was almost lost following the fall of the Roman Empire, and the only surviving manuscripts are those copied by Arab scholars during the Middle Ages. However, beginning in the Renaissance, his work was reintroduced to the West in Latin translations of Arabic and Greek texts. In the nineteenth century, German scientists began collecting the fragments and works of Theophrastus, using his work as a springboard in the creation of modern-day botany.

Jeffrey Bowman

FURTHER READING

Fortenbaugh, William W. *Theophrastus of Eresus: Sources for His Life, Writings, Thoughts, and Influence*. Boston: Brill, 2007. Print. Compiles translations and commentary of Theophrastus's texts. Includes a thorough introduction and index.

Morton, A. G. *History of Botanical Science: An Account of the Development of Botany from Ancient Times to the Present Day*. New York: Academic, 1981. Print. Covers the history of the development of botanical sciences. Discusses Theophrastus's contributions to the field.

Negbi, Moshe. "The Scientific Cradle of Botany: Theophrastus and Other Pioneers." *Israel Journal of Plant Sciences* 58.3–4 (2010): 309–18. Print. Describes the life and scientific achievements of Theophrastus, as well as the impact of his research on the work of Pliny and Dioscorides.

J. J. THOMSON

English physicist

J. J. Thomson discovered the electron, for which he received the Nobel Prize in Physics in 1906, and subsequently proposed a model for the interior of the atom. His discovery rendered false the belief in the atom as the indivisible building block of matter.

Born: December 18, 1856; Cheetham Hill, England
Died: August 30, 1940; Cambridge, England
Primary fields: Physics; mathematics

Specialty: Atomic and molecular physics

EARLY LIFE

Joseph John Thomson was the oldest son of Joseph James Thomson, a bookseller, and Emma Swindells. The young Thomson was to be apprenticed to an engineering firm, but while awaiting an opening, he entered Owens College in Manchester at the age of fourteen. Two years later, Thomson's father died, and his mother

Thomson Discovers the Electron

In 1879, English chemist William Crookes became the first to observe radiation emitted from a cathode in an evacuated glass tube through which electric discharge occurred. Noting that cathode rays cast shadows and are bent by a magnetic field, Crookes concluded that they consist of electrified particles. The following year, German physicist Eugen Goldstein countered that these rays are a form of wave. This difference of opinion regarding the nature of cathode rays became a central problem of physics.

In 1883, German physicist Heinrich Hertz found no correlation between a magnetic field within a discharge tube and the direction of the cathode rays. He also applied static electric fields both inside and outside the tube, which would presumably produce a force perpendicular to the direction of the rays and deflect them if they contained charged particles. Observing no deflection, he took this as confirmation of his original wave hypothesis.

Hoping to resolve the controversy, English physicist J. J. Thomson slightly modified Jean-Baptiste Perrin's experiment, a variation of Crookes's in which Perrin had collected negatively charged particles from cathode rays in an insulated metal cup. Using a magnetic field to bend the rays, Thomson collected them in a metal cup placed away from the direct line that the rays would have made without the magnetic field. He found that the charge in the cup reached a steady state after attaining a maximum value, which he correctly explained as having been caused by leakage into surrounding space.

Applying an electrostatic field between two conducting plates placed midway within the tube and utilizing a better vacuum technique than that available to Hertz, Thomson observed the deflection of the rays. This con-firmed that they are composed of negatively charged particles. Thompson correctly explained that an insufficient vacuum had caused Hertz's failure to observe electric deflection: Excess gas in the tube had shielded the rays from the very field meant to deflect them.

Using a cloud chamber, Thomson observed and measured the mass and velocity of these charged particles. The small mass, combined with the particles' relatively large velocity, also explained one of Hertz's observations—namely, that the rays penetrated thin sheets of metal. From Philipp Lenard's result of constancy of magnetic deflection of the rays and independence of chemical properties, Thomson soon realized that he had discovered a universal component of atoms found in radioactive substances, in alkali metals bombarded by ultraviolet light, and in a variety of gaseous discharge phenomena. Thomson's discovery that the cathode-ray particle is universal and fundamental to the structure of all matter unraveled the puzzling conductivity of gases, the nature of electricity, and the wave-particle controversy.

Thomson's discovery of the electron and its universality marked the beginning of a new period in atomic research. Based on a study of the mechanical stability of the electrons under the influence of the electrostatic force, Thomson showed that the electron circulates around the atom in concentric circles. Calling the cathode-ray particles "corpuscles" and speculating that the number of electrons in an atom increased proportionally with an element's atomic weight, Thomson attempted to explain the structure of chemical elements and their properties. His work was essential to the understanding of atomic structure and led directly to the formulation of quantum physics.

could not afford the apprenticeship fee. With scholarships, Thomson was able to remain at Owens, from which he received a certificate and prize in engineering in 1876.

Later that year, Thomson entered Trinity College at Cambridge University and spent the rest of his life there. Studying mathematics, he obtained the second-highest score in the 1880 Tripos final examination and thus earned the title second wrangler, a distinction he shared with other such illustrious physicists as James Clerk Maxwell and Lord Kelvin. In 1880, he was elected a fellow of Trinity, where his mathematical research extended some of Maxwell's earlier results in electrodynamics.

Thomson became a lecturer in mathematics at Trinity in 1882 and a university lecturer in 1883. The following year, at the age of only twenty-eight, Thomson succeeded Lord Rayleigh as Cavendish Professor of Experimental Physics and director of the Cavendish Laboratory. In 1890, he married Rose Paget, one of the first women admitted to advanced study at Cambridge. The Thomsons had two children; their son George Paget Thomson became a famous physicist as well.

LIFE'S WORK

Thomson was elected a fellow of Trinity on the basis of his thesis on energy transformation, a topic that first interested him at Owens College and that remained an important theme in his research throughout his life. From his work on electrodynamics, he published a theoretical proof that a moving electrified sphere undergoes an increase in mass because of its charge, one of the earliest indications of the relationship between mass and energy. While this was an important result itself, it was even more important in stimulating other advances from Maxwell's work, by not only Thomson but also other physicists.

In 1882, Thomson won the Adams Prize for an essay on the interaction of two closed vortices in an incompressible fluid. In *A Treatise on the Motion of Vortex Rings* (1883), he extended his results to the "vortex atom" proposed by Kelvin in 1867. After determining the arrangements necessary for the stability of two or more vortex rings in a frictionless fluid, Thomson used this model to explain the combining power of various elements in some simple molecules.

At Cavendish, Thomson chose the topic of gas discharge for experimental investigation. It had been known since the 1850s that the passage of an electric current through an evacuated tube causes the small amount of gas remaining in the tube to glow. This topic regained interest in the early 1880s as a result of new studies on cathode rays, the emanation from the cathode (negative electrode) in evacuated tubes. Some of Thomson's earlier theoretical work, in fact, was aimed at an improved understanding of cathode rays. English physicists generally believed the rays were streams of fast-moving charged particles, while German physicists generally regarded them as electromagnetic phenomena. Sir William Crookes had shown that a magnetic field deflects the path of cathode rays, and while this evidence suggested charged particles, it was not conclusive.

Thomson set out to demonstrate that an electric field could also deflect the path of cathode rays, a goal that others had not achieved, and he finally succeeded in 1897 with highly evacuated tubes. This result finally offered conclusive evidence that cathode rays are indeed particles. He also developed several methods for experimentally determining the charge-to-mass (e/m) ratio of these particles. Regardless of the source of the cathode rays, this ratio was always the same, and its value implied a very large charge or a very small mass for each particle. Although other physicists had determined similar e/m values, only Thomson assumed the charge

to be equal to the smallest-known charge of an ion and thus concluded that the mass of the particle was more than one thousand times smaller than that of a hydrogen atom (the ratio is now known to be about 1/1836). Thus, Thomson discovered the electron and received the Nobel Prize in Physics in 1906.

With the idea of the electron as the fundamental unit of electricity and a universal constituent of the atom, Thomson proposed a model for the internal structure of the atom. His model consisted of a sphere of diffuse positive charge in which were distributed negatively charged electrons that exactly balanced the positive charge. Despite drawbacks to the model, it had the advantage of being easily visualized, though it shortly gave way to the more successful nuclear atom proposed by Thomson's student, Ernest Rutherford, in 1911.

After 1906, Thomson turned his attention to "canal rays," streams of positively charged ions that travel in the opposite direction to cathode rays in discharge tubes. His investigation of their properties continued for many years and helped pave the way for Rutherford's 1914 discovery of the proton, which has an equal and opposite charge to that of the electron. As Thomson's experimental techniques grew more sophisticated, he was able to separate gaseous products differing very little in mass. In 1913, for example, the two separated species from a neon discharge proved to be the two most abundant isotopes of the element known as neon. Although different isotopes of the same element were known to exist in radioactive transformations, Thomson produced the first evidence for the existence of isotopes of a stable element.

Thomson resigned his positions at the Cavendish in 1919 and was succeeded by Rutherford. As an honorary professor, he worked daily at the Cavendish and remained master of Trinity College from 1918 until shortly before his death in 1940. Throughout his career, Thomson received numerous honors, prizes, and honorary degrees. He served as president of the Cambridge Philosophical Society, the British Association for the Advancement of Science, and the Royal Society of London.

IMPACT

Thomson's most notable and lasting scientific achievement was his discovery of the electron. Once scientists accepted the electron as a constituent of all atoms, the century-old belief in the atom as the indivisible building block of matter was rendered false. Atoms have internal structure, and much of the research in both physics and chemistry since 1897 has been to elucidate that structure.

For physicists, the electron remains of interest as one of the fundamental subatomic particles, but for chemists, the behavior of electrons, especially the atom's outermost valence electrons, is crucial in determining the properties and chemical behavior of each element.

Thomson's importance, however, extends far beyond his scientific achievements. He wrote several treatises on research topics and coauthored a widely used four-volume textbook of physics. At Cambridge, Thomson developed the Cavendish Laboratory into a preeminent research institution for subatomic physics in the early twentieth century. An outstanding teacher and leader, he trained numerous physicists, many of whom became professors themselves and seven of whom won the Nobel Prize. In introductory physics and chemistry textbooks, Thomson is often relegated to a historical footnote, but his contributions, both direct and indirect, have a direct

bearing on more of the topics in those books than many realize.

Richard E. Rice

FURTHER READING
Davis, E. A., and I. J. Falconer. *J. J. Thomson and the Discovery of the Electron*. London: Taylor, 1997. Print. A survey of Thomson's discovery of the electron within the context of his life and other achievements.
Kim, Dong-Won. *Leadership and Creativity: A History of the Cavendish Laboratory, 1871–1919*. Boston: Kluwer, 2002. Print. Traces the success of Cavendish through its leaders and scientists, with a strong focus on Thomson.
Thomson, J. J. *Recollections and Reflections*. 1936. Cambridge: Cambridge UP, 2011. Print. Thomson's retrospective of his own life and career.

SAMUEL C. C. TING

American physicist

Ting discovered the high-energy particle J/psi in 1974, with a different method used simultaneously by Burton Richter at Stanford; both physicists received the 1976 Nobel Prize in Physics for their independent discovery. In the 1990s and early 2000s, Ting led the Alpha Magnetic Spectrometer project designed to measure cosmic rays.

Born: January 27, 1936; Ann Arbor, Michigan
Also known as: Samuel Chao Chung Ting
Primary field: Physics
Specialties: Quantum mechanics; theoretical physics; astrophysics

EARLY LIFE

Samuel Chao Chung Ting was born in Ann Arbor, Michigan, on January 27, 1936, to Chinese graduate students Kuan Hai Ting and Tsun-Ying Wang at the University of Michigan. His birth in America made him a United States citizen.

In April 1936, the Ting family returned to China. Their hopes for peaceful academic careers were dashed by the Japanese invasion of China in July 1937. With his parents both working, Ting was brought up by his widowed maternal grandmother. She had raised his mother on her own and dedicated herself to her grandson.

Ting entered a formal school for the first time in his life at age twelve in 1948, when his parents settled in Taiwan

to avoid the Communist conquest of mainland China completed in 1949. In Taiwan, his father worked as engineering professor and his mother as professor of psychology.

After graduating from Chien-Kuo High School in 1955, Ting enrolled at National Cheng Kung University in Tainan City, Taiwan. However, Ting set his sights on studying in the United States. He applied to the University of Michigan, where a friend of his parents, G. G. Brown, was dean of engineering.

Ting arrived in Detroit on September 6, 1956. He spoke very little English and had only a hundred dollars in cash, believing he could work his way through college. Ting depended on scholarships and took as many classes per term as possible. His favorite pastime became watching the university's football team.

In 1959, Ting earned his bachelor of arts degree in mathematics and physics. The following year, he married American architect Kay Louise Kune. They would have two daughters, Jeanne and Amy.

Ting entered the graduate program and, after just three years, received his doctorate in physics in 1962. His doctoral advisers were American physicists Lawrence W. Jones and Martin Earl Perl.

LIFE'S WORK

As a Ford Foundation Fellow, Ting went to the European Organization for Nuclear Research (CERN) in Geneva,

Switzerland, in 1963. He worked with Italian physicist Giuseppe Cocconi at CERN's proton synchrotron.

Returning to the United States in 1964, Ting worked one year as an instructor at Columbia University before becoming assistant professor there in the fall of 1965. That year, an experiment at the Cambridge Electron Accelerator appeared to indicate a violation of quantum electrodynamics. Ting was eager to repeat this experiment on his own. In Hamburg, Germany, scientists at the Deutsches Elektronen-Synchrotron (DESY) invited Ting as a group leader to perform this experiment there in 1966, while on leave from Columbia. Ting's team constructed a double-arm spectrometer. This enabled them to measure momentum and angle of deflection and to calculate masses of both the electron and the positron created by photon collision with a nuclear target in the synchrotron. Ting's experiment proved that there was no violation of quantum electrodynamics after all.

Having developed a taste for big science, working with a large team and expensive equipment, Ting joined the Massachusetts Institute of Technology (MIT) in 1967. He became full professor there in 1969.

Ting Puts Alpha Magnetic Spectrometer into Space

In the early 1990s, Samuel C. C. Ting turned his sights on one of contemporary physics' major unanswered questions. After the Big Bang created the universe, there should have been an equal amount of matter and antimatter. However, the universe appears to be almost entirely made of matter only.

In 1994, Ting approached the director of the National Aeronautics and Space Agency (NASA), Daniel Goldin with a proposal to send a magnetic spectrometer into space, to be installed at the International Space Station (ISS). It would measure the velocity and energy of the cosmic rays it recorded and identify these high-energy particles by changing their path magnetically. Protons and antiprotons, for example, would bend in different directions. If data from the recorded and measured high-energy particles would provide evidence of an atomic nucleus heavier than antihelium as their source, this would indicate a large cosmic agglomeration of antimatter, perhaps even an antimatter galaxy.

Goldin quickly approved Ting's proposal in 1995, making him principal investigator in charge of a budget that grew to nearly $2 billion and oversight of over five hundred scientists from fifty-six institutions in sixteen countries.

On June 2, 1998, AMS-01, a prototype of the Alpha Magnetic Spectrometer, was lifted aboard the space shuttle *Discovery* to the Russian space station Mir. In space, AMS-01 operated well. However, no antihelium was discovered.

Encouraged by the operational success of AMS-01, Ting's team assembled the AMS-02. However, tragedy struck on February 1, 2003, when the space shuttle *Columbia* disintegrated. As a result, NASA shortened the shuttle program. Under new NASA director Michael Griffin, in 2005, there was no longer a shuttle flight available to lift AMS-02 into space. The expensive apparatus sat at the facilities of the European Organization for Nuclear Research (CERN) in Geneva. Although it underwent final assembly and operational testing, its future was uncertain.

Rising to the challenge, Ting successfully lobbied Congress and the public to add a final space shuttle flight to carry AMS-02 into space. On October 15, 2008, US president George W. Bush signed the bill that authorized NASA to provide another shuttle flight to transport AMS-02. In January 2009, NASA added this flight and put AMS-02 on its manifest.

Suddenly, Ting decided to prolong the lifespan of AMS-02 in alignment with the extension of the life of the ISS, up to 2028. To the horror of many scientists, worrying about lack of time or project degradation, Ting ordered replacement of the helium-cooled superconducting magnet of AMS-02 with a weaker but more durable permanent magnet that would not require cooling. The helium needed to cool the strong magnet would have been expended in two years, with no possibility for a refill in space, terminating the experiment. Ting's team exchanged the magnets, and AMS-02 was flown from Geneva to the Kennedy Space Center on August 26, 2010.

On May 16, 2011, AMS-02 rode into space inside the cargo bay of the space shuttle *Endeavor*. On May 19, 2011, AMS-02 was attached to the ISS and began operations.

By 2012, Ting and his large team of fellow scientists were analyzing the data sent by AMS-02, amounting to about 1 gigabyte per second. Their mission was to learn more about the dark matter permeating the universe, discern the nature of cosmic-ray radiation of concern to a manned mission to Mars, and seek evidence of a large source of antimatter.

In 1971, Ting assembled a team of scientists on a quest to find new heavy particles and to describe the characteristics of heavy photons. Ting's team performed their experiments at Brookhaven National Laboratory. In August 1974, they discovered evidence of high-energy electron/positron pairs that appeared with a power of 3.1 billion electron volts. Immediately, Ting realized that these pairs were the footprints of a new subatomic particle.

Ting told the Frascati Laboratory of Italy of his tentative discovery, which was confirmed there in two days. He also met American physicist Burton Richter at Stanford University, who told Ting that he had discovered the same new particle by colliding positrons and electrons at the Stanford Linear Accelerator Center (SLAC). Ting and Richter announced their independent discovery of what they termed the J/psi particle on November 11, 1974. In 1975, Ting became member of the American National Academy of Sciences and a foreign member of the Academia Sinica of Taiwan. In 1976, Ting and Richter were awarded the Nobel Prize in Physics for their discovery of the J/psi particle. The following year, Ting was given the post of Thomas Dudley Cabot Institute Professor of Physics at MIT.

Throughout the 1980s, Ting continued research and led experiments in the field of high-energy particle physics. Because of the high costs involved in these experiments, Ting became an expert in securing funding and organizing this work. In 1985, after his divorce from Kune, he married Susan Carol Marks. They would have one son, Christopher.

Ting promoted scientific exchange with the People's Republic of China, where he has received honorary professorships from Beijing Normal University, Foshan University, and Jiaotong University, among others. That year, Ting also received an honorary doctorate from the Chinese University of Hong Kong.

In the early 1990s, Ting was frustrated because he was not given a position in two major high-energy particle projects, the Large Hadron Collider at CERN and the Superconducting Supercollider in the United States. However, when the US Congress cancelled the Superconducting Supercollider in 1993, Ting presented an alternative big science project to the National Aeronautics and Space Agency (NASA) in 1994. Ting's brainchild was the Alpha Magnetic Spectrometer (AMS) to be installed on the International Space Station by a space shuttle flight. Orbiting the Earth, the AMS would serve as a cosmic-ray detector looking for proof of antimatter and dark matter and measure cosmic rays for analysis. After initial approval in 1995, it would be another sixteen years before the AMS was launched, due to administrative issues, the 2003 space shuttle *Columbia* disaster, funding, and adjustments to the AMS itself. On May 16, 2011, the space shuttle *Endeavor* brought the AMS to the International Space Station. Three days later, it was installed and began operations. Ting had finally succeeded in laying the space-born foundations for further exploration of the cosmos and its constituent matter.

IMPACT

Ting made his major scientific discovery of the J/psi particle through an unusual gift for both theoretical thought and success with practical scientific experiments. Instead of focusing on either theoretical or experimental physics, as most physicists have done since the late twentieth century, Ting has embraced both fields. In addition, Ting has proven himself a remarkably competent and successful administrator of large science projects. He has managed to coordinate the work of teams of scientists that grew steadily in number and has overseen project budgets that exceeded one billion dollars.

After winning the Nobel Prize, Ting promoted further big science projects in the United States that required the commitment of large budgets. His forceful and persuasive personality helped Ting to persuade Congress to add a space shuttle flight to transport his visionary mega project, the space-born Alpha Magnetic Spectrometer (AMS). With the AMS installed aboard the International Space Station since May 2011, Ting has been in charge of the analysis of the data it has been transmitting and remained confident of significant discoveries, particularly concerning dark matter or new high-energy particles.

R. C. Lutz

FURTHER READING

Crease, Robert P., and Charles C. Mann. "The Great Synthesis." *The Second Creation: Makers of the Revolution in Twentieth-Century Physics*. Rev. ed. New Brunswick: Rutgers UP, 1996. 311–92. Print. Describes Ting's and Richter's independent discovery of the J/psi particle and the consequences of their discovery for particle physics and efforts towards a grand unified theory for all four fundamental physical forces.

Overbye, Dennis. "A Costly Quest for the Dark Heart of the Cosmos." *New York Times*, 17 Nov. 2010: A1. Print. In-depth article showing how Ting persisted against all odds to get his Alpha Magnetic Spectrometer flown to the International Space Station aboard a space shuttle flight created for his mission. Perceptive portrayal of Ting as a determined scientist.

Panek, Richard. *The 4 Percent Universe: Dark Matter, Dark Energy, and the Race to Discover the Rest of Reality*. New York: Houghton, 2011. Print. An accessible discussion of dark matter, subject of Ting's ambitious big science project, the space-born Alpha Magnetic Spectrometer.

CLYDE W. TOMBAUGH

American astronomer

Clyde W. Tombaugh discovered the dwarf planet Pluto and several star clusters and galaxies, studied the distribution of extragalactic nebulas, searched for small natural Earth satellites, and made observations of the surfaces of several planets and of Earth's moon.

Born: February 4, 1906; Streator, Illinois
Died: January 17, 1997; Las Cruces, New Mexico
Primary field: Astronomy
Specialty: Observational astronomy

EARLY LIFE

Clyde William Tombaugh was born in Streator, Illinois, on February 4, 1906. His parents, Muron and Adella Tombaugh, operated a farm. In high school, Tombaugh became a voracious reader, devoting many hours to encyclopedias and books on mathematics and physics. His uncle, an amateur astronomer, gave him books on astronomy. Tombaugh's interest in astronomy was further stimulated in 1920 when his father and uncle bought a small refracting telescope. This eventually became Tombaugh's first telescope, and he later installed it as a finder on a sixteen-inch telescope.

A poor corn crop in 1921 led the Tombaughs to move to a farm near Burdett, Kansas, where they took up wheat farming. After the harvest of 1925, Tombaugh began the tedious process of grinding and polishing a mirror for an eight-inch reflecting telescope. After sending the mirror away for silvering, he was disappointed to learn that it had a poor figure and would not work well. He then built a testing chamber for mirrors in a family tornado cellar and began working on a seven-inch mirror for his uncle, with much better results. In 1928, he completed a nine-inch reflecting telescope for himself and began serious observation.

Tombaugh's plans to attend Kansas State University in the fall of 1928 were thwarted by a summer hailstorm that destroyed the crops. Seeking advice, he mailed his best astronomical sketches to Lowell Observatory in Flagstaff, Arizona. Observatory director Vesto Slipher, who was seeking to hire a dedicated amateur astronomer to operate a new photographic telescope for a long-exposure survey of the sky, offered Tombaugh a job. In January 1929, Tombaugh traveled to the observatory for a ninety-day trial period.

LIFE'S WORK

Tombaugh's work at Lowell Observatory built upon the predictions of astronomer Percival Lowell, who had proposed in 1905 that an unknown object he called Planet X might cause the apparent discrepancies in the orbit of the planet Uranus, which had been discovered in 1781. The study of small deviations in Uranus's orbit had led to the discovery of Neptune in 1846, but the orbital motion of Uranus did not appear to be totally explained by Neptune's presence. Therefore, Lowell postulated the existence of Planet X and initiated a series of unsuccessful searches at his observatory in Flagstaff.

Lowell died in 1916, and further searches were delayed when his widow challenged his will, which had designated funds for the Lowell Observatory. After the suit was settled a decade later, a new thirteen-inch refractor telescope and wide-angle camera were built. Tombaugh's first duties after arriving in Flagstaff on January 15, 1929, included painting the new telescope, stoking the furnace, removing snow from the observatory domes, giving tours for visitors, and training for the planet search that began in earnest on April 26.

After months spent photographing the sky and analyzing the resulting photographic plates, it occurred to Tombaugh that a new planet could best be identified when it was near its opposition point, 180 degrees from the sun. He also began to look at new regions of the sky rather than concentrating on the predicted positions that Lowell had calculated. On February 18, Tombaugh observed an object in the photographic plates that he believed could be Planet X. The observatory announced the discovery of a new planet on March 13, 1930, the seventy-fifth anniversary of Lowell's birth. Six weeks later, on May 1, Slipher proposed the name Pluto for the planet, after the Greek god of the underworld, and a

Tombaugh Discovers Pluto

While working at the Lowell Observatory in Flagstaff, Arizona, Clyde W. Tombaugh made a key astronomical discovery that further developed both the scientific community's and the public's understanding of the solar system. The observatory had been established in 1894 by astronomer Percival Lowell, who in 1905 proposed the existence of an undiscovered planet that he called Planet X. After taking a position at the observatory, Tombaugh was tasked with operating the new photographic telescope and continuing the search for Planet X.

After taking photographs with the telescope, the astronomers at Lowell used a device known as a blink comparator to examine the photographic plates. With this device, two photographic plates of the same star region taken at different times are alternately seen or "blinked" in the viewer. Stellar objects, at their great distances, do not appear to move in the time between exposures. Closer objects, such as planets or asteroids, shift on the photographic plate and appear to "blink."

Initially, observatory director Vesto Slipher told Tombaugh to search the region of the sky near the constellation Gemini, but this attempt was unsuccessful. After Tombaugh took over the task of plate blinking, he devised a technique for photographing a region of the sky when it was at opposition—that is, on the side of the Earth opposite the sun. He noticed that at oppo-

sition, asteroids shifted about seven millimeters per day. Neptune, being farther from the Earth and from the asteroid belt, shifted significantly less, only about two millimeters per day. He reasoned that any undiscovered planet beyond Neptune ought to shift even less than Neptune does. If he could find such a planet, it would truly be Planet X.

In early 1930, Tombaugh decided to photograph the Gemini region again, this time near opposition. The first exposure of the Gemini region on January 21, 1930, was disturbed by wind gusts, which shook the telescope and blurred the image. He photographed this region again on January 23 and 29 and began the tedious blink procedure. On February 18, Tombaugh compared the poor January 21 plate with the January 23 plate and found Planet X exactly where it should be. Using a hand magnifier, he then compared the plates with another taken by a smaller camera. The object was in the same corresponding position on all three plates.

Both Slipher and astronomer Carl Lampland agreed that the object could be Planet X, and Slipher asked Tombaugh to rephotograph the region as soon as possible. Based on photographs taken on the following nights, Lampland, Slipher, and Tombaugh were able to confirm the presence of Planet X. The Lowell group proposed the name Pluto on May 1, 1930, and it was soon accepted by the astronomical community.

superposed *P* on *L* was chosen as its symbol, matching the initials of Percival Lowell.

For the next two years, Tombaugh continued his search to be sure that no other planets might be missed. On June 1, 1932, he made his second major discovery when he identified a globular cluster of stars in the Milky Way Galaxy's central hub. In the fall of 1932, Tombaugh was given a leave from the observatory to study at the University of Kansas, from which he earned a degree in astronomy in 1936. While a student, he met Patricia Edson, whom he married in 1934. Returning to Flagstaff, he continued his sky survey until 1943, pausing only to complete his master's degree in Kansas. In 1937, he discovered a supercluster of galaxies and measured its shape and size, eventually cataloging nearly thirty thousand galaxies. He found five open star clusters and identified nearly four thousand asteroids, of which more than seven hundred had not been observed before.

In 1943, Tombaugh began teaching physics and navigation for the US Navy at Northern Arizona State Teachers College in Flagstaff. In 1946, he moved to Las Cruces, New Mexico, to take a position at the White Sands Proving Ground. There, he designed optical equipment and supervised the tracking of V-2 missile firings. In 1953, he received military funding to search for small natural Earth satellites, and for the next two years, he divided his time between White Sands and Lowell Observatory, where the search began.

In 1955, Tombaugh transferred the natural satellite search project to New Mexico State University to facilitate observations from Quito, Ecuador. No such satellites were discovered, but in 1957, Tombaugh and his team took some of the first photographs of Sputnik, the first artificial satellite, and provided the observational basis for the safety of an extensive artificial satellite program. From 1955 to 1973, he was a professor in the Department of Earth Sciences and Astronomy at New Mexico State

University, where he established a comprehensive observational program of the five nearest planets.

Tombaugh remained active in astronomy after his retirement in 1973, continuing to build telescopes. Over his lifetime, he ground more than thirty optical surfaces and built many telescopes. Telescopes on which he worked were later featured at the observatories at New Mexico State University and the University of Kansas, both of which were named in his honor. Tombaugh died in Las Cruces, New Mexico, on January 17, 1997.

IMPACT

Over time, scientists determined that Lowell's predictions for the position of Pluto were based on faulty calculations, and its discovery near the predicted location was only a coincidence. It was conclusively demonstrated that the mass of Pluto was far too small to cause observable deviations in the orbits of Uranus and Neptune; thus, the two larger planets' orbits could not be used to predict Pluto's position. Tombaugh's decision to search for the planet beyond the coordinates predicted by Lowell, then, proved to be crucial to its discovery. For his contributions to the field of astronomy, Tombaugh was awarded the Jackson-Gwilt Medal by the Royal Astronomical Society in 1931.

By the early twenty-first century, several icy objects were discovered beyond Pluto's orbit, in the area known as the Kuiper Belt. The objects have orbital periods of more than 300 Earth years, compared to Pluto's 248-year period. In 2006, the International Astronomical Union grouped Pluto with other large Kuiper Belt objects, classifying them as "dwarf planets." Because Pluto is extremely difficult to observe from Earth, NASA launched its New Horizons spacecraft in 2006 with the goal of studying Pluto in depth during the craft's flight past in 2015 and observing several other Kuiper Belt objects when the craft travels farther out into space.

Joseph L. Spradley

FURTHER READING

Adler, Larry, Mary Carmichael, Nomi Morris, and A. Christian Jean. "Of Cosmic Proportions." *Newsweek* 148.10 (2006): 44–50. Print. Includes discussion of Tombaugh's discovery of Pluto and examines how and why Pluto lost its planetary status and how that decision changed the shape of the solar system.

Levy, David H. *Clyde Tombaugh: Discoverer of Planet Pluto*. Tucson: U of Arizona P, 1991. Print. Provides a complete biography of Tombaugh, written by a fellow astronomer and based on thorough research and personal interviews.

Tombaugh, Clyde W., and Patrick Moore. *Out of the Darkness: The Planet Pluto*. Harrisburg: Stackpole, 1980. Print. Provides an extended account of the discovery of Pluto, written for the fiftieth anniversary of its discovery, with background information on asteroids, Uranus, and Neptune.

Weintraub, David A. *Is Pluto a Planet? A Historical Journey through the Solar System*. Princeton: Princeton UP, 2007. Print. Examines how the definition of a planet has changed throughout history and chronicles how Pluto's claim to planetary status has been challenged in the decades since its discovery.

ALAN TURING

British mathematician

Twentieth-century British mathematician Alan Turing is regarded as one of the founders of modern computing. His research into machines and human thought helped shape the field of artificial intelligence.

Born: June 23, 1912; London, England
Died: June 7, 1954; Wilmslow, England
Primary field: Mathematics
Specialties: Computability theory; logic; statistics

EARLY LIFE

Alan Mathison Turing was born in London, England, on June 23, 1912. As a student at the Sherborne School, he excelled at science and math, and he won a number of mathematics prizes despite his unconventional solutions. Turing went on to attend King's College, Cambridge, where he continued to pursue mathematics at his own pace and using his own methods, with growing success. By 1933, Turing had begun to explore mathematical logic, which focuses on proofs and computation.

In 1936, Turing completed his first major paper, "On Computable Numbers, with an Application to the Entscheidungsproblem." In the paper, published in the *Proceedings of the London Mathematical Society*, Turing describes a machine that could perform simple, carefully defined operations on paper tape. Turing modeled his machine on the action of a human following explicit instructions. This theoretical "Turing machine" was essentially a computer, although the technology did not yet exist to build the machine as described.

Also in 1936, Turing traveled to the United States and began his graduate studies at Princeton University. He earned his PhD from the university in 1938. He soon returned to Cambridge, where he began work on an analog mechanical device.

LIFE'S WORK

World War II began soon after Turing's return to England. The British Government Code and Cypher School (GCCS) asked Turing to use his mathematical skills to help decipher the codes being used by the Germans. German scientists had developed a device known as the Enigma cipher machine, which generated constantly changing codes that were nearly impossible to break. Turing helped design the Bombe, a machine that successfully deciphered the Enigma code, while working for the British government. Turing was also responsible for monitoring the communications of German submarines so that ships could be safely rerouted to avoid them.

Building on Turing's work, other members of the GCCS designed Colossus, the first electronic, programmable, and digital computer. Unlike later computers, Colossus required that those operating it change some of the machine's wiring manually to set it up for a new job. Although its functions were limited, Colossus proved that digital electronic computing machinery was feasible. For his part in the war effort, Turing was granted the title of Officer of the Order of the British Empire.

After the war, Turing went to work for Britain's National Physical Laboratory (NPL), where he designed a computer that was based on programs rather than on the rearrangement of electronic parts. Turing's proposed computer could handle many different types of tasks ranging from numerical work to algebra, file management, and code breaking. However, this computer was never built.

In 1947, Turing left the NPL for the University of Manchester, where he worked on the development of the Manchester Automatic Digital Machine, another early computer. In 1950, he published his paper "Computing Machinery and Intelligence," introducing the concept of artificial intelligence. Turing believed that it was possible to create a machine that would imitate the processes of the human brain. Turing also proposed the "Turing test," which could be used to explore the question of whether a computer can think for itself.

The Turing test challenges a machine's capability to perform humanlike conversation. During the test, a human judge conducts a conversation with a human and a machine. If the judge cannot tell which is which, then the machine passes the test. Turing originally proposed the test to address objectively the question of whether machines can think. Turing believed that if the judge cannot tell the machine from the human after a reasonable amount of time, the machine is somewhat intelligent.

During the final years of his life, Turing worked on the concept that later came to be called artificial life. Turing's main focus in biology was the physical structure of living things. He was interested in how and why organisms develop particular shapes, and he wondered how simple cells know how to grow into complex forms. Turing saw the development of natural forms such as plants and animals as nothing more than a simple set of steps, or an algorithm. He used a computer to simulate a chemical mechanism that the genes of a zygote, or egg, use to determine the anatomical structure of an animal or plant. At the same time, he was experimenting with neural networks and brain structure. Turing's ultimate goal was to merge already established biological theory with mathematics and computers.

Turing was elected a fellow of the Royal Society of London in 1951, primarily in recognition of his work on Turing machines in the 1930s. In 1952, he published a theoretical paper on morphogenesis, the formation of living organisms. He also researched such topics as quantum theory and relativity theory.

In 1952, Turing was arrested and tried for engaging in a homosexual relationship, which was considered a crime in Britain. To avoid prison, he agreed to receive estrogen injections for one year in order to "neutralize" his homosexuality. Additionally, he was perceived as a security risk and subsequently lost his security clearance and ability to work for the government. Turing died on June 7, 1954. At the time, it was ruled a suicide.

IMPACT

Turing made many contributions to mathematics, logic, and statistics. He is best remembered, however, for his contributions to computability, machine design, and artificial intelligence. His work on computability, especially the universal Turing machine concept, was the first modern work on the theory of computation and became a central idea in recursive function theory (an active area of research in mathematical logic) and in automata theory (an important theoretical discipline within computer science). The value of Turing's efforts in

Turing Describes the Turing Machine

At one level, mathematics can be viewed as a method of rearranging symbols according to a set of rules to obtain true statements about the things represented by the symbols. British mathematician George Boole showed in *An Investigation of the Laws of Thought* (1854) that conclusions about the truth or falsity of a combination of statements could be arrived at by using similar methods. In 1928, German mathematician David Hilbert posed what most mathematicians considered to be the major questions about such a symbolic system for mathematics. One of these was the issue of decidability: Can the truth of any statement be determined by the mechanical manipulation of symbols in a finite number of steps?

Alan Turing, then a researcher at King's College, Cambridge, focused on the question of exactly what is meant by a mechanical procedure as performed by a human mathematician. In 1937, he published the groundbreaking paper "On Computable Numbers, with an Application to the Entscheidungsproblem" in the *Proceedings of the London Mathematical Society.* (The German word *Entscheidungsproblem,* literally "decision problem," is the term commonly used in reference to Hilbert's question.) In his paper, Turing describes the simplest type of machine that could perform the same manipulation of symbols that mathematicians perform.

Turing's theoretical device, which came to be referred to as a "Turing machine," is similar to a typewriter in that it can print out a string of symbols but different in that it can also read symbols and modify them. In addition, its behavior is controlled by the symbols read by it rather than by a human operator. For simplicity, Turing describes the machine as acting not on a sheet of paper but on an endless paper tape that can be read only one symbol at a time. The internal workings of the Turing machine involve a memory register that can exist in only a limited number of states and a set of rules that determine, on the basis of any symbol that can be read and the state of the internal memory, what symbol will be printed to replace it on the tape, what the new state of the internal memory will be, and which direction the tape will move, if at all.

In this important paper, Turing also describes a programmable Turing machine that can read, from the tape, a description of the rules of any other Turing machine and then behave as if it is that machine. Using the properties of such a programmable, or universal, Turing machine, Turing demonstrates that the answer to Hilbert's "decision problem" is a definite no; there is no mechanical procedure that can directly demonstrate the truth or falsity of a mathematical statement.

Turing's paper played an influential role in the development of computer technology and artificial intelligence. By reducing the manipulations and mental processes of a human mathematician to operations that could be performed by a machine that could be built, Turing suggested that the thinking involved in solving mathematical problems is not very different from that used by humans in planning and in the other types of problem-solving behavior that constitute human intelligence. If this is true, then there is no fundamental reason a suitable machine could not be programmed to display intelligence.

the design of code-breaking equipment to the war effort was also significant. His work at the NPL resulted in the creation of one of the first operating modern computers, which was used for important scientific and engineering applications in the 1950s. Turing's work also influenced the design of later computers, though his design ideas largely fell outside the mainstream of computer design developments.

Turing was especially influential as the foremost champion of artificial intelligence research in the first decade of modern computing. He introduced the distinction between robotics and artificial intelligence research, arguing that the future of artificial intelligence lay in the use of the stored-program computer, not in the construction of special-purpose robots that could mimic vision or other human attributes. The Turing test has endured as the principal test of success in artificial intelligence research. In the decades since Turing's death, the field of artificial intelligence has advanced to the point at which computers can be programmed to read stories and answer questions about them, assist medical doctors in diagnoses, play chess at the expert level, and assist humans in numerous information-processing tasks that have become commonplace in society.

Bob Crepeau

FURTHER READING
Copeland, B. Jack, ed. *Alan Turing's Automatic Computing Engine: The Master Codebreaker's Struggle to Build the Modern Computer.* New York: Oxford

UP, 2005. Print. Provides a detailed history of Turing's contributions to computer science and presents diagrams and illustrations explaining the hardware, software, and other features of Turing's computers.

Graham-Cumming, John. "Alan Turing: Computation." *New Scientist* 214.2867 (2012): 2. Print. Describes Turing's scientific achievements and discusses his efforts as a code breaker during World War II and his foundational work in computer science.

Hodges, Andrew. *Alan Turing: The Enigma—The Centenary Edition*. Princeton: Princeton UP, 2012. Print. Offers a biography of Turing, covering his influence on modern computer sciences, artificial intelligence, and the gay rights movement.

Petzold, Charles. *The Annotated Turing: A Guided Tour through Alan Turing's Historic Paper on Computability and the Turing Machine*. Hoboken: Wiley, 2008. Print. Guides readers through Turing's landmark paper, offering detailed explanation and examples.

Turing, Alan. "Computing Machinery and Intelligence." *Mind* 59 (1950): 433–60. Print. Provides Turing's counterarguments to common objections against artificial intelligence and introduces the Turing test, which decides when a computer has achieved intelligence.

HAROLD C. UREY

American chemist

Urey discovered deuterium, the heavy isotope of hydrogen, as well as methods of isotope separation. He founded the modern science of cosmochemistry, devoted to understanding the origin and development of the solar system.

Born: April 29, 1893; Walkerton, Indiana
Died: January 5, 1981; La Jolla, California
Primary fields: Chemistry; physics; astronomy
Specialties: Physical chemistry; cosmochemistry

EARLY LIFE

Harold Clayton Urey lived a life and had a career that spanned a period of rapid change and development in the United States and the world. By his own account, he was seventeen years old when he first saw an automobile; less than sixty years later, he held in his hand a rock from the surface of the moon.

After finishing high school, he spent three years as a teacher in country schools before entering the University of Montana, where he majored in biology. He had to work to stay in college; this included periods of employment as a waiter, a construction worker, and a biology instructor. When the United States entered World War I, Urey found a job as an industrial chemist in Philadelphia. He later said that this was one of the experiences that nudged him back toward a university career. He returned first to the University of Montana as an instructor for two years. Then, in 1921, he was admitted to graduate school in chemistry at the University of California, Berkeley.

Urey completed his PhD work in 1923 and moved on to the Niels Bohr Institute in Copenhagen on a fellowship. Danish physicist Niels Bohr was already established as the central figure in atomic and nuclear physics. Urey met many other leaders in physics and chemistry while in Europe.

LIFE'S WORK

Urey returned to the United States to take a teaching position at Johns Hopkins University. As a chemist with a strong grasp of physics, he had many lines of work open to him. His early papers were mainly related to the way molecules interact with light, using the then-new concepts of quantum theory to study a wide range of phenomena. In 1929, he moved to Columbia University.

Urey's most important discovery came two years later. Chemists were searching the periodic table for stable isotopes, which are variants of any chemical element with the same number of protons as the element but different amounts of neutrons. Urey followed this subject closely, since he foresaw the potential significance of these isotopes to many fields. After the discovery of the heavy isotopes of oxygen, he saw what had not been seen by others, namely, that this implied the existence of a rare heavy isotope of the lightest element, hydrogen. This had been searched for earlier, as part of a general survey, but not with the intensity and skill Urey and his collaborators then brought to the task. In a matter of months, they succeeded.

This isotope is so distinct from light hydrogen that Urey gave it a special name, deuterium (meaning "the second one"). Water made with it ("heavy water") boils at a temperature a few degrees higher than the usual kind and even looks slightly different. The chemical properties

Urey Discovers Deuterium and Heavy Water

Atoms are generally composed of three particles: protons, neutrons, and electrons. The periodic table of elements ranks elements according to the number of protons they contain. Thus, hydrogen, which has only one proton in its nucleus, has the atomic number one. An isotope is a variant of a given element that has the same number of protons but a different number of neutrons, as its original element. The term "isotope" comes from the Greek words *iso* (same) and *topos* (space), reflecting the fact that all isotopes of a particular element occupy the same spot on the periodic table.

The concept of isotopes was first introduced in 1913 by Frederick Soddy, who provided evidence that different elements can occupy the same position in the periodic table. In the early 1920s, Francis William Aston found that hydrogen has one proton, no neutrons, and no electrons, whereas oxygen has eight protons, eight neutrons, and eight electrons. Soon afterward, William Francis Giauque discovered the existence of oxygen isotopes that had more than eight neutrons. As a result, he declared the standards for physical and chemical measurements inaccurate. Several other scientists suggested that a hydrogen isotope with an atomic weight of two—that is, a species consisting of one proton, one neutron, and one electron—might exist. It was expected, however, that this isotope would be much less common than the hydrogen isotope that had no neutrons.

The different physical properties of the oxygen isotopes led Harold Urey and his coworkers Ferdinand Brickwedde and George M. Murphy to suggest that the vapor pressures of the hydrogen isotopes, if they existed, would be different. If this were true, they reasoned, the isotopes would boil at different temperatures. In December 1931, Urey and his coworkers announced that they had isolated deuterium, a hydrogen isotope containing one neutron, by distilling liquid hydrogen. Urey proved the success of his procedure by using emission spectroscopy, a technique that can be used to demonstrate the existence of any gas. In 1934, Urey, then forty-one, was awarded the Nobel Prize in Chemistry for his work.

Water obtained from natural sources contains one deuterium atom for every 6,760 ordinary hydrogen atoms. When electricity is passed through water, hydrogen and oxygen separate as gases. This process, called electrolysis, is performed in an electrolytic cell. Hydrogen is isolated at the cathode end of the cell. When naturally obtained water is electrolyzed, ordinary hydrogen is deposited at the cathode, whereas deuterium remains in the liquid form. This result occurs because the isotopes have different properties.

Until 1943, electrolysis was the only method used to prepare deuterium and heavy water on a large scale. Since then, it has been replaced by less expensive processes, such as the process of fractional distillation that Urey used in his discovery of deuterium. This process works because ordinary water has a boiling point of 100 degrees Celsius at 1 atmosphere of pressure, whereas deuterated water has a boiling point of 101.42 degrees Celsius at the same pressure.

Urey also demonstrated that the isotopes of other elements could be isolated by taking advantage of their different physical properties. His studies led to the identification of the boron isotopes, and in the fall of 1940, he succeeded in isolating the heavier isotope of sulfur.

of hydrogen and deuterium are different enough that aquatic organisms cannot live in pure heavy water.

The award of the Nobel Prize to Urey in 1934 sealed his reputation as a leader in his field. In the remaining years before World War II, Urey centered his efforts on the practical separation of isotopes on a scale large enough to permit the power of isotopic methods to be exploited in physical and chemical research. He worked with deuterium and with heavy isotopes of carbon, nitrogen, oxygen, and chlorine, all essential elements for life. He also served as the first editor of the *Journal of Chemical Physics*, which became the most widely read journal in the field.

When atomic energy and atomic weapons became popular around 1940, Urey's Columbia colleagues Enrico Fermi and Leo Szilard were among the first to undertake work in the field. Urey led the effort to separate the fissionable isotope of uranium, U-235, from the much larger mass of U-238 in the natural element. He also became the director of the Special Alloyed Materials (SAM) Laboratory at Columbia.

Urey always had a strong interest in politics, and the destruction of Hiroshima and Nagasaki gave him a feeling of personal responsibility that he never lost. Especially in the early postwar years, when he had moved to the University of Chicago together with Fermi, the Mayers,

Szilard, Willard Libby, Edward Teller, and others, he spent much of his time writing, speaking, and lobbying in an effort to bring nuclear weapons and nuclear power under control in some internationally viable way.

Returning to the laboratory, he found that his prewar research interests had lost their excitement for him, and he looked for new directions. He found them in the natural world. His deep knowledge of isotopic processes was first applied to the Urey temperature scale, a method of determining the temperatures at which organisms grew (or rocks formed) in ancient periods, using the subtle isotopic patterns of oxygen found in fossil shells or rocks. With his students, he pioneered studies that made clear the history of ice ages and even of the life cycles of species long extinct.

Meanwhile, Urey broadened this historic interest to a general search for understanding of the earliest records of the origin of the Earth, sun, and planets, and of the origin of life. Immersing himself in the literature of the subject, he quickly came to believe that he could do better. His resulting book, *The Planets: Their Origin and Development* (1952), raised the discussion of the subject to a new level and contributed to the early development of cosmochemistry, the study of the chemical properties of the matter that makes up the universe. Two other landmark papers, one with his student Harmon Craig on meteorites and one with Hans Suess on the abundance of the elements, marked further progress. Urey's student Stanley Miller performed a classic experiment that gave support to Urey's ideas on the origins of life.

In 1958, Urey moved to the new campus of the University of California, San Diego. The rapid growth of this university's standing in science owed much to his inspiration and efforts. At the age of eighty, he was still working and publishing regularly. He published his last scientific paper at age eighty-four, after a long career during which he received many honors and medals.

Married for almost sixty years to Frieda Daum Urey, he had four children and numerous grandchildren.

IMPACT

Thanks to Urey's findings, stable isotopes such as deuterium have become important tools in many fields of scientific research. The discovery of deuterium has had a great impact on both science and life in general; a central use is in the hydrogen (fusion) bomb. Heavy water, on the other hand, has a central role in nuclear reactor proceedings. Heavy-water reactors are manufactured in many countries, and heavy water may become even more important as nuclear energy becomes more widely used throughout the world.

The use of deuterated solvents (solvents whose hydrogens have been replaced with deuterium) has helped organic and analytical chemistry significantly in the identification of unknown compounds. The operation of certain sophisticated pieces of scientific equipment, such as the nuclear magnetic resonance (NMR) spectrometer, is based on the existence of isotopes such as deuterium.

Medicine has used deuterium to study biochemical and physiological changes in the human body. Successful results with deuterium have led to the use of other isotopes, such as carbon 14, in biochemistry.

Finally, the possible existence of a relationship between isotope abundance and temperature has aided research into the nature of the Earth's climate from thousands and millions of years ago, as well as research intended to determine the age and formation of the solar system.

James R. Arnold

FURTHER READING

Brian, Denis. *The Voice of Genius: Conversations with Nobel Scientists and Other Luminaries*. 1995. Cambridge: Perseus, 2001. Print. Contains interviews with prize-winning scientists, including Urey.

Cohn, Mildred. "Harold Urey: A Personal Remembrance Part I." *Chemical Heritage* 23.4 (2005): 8–48. Print. Presents the author's experience of working with Urey, describing Urey's research, teaching, and legacy for the next generation of scientists at Columbia University.

Rigden, John S. *Hydrogen: The Essential Element*. Cambridge: Harvard UP, 2000. Print. Outlines scientific discoveries about the element of hydrogen. Includes a chapter about Urey.

JAMES VAN ALLEN

American physicist

James Van Allen pioneered the use of artificial satellites for Earth studies, applying his expertise to help deploy planetary probes to enhance space exploration and knowledge. His discovery of radiation belts around the Earth initiated the field of magnetospheric physics.

Born: September 7, 1914; Mount Pleasant, Iowa
Died: August 9, 2006; Iowa City, Iowa
Primary field: Physics
Specialties: Astrophysics; nuclear physics

EARLY LIFE

James Alfred Van Allen was born to lawyer Alfred Morris Van Allen and schoolteacher Alma Olney Van Allen in Mount Pleasant, Iowa. He excelled at school, particularly in mathematics and science, and studied Latin and woodworking. Van Allen developed his innate curiosity by reading *Popular Science* and *Popular Mechanics* magazines, which encouraged him to construct motors, a crystal radio, and a Tesla coil. Learning about planets, Van Allen became interested in astronomy and space.

After graduating from high school in 1931, Van Allen enrolled in Iowa Wesleyan College as a physics major. He came to admire his future mentor, physics professor Thomas C. Poulter, who urged his pupils to pursue innovative research. Poulter taught Van Allen skills that would prove useful for making scientific instruments, and he later hired Van Allen as an assistant. Supplied with a magnetometer by the Carnegie Institution's Department of Terrestrial Magnetism (DTM), Van Allen gathered magnetic data for a field survey of

Henry County, Iowa. Explorer Richard E. Byrd named Poulter chief scientist for his second Antarctic expedition in the early 1930s, and Van Allen served as Poulter's aide while he prepared for the project. Van Allen earned his bachelor's degree in 1935.

Interested in pursuing a scientific career, Van Allen expanded his physics knowledge by pursuing graduate degrees at the University of Iowa in Iowa City. He worked with adviser Edward P. T. Tyndall, earning a master's degree in 1936, and studied under professor Alexander Ellett as a doctoral student, completing his PhD in 1939.

LIFE'S WORK

Van Allen accepted a position at the DTM as a Carnegie Research Fellow in a nuclear physics laboratory. After World War II began, Van Allen devised radio proximity fuses for the US Navy to use for antiaircraft tactics. Beginning in April 1942, he conducted that work in the new Applied Physics Laboratory (APL) at Johns Hopkins University. In November of that year, Van Allen was commissioned as a lieutenant in the Naval Reserve to serve in the South Pacific as an evaluator of the naval deployment of radio proximity fuses. Van Allen married Abigail Fithian Halsey on October 13, 1945, in Southampton, New York, and they later had three daughters and two sons.

After the war, Van Allen returned to the Applied Physics Laboratory to establish and chair the high-altitude research group. The group used German V-2 rockets to assess cosmic rays and other areas of interest within the upper atmosphere. By 1946, Van Allen

Van Allen Discovers Earth's Radiation Belts

Until the late 1950s, studies of Earth's magnetic field could be performed only from Earth's surface. This hindered the understanding of how the field is generated as well as the determination of the field's shape and strength and the volume of space that it occupies. This changed, however, with the development of artificial satellites. Scientists designated the time period from July 1, 1957, to December 31, 1958, as the "International Geophysical Year" (IGY). During this time period, the Earth and its surrounding area were to be studied intensely by scientists around the world to learn more about the planet. In 1955, the US government announced that the United States would launch an artificial satellite during the IGY. This effort took on additional importance following the Soviet Union's successful launch of the satellite Sputnik 1 on October 4, 1957.

James Van Allen and his colleagues developed instruments to be carried on the satellites launched as part of the IGY effort. Hoping to study cosmic rays, Van Allen included a Geiger counter, a device used to measure the presence of radiation or radioactive materials, among the instruments. On January 31, 1958, the satellite Explorer 1 launched, carrying the Geiger counter. When the counter's radio signal was transmitted to Earth for analysis, it did something strange: It increased to a maximum, decreased to zero, and then increased again to maximum. Van Allen correctly interpreted this not as a result of an actual decrease in radiation but as a result of the instrument's inability to handle high levels of radiation. This is analogous to the distortion one hears when the volume of a radio is turned too high, driving the electronics beyond their design limits.

Further study revealed the nature of the radiation. Earth's magnetic field temporarily traps electrons and other electrically charged particles emitted by the sun. Some of the particles also may come from Earth's upper atmosphere as its gases interact with the solar particles. Earth's magnetic field fans out at the magnetic pole in the Southern Hemisphere, arcs over Earth's equator, and converges on the magnetic pole in the Northern Hemisphere. The field is strongest at the poles and weakest halfway between them. Particles such as electrons enter the field, and as the field strength increases near the poles, the particles bounce off this area and toward the opposite poles. The particles may perform this bounce motion many times before escaping into space.

Because of this effect, there are two broad bands, or "belts," in Earth's magnetic field that have high radiation levels. Aligned with the center of Earth, they are both doughnut shaped, with crescent-shaped cross sections. Although the electrically charged particles consist mostly of electrons, the inner belt does contain some protons and other particles. In honor of Van Allen's discovery, these belts of high radiation were named the Van Allen radiation belts.

---

oversaw the use of new Aerobee rockets. Early in the 1950s, however, administrative changes at the APL led to a shift in research focus away from high-altitude research.

Tyndall, one of Van Allen's former advisers, urged him to apply for the position of Physics Department chair at the University of Iowa, a position he filled beginning in January of 1951. At Iowa, Van Allen used balloons to transport instruments aloft to investigate cosmic rays. He created "rockoons," balloon-rocket devices used to launch instruments to high altitudes above Earth. During the 1950s, Van Allen launched rockoons on several expeditions near Greenland and the North Pole to measure cosmic radiation. During this time, he also served as adviser for a number of students pursuing graduate-level research in this area.

Van Allen served as chair of a satellite instrumentation group during the International Geophysical Year, which extended from July 1957 to December 1958. Aware of military efforts to deploy an artificial satellite, he developed instrumentation compatible with both Navy and Army satellites in development. In October 1957, while on a rockoon expedition in the Pacific, Van Allen heard the signal of the Soviet satellite Sputnik on the radio. After returning from the expedition, Van Allen resumed his work with satellites. Under Van Allen's direction, a Geiger counter, an instrument used to detect and measure radiation, was placed on the Explorer 1 satellite, which launched on January 31, 1958.

Assessing information collected from Explorer 1, Van Allen noticed first an absence and then a surge of data and concluded that radiation was affecting the measurements. He later gathered information from instruments on Explorer 3 and 4, determining that two "radiation belts" existed around Earth. On May 1, Van Allen publicly announced his detection of the radiation belts, which were later named in his honor, in a paper at an American Physical Society and National Academy of Sciences meeting. In March 1959, Van Allen published an article describing the radiation belts in *Scientific American*. Van Allen's work inspired the field of magnetospheric physics, which intrigued researchers worldwide.

Beginning in 1958, Van Allen chaired a space scientists' group that supported a piloted lunar landing, but he eventually decided robotic missions were preferable for space exploration because he thought few significant scientific results had been achieved by human space travelers. Van Allen devised instrumentation for the Mariner spacecraft deployed to Venus, and as principal investigator, he developed instruments for Pioneer 10 and Pioneer 11, detecting and surveying radiation belts associated with Jupiter and Saturn in the 1970s. He later supported deploying the Voyager probes, which expanded exploration to the outer planets, and the Galileo craft that orbited Jupiter.

Although Van Allen retired in 1985, he remained active in his department and profession. Mount Pleasant citizens restored Van Allen's boyhood home during the late 1990s, and he participated in its dedication as a historical site. Van Allen received numerous recognitions for his accomplishments, including the Royal Astronomical Society Gold Medal, the Royal Swedish Academy of Sciences Crafoord Prize, the National Air and Space Museum Trophy, and US National Medal of Science.

On October 9, 2004, the University of Iowa hosted a ninetieth-birthday celebration for Van Allen, who continued to research and evaluate satellite data in his office in Van Allen Hall. Van Allen died on August 9, 2006, in Iowa City. The university sponsored a public memorial and established a scholarship in his honor.

IMPACT

Van Allen shaped space science as it emerged in the mid-twentieth century. His contributions revealed new information about the universe, providing crucial data that enabled spacecraft to maneuver in the solar system. His work highlighted the potentials of space and influenced students to seek careers in space science. Many of his students and colleagues became prominent NASA

investigators and administrators. His opinions also influenced NASA policy, especially the increase in unpiloted space missions during the 1990s. While some historians consider Van Allen's detection of Earth's radiation belts to have strengthened the position of the United States in the Cold War space race, his investigations were motivated by scientific curiosity rather than political ambition. He nurtured a sense of scientific community in the United States, and he worked with rocket scientists and other researchers from a variety of countries, sharing insights into advancing science and technology.

Elizabeth D. Schafer

FURTHER READING

Beatty, J. Kelly, Carolyn Collins Petersen, and Andrew Chaikin, eds. *The New Solar System*. 4th ed. Cambridge: Sky, 1999. Print. Includes a chapter written by Van Allen and astrophysicist Frances Bagenal describing their work with magnetospheres and incorporating examples from throughout Van Allen's career, including planetary exploration with probes.

Bille, Matt, and Erika Lishock. *The First Space Race: Launching the World's First Satellites*. College Station: Texas A&M UP, 2004. Print. Provides biographical details on Van Allen and his research as well as historical context for US and Soviet aerospace research conducted in the 1950s.

Foerstner, Abigail. *James Van Allen: The First Eight Billion Miles*. Iowa City: U of Iowa P, 2007. Print. Chronicles Van Allen's scientific curiosity, space research philosophy, and achievements from childhood through his radiation discoveries with satellites and probes.

O'Brien, Brian. "Radiation Belts." *Scientific American* 208 (1963): 84–96. Print. Provides a wealth of information about the discovery of the Van Allen radiation belts, including maps of the belts and the shape of the magnetic field.

Van Allen, James A. *Origins of Magnetospheric Physics*. Iowa City: U of Iowa P, 2004. Print. Offers a detailed account of Van Allen's research and experiences and includes images from his field notebooks, radiogram and correspondence transcripts, diagrams, and research proposal excerpts.

Harold E. Varmus

American biologist

Oncogenes, genetic information associated with the conversion of normal cells into cells that are malignant, had been found in viruses during the 1960s and 1970s. In 1975, Varmus and his colleague, J. Michael Bishop, discovered that viral oncogenes actually originated from normal cells, where they played a role in regulating cell division.

Born: December 18, 1939; Oceanside, New York
Primary field: Biology
Specialties: Genetics; oncology

Early Life

Harold Elliot Varmus was the first of two children born to Dr. Frank Varmus, a general practitioner, and Beatrice (Barasch) Varmus, a psychiatric social worker. Varmus grew up in Freeport, New York. Following high school, he enrolled at Amherst College and graduated with a BA in English in 1961.

Awarded a Woodrow Wilson Fellowship, Varmus enrolled at Harvard University and began his graduate studies in Anglo-Saxon and metaphysical poetry. However, he soon developed an interest in the medical sciences and decided to enter the Columbia College of Physicians and Surgeons to study psychiatry and international health. His work as a medical student at a hospital in India made him reconsider his interest in being a doctor overseas, and he eventually focused on internal medicine, in which he received his medical degree in 1966.

After his service as medical house staff at Columbia-Presbyterian Hospital between 1966 and 1968, Varmus joined the laboratory of Ira Pastan at the National Institutes of Health (NIH), in Bethesda, Maryland. As a clinical associate at NIH he investigated the role of cyclic nucleotides in gene regulation in bacteria. The work spurred Varmus's interest in the newly expanding field of molecular biology, the cutting edge of which was developing in laboratories such as that of J. Michael Bishop at the University of California, San Francisco (UCSF).

Life's Work

Varmus joined Bishop's laboratory at UCSF as a postdoctoral fellow in 1970 and was promoted to full professor in the Department of Microbiology and Immunology by 1979. It was in Bishop's lab that Varmus began working on RNA tumor viruses. He and Bishop studied the genetic makeup of tumor viruses to find out why they contained cancer-causing genes and where the genes came from. Their research showed that tumor viruses did not originally have cancer-causing genes, called oncogenes, but acquired such genes from normal cells. In 1989, Varmus and Bishop shared the Nobel Prize for Physiology or Medicine for their work on oncogenes.

In addition to his work with Bishop on oncogenes, Varmus and his UCSF colleagues demonstrated exactly how some modifications of genes in normal cells, called proto-oncogenes, could result in cancers. Some of the gene products were cellular growth factors, which induced the cycle of cell division. Others were receptors for those factors, situated on the cell membrane. Still other proto-oncogene products were DNA binding proteins, which regulated DNA expression and replication. Varmus and his colleagues also became well known for their studies of hormone actions, hepatitis B viruses, and various blood disorders.

Winning the Nobel Prize helped Varmus gain influence in the scientific community, and he started to become more involved in policy issues. In 1993, Varmus left UCSF and returned to NIH, where he had started his career, when US Secretary of Health and Human Services Donna Shalala chose him to be the organization's director. Serving as NIH director from 1993 to 1999, Varmus helped double its budget and instituted many positive changes in the way the organization conducted its research.

Varmus has been an ardent advocate for making scientific papers accessible to everyone, proposing that scientists, rather than journal editors, should maintain control over the publication of scientific research. After several failed attempts at creating an open-access publication system, in 2000 he cofounded the Public Library of Science (PLoS), a publisher of open-access biomedical journals, and serves as the chairman of its board of directors.

Also in 2000, Varmus was hired as the president of Memorial Sloan-Kettering Cancer Center, a National Cancer Institute–designated cancer center, in New York City. Despite his successful leadership of the center, Varmus stepped down from this position in early 2010, saying he felt the institution needed a fresh vision for the next decade. On May 18, 2010, President Barack Obama appointed Varmus to be the fourteenth director of the National Cancer Institute, which is part of the

NIH. He took his oath of office as NCI director on July 12, 2011.

Varmus has received numerous awards in recognition of the significance of his work. In addition to the Nobel Prize in Physiology or Medicine (1989) that he shared with Bishop, his other significant honors are the Albert Lasker Basic Medical Research Award (1982), the Armand Hammer Cancer Prize (1984), the Alfred P. Sloan Prize (1984), the American College of Physicians Award (1987), and the 2001 National Medal of Science. Varmus gained membership in the National Academy of Science (1984), the American Academy of Arts and Sciences (1988), and the Institute of Medicine (1991). In 2009, President Obama appointed him cochair of the President's Council of Advisors on Science and Technology.

IMPACT

Oncogenes were first discovered in viruses, but the work of Varmus and his colleagues demonstrated these regions of genetic information had originated as cellular genes, the function of which was to regulate cell division. Cancer is not a single disease but one characteristic of a specific type of malignant cell. However, a common feature among many cancers is an improper regulation among the genes that regulate cell division.

Since Varmus and Bishop first demonstrated in the 1970s the origin of a few examples of oncogenes, well over one hundred such genes have been described and located. Understanding the function of oncogenes has helped in the process of learning the origin of a diverse group of malignancies. Knowing these functions also has led to a significant understanding of cell regulation

Varmus Discovers Proto-Oncogenes in Normal Cells

By the time Harold Varmus and Michael Bishop attempted to figure out how RNA tumor viruses—viruses that cause tumors and whose genes are comprised of ribonucleic acid—caused tumors in the early 1970s, many scientists accepted the theory that these viruses contained cancer-causing genes, or oncogenes, that copied RNA onto host cell DNA via an enzyme called reverse transcriptase. Other scientists thought that normal host cells contained cancer-causing genes that were activated by viruses or other external carcinogens. Varmus and Bishop wanted to know whether viral oncogenes or host cell oncogenes were responsible for causing tumors. The two scientists also wanted to know why viral oncogenes had evolved and what purpose they served.

Harold Varmus's first attempts to clarify the oncogene puzzle involved preparation of a nucleic acid probe to measure viral DNA in cells. Since the virus being tested was the Rous sarcoma virus, which infected chickens, the initial experiments utilized chicken cells. The specific gene that carried out the cell transformation became known as the "sarc" gene. Varmus obtained questionable results until he switched from chicken cells to those of other species: duck cells and even mammalian cells. He was able to demonstrate that following infection, the viral RNA is indeed copied into DNA and integrates into the host chromosome. When a colleague, Dominique Stehelin, was able to prepare a pure *sarc* probe, one that was only capable of combining with the sarc gene (v-src) of the retrovirus, Varmus and Bishop were then able to test for the pres-

ence of a cellular version, a c-src, of the viral oncogene.

The results were clear. The sarc probe combined with DNA obtained from bird cells, indicating the presence of the src gene in the DNA even in the absence of viral infection. In other words, the oncogene did not originate as a viral gene, but was a normal cell gene the virus had likely acquired. The cell version of the oncogene became known as a proto-oncogene.

Varmus and Bishop found that the src genes had been present in birds at least for one hundred million years. Further analysis provided a possible explanation for the presence of the gene in retroviruses. The virus did not introduce the sarcoma gene into the cells it infected. Instead, the gene was picked up by the virus following infection and integration. Subsequent experiments demonstrated the presence of homologous sarc genes in other species, including mammals such as humans.

The team also found that proto-oncogenes were not randomly placed within the cell genome but were found at specific positions. Unlike the form of the gene in the virus, which was a continuous genetic entity, the proto-oncogene had the characteristic of other genes in being subdivided into separate domains, with each segment separated by stretches of DNA. As more oncogenes were discovered, and their functions investigated, it was found that these genetic elements regulate, at various levels, the ability of cells to replicate. Mutations in the genes, or their over-expression, could in some cases account for the malignant transformation of the cell.

in general. In particular, the role of oncogene products involved in each step leading up to, and controlling, cell division has resulted in a significant understanding of the process as a whole.

One of the main goals of cancer research is the development of a means to control or block cell division. For example, the anticancer drug herceptin, used in the treatment of certain forms of breast cancer, works by competing with an oncogene product that induces cell division. The ability to block the action of oncogene products may not necessarily result in a cure for the disease, but it could be a means to control cancer as a chronic disease.

Richard Adler

FURTHER READING

Colome, Jaime S. "Harold E. Varmus." *The Nobel Prize Winners: Physiology or Medicine*. Vol. 3. Pasadena: Salem, 1991. Print. A scientific biography of Varmus that includes a summary of his 1966 Nobel Prize lecture.

Pelengaris, Stella, and Michael Khan, eds. *The Molecular Biology of Cancer*. Malden: Blackwell, 2006. Print. Collection of articles addressing causes and treatments of cancers, the role of viruses in some cancers, and a brief history of the subject.

Weinberg, Robert. *The Biology of Cancer*. New York: Garland Science, 2006. Print. Definitive work on research into the molecular basis of cancer. Extensive discussion on the roles of oncogenes.

J. CRAIG VENTER

American biologist

Prominent genomics researcher and entrepreneur, J. Craig Venter is recognized for a wide array of accomplishments that includes the first complete sequencing of the human genome, as well as his 2010 creation of the first self-replicating bacterial cell with synthetic DNA.

Born: October 14, 1946; Salt Lake City, Utah
Primary field: Biology
Specialties: Genetics; biochemistry

EARLY LIFE

John Craig Venter was born on October 14, 1946, in Salt Lake City, Utah, but he spent his childhood in the city of Millbrae, California. He was the second of four children born to John and Elizabeth Venter, who were both members of the United States Marine Corps during World War II.

As a child, Venter was a self-described mischief-maker who loved playing around the railroad tracks near his house. He displayed a strong mechanical and engineering ability, excelling at such projects. Venter was an exceptionally competitive swimmer but did not shine academically. At Mills High School, where he enrolled in 1960, he was rebellious, bored, and frequently in trouble. (In 2007, when his genome became the first individual human genome to be completely sequenced, Venter would discover a possible explanation for his behavior: a genetic anomaly associated with Attention Deficit Hyperactivity Disorder.)

At seventeen, Venter dropped out of high school and moved alone to Costa Mesa, California, but was soon drafted into the military. He enlisted in the United States Navy and began serving as a senior corpsman in a field hospital in Da Nang, South Vietnam. The exposure to death and critical injury had a profound impact on him, and when Venter returned to the United States in 1968, he began taking steps toward a medical career. Venter first took classes at the College of San Mateo, a community college in California, and later he was accepted as a student at the University of California, San Diego (UCSD).

In 1972, he received his BS degree in biochemistry and remained at UCSD to pursue graduate studies. He earned a PhD in physiology and pharmacology in 1975. By this time, his ambitions had turned from practicing medicine to laboratory research. His doctoral dissertation focused on how the hormone adrenaline interacts with cells.

LIFE'S WORK

After completing his doctorate, Venter accepted a position as a junior faculty member at the medical school of the State University of New York. In 1982, he became the deputy director of the molecular immunology department at the Roswell Park Cancer Institute. Venter joined the National Institutes of Health (NIH), a government research body based in Bethesda, Maryland, in 1984. It was during his tenure there that the focus of his work turned toward genetic sequencing.

Genetic sequencing is the attempt to map out the structure and function of the chemical building blocks, or base pairs, that form strands of DNA (deoxyribonucleic acid). DNA is the carrier of the genetic instructions that drive the development of most living organisms. A DNA base pair consists of either a molecule of cytosine paired with one of guanine, or a molecule of adenine paired with one of thymine. These bases are abbreviated with the letters A, T, C, and G; a sequenced genome looks like a series of letters, such as "CCAAGTAC."

One of Venter's early projects was the development of so-called expressed sequence tags (ESTs). An EST consists of a small, unique sequence of DNA, a few hundred base pairs in length. This sequence is a portion of a gene that expresses, or contains instructions for producing, a particular protein. By matching ESTs to a longer stretch of genomic information, researchers can quickly identify full-length genes that serve known functions.

In 1992, Venter left the NIH to start his own non-profit research foundation, the Institute for Genomic Research (TIGR). TIGR made the news in 1995 when it published the first complete genome sequence belonging to a free-living organism—that of *Haemophilus influenzae*, a bacterium that causes various human infections. Although others had managed to sequence virus genomes completely, *Haemophilus influenzae* was a much more complex organism. Venter's success in mapping all of its base pairs in one year was considered remarkable.

Venter had sequenced the bacterium genome using a technique known as "shotgun sequencing." At the time, the traditional method of DNA-sequencing relied on sequencing large chunks of a genome, cloning them in bacterial artificial chromosomes (BACs), a type of engineered DNA molecule, and breaking those down again into smaller pieces. Only after every piece has been sequenced could they be fitted back together. This technique is highly accurate but expensive and time-consuming. Venter's much faster and cheaper shotgun technique breaks a genome into much smaller pieces, which can be sequenced and aligned simultaneously.

In 1998, Venter founded a private company called Celera Genomics. Celera's main goal was to speed up the completion of the sequencing of the entire human genome. This information would provide a database for medical researchers in developing diagnostic tests for diseases based on genetic markers, as well as personalized therapies targeting specific genetic anomalies. The publicly funded Human Genome Project, which

consisted of a consortium of international research groups, had been working on this endeavor since 1990 but continued to use the BAC-to-BAC technique. Venter believed the shotgun method would provide a quicker and less expensive solution.

In 2000, what had been a very visible and sometimes contentious race between the public and private sectors to map the complete human genome ended on a collaborative note, with Venter and Francis Collins of the Human Genome Project jointly announcing that both groups had finished draft sequences. It was generally accepted that Celera "won" the race, since its draft was completed several months before that of the Human Genome Project. In the years that followed, Celera scientists would go on to publish the genomes of other organisms, including the mouse and the fruit fly.

Leaving Celera in 2002, Venter threw himself into the field of synthetic biology: the attempt to build living biological systems using standardized parts, such as DNA sequences, proteins, and other organic compounds. Among other projects, Venter has been sailing around the world collecting undersea microbes to help build a library of organic building blocks. In 2010, he made the headlines again for creating the first living cell with an entirely synthetic genome. He continues to work on cutting-edge genomics research at the J. Craig Venter Institute, the merged incarnation of several organizations he had founded previously.

Venter has been married three times. He has one child, Christopher Emrys Rae Venter, with his former wife Barbara Rae. He lives in San Diego, California.

IMPACT

Venter has received numerous scientific prizes and awards, including the National Medal of Science in 2008. He has twice been named as one of *Time* magazine's most influential people in the world. Many of the tools he has worked on developing or promoting are now widely used throughout biological research. The EST technique for rapid gene identification, for instance, has been used to pinpoint the genes involved in several human diseases, including Alzheimer's and a particular form of colon cancer. The initially controversial technique of shotgun sequencing is, more recently, a conventional tool of genomics. Most current approaches to whole-genome sequencing use some hybrid form of shotgun and BAC-to-BAC sequencing.

Although Venter's bacterium with a synthetic genome was not, as it was sometimes described, the first "synthetic life," it represented a step toward a host of

Venter Creates the First Self-replicating Cell with Synthetic DNA

In May 2010, the J. Craig Venter Institute announced its successful creation of the first self-replicating bacterial cell with an entirely synthetic genome. While Venter's team had replicated the bacterium *Myocoplasma genitalium* in 2008, this new genome represented the longest set of DNA yet to be produced. Venter's team had been working on this line of research since 1995. The release of the paper in which Venter described the achievement received a great deal of media attention. Venter had designed and built a complete artificial bacterial chromosome, inserted it into a living bacterial cell that already possessed its own DNA, and watched the synthetic DNA replace the cell's original genetic code. The synthetic DNA provided the instructions that the bacterium used as it replicated. This replication formed new copies of the cell, copies that also featured the synthetic DNA.

Venter assembled the design for the artificial chromosome on a computer, using the actual DNA of the bacterium *Mycoplasma mycoides* as a reference. He made several changes to the natural genome, deleting several genes and adding new segments of genetic code that served no practical function but stood for the names of the researchers, their contact information, and a series of famous quotations from such figures as physicist Richard Feynman and author James Joyce. These changes served as watermarks—identifying markers that would distinguish the synthetic genome from that of the original cell.

The first practical problem Venter and his colleagues had to overcome was the question of how they could build a complete bacterial chromosome, which would consist of over one million base pairs of DNA. Existing techniques only enabled the synthesis of partial genomes, consisting of a few thousand base pairs. Venter solved this problem by cutting the code for the synthetic DNA into over a thousand smaller pieces. He added additional overlapping base pairs at the ends of each piece that would later be used to stitch them back together as well as providing a sequence that would enable them to survive in yeast cells. Once these pieces were synthesized, Venter began inserting them into yeast cells. The yeast took in and recombined the DNA pieces into larger wholes until the entire synthetic genome formed a single continuous chromosome.

Finally, the completed synthetic genome was inserted into a living bacterium—not *Mycoplasma mycoides*, but the related *Mycoplasma capricolum*. After several unsuccessful trials, Venter's team finally managed to grow a colony of bacteria that possessed the synthetic genome. The cells were producing *Mycoplasma mycoides* proteins instead of those typical of *Mycoplasma capricolum*. Their native genetic code had been completely replaced by Venter's synthetic code.

In spite of the breakthrough, Venter admitted that the synthetic genome was a mere "plagiarism" of nature, a copy of a naturally occurring organism. As of 2012, the J. Craig Venter Institute aspired to develop more advanced synthetic organisms for ecological and industrial purposes—organisms, for example, that could repair the environmental damages of pollution and supply sources of fuel.

potential applications. The ability to design and manipulate pieces of genetic code like building blocks could enable the creation of clean, renewable sources of alternative energy, self-repairing materials, or highly effective vehicles for drug-delivery. Because of the potential for the tools of synthetic biology to be used in harmful ways, Venter's announcement prompted President Barack Obama to create a bioethics commission to study the regulatory implications of this emerging field.

M. Lee

FURTHER READING

Biello, David, and Katherine Harmon. "Tools for Life: What's Next for Cells Powered by Synthetic Genomes?" *Scientific American* 303.2 (2010): 17–18. Print. Brief commentary on the impact that synthetic biology, such as Venter's artificial bacterial genome, may have on the study of life.

Lesk, Arthur M. *Introduction to Genomics.* New York: Oxford UP, 2007. Print. Student-focused volume covering human genomics, comparative genomics, evolution and genomic change, sequencing techniques, proteomics, and systems biology. Includes extensive full-color illustrations, sidebars, and end-of-chapter problems and exercises.

Pennisi, Elizabeth. "Synthetic Genome Brings New Life to Bacterium." *Science* 21 (2010): 958–59. Print. Explanation of the steps involved in Venter's 2010 creation of the first entirely artificial (bacterial) genome and successful insertion into a recipient cell.

Shreeve, James. *The Genome War: How Craig Venter Tried to Capture the Code of Life and Save the World*. New York: Knopf, 2004. Print. Behind-the-scenes account of the race between Venter's company, Celera, and the US government-backed Human Genome Project, to sequence the entire human genome.

Venter, J. Craig. *A Life Decoded: My Genome, My Life*. New York: Penguin, 2007. Print. Privides a look at Venter's personal story, scientific discoveries, and the politics that surround genomic research.

GIOVANNI BATTISTA VENTURI

Italian physicist

Italian priest, physicist, teacher, and diplomat Giovannia Battista Venturi's career spanned the late eighteenth century to the early nineteenth century. In addition to exploring optics and acoustics, Venturi discovered a hydraulic principle that provided multiple practical—and commercial—applications. He also published works on the scientific contributions of Leonardo da Vinci and Galileo Galilei.

Born: March 15, 1746; Bibbiano, Italy
Died: April 24, 1822; Reggio Emilia, Italy
Also known as: Giambattista Venturi; Abbé Venturi
Primary field: Physics
Specialties: Hydrology; mechanics; optics; acoustics

EARLY LIFE

Giovanni Battista Venturi was born on March 15, 1746 into a wealthy family in the small northern Italian town of Bibbiano, northwest of Bologna. He received his early education at the Jesuit seminary in his hometown, where he excelled as a student.

After the age of ten, Venturi transferred to the seminary in the larger town of Reggio Emilia, where he took courses in logic, metaphysics, and mathematics. As a teenager, he enrolled at the University of Reggio Emilia (in operation from 1752 to 1772, and after 1998 incorporated into the University of Modena). At the university, he took classes from physicist Bonaventura Corti, and biologist Lazzaro Spallanzani.

Venturi graduated from the University of Reggio Emilia in the mid-1760s and returned to the Reggio Emilia seminary where, in 1769, he was ordained as a priest. The same year, he began teaching logic at the seminary. In 1774, he moved to the University of Modena, where he taught philosophy and geometry. Two years later, Venturi began teaching physics at Modena, with an emphasis on hydrology.

Venturi's reputation as a scholar brought him to the attention of nobleman Gherardo, Marquis of Rangoni, magistrate of studies and minister to Francesco III d'Este, Duke of Modena and Reggio. In the late 1770s, under the patronage of the duke, Venturi was appointed state mathematician, auditor, and engineer.

LIFE'S WORK

As state engineer during the reign of Duke Francesco III (died 1780) and his successor, Duke Ercole III, Venturi was put in charge of numerous public works projects in addition to his regular teaching duties. He oversaw the building of bridges, and supervised the rechanneling of rivers and the draining of swamplands. Venturi also wrote the official regulations governing the construction of dams on waterways within the dukedom. As an authority on hydraulics, he was often consulted in matters of arbitration.

When Ercole III founded the Atesine Academy of Fine Arts, a cultural and scientific organization, in 1785, Venturi was recruited a member. The following year, he was appointed as professor of experimental physics at the University of Modena. As part of his responsibilities in the new post, Venturi was charged with setting up a modern laboratory; the duke's funding allowed him to equip the lab with the latest instruments. Another task the versatile Venturi accepted was the completion of a chronicle of literary accomplishments of the community of Modena, which had been left unfinished at the death of its original author, historian and critic Girolamo Tiraboschi, in 1794.

In early 1796, during the French Revolutionary War of the First Coalition (1792–97), French general Napoleon Bonaparte, on his first command, invaded northern Italy, where he successfully defeated a superior force of combined Austrian and Italian troops. Duke

877

The Venturi Effect: A Simple Principle for a Myriad of Complex Tasks

In the late 1790s, Giovanni Battista Venturi published his magnum opus in hydraulics, *Recherches experimentales sur le principe de la communication laterale du mouvement dans les fluides appliqué à l'explication de différens phénomènes hydrauliques* (1797; *Experimental enquiries concerning the principle of the lateral communication of motion in fluid*, 1799). The work was the result of years of investigations into fluid mechanics in the process of solving particular problems related to engineering projects that involved the flow of water.

The book discussed numerous experiments undertaken to show the effects of internal fluid friction in various circumstances, including eddies, discharges from pipes and fluid density. A centerpiece of the book was an extension of a principle first described by Daniel Bernoulli (a Venturi correspondent), which states that a decrease in flow produces an increase in pressure, while an increase in flow produces a decrease in pressure. Venturi's contribution was the observation that a fluid flowing through a pipe, when forced through a constriction increases in velocity—towards the speed of sound—in direct proportion to a decrease in pipe diameter. At the same time, the pressure of the fluid decreases, in response to the law of conservation of energy.

Venturi's principle can be simulated easily by placing a thumb over the open end of a working garden hose: the thumb constricts the normal flow of water, increasing its kinetic energy, thus its velocity, and propelling the liquid a greater distance. At the same time, the constriction creates a vacuum in the flow of the water, reducing the pressure within the hose.

Venturi's discovery went unnamed until 1887, when hydraulic engineer Clemens Herschel (1842–1930) of Builders Iron Foundry (originally out of Providence, Rhode Island, now headquartered in Akron, Ohio), after reproducing Venturi's experiments, termed it the Venturi effect. Herschel subsequently invented and patented a pipe featuring constricted sections, and a meter to measure flow or water or wastewater through the pipe. In honor of the scientist who inspired the inventions, Herschel named the items the Venturi tube and the Venturi meter, respectively. The Venturi tube, which uses a pipe constriction to increase velocity and decrease pressure, and the Venturi meter, which measures the speed of a fluid within a pipe, are both still widely used in engineering and industry.

Since then, numerous additional applications have been devised that take advantage of the increased velocity-decreased pressure tradeoff of the Venturi effect. Equipment that mixes air and flammable gas—for example, gas grills and Bunsen burners—use constricted tubes to achieve an optimum blend of velocity and pressure. Likewise, vehicle carburetors employ the Venturi effect to vacuum fuel into the intake airstream of an engine. Foam fire extinguishers also use the effect, as do perfume atomizers, industrial vacuum cleaners that operate off compressed air, sand blasters, spray painters, steam injectors, scuba-diving regulators and a host of other specialized apparatus.

The Venturi effect is even found in musical instruments. Contemporary B-flat clarinets are manufactured with a reverse taper in the barrel, which increases the velocity of exhaled air down the tubular form, increasing responses to fingered notes while enhancing tone. Trombones usually have leadpipes—double tapered tubes available in several sizes, shapes, and metals—in the upper slide tube to improve response and tone.

The Venturi effect is particularly useful in medicine. Modern vaporizers and ventilators use the principle. Respiratory therapy—employing the eponymous Venturi air entrainment mask and the mechanism of the Italian scientist's discovery—saves lives by delivering measurable oxygen concentrations to patients with breathing difficulties.

Ercole III of Modena was forced to flee his domain, and named Venturi as secretary to an Italian legation sent to Paris to negotiate favorable terms for peace. The drawn-out, contentious negotiations culminated in the Peace of Tolentino on February 19, 1797.

During an eighteen-month stay in Paris, Venturi exchanged ideas with many leading French scientists, among them physicist, astronomer, and mathematician Jean-Baptiste Biot, zoologist Georges Cuvier, mineralogist Abbé René Haüy, astronomer Joseph Jérôme Lalande, and mathematician Gaspard Monge. In Paris, Venturi published several scientific treatises on hydrology, including one that dealt with the movement of camphor on water, and his major work concerning lateral movement of fluids, which gave rise to what became known as the Venturi effect.

After returning to Modena, Venturi was briefly imprisoned because of what were perceived as unfavorable terms in the treaty he had helped to create. In addition, a movement sprang up to deny him a teaching position at the university. However, astronomer Pierre-Simon Laplace wrote in glowing terms of Venturi's abilities to First Consul Napoleon Bonaparte. Napoleon responded to Laplace's recommendations—and silenced Venturi's critics—by making him an adjunct member of the French revolutionary law-making body called the Corps législatif. Venturi was also appointed as a professor at the military school in Modena, and was named a chevalier of the Legion of Honor. Venturi was later given a professorship of physics at the University of Pavia, in which capacity he was consulted to lend his expertise to mining and hydraulic projects.

Napoleon grew to trust Venturi to such a degree that he was sent on several diplomatic missions. At the beginning of the nineteenth century he was made diplomatic agent to the Helvetic Confederation to help sort out the governing principles of the French conquest known as Helvetic Republic. During his years in the Swiss Confederation, Venturi worked to develop constitutional tenets and achieve unity among a loose collection of self-governing cantons, helping to lay the foundation for what became the nation of Switzerland.

When his health began to fail, Venturi retired in 1813 and returned to Reggio Emilia. Napoloeon granted him a handsome pension. In his later years, Venturi devoted his time to the publication of scientific works. He died soon after his seventy-sixth birthday.

IMPACT

A multitalented individual with far-ranging interests, Venturi was one of Italy's leading civil engineers, and considered Europe's foremost expert on hydraulics. Equally at home in the fields of physics and philosophy, literature, and history, he earned considerable respect and admiration among colleagues throughout the scientific community, and gained the trust of rulers both at home and abroad. Despite his many abilities, Venturi was by all accounts a modest, humble man. One of his greatest and longest-lasting accomplishments was his promotion of the work of other scientists.

During his sojourn in Paris, Venturi was allowed to examine twelve volumes of Leonardo da Vinci's notes. Napoleon's troops had looted the Ambrosian Library in Milan and had carried off da Vinci's notebooks as war trophies. Venturi deciphered da Vinci's mirror writing then decoded and translated his work into French, adding a new dimension to da Vinci's reputation as an artist by disseminating information for the first time about Leonardo's studies on fluid dynamics, lift and drag in aerodynamics, anatomical and physiological research, and other scientific topics.

Venturi's essay, *Commentaries on the History and Theory of Optics* (1814), was focused primarily on the *Dioptra*, a treatise from Heron of Alexandria regarding his invention of an instrument for surveying and measuring. Likewise, Venturi's final major written work was intended to lend acclaim to a predecessor: the two-volume *Memoirs and Hitherto Unpublished* or *Missing Letters* by Galileo Galilei, *Ordered and Explained with Annotations*.

Jack Ewing

FURTHER READING

Darrigol, Olivier. *Worlds of Flow: A History of Hydrodynamics from the Bernoullis to Prandtl*. New York: Oxford UP: 2009. Print. Illustrated overview of the development in the field of fluid mechanics, from its beginnings in the eighteenth century, with an emphasis on individual landmarks that helped advance understanding of the science involved.

Downie, Neil A. *The Ultimate Book of Saturday Science: The Very Best Backyard Science Experiments You Can Do Yourself.* Princeton: Princeton UP, 2012. Print. An engaging how-to book gives instructions for conducting independent experiments to demonstrate scientific principles, including the Venturi effect. Illustrated.

Landrus, Matthew Hayden. *Leonardo da Vinci's Giant Crossbow*. Berlin: Springer, 2010. Print. Includes reproductions of da Vinci's notebook drawings. This focuses on the artist-scientist's designs for proposed military weapons, incorporates information on Venturi's decoding and translations of da Vinci's work, and analyzes the technological aspects of the invented weapons.

ANDREAS VESALIUS

Flemish physician and anatomist

Sixteenth-century Flemish physician Andreas Vesalius published the first modern comprehensive text of human anatomy. His accurate description of the structure of the human body, which was the result of firsthand dissection, is the basis of the modern scientific study of human anatomy.

Born: December 31, 1514; Brussels, Belgium
Died: October 15, 1564; Zakynthos, Greece
Primary field: Biology
Specialty: Anatomy

EARLY LIFE

Andreas Vesalius was a fifth-generation physician. He attended the University of Louvain in Brussels from 1529 to 1533, where he studied Latin and Greek. From 1533 to 1536, Vesalius attended the University of Paris to study medicine. The focus of the medical faculty at the university was based solely on the works and teachings of Galen, the great second-century Greek medical writer, whose authority in anatomical matters was then unchallenged.

At the University of Paris, Vesalius found that there was little practical teaching of anatomy. Human corpses were dissected only twice a year, and Vesalius found the procedure disappointing. The professor of anatomy never performed the dissection himself but merely read passages from Galen as an assistant dissected the cadaver. In most cases, pigs or dogs were dissected. Eager to obtain human skeletons, Vesalius sought them from cemeteries and gallows outside the city, obtaining corpses of criminals in various states of decay. He became skilled at dissection and gained a firsthand knowledge of human anatomy. He began to acquire a reputation as an anatomist and even conducted a public dissection.

Vesalius left Paris in 1536 and returned to Louvain where he completed his baccalaureate degree the following year. He then traveled to Italy and enrolled in the University of Padua, and on December 5, 1537, Vesalius received his medical degree with highest distinction. On the following day, he was appointed professor of surgery, which included the teaching of anatomy. He was twenty-three years old.

LIFE'S WORK

Vesalius lectured daily at the University of Padua to some five hundred students, professors, and physicians. Dispensing with an assistant, he personally dissected cadavers. He also prepared four large anatomical charts to illustrate his lectures, and in 1538, he published three of them and three skeletal views, which have come to be known as *Tabulae anatomicae sex* (*Six Anatomical Tables*, 1874). The publication of these accurate and detailed plates marked a major advance in anatomical illustration. In the same year, he published a dissection manual based on Galen, *Institutiones anatomicae* (The institutions of anatomy), and in the following year, he published *Epistola, docens venam axillarem dextri cubiti in dolore laterali secandam* (1539; *The Bloodletting Letter of 1539*, 1947), in which he argued for the importance of the direct observation of the body.

In his lectures on anatomy, as was then customary, Vesalius expounded the views of Galen, whose authority was accepted in virtually every medical faculty in Europe. In the dissections he performed, however, he began to notice discrepancies between what he observed and what Galen had described. At first, so few cadavers were available that there was only limited opportunity for dissection, but by 1539, corpses of executed criminals were made available to him. Repeated dissections made it increasingly apparent to Vesalius that Galen's descriptions were erroneous and that Galen had based his descriptions on the anatomy of animals, primarily apes, pigs, and dogs. Vesalius expounded his discoveries first at Padua (in his fourth public dissection, at which he ceased to use Galen as a text) and then in 1540 at Bologna, where he was invited to lecture.

As early as 1538, Vesalius had apparently contemplated a major work on anatomy, and as his dissections began to reveal discrepancies between Galen's anatomy and his own discoveries, Vesalius recognized the need for a new, comprehensive text to replace Galen, which he began work on in 1540. Vesalius had woodcut illustrations for the work prepared in Venice, probably in the artist Titian's studio. To produce at least some of the illustrations, he chose a compatriot, Jan Steven van Calcar, who belonged to the school of Titian and had drawn the skeletal figures for the plates in *Tabulae anatomicae sex*. Other painters associated with the school of Titian almost certainly had a hand in the illustrations as well. Vesalius selected a firm in Basel to print the work, and the woodblocks for the illustrations were transported by donkey.

In the summer of 1542, Vesalius went to Basel to oversee the printing of *De humani corporis fabrica libri*

Andreas Vesalius Disproves Galen's Views of Anatomy

Until the sixteenth century, students of anatomy in European universities studied the writings of ancient Greek philosopher and physician Galen of Pergamum. Although dissection was not common, when it did occur, professors traditionally read to students from Galen's works while their assistants dissected the cadavers. The ways in which the dissection confirmed Galen's theories were pointed out, and students, who were unable to view or participate in the procedure, had little opportunity to corroborate or refute the instruction. Thus, Galen's ideas about the various systems of the human body, as well as certain medical practices such as bloodletting and cataract surgery, provided the foundation for much of the early anatomy and medical science instruction.

Vesalius also studied Galen as a student in Paris, but by the time he became a lecturer in Padua, Italy, he was instrumental in not only changing the way anatomy was taught, but also challenged and refuted a number of Galen's most important ideas.

Vesalius, who was provided bodies of executed criminals, was noted for dissecting cadavers himself as his students gathered around him to observe the details of human anatomy. Also, since Galen had based his theories on the dissection of primates (human dissection was prohibited under the Roman law during Galen's time), Vesalius was able to show the sometimes dramatic anatomical differences between humans and apes. Not only did Vesalius's practice encourage learning by hands-on experience, it also uncovered key shortcomings of Galen's works. Even more important,

though, were the charts that Vesalius prepared for his students to study, which dramatically altered the way in which human anatomy was taught.

In 1543, Vesalius published his groundbreaking anatomy textbook, *De humani corporis fabrica* (*On the Fabric of the Human Body in Seven Books*, 1998-2009), in seven volumes. The lavish and intricately detailed illustrations of human anatomy distinguished this book, making it the first significant textbook of human anatomy in the modern world. A highly unusual feature of the volumes was that the artists who drew the illustrations were likely present at the dissections themselves and did not work from someone else's depictions of the events.

In *De humani corporis fabrica*, Vesalius disproved many of Galen's ideas. Regarding the skeletal system, for instance, Vesalius showed that the jaw consists of one bone, not two separate bones as Galen thought. Additionally, while Galen believed that the human breastbone is composed of seven segments, Vesalius showed that it is made up of only three parts. Vesalius also disproved Galen's theory of the circulatory system, showing that both arteries and veins originate in a four-chambered heart, rather than in the liver as Galen believed, and that valves, including the mitral valve Vesalius discovered, regulate the flow of blood in and out of the heart.

As many scientists have pointed out, Vesalius's recognition of the differences between the anatomy of humans and other species represents the earliest step toward establishing the science of comparative anatomy in which scientists recognize the differences as well as the common shared traits among humans and other species.

septem (*On the Fabric of the Human Body in Seven Books*, 1998–2009), better known as *De fabrica*, which was published in August 1543. In *De fabrica*, Vesalius corrected more than two hundred errors of Galenic anatomy and described certain features that either were previously unknown or had been described only partially. He was not the first to find mistakes in Galen, but he went beyond mere correction by insisting that the only reliable basis of anatomical study was dissection and personal observation. *De fabrica* was the first modern treatise on human anatomy that was not based on Galen or drawn from dissected animals, and it surpassed all previous books on the subject, revolutionizing the study of anatomy with its use of illustrations. The woodcuts, showing skeletons and flayed ("skinned") human fig-

ures, represented the culmination of Italian painting and the scientific study of human anatomy. They were meant to be studied closely with the text and were so successful that they were frequently plagiarized.

Vesalius's fame spread rapidly, and many Italian physicians came to accept his views. Yet Galen's supporters reacted with strong attacks. Jacobus Sylvius, the leading authority on anatomy in Europe and Vesalius's former teacher, published a vitriolic pamphlet against Vesalius. Disappointed by the opposition, Vesalius abandoned his anatomical studies, burned all his manuscripts, and resigned his chair at Padua. He then left Italy to accept the position of third court physician to the Holy Roman Emperor, Charles V, which he maintained for the next thirteen years.

In 1544, his father, who had been an apothecary to Charles V, died and left a substantial inheritance to Vesalius, who then married Anne van Hamme. About a year later, a daughter, his only child, was born. Vesalius spent much of his time traveling with the emperor, who suffered from gout and gastrointestinal disorders. Vesalius also served as a military surgeon during this time and introduced several new procedures, the most notable of which was the surgical drainage of the chest. Vesalius enjoyed the full confidence of the emperor, and his professional reputation continued to grow. On Charles's abdication from the Spanish throne in 1556, he granted Vesalius a pension for life.

When King Henry II of France was severely wounded in the head during a tournament in 1559, Vesalius was summoned to Paris, where he joined the distinguished French surgeon Ambroise Paré in treating the king. The wound proved fatal, and the king died ten days later. Vesalius's reputation was secure, however, and his medical opinion continued to be sought.

In 1562, Don Carlos, heir to the throne of Spain, received a severe head injury as the result of a fall. As his condition grew worse, the king summoned Vesalius to join several Spanish physicians in attendance on the infant. Although they distrusted him from the beginning, the Spanish physicians eventually allowed Vesalius to administer a treatment that resulted in a rapid improvement of the prince, who recovered.

In the spring of 1564, Vesalius left for a trip to the Holy Land by way of Venice, Italy. He proceeded to Palestine by way of Cyprus, Greece, but he became ill on the return journey and died on October 15, 1564. He was buried on the Greek island of Zakynthos.

Impact

Although Vesalius was trained in the Galenic system, he gradually began to see why Galen's anatomical descriptions, which were based on the dissection of animals, needed correction. Even then, he was not wholly able to escape Galen's influence, for he sometimes reproduced Galen's errors. His great contribution to medicine was his insistence that anatomical study be based on repeated dissection and firsthand observation of the human body.

Vesalius has been called the founder of modern anatomy. The importance that he placed on the systematic investigation of the human body led to dissection becoming a routine part of the medical curriculum. His *De fabrica* revolutionized the study of anatomy, and its anatomical illustrations became the model for subsequent medical illustrators. Its publication marked the beginning of modern observational science and encouraged the work of other anatomists. Vesalius's ideas spread rapidly throughout Italy and Europe and came to be widely accepted within a half century, in spite of the continuing influence of Galen.

Gary B. Ferngren

Further Reading

Friedman, Meyer, and Gerald W. Friedland. *Medicine's Ten Greatest Discoveries*. New Haven: Yale UP, 2000. Print. Discusses ten major scientific discoveries, including Vesalius's invention of the modern science of anatomy. Includes illustrations, bibliographic references, and index.

Joffe, Stephen N. *Andreas Vesalius: The Making, the Madman, and the Myth*. Bloomington: Persona, 2009. Print. Provides an extensive biography of Andreas Vesalius, covering his childhood, his scientific career, his publications, and later life.

Persaud, T. V. N. *A History of Anatomy: The Post–Vesalian Era*. Springfield: Thomas, 1997. Print. Reviews Vesalius's legacy and the development of the science of anatomy. Includes illustrations, bibliographic references, and index.

Rudolf Virchow

German pathologist

Nineteenth-century German pathologist Rudolf Virchow is known as the "father of pathology" for his pioneering use of cell theory to analyze and explain the body's response to disease. As a politician, he instituted many public health reforms. He also helped advance the organization of anthropology within Germany.

Born: October 13, 1821; Schivelbein, Prussia (now Poland)
Died: September 5, 1902; Berlin, Germany
Primary field: Biology
Specialties: Pathology; anthropology

EARLY LIFE

Rudolf Ludwig Karl Virchow was born in Schivelbein, a small town in rural Pomeranian Prussia (now Poland) on October 13, 1821. His father was a merchant who encouraged his only son to pursue an education. Young Virchow excelled academically and was awarded a military fellowship at the Friedrich Wilhelm Institute in Berlin in 1839. At the institute, he studied under Johannes Peter Müller, a famous physiologist. Virchow received his medical degree in 1843 and was soon appointed company surgeon at Charité Hospital in Berlin.

LIFE'S WORK

In 1845, Virchow gave speeches in which he outlined his vision for medical progress. Virchow claimed that progress could only occur through clinical observation, animal experimentation, and the study of pathological anatomy, the physical expression of diseases, at the microscopic level. During this period, Virchow also published a classic paper in which he described one of the first reported cases of leukemia.

At the time Virchow presented these conclusions, some medical authorities still believed that the body's so-called humors (blood, phlegm, black bile, and yellow bile) controlled physical and mental health, even though this ancient theory had never been validated by scientific experimentation. Consequently, Virchow's modern ideas were criticized by older members of the faculty, and some editors of medical journals refused to publish his work.

In 1847, Virchow and his friend Benno Ernst Heinrich Reinhardt created their own journal, *Archiv für pathologische Anatomie und Physiologie und für klinische Medizin* (Archives of pathological anatomy and physiology and of clinical medicine). In 1903, the journal later became known as *Virchows Archiv*, and is a respected periodical that continues to be published into the twenty-first century.

Virchow finished his military obligation and became an instructor at the University of Berlin, where Müller was dean, in 1847. During this period, he continued to challenge many established medical conventions. In 1848, he disproved the theory that inflammation of the veins (phlebitis) caused most diseases. Instead, he revealed that matter could collect in the veins and that this matter, which he termed *thrombus*, could detach in the blood's current and form what he called an "embolus" or embolus. Virchow noted that the free-floating embolus could then become stuck in smaller vessels, which could give rise to embolisms, which are lesions in the vessels.

From 1848 to 1849, he also published a weekly paper called *Die Medizinische Reform*, which called for more clinical training for medical students and a unified system of standards for all physicians.

In 1848 the Prussian government sent Virchow to Upper Silesia to investigate an outbreak of typhus. In Upper Silesia, he became convinced that the outbreak was the result of the population's squalid living conditions. His report condemned the Prussian government for allowing these conditions to exist and suggested broad political and economic reforms. His efforts in Silesia had an impact, and the same year, he was asked to represent a Prussian borough, although he was still too young to accept the post.

Virchow's liberal politics made him a target of the conservatives in Berlin. In 1849, he was suspended from his position at the Charité Hospital. He found support in the city of Würzburg and moved there to assume the chair of pathological anatomy at the University of Würzburg. He stayed at the university for the next seven years, marrying Rose Mayer in 1850, and fathering six children.

Virchow was extremely productive during this period, making significant progress in his investigation of cellular pathology and pathological anatomy. He was a popular academic, and helped the university expand by nearly quadrupling the number of medical students during the course of his tenure. In addition, in 1854, he began editing the six-volume *Handbuch der speziellen Pathologie und Therapie* (Handbook of special pathology and therapeutics). It was also at Würzburg that Virchow first demonstrated an interest in anthropology by studying the skulls of the mentally disabled in order to determine how the skull developed.

In 1858, Virchow published his influential theory, *Omnis cellula e cellula* ("all cells from cells"), which states that every cell originates from another existing cell like it. Contrary to the prevailing medical beliefs, Virchow argued that diseases resulted from changes in cells caused by external influences, then spread through cellular division. Therefore, only specific tissues became infected, and not the entire organism as was commonly thought.

Virchow's theory was actually based on discoveries made by John Goodsir and Robert Remak, but it was not until Virchow published *Cellular Pathology as Based upon Physiological and Pathological Histology* (1858) that cellular pathology gained substantial acceptance in the scientific community.

Virchow was offered a professorship at the University of Berlin in 1856. He was instrumental in the creation of the university's pathological institute. Virchow

Virchow Proposes *Omnis cellula e cellula* ("All cells from cells") Theory

Rudolf Virchow is widely considered among the most important of the nineteenth-century pathologists. He was among the first to apply microscopic observations in the study of disease and cellular pathology, a method he passed on to his students, many of whom became leading figures in medicine.

In 1839, German physiologist Theodor Schwann published his studies on the spinal notochord, noting that its composition was that of cells, an observation that became the basis of cell theory: all life is composed of cells. Similar observations were made by German botanist Matthias Schleiden in his studies of plant structures. Virchow developed Schwann's work while applying it to the human body, which in 1855 resulted in the concept of cell theory, that human beings are composed of cells, and *omnis cellula e cellula*, which roughly means that all cells originate from other cells.

The idea that humans are composed of cells had been proposed by German embryologist Robert Remak several years earlier as a result of his observations that tissues originated through the reproduction of cells. Remak's work had been largely ignored by the medical community, however. While the Latin aphorism *omnis cellula e cellula* is widely attributed to Vir-chow, it likely originated with French chemist and physiologist Francois-Vincent Raspail in 1825.

Virchow's contributions to cell theory also included the recognition of leukemia as a distinct disease, rather than the ill-defined "suppuration of the blood." Observing a case in a young cook, Virchow reported the overwhelming presence of *weisses blut*, "white blood," in a sample from the patient; the term later became *leukemia*. Believing that if cells arise only from replicating cells, growth can take place only through hyperplasia, an increase in the number of cells, or hypertrophy, an increase in the size of cells, terms that he coined. Leukemia and cancer in general were the result of hyperplasia, an increase in the actual number of cells. Virchow called the unusual characteristic of these cells *neoplasia*, or "new growth."

Virchow's scientific views ultimately developed into a conflict with the new germ theory of disease, the idea that diseases resulted from the presence of infectious agents. Nevertheless the present-day belief that pathological changes within the cells and tissues of the body can be used to diagnose disease and understand symptoms largely reflects the work that began with Virchow.

---

used the lab for decades where he trained numerous medical students and established the center as one of Europe's leading facilities.

Upon his return to Berlin, Virchow became active in politics and in 1859 he was elected to the Berlin City Council. As a politician, Virchow created policies in line with his belief that many diseases are the result of social problems. While in office, Virchow instituted a variety of public health measures. He enacted school hygiene ordinances and made improvements to the city's water and sewage systems. He supervised the construction of two new hospitals in Berlin, the Moabi and the Fried-richshain, and established a nursing school. His study of trichina, a parasitic worm found in pork, led to rigorous meat inspection policies in order to prevent human infection. The success of these programs led to an invitation from the Norwegian government in 1859 to examine an outbreak of leprosy in Bergen. As a result of the expedition, he identified the lepra cell, which is also known today as Virchow's cell.

In order to expand his social reforms, Virchow and some friends founded the liberal Progressive Party.

Virchow represented the party and was elected to the Prussian Diet in 1861. While in office, Virchow was a relentless opponent of conservative politician (and later, first chancellor of Germany) Otto von Bismarck. Virchow's impact was so great that in 1865, Bismarck actually challenged him to a duel, which Virchow refused. Virchow did, however, help the Prussian army by organizing hospital trains, the first of which he personally led to the frontlines during the Franco-Prussian War (1870–71).

Virchow's interest in anthropology and archaeology became more pronounced during this period. In 1869, he helped create the German Anthropological Society and the Berlin Society for Anthropology, Ethnology, and Prehistory and served as president of the latter for the remainder of his life. By 1870, Virchow was directing his own excavations, and in 1886, he helped establish the Berlin Ethnological Museum and founded the Museum of German Folklore in 1888.

Virchow remained active in politics and medicine until his death in 1902. He died in Berlin while recovering from a broken hip that he had received from jumping off a moving streetcar at the age of eighty-one.

IMPACT

During the mid-nineteenth century, Virchow's work on cellular pathology modernized German medicine, reducing the influence of medieval theory and positioning Germany as one of Europe's leading centers of clinical practice. He developed one of the two main autopsy procedures still in use, penned more than two thousand works, and coined more than fifty medical terms, including *hyperplasia*, *leukemia*, and *giant cell*. Even as a politician, Virchow used his medical knowledge to improve public health. He also made significant contributions as a teacher, inspiring students such as Paul Langerhans, Friedrich Daniel von Recklinghausen, Julius Friedrich Cohnheim, Edwin Klebs, and Felix Hoppe-Seyler.

Virchow's influence on German anthropology was also considerable. In addition to the anthropological organizations he helped to establish, his own work would have an impact beyond his lifetime. While investigating German heritage, he conducted a census of hair and eye color of six million school children and examined skull deformities and other physical characteristics of ancient remains. Virchow concluded that modern Germans had inherited traits from multiple races. Later, in the 1930s, the Nazis tried to conceal Virchow's findings, which conflicted with their party's ideology of Aryan superiority and "pure lineage" propaganda.

Tom Fields

FURTHER READING

Brown, Theodore M., and Elizabeth Fee. "Rudolf Carl Virchow." *American Journal of Public Health* 96.12 (2006): 2104–5. Print. Presents a brief biography of Virchow and describes his major scientific achievements.

Kumar, David R., et al. "Virchow's Contribution to the Understanding of Thrombosis and Cellular Biology." *Clinical Medicine and Research* 8.3/4 (2010): 168–72. Print. Presents an overview of Virchow's research on thrombosis and cellular biology.

Taylor, Rex, and Annelie Rieger. "Rudolf Virchow on the Typhus Epidemic in Upper Silesia: An Introduction and Translation." *Sociology of Health and Illness* 6.2 (1984): 201–17. Print. Discusses Virchow's report on the 1848 typhus epidemic and describes his influence on the field of social medicine.

HUGO DE VRIES

Dutch botanist

Working in the late nineteenth and early twentieth centuries, Dutch botanist Hugo de Vries was instrumental in rediscovering geneticist Gregor Mendel's laws of heredity. In addition, de Vries helped establish the modern science of genetics with his theory of intracellular pangenesis, and his mutation theory paved the way for debates about the nature of evolutionary change.

Born: February 16, 1848; Haarlem, Netherlands
Died: May 21, 1935; Lunteren, Netherlands
Primary field: Biology
Specialties: Botany; genetics; evolutionary biology

EARLY LIFE

The oldest son of Gerrit de Vries and Maria Everardina Reuvens, Hugo de Vries was born into a family of scholars, lawyers, religious figures, and statesmen. After working as a lawyer for some time, Gerrit was appointed to the Council of State and moved his family to The Hague; he later became prime minister of the Netherlands, serving from 1872 to 1874.

During his childhood, de Vries attended a private Baptist grammar school in Haarlem and later attended the local gymnasium, or secondary school. He spent his free time and his longer vacations exploring the countryside, searching for plants to fill his herbarium. Due to his burgeoning interest in botany, he built numerous herbariums, occasionally winning prizes for them. After the family moved to The Hague, the young de Vries occasionally spent time in Leiden, where he met the botanist Willem Suringar. Suringar asked de Vries to help him classify the plants kept by the Netherlands Botanical Society.

In 1866, de Vries entered Leiden University. Under the influence of Julius Sachs's 1868 botany textbook *Lehrbuch der Botanik*, de Vries developed an interest in plant physiology. During these years, he also discovered Charles Darwin's treatise *On the Origin of Species* (1859), which piqued his interest in evolution.

LIFE'S WORK

In 1870, de Vries moved to Germany's Heidelberg University to study chemistry with Wilhelm Hofmeister.

Six months later, in the spring of 1871, he moved to Würzburg, Germany, where he studied with Julius

Hugo de Vries Develops His Mutation Theory of Evolution

Much like English naturalist Charles Darwin, Hugo de Vries developed his ideas about evolution after a long period of experimentation and reports on those experiments. In Darwin's case, his observations of animals and plants over the course of his travels enabled him to formulate his theories of adaptation, heritability, and natural selection. Similarly, Vries's lengthy experiments with a species of the evening primrose (*Oenothera lamarckiana*) led to his conclusions regarding mutation as the mechanism driving the evolution of species.

In 1886, de Vries discovered a plot of land overgrown with evening primrose. He noticed that a number of the plants looked remarkably different from others, so he took seeds from the normal plants and from two of the plants with differences. He planted them in his experimental garden and began his observations.

As he watched the plants develop, he noticed that the seeds that he had collected started to produce new forms, which he thought were clearly and sufficiently different enough from the parent plant to be considered a new species. He later referred to these single variations as mutations and gave them a scientific name that reflected their form. Thus, he named a giant plant *Oenothera gigas*; one with red veins in the leaves, *Oenothera rubinervis*; and one with narrow leaves on long stalks, *Oenothera oblonga*.

De Vries argued that a species produces mutants over isolated short periods of time in its evolutionary life. Furthermore, he theorized that permutation periods in which mutant traits are developed precede these periods of mutation. On the basis of his research, he distinguished between progressive and retrogressive mutants; the mutants that possessed retrogressive traits did not contribute to the evolution of the species, while those possessing progressive traits did.

While some of de Vries's critics contended that these single variants were not mutants but simply hybrids, later scientists followed in de Vries's footsteps with their own experiments in an effort to confirm mutation theory as a genetic mechanism by which evolution proceeds.

Sachs and worked in his laboratory and contributed to Sachs's journal by writing a number of reports on his experimental work. Although he taught natural history at the First High School in Amsterdam from 1871 to 1878, de Vries returned in the summers to Sachs's laboratory at Würzburg in order to continue his experiments in plant physiology. Over the course of these seven years, de Vries produced a number of monographs on red clover, potatoes, and sugar beets, and his articles on cell growth in plants attracted wide attention. His article on the mechanism that causes tendrils to curve in plants prompted Darwin's admiration for de Vries and the two men began a long correspondence.

De Vries moved to the University of Amsterdam in 1878, becoming the equivalent of a tenured professor in 1881. It was there that he conducted his famous experiments on protoplasm, plasmolysis, and plant osmosis. Through these experiments, he discovered that the inner lining of the cell wall, the protoplast, consisted of three layers, not two, as most plant physiologists believed at the time. He also determined that vacuoles, small cavities containing fluid in the cell, have their own linings, and he performed research on protoplasm in insectivorous plants.

Late in the 1880s, de Vries's interests, influenced by his deep reading of Darwin, shifted to questions regarding inheritance and variability. In his book *Intracellular Pangenesis* (1889), de Vries argued that hereditary traits of living organisms are independent units (pangenes) that reside in cells' nuclei. De Vries used this theory to explain how a cell develops into an organ, how metamorphosis occurs, and how offspring develop and maintain uniformity with parents. He argued that hereditary traits of a genus can be traced to large aggregates of pangenes that remain unchanged in the offspring; extraordinary changes during the division of cells, however, result in the creation of a different pangene, which results in a new characteristic of an organism. Thus, according to de Vries, evolution proceeds by this pangenetic mechanism. Twenty years later, Danish botanist Wilhelm Johannsen shortened de Vries' term *pangenes* to *genes*.

In order to support his own work on pangenesis, de Vries conducted numerous experiments involving the hybridization of several plant species. Through such experiments and his reports on them, he rediscovered Mendel's 1866 paper on the experiments with peas that led to Mendel's formulation of his genetic laws. Following de Vries's rediscovery of Mendel's laws, many other scientists took up Mendel's ideas regarding hybridization and genetics. However, de Vries believed that hybridization failed to account for the appearance of new species, and rather than building on Mendel, he set out to explore the phenomenon of mutation, which he thought provided the details for and advanced the theory of evolution.

Beginning his experiments with a species of evening primrose in 1886, de Vries noticed new variants in the species. Amongst a garden plot in which the parent primrose grew, a number of offspring grew that were distinct enough to be single variations of the parent and for de Vries to call mutants. He hypothesized that during its evolutionary life, a species produces mutants over isolated and relatively short periods of time. Sometimes permutation periods, during which the hereditary traits are formed, precede the periods of mutation. De Vries developed his ideas at length in a two-volume work, *Mutation Theory* (1900–1903), which became the foundation of an evolution theory that proposed that abrupt periods of mutations were responsible for propelling evolution, rather than a gradual, continuous process of adaptation and selection.

In May 1905, de Vries was elected Foreign Member of the Royal Society of London. He also acted as a correspondent for and member of various other societies, including the Russian Academy of Sciences, the Prussian Academy of Sciences, and the Academia dei Lincei in Rome, Italy. He retired from the University of Amsterdam in 1918 to his estate in Lunteren, where he continued to conduct experiments in his vast experimental gardens until his death in 1935.

Impact

While de Vries may be best known today for his rediscovery of Mendel at the end of the nineteenth century, his work on mutation theory and evolutionary biology continues to have significant and lasting ramifications for the subject. While numerous scientists posit that evolution develops through a gradual process of adaptation and the inheritance of adaptive traits, others argue that evolution advances by jumps or macromutations, a theory known as saltationism. De Vries was one of the first saltationist geneticists to advocate for mutations as the mechanism that drives the evolutionary process.

De Vries's ideas about the genetic basis of mutation, including his isolation of the pangene as the unit in which mutation occurs, anticipate much modern scientific work on the genetic basis of evolution. The mutation research performed by de Vries and other early geneticists provided the foundation for work by later evolutionary biologists such as Richard Dawkins. De Vries's work may also have influenced American geneticist T. H. Morgan, who, with a group of other scientists, conducted experiments on the genetics of fruit flies (*Drosophila*) that became the foundation for the modern chromosome theory of heredity.

Henry L. Carrigan Jr.

Further Reading

Bowler, Peter J. *Life's Splendid Drama: Evolutionary Biology and the Reconstruction of Life's Ancestry, 1860–1940*. Chicago: U of Chicago P, 1996. Print. Offers an account of how various scientists have used de Vries's ideas about mutation as the basis for evolutionary theory in contemporary debates about the history of evolution.

Ridley, Matt. *The Agile Gene: How Nature Turns on Nurture*. New York: Harper, 2004. Print. Provides an account of genes as the foundation of an evolutionary theory of behavior, proceeding from de Vries's early theory of genetics.

Ruse, Michael, and Joseph Travis, ed. *Evolution: The First Four Billion Years*. Cambridge, MA: Harvard UP, 2009. Print. Contains short essays on major scientists who have made an impact on the study of evolution, including a brief introduction to de Vries's work and his role in shaping the conversation about evolution.

JOHANNES DIDERIK VAN DER WAALS

Dutch physicist

Educator and physicist Johannes Diderik van der Waals received the Nobel Prize in Physics in 1910 for his work showing the continuity of state between liquids and gases. The weak electric forces that attract neutral molecules to one another are named after him.

Born: November 23, 1837; Leiden, Netherlands
Died: March 8, 1923; Amsterdam, Netherlands
Primary field: Physics
Specialty: Atomic and molecular physics

EARLY LIFE

Johannes Diderik van der Waals was born on November 23, 1837, the first of ten children in a working-class family in Leiden, the Netherlands. His father, Jacobus van der Waals, was a carpenter, and his mother was Elisabeth van den Burg. Due to his family's financial situation, van der Waals was not able to enroll in a secondary school, the standard pathway to a university education. Instead, he completed primary school in his hometown and then proceeded to an advanced primary school, which he left at around age fourteen to become a teacher in a primary school.

Van der Waals began studying part time at the University of Leiden starting in 1862. However, he did not know Latin, a prerequisite for taking formal university examinations and pursuing doctoral studies. Nevertheless, his pursuit of further education enabled him to obtain teaching certificates in mathematics and physics. He became director of a primary school in 1864, at the age of twenty-four. A year later, he was appointed to a teaching position at one of Hogere Burger secondary schools in

Deventer, which provided schooling for upper-middle-class children. In 1866, van der Waals moved to the Hague, where he continued his teaching career.

Throughout his early education and work as a teacher, van der Waals focused on the fields of mathematics and physics. New legislation was eventually passed, allowing van der Waals to apply for—and obtain—an exemption from the classical languages requirement for university examinations at the University of Leiden.

LIFE'S WORK

On June 14, 1873, the thirty-five-year old van der Waals defended his thesis, "On the Continuity of the Gas and Liquid State," at the University of Leiden. No one could have guessed how influential his thesis—which proposed a revolutionary equation of state showing the continuity of liquid and gaseous states of matter—would become. At that time, the paper simply earned van der Waals a doctorate degree and entry into the community of professional scientists.

For the next several years, van der Waals continued to advance his work in education and science in tandem. In 1875, he was elected a member of the Royal Netherlands Academy of Arts and Sciences. In 1877, he was named director of secondary education in the Hague. Meanwhile, "On the Continuity of the Gas and Liquid State" was gaining the attention of a wider audience, spawning papers in response, and earning recognition from Scottish physicist James Clerk Maxwell, the author of classical electromagnetic theory, in the pages of *Nature*.

During the late nineteenth century, the field of molecular science was still taking shape. Not all scientists

Van der Waals Proposes the Equation of State

When Dutch physicist Johannes Diderik van der Waals published his thesis in 1873, the key element was this equation:

$$(P + a\,/\,V^2)\,(V - b) = RT$$

Here, P is the pressure of a gas or liquid, V is the molar volume, and T is the temperature, with a and b characterizing the critical point of the gas or liquid—the conditions of temperature and pressure at which a liquid becomes a gas and vice versa. R is the ideal gas constant.

What made van der Waals's equation of state revolutionary was that it was applicable for both gases and liquids, demonstrating that the two states exist on a continuum, with fundamental similarities to their behavior. Apply enough pressure to a gas, and it will become a liquid; heat up a liquid enough, and it transform into a gas. Van der Waals's equation quantified this relationship better than any that had come before.

The concept that gases and liquids both behave as fluids is now considered a fundamental concept of science. However, at the time of van der Waals's thesis, the nature of matter was still the subject of contention—many prominent scientists did not believe in atoms. The chief conceptual innovation of van der Waals's equation is a direct consequence of his belief in atoms and molecules. To come up with his equation of state, van der Waals had taken into account a strictly molecular view of gases and liquids, where their particles took up space and interacted with one another. It performed much better in making predictions than the ideal gas law, which had been the standing paradigm but failed to take into account the volume of gas particles or their ability to interact.

Throughout his lifetime, van der Waals would continue to refine his equation, eventually developing a generalized form that united solid, liquid, and gaseous states of matter into one equation, the law of corresponding states. Although in modern terms van der Waals's original equations are obsolete, they represent an essential step in the development of our modern understanding of the states of matter.

agreed that atoms and molecules were the basis of matter. Van der Waals was a dedicated atomist, however, and the fact that he took into account the "thickness" of the particles in gases and liquids was essential to the insight of his thesis. Van der Waals's name would eventually be immortalized in the term "van der Waals forces," the weak electric forces that attract neutral molecules to one another. These are the forces that allow geckos and small spiders to cling to surfaces.

Later in 1877, some six months after his directorship in the Hague, van der Waals was chosen as the first professor of physics at the newly created University of Amsterdam, where he worked to establish the department of physics.

Van der Waals helped to create the field of molecular physics. In 1880, he published the law of corresponding states, which generalized his equation of state, previously limited to gases and liquids, to all substances. In 1891, van der Waals published a paper entitled "Théorie moléculaire d'une substance composée de deux matières différentes" (A molecular theory of a substance composed of two different species), which showed how his original equation could be applied to liquid mixtures.

In 1881, van der Waals's wife, Anna Magdalena Smit, succumbed to tuberculosis. Her death deeply affected him, and he never remarried. The couple had four children: Anne Madeleine, Jacqueline Elisabeth, Johanna Diderica, and Johannes Diderik Jr.

Van der Waals accumulated many honors during his career. He served as general secretary of the Royal Netherlands Academy of Arts and Sciences from 1896 to 1912. He was also granted an honorary doctorate from the University of Cambridge and honorary membership in the Imperial Society of Naturalists of Moscow. Van der Waals was a member of the Royal Irish Academy, the American Philosophical Society, the Institut de France, the Royal Academy of Sciences of Berlin, and the Royal Flemish Academy of Belgium for Science and the Arts. Van der Waals was granted foreign membership in the Chemical Society of London, the American National Academy of Sciences, and the Accademia dei Lincei of Rome.

In 1910, at age seventy-two, van der Waals was awarded the Nobel Prize in Physics for his equation of state. He died on March 8, 1923, in Amsterdam.

IMPACT

Van der Waals has been cited as the founder of modern molecular physics for revolutionizing scientific understanding of gases and liquids. Van der Waals's work enabled another Dutch physicist, Kammerling Onnes, to liquefy helium in 1908. Onnes went on to use liquid helium as a coolant to discover superconductivity in mercury in 1911. (Onnes was awarded the Nobel Prize in Physics in 1913.) Over a century and a half after the publication of his thesis, van der Waals's generalized law of corresponding states and a modified version adapted for quantum physics are in use in both theoretical physics and engineering applications.

Van der Waals was a primary player in what has been called the Second Golden Age of Dutch sciences. His time at Amsterdam helped prepare a generation of Dutch students who became world leaders in experimental molecular sciences. Van der Waals continues to receive frequent mention in modern scientific papers, both in retrospective praise and in providing the foundation for new research.

Van der Waals's demonstration of the molecular nature of matter is his greatest scientific achievement. He was the first to account for the importance of intermolecular forces in a given substance, calculating that they affect important and practical properties such as volume and pressure. As the accuracy and importance of his approach was revealed through experimentation,

van der Waals's work became a compelling argument for a molecular composition of matter.

Kenrick Vezina

FURTHER READING

Shalom, Eliezer, Ajoy Ghatak, and Heinrich Hora. *Fundamentals of Equations of State*. Hackensack: World Scientific, 2002. Print. An advanced review of the science behind equations of state. Includes a discussion of how the equation of state has influenced other branches of science.

Tang, Kwong-Tin, and Jan Peter Toennies. "Johannes Diderik van der Waals: A Pioneer in the Molecular Sciences and Nobel Prize Winner in 1910." *Angewandte Chemie* 49.50 (2010): 9574–79. Print. An accessible scholarly essay that breaks down van der Waals's thesis and provides a particularly intriguing description of van der Waals the person, including his teaching style.

Valderrama, José O. "The legacy of Johannes Diderik van der Waals, a hundred years after his Nobel Prize for physics." *Journal of Supercritical Fluids* 55.2 (2010): 415–20. Print. Highlights the importance of van der Waals's work, particularly its use in applied science and engineering.

ALFRED RUSSEL WALLACE

English biologist

Nineteenth-century naturalist and explorer Alfred Russel Wallace developed a theory of evolution based on the principle of natural selection at the same time as fellow investigator and theorist Charles Darwin. Wallace also made significant contributions in the field of biogeography.

Born: January 8, 1823; Usk, Wales
Died: November 7, 1913; Broadstone, England
Primary field: Biology
Specialty: Evolutionary biology

EARLY LIFE

Alfred Russel Wallace was born in Usk, southeast Wales, and was raised in Hertford, where he attended the Hertford School. At age fourteen, Wallace went to live with an older brother in London, where he apprenticed as a surveyor. He developed his skills in math and science and also bore witness to social injustice while traveling across the country to surveying sites with his

brother. Influenced by the theories of social reformer Robert Owen, Wallace became involved with Mechanics Institutes, which provided education to working men. He also read numerous scientific books, including Charles Lyell's *Principles of Geology*, which, contrary to creationist theories of the period, posited that the Earth had been forming for millennia.

In 1844, Wallace accepted a teaching post at Leicester. While in Leicester, he became interested in mesmerism, a type of social science hypnotism developed by German physician Franz Mesmer. Wallace also became interested in travel literature, specifically the work of scientists and naturalists who had visited remote corners of the globe and reported their findings on the varieties of animal and plant life in these regions. Wallace became acquainted with Henry Bates, who would later become a renowned naturalist and explorer. Although Wallace continued to work as a surveyor after the unexpected death of his brother, his interest in science remained high. In 1845, he read Charles Darwin's exploration memoir *The*

Voyage of the Beagle, as well as Robert Chambers's *Vestiges of Creation*, which proposed that species were not static but developed gradually over time. Wallace made the decision to become a naturalist and planned a journey up the Amazon River in South America. He set off for Brazil with Bates in April 1848.

LIFE'S WORK

Wallace's trip to South America transformed him from an amateur to a professional scientist. For four years, he traveled the Amazon and its tributaries, collecting and observing the natural life on the Rio Negro. He was methodical in gathering specimens of the birds and insects he found there, preparing them carefully and occasionally shipping samples to an agent in England. Throughout his explorations, Wallace planned a series of publications. He kept extensively detailed journals about his discoveries. Wallace also accumulated a collection of specimens to bring back to England, where he intended to sell them in order to fund future work. However, this collection and much of his paperwork was lost when the ship transporting him back to England in 1852 caught fire and sank. Wallace managed to find a lifeboat and survive.

Wallace did not let the shipwreck of 1852 set him back. Upon returning to England, he began writing about his travels, producing two books that were well received by the scientific community. He was introduced to a number of influential scientists who saw promise in the field studies he had done. Within this community of scientists, Wallace sought support for another expedition to the East. In March 1854, he set out for the Malay Archipelago, where he spent eight years conducting observations and collecting specimens. Wallace's work in Southeastern Asia established his reputation as one of the century's premier natural scientists.

Years of study had convinced Wallace that evolution, not creationism, best explained the extensive variations among the many species of animal life he had observed during his years as an explorer. In 1855, he published a paper that made public his commitment to the theory of evolution. Three years later, Wallace came up with an explanation for the mechanism that drove this evolutionary process. It appeared to him that, through a process of natural selection, organisms that had more effectively adapted to their environments were more capable of surviving and reproducing. In February

---

Wallace's Discovery of Natural Selection

Alfred Russel Wallace's scientific studies convinced him that creationism was an inadequate explanation for the immense variety of living species he observed in nature. His explorations in South America and the Malay Archipelago reinforced his conviction that species evolved in some complex way. Intending to turn his notes and speculations into a major study on the topic, he published a paper supporting the principle of evolution in 1855. However, at that time, he had not yet discovered the mechanism that controlled the process. In 1858, while recuperating from illness on the island of Ternate, in what is now eastern Indonesia, Wallace came up with an explanation for the variety of species he had observed in the field. It appeared to him that a process of natural selection caused species to evolve over time, developing characteristics that would allow them to thrive in a changing environment. Species that failed to adapt slowly decreased in number, and gradually became extinct. Over two nights, Wallace drafted "On the Tendency of Varieties to Depart Indefinitely from the Original Type," a paper explaining how natural selection favored species that adapted best to changing environments. He sent his paper to Charles Dar-

win, whom he greatly admired. Darwin was known to have been working on the problem of evolution for two decades but had hitherto published little beyond the journal that he kept during his nearly five-year voyage aboard the HMS *Beagle* from 1831 to 1835. When Wallace wrote his paper in 1858, he had no way of knowing that Darwin had independently come to the same conclusions.

Darwin acted honorably and generously when he received Wallace's paper. With the help of fellow scientists Charles Lyell and Joseph Dalton Hooker, he arranged to have Wallace's paper read at a meeting of the Linnaean Society in London on April 1, 1858. Darwin's work was also presented at the meeting. The joint presentation gave the two scientists equal claim to being first in "discovering" the principle of natural selection at work among living species. A year later, Darwin published *On the Origin of Species*, a work that revolutionized accepted ideas about the natural world. When Wallace received a copy of Darwin's book, he abandoned plans to develop his own ideas more fully. Instead, he became a champion of Darwin's works and of the principles of natural selection.

1858, Wallace drafted a paper outlining his theory and sent it to Charles Darwin in England. Darwin, who had reached the same conclusion independently, arranged for a joint public reading of Wallace's paper and one of his own in April 1858.

Wallace was not in England when controversy erupted over the publication of Darwin's *On the Origin of Species* (1859), which laid out the theory of evolution in detail. He continued working in the Malay Archipelago, recording his observations about natural life in the region and taking notes for a series of publications discussing his theories about how animal species came to be distributed around the globe. After returning to England in 1862, Wallace spent the next fifteen years as a public champion of evolution, while composing a series of works explaining his own ideas about geographical species distribution. His book *The Malay Archipelago* (1869) was hailed as one of the most important scientific travelogues of the age, and *The Geographical Distribution of Animals* (1875) became the standard work in zoogeography for nearly a century. In 1866, Wallace married Annie Mitten. The couple had three children.

In the early 1860s, Wallace began to fall out of favor with some in the scientific community over his support for the practice of spiritualism. Inspired by his interest in mesmerism, Wallace attended séances and wrote about the possibility of contacting the dead. Though he realized he could produce no proof sufficient to convince fellow scientists that such contact was possible, Wallace argued that failure to find scientific evidence did not automatically signify that such communication was impossible. An even more serious breach between Wallace and fellow scientists occurred over his profession that, while evolution explained changes among subhuman species, the development of the human brain and of human morality was the result of intervention into the natural order of evolution by a higher intelligence. Many saw this theory as nothing more than a reversion to creationism.

Later in his life, Wallace became an active proponent of a number of radical social causes. He introduced land reform plan that called for the government to take over ownership of all land. He also joined a group opposing mandatory smallpox vaccination. Nonetheless, he remained an active author, publishing a number of scientific studies, including an influential collection of essays entitled *Darwinism* in 1889, and a two-volume autobiography in 1905.

Despite Wallace's controversial support of human exceptionalism, the scientific community recognized his contributions to the advancement of evolutionary theory. He was awarded the Royal Medal in 1868, elected a Fellow of the Linnaean Society in 1872, and awarded an Honorary Doctor of Civil Law degree by Oxford University in 1889. In 1908, King Edward VII conferred on him the Order of Merit. Following his death in 1913, Wallace's reputation waned and Darwin earned notoriety as the sole father of evolutionary biology. Only at the beginning of the twenty-first century was his reputation restored by scientists who recognized his important contributions across the spectrum of the biological sciences.

IMPACT

The development of the theory of natural selection revolutionized the study of biology and led to advancements in other fields such as paleontology and genetics. Additionally, while Thomas Henry Huxley became known as the most influential champion of Darwin's theory of evolution, Wallace was equally active and influential in speaking and writing in defense of natural selection in the face of many detractors. Even after he fell out with Darwin over the issue of human origins, he continued to publish works in support of Darwin's ideas about evolution.

Wallace was a leading figure in providing animals and insects for study by naturalists in England. Over the course of his career, he collected more than 120,000 prepared specimens and living animals for zoos, museums, and scholars. His pioneering work in constructing a theory to explain the geographical distribution of animals earned him recognition as the father of zoogeography. Wallace's theory that migration occurred over land masses that were once connected but were later separated by large bodies of water was proven feasible in 1915, when German geophysicist Alfred Wegener developed the concept of continental drift.

Wallace also made contributions in the areas of exobiology, animal mimicry and coloration, and bird migration. While his work as a social reformer did not have the same impact as his efforts in science, many of his ideas, including the encouragement of employee buyouts and payment of double wages for overtime work, became important to labor relations activities in the twentieth century.

Laurence W. Mazzeno

FURTHER READING

Fichman, Martin. *An Elusive Victorian: The Evolution of Alfred Russel Wallace*. Chicago: U of Chicago P, 2010. Print. Examines Wallace's major intellectual and cultural views and activities. Explains how Wallace's pursuit of scientific knowledge coalesced with his social, political, ethical, and theological interests.

Raby, Peter. *Alfred Russel Wallace: A Life*. Princeton: Princeton UP, 2001. Print. Detailed biography providing extensive discussion of Wallace's travels and analysis of his contributions to science and social policy.

Shermer, Michael. *In Darwin's Shadow: The Life and Science of Alfred Russel Wallace*. New York: Oxford UP, 2011. Print. Psychological study of Wallace, stressing his iconoclasm and providing insight into the methodologies that led him to embrace scientific study, social activism, and spiritualism with equal vigor.

Slotten, Ross. *The Heretic in Darwin's Court: A Life of Alfred Russel Wallace*. New York: Columbia UP, 2004. Print. Presents a comprehensive biography of Wallace, including a discussion of his involvement in various social and political causes and his lifelong interest in spiritualism.

Smith, Charles H., and George Beccaloni, eds. *Natural Selection and Beyond: The Intellectual Legacy of Alfred Russel Wallace*. New York: Oxford UP, 2008. Print. Presents twenty essays by leading scientists exploring aspects of Wallace's career and contributions to evolutionary biology.

JAMES D. WATSON

American biologist

James Watson, working with British biologist Francis Crick, helped identify the double-helix structure of the deoxyribonucleic acid (DNA) molecule, and codiscovered the process of replication responsible for heredity. He also conducted significant research on protein synthesis and the role of viruses in cancer.

Born: April 6, 1928; Chicago, Illinois
Also known as: James Dewey Watson
Primary field: Biology
Specialties: Genetics; virology

EARLY LIFE

James Dewey Watson was born on April 6, 1928, in Chicago, Illinois, and was named after his father, a businessman. Although the Great Depression impacted the family financially, the Watson home was filled with books. As a child, Watson read classic Russian and English literature and became absorbed in almanacs and other reference books. He spent his early years in Chicago and attended the University of Chicago Nursery School, Horace Mann Elementary School, and South Shore High School.

A gifted student, Watson received a scholarship to an experimental program at the University of Chicago for students who had completed two years of high school. He chose to major in zoology and graduated with a bachelor of science degree in 1947, at the age of nineteen.

Watson became interested in genetics during his senior year of college. Like Francis Crick, he was inspired by the book *What Is Life?* (1946) by Nobel Prize–winning physicist Erwin Schrödinger. In his

book, Schrödinger proposes that genetic material may be found in a molecule, meaning that molecular biology holds the answers to the question of the evolution of life on Earth. Instead of becoming an ornithologist or a naturalist, Watson began entertaining thoughts about studying DNA.

Watson obtained a fellowship to attend graduate school at the University of Indiana at Bloomington, where he studied genetics with Hermann J. Muller. His adviser for his thesis on bacteriophages was Salvatore Luria, a prominent microbiologist. Watson spent one summer at Cold Spring Harbor Laboratory on Long Island, New York, with Luria, learning about bacteriophages.

In 1950, Watson received his PhD in zoology and obtained a Merck Fellowship from the National Research Council to study bacteriophage-infected cells at the University of Copenhagen. He analyzed DNA in bacterial viruses with biochemist Herman Kalckar, who took Watson to a symposium on micromolecules held at the Zoological Station in Naples, Italy, in the spring of 1951. It was there that he first saw an X-ray diffraction photograph of DNA that depicted a helical structure, taken by Maurice Wilkins, a physicist and X-ray crystallographer at King's College in London. It was well known that Wilkins and Rosalind Franklin, his colleague at King's College, had been researching DNA, and suddenly Watson became interested in the research.

LIFE'S WORK

In October 1951, Watson joined a group of scientists researching proteins at Cambridge University's Cavendish

Laboratory, not far from King's College. There, he met Francis Crick, a British physicist who had returned to graduate school after World War II and was still working on his PhD.

Crick and Watson struck up a friendship based on their mutual interest in DNA. Crick shared everything he had heard about the King's College team, which had been making considerable progress in cracking the genetic code. Watson mentioned his experience at the symposium in Naples earlier that year and raved about Wilkins's X-ray diffraction photograph. Despite the fact that neither scientist was assigned to research heredity, they decided to enter the race to determine the structure of the DNA molecule. Watson's background in biology complemented Crick's background in physics. However, it would take time for the pair to reach the necessary level of expertise. In addition, Crick had to teach Watson about X-ray crystallography, which was the chief means of recording and investigating the structure of molecules at the time.

Watson and Crick had a number of problems to solve before the basis of human heredity could be revealed. Even with the aid of X-ray diffraction techniques, molecular analysis is very difficult. The technique Watson and Crick used was to make physical models of molecular structures. In the spring of 1952, Watson and Crick saw another X-ray diffraction photograph taken by Rosalind Franklin, the chemist and expert X-ray crystallographer working with Wilkins at King's College. Her photograph clearly depicted the double-helix structure of DNA. Based on her photograph, Watson and Crick were able to put together a model showing the correct structure of DNA.

Crick and Watson submitted their findings, titled "A Structure for Deoxyribose Nucleic Acid," to the scientific journal *Nature*. They were published on April 25, 1953, followed by another article on May 30. Watson and Crick had beaten the King's College team, as well as the distinguished American chemist Linus Pauling, who had also been close to solving the DNA puzzle.

In 1962, Watson, Crick, and Wilkins were awarded the Nobel Prize, although many scientists believe that Rosalind Franklin, had she not died prior to 1962, would have been named instead, for it was her X-ray diffraction photograph that depicted the double helix.

After his work at Cambridge, Watson returned to the California Institute of Technology (Caltech) as a senior research fellow. He worked with students on bacteriophages and conducted additional research in X-ray diffraction studies of ribonucleic acid (RNA).

In 1955, he returned to Cambridge, where he studied tobacco mosaic virus using X-ray diffraction and worked with Crick on a theory about the structure of DNA in viruses. In 1956, Harvard University offered Watson an assistant professorship in the biology department; he became a full professor in 1961. He wrote the first undergraduate textbook on genetics, *Molecular Biology of the Gene* (1965). After several revisions, it is still in use more than forty years later.

Watson remained a bachelor until 1968, when he married Elizabeth Lewis, a sophomore at Radcliffe College. That year, Watson was named director of the Cold Spring Harbor Laboratory. At the time, the institution was suffering from financial problems. Watson turned it into a premier academic institution specializing in cancer research. In 1994, Watson was named president of the institution and worked to obtain accreditation for its doctoral programs. The Watson School of Biological Sciences is now named for him, and he watched the first graduate students obtain their doctorates in June 2004.

In 1968, Watson published his memoir of the DNA discovery, *The Double Helix: A Personal Account of the Discovery of DNA*. The book was controversial for its depiction of Watson's colleagues, and women's groups disapproved of his portrayal of Rosalind Franklin. In his memoir *Genes, Girls, and Gamow: After the Double Helix* (2002), Watson gives Franklin credit for her important role in solving the DNA puzzle.

In 1989, Watson was asked to direct the National Center for Human Genome Research at the National Institutes of Health. For three years, he oversaw the initial development of the Human Genome Project, which led to the draft sequencing of the human genome in 2003 and the finished sequencing in 2006. Concerned about the project's ethical implications, Watson created the Ethical, Legal, and Social Issues Research Program (ELSI).

In addition to the Nobel Prize, Watson has been awarded many other honors, including the Presidential Medal of Freedom in 1977, the National Medal of Science in 1997, and a number of honorary degrees. In 2007, the 454 Life Science Corporation presented Watson with his personalized, full sequence genome—or specific genetic makeup. Watson published the genome online.

IMPACT

The discovery of DNA's double-helix structure brought about a revolution in biochemistry because it allowed scientists to analyze the genetic makeup of all living organisms. Without the discovery of the double helix, sequencing the human genome would have been

Watson and Crick Discover DNA's Double Helix Structure

In the fall of 1951, when James D. Watson began work at the Cavendish Laboratory at Cambridge University in England, there was no agreed upon understanding of how human genetic information was stored and transmitted. Some biologists believed that genes were protein molecules; others thought that DNA (deoxyribonucleic acid), which was already known to exist in the chromosomes of all cells, was the carrier of genetic information. Watson and his colleague Francis Crick became convinced that research into DNA was most likely to provide the answer to this central question. However, the structure of the DNA molecule was unknown.

The DNA molecule consists of long chains of sugar and phosphate bases. The four different types—adenine (A), cytosine (C), guanine (G), and thymine (T)—are attached to the sugar and sugar phosphates in chemically complex ways. The length of these chains is astonishing; the largest human chromosome contains about three billion base pairs.

Watson and Crick made physical models of the DNA molecule using parts representing these different chemical components. These parts were constructed so that they could not be physically connected to other parts if the chemical bond could not exist in nature. The structure of the model was verified by comparing the angles of the connections to the angles revealed by X-ray diffraction photographs of the actual DNA molecule.

Watson and Crick built their first model out of cardboard and wire, relying on Watson's memory of rival Maurice Wilkins's X-ray diffraction photograph. This first model depicted three strands, or spirals, rather than the two-strand, double helix model that they would later determine to be correct. In addition, the bases were positioned incorrectly and were lacking the right chemical structures.

After they saw rival Rosalind Franklin's X-ray diffraction photograph that clearly showed the double helix structure in 1952, Watson and Crick set about determining the correct placement and pairing of the A, C, G, and T bases. While visiting Cambridge, Austrian chemist Erwin Chargaff took a look at the model and explained his recent determination regarding ratios between the bases, which stated that base A was equivalent to base T and that base C was equivalent to base G. These are now known as Chargaff's rules. Another chemist, Jerry Donohue, assisted Watson and Crick by showing them the correct chemical structure of the bases. The bases form what are now called the "rungs of the ladder," whereas in the first model Watson and Crick had placed the bases along the backbone, or the "rails of the ladder."

From his work on proteins, Crick guessed that the two strands of DNA move in opposite directions and then determined correctly that DNA replicates when the two strands "unzip" and copy themselves. The partners had put together the final, correct model of DNA by March 7, 1953.

---

impossible. Having a complete sequence of the human genome is a major scientific achievement. However, researchers have much to learn about the number, exact location, functions, and expressions of human genes. As scientists increase their knowledge of how genetic variations affect individuals, new genetic therapies and technologies will become possible. Watson's own work in genetics and molecular biology has had direct implications for poliomyelitis research and the fight against cancer.

In anticipation of these and other breakthroughs made possible by genetic research, Watson and others have begun to address the host of often complex ethical, legal, and social issues that have already arisen, including fair use, privacy and confidentiality, reproductive rights, medical and public health education,

environmental concerns, commercialization, and human responsibility.

Sally Driscoll

FURTHER READING

Ridley, Matt. *Francis Crick: Discoverer of the Genetic Code*. New York: Harper, 2006. Print. Eminent Lives series. Provides a succinct account of Crick's work on DNA with Watson.

Watson, James D. *Avoid Boring People: Lessons from a Life in Science*. New York: Knopf, 2007. Print. Discusses Watson's own recollections of his early life and scientific achievements up to the mid-1970s.

---, and Andrew Berry. *DNA: The Secret of Life*. New York: Knopf, 2003. Print. Traces the evolution of the study of DNA.

ALFRED WEGENER
German meteorologist and geologist

Wegener's theories gave scientific credence to the idea of continental drift. Wegener concluded that the continents were once part of a so-called supercontinent known as Pangaea sometime during the Mesozoic era.

Born: November 1, 1880; Berlin, Germany
Died: November 1930; Greenland
Primary field: Earth sciences
Specialties: Geology; meteorology

EARLY LIFE
Alfred Lothar Wegener was born in Berlin, Germany, on November 1, 1880. As a young man, Wegener dreamed of adventure and of being an explorer. He was physically active and a skilled mountaineer, and would hike in the Alps while attending the University of Innsbruck in Austria.

Wegener graduated from secondary school in 1899. He then studied mathematics and the natural sciences at the Friedrich Wilhelm University in Berlin, where he focused especially on astronomy. Between 1901 and 1902, Wegener volunteered in the Queen Elizabeth Guard-Grenadier Third Regiment. He earned his doctorate from the University of Berlin in 1904; his doctoral dissertation, titled "The Alfonsine Tables for the Use of a Modern Calculator," focused on astronomy.

Wegener's first adventurous exploits took place in April 1906. He had moved to Lindenberg with his brother, where they worked together at the Royal Prussian Aeronautic Observatory. They were able to assist in atmospheric experiments, and completed a record-breaking 52-hour hot-air balloon flight. That same year, Wegener had the chance to participate in his first polar expedition to the northeastern coast of Greenland with a group of explorers from Denmark.

Among the party was Russian meteorologist Wladimir Köppen, who would become one of Wegener's mentors and an important collaborator. Wegener married Köppen's daughter, Else, in 1913. During the two-year journey through Greenland, Wegener learned how to survive in and travel through polar environments. The polar expeditions provided opportunities for Wegener to gain meteorological information, such as measurements of ice thickness.

LIFE'S WORK
Wegener's academic career began in 1908 at the University of Marberg, where he taught courses in astronomy and meteorology. While looking at a map of the world in 1910, he noticed the correspondence between the coastlines of the continents separated by the Atlantic Ocean. Although he was struck by how the opposing coastlines seemed to fit together like a jigsaw puzzle, he was not convinced at the time that continental drift was the probable explanation.

In 1911, Wegener came across information describing a theoretical land bridge that once linked Brazil with Africa. This discovery renewed his interest in continental drift—which describes the phenomena of the formation, change, and movement of the continents across the Earth's crust. He began to conduct research in geology and paleontology in order to learn more. The information he gathered in this research convinced him that continental drift was worth consideration. That year also saw the publication of his first book, *Thermodynamics of the Atmosphere*.

In January 1912, Wegener addressed the Geological Association in Frankfurt, Germany, with a talk called "The Geophysical Basis of the Evolution of the Large-scale Features of the Earth's Crust (Continents and Oceans)." He spoke again a few days later to the Society for the Advancement of Natural Science in Marburg on the topic of "Horizontal Displacements of the Continents." His talks rejected the land-bridge theory that connected continents in favor of the theory of continental drift, which suggests that landmasses actually moved away from each other over a long period of time.

Later that year, Wegener's research was interrupted by another journey to Greenland, this time with Johann Peter Koch, Vigfus Sigurdsson, and Lars Larsen. The purpose of the 1912 trip was to cross the island at its widest point. Using Icelandic ponies, the group was able to spend the winter at a camp on the inland ice sheet. The expedition nearly ended in disaster when they traversed the inland glacier; they had nearly run out of food, and without the help of a group of Eskimos, they might never have made it. Wegener's third expedition in 1929 was a preliminary scouting trip for an ambitious 1930 trip, during which he hoped to climb to the interior ice sheet.

Wegener's scientific work was interrupted again when World War I began in 1914. He was drafted into the Queen Elisabeth Grenadier Guards' Third Regiment as a junior officer, and was sent into the field. Despite two injuries, he continued to serve the German military

Wegener Proposes the Theory of Continental Drift

The concept of continental drift was developed, at least in part, to explain the striking similarities between the parallel coastlines bordering the Atlantic Ocean, which seem as though they could fit together like pieces of a giant jigsaw puzzle.

As early as 1620, English philosopher Sir Francis Bacon discussed the possibility that the Western Hemisphere had once been joined to Africa and Europe. French geographer Antonio Snider-Pellegrini, in his book *La Creation et ses Mysteres Devoiles* (Creation and its mysteries revealed, 1859), recognized the similarities between American and European fossil plants of the Carboniferous period and proposed that all continents were once part of a single landmass. Nineteenth-century Austrian geologist Eduard Suess noticed the close correspondence between geological formations in the Southern Hemisphere, grouping them together into a single landmass he termed Gondwanaland. In 1910, Alfred Wegener suggested mechanisms that could account for large, lateral displacements of the Earth's crust and, therefore, how continents could be driven apart.

The concept of continental drift was best expressed by Wegener in his book *Die Entstehung der Kontinente und Ozeane* (1915; The Origin of Continents and Oceans, 1924). He based the theory on the shape of the continents and geologic evidence, specifically similarities in fossil fauna and flora found in both Brazil and Africa. A series of maps was developed to show three stages of the drift process, and the original supercontinent was named Pangaea (meaning "all lands").

Wegener believed that the continents, composed of light-density granitic rocks, were independently propelled, driven by forces related to the rotation of the Earth. He provided evidence based on detailed geological correlations that indicate a common historical record on both sides of the Atlantic.

The split of Pangaea was visualized as beginning during the Jurassic period, with the southern continents moving westward and toward the equator. South America and Africa began to drift apart during the Cretaceous period, and the opening of the north Atlantic took place during the Pleistocene epoch. Greenland and Norway started to separate as recently as 1.5 million years ago. Continental collisions led to the folded mountains of the Himalayas. According to Wegener, as the drifting continents met the resistance of the ocean floor, their edges were compressed and folded into mountains. Periods of glaciation found in the southern part of South America, Africa, Australia, peninsular India, and Madagascar provided further evidence of drift.

Detailed studies by the South African geologist Alexander Logie Du Toit provided strong support to Wegener's concepts. Du Toit postulated two continental masses rather than one and visualized the northern supercontinent of Laurasia and its southern counterpart Gondwanaland as separated by a seaway called "Tethys." His ideas were published in *Our Wandering Continents* (1937), a book he dedicated to Wegener.

Although Wegener and Du Toit provided compelling evidence, one problem remained: What forces could be strong enough to rupture, fragment, and propel the continents? Arthur Holmes developed the concept that thermal convection in the earth's mantle is the main cause of drift. Published in 1931, Holmes's model is very similar to the now widely accepted theory of plate tectonics. Holmes was the first to introduce the idea that the continents are being carried along by a moving mantle in a conveyor-belt motion.

as a field meteorologist, working in Dorpat, Estonia, at the German university. When the war ended, he became head of the Department of Theoretical Meteorology at the German Marine Observatory in Hamburg, where he began collaborations with Köppen on an important book, *Climates of the Geological Past* (1924).

Wegener's most famous work, *Die Entstehung der Kontinente und Ozeane* (*The Origin of Continents and Oceans*, 1924), was published in German in 1915. The book would go through three more German editions and was translated into French, Spanish, Swedish, Russian, and English. His central argument brought together geophysics, geography, and geology in order to examine and explain Earth's early geography. This was an important step during a time when these fields were largely divorced from one another by specialist studies. Wegener did not believe that evidence from any one of the Earth sciences could substantiate continental drift, and saw the importance in looking to all fields for answers.

After 1922, scientists began to investigate the question of continental drift more extensively. In his own research, Wegener found empirical evidence for the shift of Greenland. Like the science of its time, the

1929 edition of *The Origin of Continents and Oceans* focuses on moving beyond an outline of continental drift theory. Ultimately, Wegener felt that his role in examining continental drift was limited because the questions raised by his research were too big for him to address alone.

The theory of continental drift, as Wegener understood it, centered on the idea that continental crusts are based on a lighter kind of rock, known as sial. Sima, the rock that makes up the ocean floor, is denser. This idea had been put forth first by Austrian geologist Eduard Suess, but it was Wegener who used the theory to argue that the sial layer was able to float on the sima, and was thus able to move across it. After establishing that the less-dense layer was capable of movement, Wegener also tried to explain why continents move. One force that he believed was the cause of continental movement was *pohlflucht*, or pole-fleeing—a force created by the rotation of the Earth and causing the continents to shift toward the equator. Wegener also argued that the force of the tides caused the continents to move laterally.

As Wegener's work continued, he realized that these two forces alone were not enough to explain the movement of the continents. In 1929, he hypothesized that currents in the Earth's magma may also be responsible for landmass movement, an explanation that remains in the twenty-first century. Additionally, he pointed to the Atlantic Ocean as an example of a widening gap between separating continents, and argued that continental movement had created mountain ranges such as the Alps and Himalayas.

Wegener's tragic death occurred during his fourth journey to Greenland in 1930. The journey's scientific goals included meteorological and geophysical experiments on the ice sheet. The group attempted to move across the ice sheet using motorized sleds, dog sleds, and Icelandic ponies. Unfortunately, due to problems caused by ice conditions, equipment failure, and supply shortages, the expedition became much more difficult than expected. After a heroic attempt to resupply a way station that had been cut off by weather and ice conditions, Wegener died while attempting to return.

IMPACT

In spite of Wegener's tragic end, he and his companions gathered valuable scientific information about polar regions through their explorations of Greenland. He pioneered research methods in polar science, as well as seismic methods for measuring the thickness of the ice sheet. While this exploratory work was important, it was Wegener's research on continental drift that made the greatest impact on the history of science. For years, geologists were skeptical of his theories, but over time his theories have made significant impacts on climatology and other Earth sciences. American geologist Harry Hammond Hess and geophysicist Robert Sinclair Dietz introduced the theory of seafloor spreading in the early 1960s, building upon the basic premise of Wegener's drift theory. The theory of plate tectonics, which emerged in the 1930s, also built upon Wegener's legacy. The theory of continental drift, with its subsequent modifications, remains one of the most significant theories in Earth science. Although not without its problems, it is the most complete theory of global tectonics in existence.

Christina Healey

FURTHER READING

Gramling, Carolyn. "September 21, 1930: Alfred Wegener Begins a Fateful Polar Expedition." *Earth* 55.9 (2010): 72–75. Print. Describes Wegener's last expedition to Greenland to study polar air circulation patterns.

Hughes, Patrick. "The Meteorologist Who Started a Revolution." *Weatherwise* 47.2 (1994): 29–30. Discusses Wegener's life and career. Discusses Wegener's papers promoting the theory of continental drift.

McCoy, Roger M. *Ending in Ice: The Revolutionary Idea and Tragic Expedition of Alfred Wegener*. New York: Oxford UP, 2006. Print. Presents a compelling biography of Wegener. Describes the development of the theory of continental drift and Wegener's four research expeditions to Greenland.

Yount, Lisa. *Alfred Wegener: Creator of the Continental Drift Theory*. New York: Chelsea, 2009. Print. Describes the life and work of Wegener, continental drift, and the critical reception of Wegener's theory.

KARL WEIERSTRASS

German mathematician

A pioneer in the field of mathematics, Weierstrass is often called the "father of modern analysis" for having provided a solid arithmetical foundation for calculus.

Born: October 31, 1815; Ostenfelde, Bavaria (now Germany)
Died: February 19, 1897; Berlin, Germany
Primary field: Mathematics
Specialty: Calculus

EARLY LIFE

Born in 1815, Karl Theodor Wilhelm Weierstrass was the oldest of four children. His father was a customs official whose employment necessitated many family relocations during Weierstrass's childhood. His mother Theodora died in 1827, an event that strengthened his father's already powerful influence on the boy. When Wilhelm secured employment in the Paderborn tax office, the family's frequent movement came to an end. In 1829, young Karl entered the Catholic Theodorianum, where he proved an excellent student, especially in mathematics. As he worked on his education, the young pupil found part-time employment as a bookkeeper to assist in paying his family's expenses.

Despite Weierstrass's interest in developing his talents in math, his father had a different path chosen for him. Wilhelm desired that his son follow in his footsteps and chose a conservative career path as a civil servant. His father's influence was such that the nineteen-year-old Weierstrass enrolled in the University of Bonn in 1834 to study public finance and law. Although he continued with the interest in mathematics that he had demonstrated in his youth, he struggled with his education on the college-level not from lack of talent but from lack of interest. Fencing and beer dominated his days, while studies took a back seat. Much to the dismay of his demanding father, Weierstrass returned home without a degree after four years at the university.

With few options available for the seemingly disinterested student, Weierstrass, with the help of a family contact, was admitted into Münster's Theological and Philosophical Academy in 1839, where he received a teaching certificate in secondary education. Münster proved an agreeable sojourn for Weierstrass; there, he came into contact with the German mathematician Christof Gudermann. Gudermann introduced Weierstrass to the revolutionary field of elliptic functions.

In 1841, Weierstrass received his teaching certificate and began a fifteen-year career as a secondary school teacher.

LIFE'S WORK

Weierstrass's extended career as a high school teacher brought with it much professional isolation. The distance from academic mathematicians afforded him the opportunity to develop his own thinking in the field of calculus, free from the prejudices and constraints typically encountered in professional fields. Weierstrass blossomed as an intellectual, while, at the same time, he taught a dizzying array of subjects that included history, botany, German, and mathematics. His days were filled tending to the needs of his students, while his evenings were spent in pursuit of mathematics.

Every night, despite bouts of dizziness that appeared intermittently from 1850 onward, Weierstrass explored the implications of abelian functions (named for Norwegian mathematician Niels Abel), which offered a generalized understanding of elliptic functions. These nocturnal studies ultimately paved the way for his own pioneering work in the field. Until 1848, Weierstrass's work in mathematics occurred in complete isolation, but he was soon to share his findings with the world. His first publication was part of a recruitment prospectus for the Collegium Hoseanum in Braunsberg, where he worked, and it attracted little attention save for convincing a few parents to send their children to the school. He made his first major impact on the mathematics community with the 1854 publication of "Zur Theorie der Abelschen Funktionen" (On the theory of abelian functions), originally published in the *Journal for Pure and Applied Mathematics*. In its examination of abelian functions as a convergent power series, the work underscores Weierstrass's rigorous and pioneering methodological approach. His study attracted much attention and finally earned the mathematician the opportunity for university employment that he had been looking for.

In 1854, the University of Königsberg granted Weierstrass an honorary doctoral degree. After several failed attempts to secure a prestigious university post, Weierstrass settled on an appointment at the Industry Institute of Berlin in June 1856. Several months later he was offered and accepted a post at the University of Berlin—a position he truly coveted—but could not actually fill the chair for several years due to contractual

Weierstrass Develops Early Form of Modern Calculus

Until the pioneering work of German mathematician Karl Weierstrass, the main tenets of calculus only hinted at an arithmetical understanding of limits—the value that a function approaches as the input approaches a value—but this understanding remained unproven. The precepts that pertained to limits offered reasonable certainty within the study of calculus, but as foundational theorems they lacked the rigor that is typically associated with modern mathematics. Nineteenth-century scholars such as Bohemian mathematician Bernard Bolzano had made strides in defining limits in a more rigorous fashion; however, such work remained controversial, even as it anticipated modern definitions of limits. As a result, nineteenth-century understandings of functions remained equally muddled, and intuition rather than mathematics shaped most work on the subject.

Weierstrass would change all of this in his approach to analysis—the branch of mathematics that deals with limits and other types of continuous change. Weierstrass sought to use only real number systems, rather than geometric extrapolations, to conduct his work. Owing to his unique training and early career spent as a secondary school educator, isolated from prominent mathematicians, Weierstrass was free of the kinds of thinking and the restraints that shaped the work of his peers. As such, he took a novel approach to what amounted to an old problem and was perhaps more willing to break from accepted notions.

Weierstrass deconstructed existing rules regarding limits, especially functions (that is, expressions of relationships between dependent and independent variables), reducing them to their basic element. He then began to rebuild the constituent parts to construct proofs that remain the basis of our understanding of functions in the twenty-first century. In 1861, his development of a continuous function with no derivatives—the measurement of the change of a function as another quantity changes—demonstrated his strict adherence to real numbers. This adherence offended mathematicians who depended on more intuitive methods. Nevertheless, his construction came to be known as the Weierstrass function (even though mathematicians had attempted to develop a continuous function with no derivatives earlier in the nineteenth century). Weierstrass's rigid analytical method soon became the standard practice by which mathematicians conducted their work. Modern analysis remains a fixture of collegiate baccalaureate teaching and training in mathematics. Contemporary understanding of most functions, whether Abelian or elliptic, stem from Weierstrass's work, while fields such as the calculus of variation owe much to the German thinker as well. Weierstrass remains a respected pioneer in the field of mathematics and a critical innovator of the mid-nineteenth century.

obligations incumbent upon his earlier acceptance of the post at the Industry Institute. In the same year that he became a university professor, he published another groundbreaking article that expanded upon his earlier work on abelian functions, this time examining the inversion of hyperelliptic integrals. It was this work that made him an even more prized commodity in the German university community.

In Berlin, Weierstrass finally found himself in the presence of fellow mathematicians. He threw himself into his new position and found his passion for mathematics heightened by the presence of such esteemed peer mathematicians as Ernst Eduard Kummer and Leopold Kronecker, both of whom challenged and supported Weierstrass. The three educators helped to make the University of Berlin the premier institution for the study of mathematics in Europe. Weierstrass regularly taught before packed classrooms, as he developed offerings in calculus with an emphasis on analytic functions.

Despite his professional success, Weierstrass found his health failing. In 1861, his growing problem with vertigo led to his collapse and year-long hiatus from the university. Upon his return, the bouts of dizziness largely disappeared, only to be replaced by chronic chest pains. No longer able to lecture in the traditional fashion, Weierstrass addressed his students from a seated position, while advanced students wrote on the board for him. He published little but commanded a profound influence. Over the course of his work at the University of Berlin, several of his students published their lecture notes from Weierstrass's class, which brought the professor international acclaim. From these lectures, collected in *Gesammelte Abhandlungen* (Collected works, 1894–1927), Weierstrass's role in developing modern analysis becomes apparent.

He carefully defined calculus functions in terms of inequalities, which allowed mathematicians to approach problems in a far more rigorous manner than was permitted by the theoretical geometric approach popular in the mid-nineteenth century.

The collegial culture of the University of Berlin continued into the 1880s, but a schism between Weierstrass and his colleague Leopold Kronecker over the concept of infinity produced much acrimony and nearly resulted in Weierstrass seeking an appointment in Switzerland. He opted instead to stay in Berlin, where he would oversee the publication of his complete works. Failing health and near immobility marked the final three years of his life. He died in Berlin from pneumonia in 1897.

IMPACT

Weierstrass was widely recognized as one of the preeminent mathematicians of his era, and he is now remembered as the "father of modern analysis." His rigorous approach to calculus created a solid arithmetical foundation for the discipline, which had previously been governed by vague, poorly defined theories that lacked the rigor of other mathematical fields. Modern calculus owes much of its theoretical foundation to his work. Some of his discoveries, such as the nondifferentiable function, proved highly controversial when first introduced, while others provided a solid basis for preexisting, yet tenuously stated, concepts. Many questioned the validity of the construction, but time has proven the soundness of his theory, which is today known as the Weierstrass function.

He is also famous for the Weierstrass M-test for detecting the uniform convergence of a series of functions, as well as advances in abelian functions. What remains most remarkable about Weierstrass's career is that he spent fifteen years of his adult life laboring as a high school educator. Through diligent effort, and despite having failed in college, Weierstrass worked nightly in isolation to develop the foundation of the mathematical work that would make him famous and inspire the research of a generation of scholars. Once established at the University of Berlin, Weierstrass and his colleagues helped to train some of the most influential mathematicians of the late nineteenth century. Weierstrass's students included Georg Cantor, Sofia Kovalevskaya, Ludwig Boltzmann, and Max Planck, all of whom went on to revolutionize mathematics.

Keith M. Finley

FURTHER READING

Aczel, Amir D. *A Strange Wilderness: The Lives of Great Mathematicians*. New York: Sterling, 2011. Print. Explores the lifestyles of mathematicians from the ancient to the modern world, including that of Weierstrass.

Bartle, Robert G., and Donald R. Sherbert. *Introduction to Real Analysis*. Fourth Ed. New York: Wiley, 2011. Print. Standard modern textbook underscores the seminal role that Weierstrass played in the development of calculus. Features his ideas and advances on nearly every page.

Hawking, Stephen, ed. *God Created the Integers: The Mathematical Breakthroughs that Changed History*. Philadelphia: Running, 2007. Print. Tracks the evolution of modern mathematics, posing Weierstrass as a figure who demands attention. Offers a thorough treatment of the German mathematician.

Watson, Peter. *The German Genius: Europe's Third Renaissance, the Second Scientific Revolution, and the Twentieth Century*. New York: Harper, 2010. Print. Explores the vibrant milieu of German intellectual thought inspired by trailblazing nineteenth-century thinkers such as Weierstrass.

STEVEN WEINBERG

American physicist

Weinberg, along with Sheldon Glashow and Abdus Salam, developed the theory that unified the electromagnetic and weak nuclear interactions into the electroweak force. Weinberg also helped develop the theory of strong nuclear interactions known as quantum chromodynamics, or QCD. The electroweak theory and QCD provide the foundation for the standard model of matter.

Born: May 3, 1933; New York, New York
Primary field: Physics
Specialties: Theoretical physics; electromagnetism; quantum mechanics

EARLY LIFE

Steven Weinberg was born in New York City to Frederick and Eva Weinberg. The young Weinberg was encouraged in his scientific pursuits by his father. While attending Bronx High School of Science, Weinberg became highly interested in theoretical physics. He graduated from high school in 1950 and attended Cornell University, where he earned a BS in physics in 1954. That same year, he wed his college girlfriend, Louise Goldwasser; they would have one daughter, Elizabeth.

After attending the Institute for Theoretical Physics in Copenhagen, Denmark, for a year, Weinberg earned his doctoral degree in physics from Princeton University in 1957. From 1957 until 1959, he taught physics at Columbia University. For the next seven years, he taught physics and participated in theoretical physics research at the University of California, Berkeley. At Berkeley he became an expert in the application of Feynman diagrams and worked on current algebra research and understandings of the strong nuclear force.

Between 1966 and 1969, Weinberg took a leave from Berkeley and served as the Morris Loeb lecturer at Harvard University and as a visiting professor of physics at the Massachusetts Institute of Technology (MIT). In 1969, he received an appointment as a professor of physics at MIT, where he remained until 1982. From 1960 to 1973, he was a consultant at the US Institute for Defense Analysis, and from 1971 to 1973 he consulted for the US Arms Control and Disarmament Agency. When Julian Schwinger left Harvard in 1973, Weinberg accepted the university's position as Higgins Professor of Physics as well as an appointment as a senior scientist at the Smithsonian Astrophysical Observatory.

LIFE'S WORK
During his stay at MIT, Weinberg embarked on his most significant work in theoretical physics. After concentrating for several years on unifying the theory of electromagnetic forces with that of strong nuclear forces, he realized that he instead needed to apply his mathematical formalism to the electromagnetic and weak nuclear forces. In 1967, he published the short paper "A Model of Leptons" in *Physical Review Letters*, in which he predicted two weak particles (massive bosons) that might generate the weak nuclear force. With this insight and sufficiently high energies, the electromagnetic and weak interactions would merge into a single interaction, the electroweak force.

Weinberg's paper went relatively unnoticed, however, because of some mathematical inconsistencies in his theory that he had claimed could be resolved. In 1971, Gerard 't Hooft, a prominent theoretical physicist, showed that Weinberg's scheme could indeed be renormalized to eliminate the mathematical difficulties and produce physically viable results.

The electroweak theory developed by Weinberg also was proposed independently by Abdus Salam and Sheldon Glashow. The theory postulates that the weak and electromagnetic interactions have the same strength at very high particle energies. Thus, these two apparently independent interactions are just different manifestations of a single unifying electroweak interaction, which was confirmed by Carlo Rubbia and Simon van der Meer at the European Organization for Nuclear Research Laboratory (CERN) in Geneva, Switzerland, in 1983.

The electroweak theory forms a major part of the so-called standard model of elementary particle physics. This model provides a comprehensive picture of the fundamental particles of matter and how they behave and interact. It also explains a vast majority of the experimental data that have been collected by elementary particle physicists.

The theory made a number of important predictions that were confirmed during the 1970s. The first, the existence of a weak neutral current, was discovered in 1973 at the Fermi National Accelerator Laboratory and at CERN. The second, the existence of a fourth quark that was necessary to account for the predicted rate of neutral weak interactions, was discovered in 1974. The third, the violation of atomic parity, was established in 1978.

In 1979, Weinberg, Salam, and Glashow shared the Nobel Prize in Physics for their development of the electroweak theory. In 1982, Weinberg was appointed as the Jack S. Josey-Welch Foundation Chair of Science and Regental Professor of Physics at the University of Texas at Austin, where he founded the theoretical physics group.

For his many contributions to research in cosmology and the unification of elementary-particle forces, Weinberg has received numerous honors and awards. In addition to winning the Nobel Prize, Weinberg has been awarded the J. R. Oppenheimer Prize (1973), the Dannie Heineman Mathematical Physics Prize (1977), the Elliott Cresson Medal (1979), the James Madison Medal of Princeton University (1991), the National Medal of Science (1991), the Lewis Thomas Prize (1999), and the Benjamin Franklin Medal of the American Philosophical Society (2004).

Weinberg gained membership in the National Academy of Sciences, the American Academy of Arts and Sciences, the American Physical Society, the American Astronomical Society, the Royal Society of London, and the American Philosophical Society. He received honorary degrees from sixteen institutions,

The Weinberg- Salam-Glashow Model

Steven Weinberg was a member of the venerated trio of particle physicists, including Abdus Salam and Sheldon Lee Glashow, who were jointly awarded the 1979 Nobel Prize in Physics for their pioneering work in the arena of particle physics referred to as "weak force." The trio put forth the first definitive theory illustrating unified weak and electromagnetic interactions between elementary particles. The Weinberg-Salam-Glashow model, or WSG model, was one of the first cohesive theories in the field of particle physics regarding the nature of interactive forces at work in the universe.

Elementary particle physics is initially described through the ways that the universe's most basic molecular particles interact with each other. This concept is referred to by physicists as the "fundamental interactions" of matter. Such interactions are non-contact interactions—forces that, unlike many other chemical and physical relationships in the scientific world, interact without direct unification at a molecular level.

The concept of weak force was first alluded to in the work of the American physicist Enrico Fermi. The force was dubbed "weak" because it is believed to be weaker in strength, range, and sustainability than the forces at work in stronger fundamental actions such as nuclear force and electromagnetism. Prior to the findings presented in the WSG model there were only three known fundamental interactions in the universe. These three forces were gravity, or the force with which matter attracts forces proportional to its mass; electromagnetism, or the interaction between electrically charged particles; and strong nuclear force, or the force between two or more nucleons that creates atomic power.

The WSG model shed light on an interaction that the researchers deemed responsible for the radioactive beta decay, or the slow breakdown of subatomic matter via particle emission. Weinberg and his colleagues deduced that the concept of weak interaction has a widespread influence on all fermion particles, or particles that obey the Fermi–Dirac principals of physical mechanics.

The WSG model is of particular relevance to physicists who are searching for the fundamental particles from which the universe is constructed and examining how they interact with each other. Numerous theories exist that hypothesize a potential relation between Weinberg, Salam, and Glashow's conception of electroweak interaction and the massless subatomic particles that inhabit the universe.

including the University of Chicago, Yale University, Columbia University, and Dartmouth College.

Weinberg's prolific writings include more than three hundred published papers on elementary particle physics. He has also authored several books, including *Gravitation and Cosmology: Principles and Applications of the General Theory of Relativity* (1972) and the highly regarded three-volume series *The Quantum Theory of Fields* (1995–97). Weinberg made many public appearances to discuss scientific topics, and he wrote many scientific articles and books for the general public, including *Dreams of a Final Theory* (1992), *Facing Up: Science and Its Cultural Adversaries* (2001), and *Glory and Terror: The Growing Nuclear Danger* (2004).

IMPACT

Progress in science is often coupled with the unification of apparently independent phenomena in terms of a few fundamental principles. One of the most important problems in physics has revolved around the unification of the four basic forces of nature—gravitational, electromagnetic, weak nuclear, and strong nuclear—into one fundamental force. Weinberg played a prominent role in accomplishing part of this task by unifying the electromagnetic and weak nuclear forces into the electroweak force.

In addition to the electroweak theory that earned Weinberg a Nobel Prize, he made many other significant contributions to physics. He played a major role in the development of the theory of the strong nuclear force known as quantum chromodynamics and in the development of the grand unified theory to unite the four basic forces into one fundamental force that governs all particle interactions. Weinberg also made important contributions to quantum field theory, cosmology, astrophysics, and the theories of supersymmetry and supergravity. He wrote significant papers concerning relativistic astrophysics, fluctuations in the cosmic microwave background radiation that is a remnant of the big bang, the survival of protogalaxies in an expanding universe, and problems associated with the value of the cosmological constant.

Alvin K. Benson

903

FURTHER READING

Close, Frank. *Particle Physics: A Very Short Introduction*. New York: Oxford UP, 2004. Print. Contains a biography of Weinberg and discusses his many contributions to elementary particle physics. Examines his role in physicists' effort to develop a unified field theory of the fundamental forces of nature and a standard model of matter.

Crease, Robert P., and Charles C. Mann. *The Second Creation: Makers of the Revolution in Twentieth-Century Physics*. Rev. ed. New Brunswick: Rutgers UP, 1996. Print. A history of theoretical physics and grand unified theory that examines Weinberg's

important role in scientific discoveries that have greatly affected the world.

Giberson, Karl, and Mariano Artigas. *Oracles of Science: Celebrity Scientists versus God and Religion*. New York: Oxford UP, 2007. Print. Six prominent scientists, including Weinberg, contrast their respective philosophies of science and religion. Examines Weinberg's views of religion and the theory of intelligent design.

Hargittai, Magdolna. *Candid Science IV: Conversations with Famous Physicists*. London: Imperial College, 2004. Print. Cites some of the details of Weinberg's life and many of his important scientific insights into unified field theory and other relevant subjects in physics.

AUGUST WEISMANN

German physician and embryologist

Weismann is most noted for his development and refinement of the theory of the continuity of the germ-plasm, his devout support of Darwinism and the principle of natural selection, and his discrediting of the idea of the inheritance of acquired characteristics.

Born: January 17, 1834; Frankfurt am Main, German Confederation (now Germany)
Died: November 5, 1914; Freiburg im Breisgau, Germany
Also known as: August Friedrich Leopold Weismann
Primary field: Biology
Specialties: Zoology; cellular biology

EARLY LIFE

August Friedrich Leopold Weismann was the son of Johann Konrad August Weismann, a classics teacher at the gymnasium in Frankfurt, and Elise Eleanore Lübbren Weismann, a musician and painter. He was the eldest of four children, and his home life was simple and happy. As a young boy, Weismann showed an active interest in nature. He collected butterflies, caterpillars, beetles, and plants, and he assembled a herbarium.

Weismann was interested in chemistry and physics as a young adult and wanted to pursue studies in that direction. His father and friends of the family, however, suggested that he pursue medicine because a career in medicine would be more lucrative. To this end, he entered the University of Göttingen in 1852, where he studied with Friedrich Henle and Friedrich Wöhler in an atmosphere that emphasized research rather than broader problems. He received his medical degree in 1856.

Following graduation, Weismann continued his research while working as an assistant in the medical clinic at Rostock. In 1857, he transferred to the Rostock Chemical Institute so that he could pursue his interest in chemistry. This was followed by a tour of four German universities and a more extensive stay in Vienna.

Weismann entered private medical practice in Frankfurt in 1858. His practice allowed him sufficient time to pursue studies on heart-muscle fibers. His private practice was interrupted in 1859 by the war between Austria and Italy, at which time he entered the German army and served as a surgeon at the field hospital in Italy. He resumed private practice in 1860.

LIFE'S WORK

In 1861, Weismann abandoned medicine to pursue what had become his main interest, the biological sciences. He attended the University of Giessen for two months in 1861 and was profoundly influenced by Rudolf Leuckart, under whom he began his studies in insect embryology. He considered the two months he spent with Leuckart to be the most important and inspiring time of his career.

Following his stay at Giessen, Weismann became the private physician of Archduke Stefan of Austria. While in this position, from 1861 to 1863, Weismann had ample time to pursue his interest in insect development and completed his first major work, *Die Entwicklung der Dipteren* (On the development of the dipteran in the egg), in 1864. He also had time to read Charles Darwin's *On the Origin of Species by Means of Natural Selection*

August Weismann Develops Germplasm Theory

German physician and naturalist August Weismann (1834–1914) was active professionally during a significant era in the area of biology. The theory of evolution was developed and published by British naturalist Charles Darwin, and German biologists made groundbreaking observations of cellular organelles. During the first half of the nineteenth century, cell theory was primarily that espoused by biologist Theodor Schwann and botanist Matthias Schleiden, who proposed that cell formation in animals and plants involved the crystallization of structures around the nucleus. However, by the latter half of the century, it became clear that cells were duplicated through a process of binary fission. Weismann's contemporary Walther Flemming witnessed the duplication and separation of chromosomes (a term coined by Heinrich Waldeyer-Hartz in 1888) in cells while observing mitosis, the process of cell division. At the same time, embryologists Oscar Hertwig and Edouard Van Beneden observed the process of meiosis in egg formation in sea urchins and nematodes, respectively.

Weismann spent the last decades of his professional life observing the process of egg formation, following up Hertwig's work on sea urchins and applying those observations to fertilization events. He observed, for example, that egg formation required two stages of cell division, resulting in a halving of the chromosome number in the cells—a "reduction division," as he termed the process. This, he thought, was to prevent doubling of the germplasm, or germ cells (sperm and egg), at each generation. This is considered by many to be his most significant and effective scientific contribution. Weismann believed that during fertilization, individual ancestral germplasms, each carrying variations, were combined. He thought that, as well as introducing new variations, this process created new combinations of variations.

While Weismann did not fully understand the structure of the chromosomes or their function in transmission of traits (that would not be determined for another forty years), he did theorize correctly that genetic characteristics are transmitted from parent to offspring through the germplasm. Weismann also theorized the source of the germplasm was in the cell nucleus. He contended that the germplasm was to be found on the chromatin threads, the idants (chromosomes) in the nucleus of the cell. He hypothesized that the idants were composed of smaller units called "ids," which in turn were composed of "determinants," the individual hereditary units, which he correctly envisioned as being linearly arranged. The determinants, he thought, were composed of still smaller, more basic units, called "biophors."

Further, Weismann recognized that the characteristics within the germ cells are not affected by events taking place in somatic cells, the cells found elsewhere in the body and not involved in inheritance; the independence of germ cells from the rest of the body became known as the Weismann barrier.

The process of sexual reproduction through germ cells also provided an explanation for the variation within in a species that formed the basis for Darwin's natural selection. Through production of individual sperm and eggs with unique characters, genetic variation was the logical outcome. Weismann published many of his ideas in *Vorträge über Descendenztheorie* (1902; *The Evolution Theory*, 1904), as well as in earlier books and published manuscripts.

(1859). Like so many scientists of the time, Weismann was profoundly influenced by Darwin's book.

In 1863, Weismann became a lecturer at the University of Freiburg and taught zoology and comparative anatomy. In 1866, he was appointed extraordinary professor and, in 1874, professor. He was the first to occupy the chair of zoology at Freiburg. He soon became director of the zoological institute at the university.

Weismann's first research papers examined insect histology and embryology. Several papers on these subjects were published between 1862 and 1866. One important discovery he made was that, during metamorphosis, tissues completely dedifferentiate and then redifferentiate during the formation of the adult. Weismann was also interested in the origin and fate of the germ cells of hydrozoans. The germ cells of multicellular organisms such as hydrozoans are set aside from the somatic cells early in development and provide for the continuity of the organism through the sperm and the egg. The somatic cells will eventually die, but the germ cells live on in a new individual. Only the reproductive cells have the capacity to form a complete, new individual. From these observations, Weismann developed the theory for which he is most noted, that of the continuity of the germplasm. Though his eyesight failed in 1864, further work on the theory of the continuity of the germplasm occupied the last thirty years of his life as an active scientist. The theory encompassed many areas but primarily focused on heredity and evolution. He first published on these topics in 1883.

Weismann's ideas on the continuity of the germplasm put him in direct conflict with many other scientists of the time. By then, many had come to discredit natural selection as a mechanism of evolution and advocated Lamarckism, the inheritance of acquired traits, as an alternative. Weismann investigated many cases of reported inheritance of acquired characteristics and could find no authenticated instance of such inheritance. His own classic experiments, in which he cut off the tails of mice over several generations but found no tendency for the tail to shorten in succeeding generations, were instrumental in challenging Lamarckism. He thought that the only way acquired characteristics could be passed to the offspring was if the germ cells were affected. He became more devoted to the theory of natural selection than did Darwin. Weismann did not believe that the environment in any way affected heredity.

Weismann extended Darwin's theory of natural selection to the germ cells in a theory called germinal selection. He thought that the "determinants" (his term for genes) struggled with one another for nutriment and that the stronger ones would triumph and eliminate the weaker ones. Thus, only the stronger ones would survive in the germplasm and be passed to the offspring. This, he thought, could account for the loss of organs during evolution. Later work failed to support his idea of germinal selection.

Extending his germplasm theory to development, Weismann correctly thought that the determinants directed differentiation in individual cells but incorrectly envisioned that this was a result of the distribution of different determinants to different cells during cell division. He therefore thought that mitosis could be qualitatively unequal while being quantitatively equal.

Weismann's main works on heredity and evolution were published in *Studien zur Descendenztheorie* (1875–1876; *Studies in the Theory of Descent*, 1882), *Essays upon Heredity and Kindred Biological Problems* (1889–1892), *Das Keimplasma: Eine Theorie der Vererbung* (1892; *The Germ-Plasm: A Theory of Heredity*, 1893), *On Germinal Selection as a Source of Definite Variation* (1896), and *Vorträge über Descendenztheorie*

(1902; *The Evolution Theory*, 1904). *The Evolution Theory* became an important and widely read book. Given the importance of Weismann's theoretical contributions to science, his experimental and observational work was often overshadowed.

Weismann retired from the faculty of the University of Freiburg in 1912. He died peacefully at Freiburg im Breisgau, Germany, on November 5, 1914, at the age of eighty.

IMPACT

Weismann was one of the most respected biologists of the latter part of the nineteenth century and the early part of the twentieth century. His ideas stimulated considerable discussion and research. His theories on heredity and development were far-reaching. He correctly recognized that the hereditary material was contained within the nucleus of the sperm and egg and that the hereditary material of the germ cells is reduced to one-half during the maturation of the sperm and egg. In a single theory, the germplasm theory, he explained the meiotic reduction division, sexual reproduction, development, and natural selection. It has been said that Weismann's ability to synthesize these scientific elements ushered in twentieth-century genetics.

Charles L. Vigue

FURTHER READING

Rheinberger, Hans-Jörg. "Heredity and Its Entities around 1900." *Studies in History and Philosophy of Science Part A* 39.3 (2008): 370–74. Print. Describes the state of scientific understanding at the beginning of the twentieth century of the process of hereditary transmission. Reviews the contributions of Weismann and others.

Weismann, August. *Essays upon Heredity and Kindred Biological Problems.* Ed. Edward B. Poulton, Selmar Schönland, and Arthur E. Shipley. 2 vols. Oxford: Clarendon, 1891–92. Print. Contains some of Weismann's most important theoretical contributions on heredity, the continuity of the germplasm, sexual reproduction, and evolution.

---. *The Germ-Plasm: A Theory of Heredity.* 1893. Trans. W. Newton Parker and Harriet Rönnfeldt. Bristol: Thoemmes, 2003. Print. Addresses the most significant theoretical contributions Weismann made to science.

JOHN ARCHIBALD WHEELER

American physicist

American physicist John Archibald Wheeler made important contributions to the theories of general relativity, quantum gravity, and quantum electrodynamics. He is known for his role in the development of both the atomic and the hydrogen bombs, as well as for naming one of the strangest astronomical bodies known to science: the black hole.

Born: July 9, 1911; Jacksonville, Florida
Died: April 13, 2008; Princeton, New Jersey
Primary field: Physics
Specialties: Quantum mechanics; relativity; nuclear physics

EARLY LIFE

Wheeler was born on July 9, 1911, in Jacksonville, Florida. As a child he showed an aptitude for mathematics and was always attracted to scientific topics in his reading. At the age of sixteen Wheeler enrolled at Johns Hopkins University in Baltimore, Maryland, as an engineering student but soon realized that his real passion was for the science of physics.

He graduated with a PhD in physics in 1933 and went on to become a professor of physics at the University of North Carolina. In 1938 Wheeler was invited to teach at Princeton University, where he would write, give lectures, and conduct research for nearly four decades.

Although Princeton had become his professional home, in the late 1930s Wheeler spent a year abroad working with the Danish physicist Niels Bohr at the University of Copenhagen. It was at that point that his work on nuclear physics began in earnest.

During the same period, the rumblings of the Second World War could be heard in the background. Scientists and politicians all over the world were starting to realize that nuclear fission—a complex process by which the nucleus of an atom can be split apart, creating a tremendous burst of energy—could potentially be used to create a bomb that would be more powerful than any that had been made before. They called this hypothetical weapon an atomic bomb.

LIFE'S WORK

Wheeler and Bohr wrote a paper in 1939 explaining their theory of how nuclear fission actually takes place. The paper also suggested that if one were to build a bomb using nuclear fission, the best possible source of atoms and nuclei would be the artificial element known as uranium-235—the substance that is, in fact, the major ingredient used to make an atomic bomb.

The US government sponsored the development of the first atomic bomb through a World War II–era venture known as the Manhattan Project. In 1951, Project Matterhorn was initiated to develop the even more powerful hydrogen bomb, based on similar scientific principles. Wheeler worked on both projects and was awarded the Atomic Energy Commission's 1968 Enrico Fermi Award for his contributions to national defense. Beginning in the 1940s, Wheeler became interested in a theory known as quantum physics, or quantum mechanics. This branch of physics emerged in the early years of the twentieth century and was still developing at the time that it caught Wheeler's attention (his mentor, Bohr, had helped to establish the field).

In the 1950s and 1960s Wheeler became involved in an area of quantum mechanics called quantum electrodynamics. Together with Richard Feynman, a graduate student at Princeton who went on to win the Nobel Prize in Physics in 1965, Wheeler made various contributions in this field.

In addition, Wheeler had become interested in Albert Einstein's theory of general relativity and its relationship to quantum mechanics; Wheeler is commonly credited with reviving interest in general relativity. With these two theories in mind, he started to wonder about the nature of space-time, which is the term physicists use to describe the cosmic backdrop of the universe. Space-time can be thought of as the background setting for every event that takes place, anywhere; it includes all three dimensions of space, plus time. Thinking in quantum terms, Wheeler tried to imagine space-time on an extremely small scale; specifically, he thought about the level of the Planck length. This is an unimaginably tiny unit of measurement, about 10 to the power of minus 35 meters.

The basis of Wheeler's hypothesis is that gravity's force works through fields, like the magnetic fields that surround a magnet. General relativity states that gravity comes about as a result of the way space-time curves. Quantum mechanics has demonstrated that fields constantly experience tiny variations, or quick random jumps in the level of their energy. Combining general relativity and quantum mechanics, Wheeler put forward the theory that, on a scale as small as the Planck length, space-time itself experiences uncountable sudden changes in its shape and structure that make it look almost like it is boiling. He called this *quantum foam*. No one has ever found any evidence for quantum foam, but it is an example of Wheeler's ability to make connections between different scientific theories.

In the late-1960s Wheeler famously coined the term "black hole" for the mysterious space objects he was studying—which had until then been called frozen stars, dark stars, or collapsed stars. The notion of a black hole dated back to eighteenth-century natural philosopher John Michell, who speculated about what might happen if an object the size of the sun increased in mass so much that its "escape velocity" was greater than the speed of light. Due to gravitational pull, the more dense and massive an object is, the more powerfully it tends to tug anything around it (dust, asteroids, light) toward itself; additionally, the more dense and massive an object is, the faster other things around it have to travel away from it in order to escape the tremendous pull of its gravity. In the case of a star, any light traveling away from the object would simply be pulled back towards it. Since light could never bounce off the object and be seen by the human eye, Michell realized that the object would be invisible.

In 1939, scientists Robert Oppenheimer and Hartland Snyder guessed that such an object might be

Wheeler Coins the Term "Black Hole"

In the spring of 1968, John Archibald Wheeler used the term "black hole" in a paper that was published in the journals *American Scholar* and *American Scientist*. This was the first time that the term had been used. In the paper, Wheeler rejected the idea that some force would prevent a massive star from collapsing beyond a certain point once it ran out of energy. He suggested that it was possible for a star to collapse into a singularity (an object of no size, with infinite density). Since the gravity of such a singularity would be so strong that no light could escape, the term black hole seemed to fit.

Wheeler's interest in black holes began when he turned his research toward general relativity, trying to form a link between astrophysics and quantum physics—that is, the study of atomic particles. The most interesting connection he found was in the idea of gravitational collapse. Scientists had long theorized that a large enough body of dense matter, such as a "cold" star, should be forced to collapse in upon itself. Not much was known, however, about how matter was affected by such extremely high pressure.

Early twentieth-century researchers had speculated about the conditions of space and time around stars and the hypothetical spheres within them. If a star collapses and becomes smaller than that sphere, the star will be separated from space-time. Light and matter can enter this sphere, but nothing—not even light—can escape. This sphere came to be called an "event horizon"; the existence of event horizons is now an accepted part of physics.

Before Wheeler's paper, black holes had been called "Schwarzschild's singularity," "collapsed stars," or "frozen stars." These names had to do with what these objects would look like outside the event horizon. For Wheeler, the event horizon was only the surface; he was also interested in black holes themselves.

Wheeler continued his studies and found that black holes were relatively simple objects, having only mass, electric charge, and a rate of spin. Two major questions, however, remained unanswered: Were there conditions in the universe that would actually create black holes? If so, would black holes be stable—that is, would they last a long period of time and act predictably?

It was well established that there were stars in the universe that were, in theory, big enough to form black holes if such stars ever burned out. The question of stability was more troubling, but Wheeler and other physicists calculated that black holes should be stable. It began to seem that black holes had to exist—but none had ever been discovered.

The next step was to find them. Wheeler suggested that a black hole might be found by looking for the way in which its gravity would affect the things around it. He also suggested that astronomers should look for the huge amounts of energy that some objects would give off just before they were sucked into a black hole.

Wheeler is an important figure in twentieth-century particle and gravitational physics. Along with Karl Schwarzschild, J. Robert Oppenheimer, Roy Kerr, and Stephen Hawking, he stands as a pioneer in the understanding and theory of black holes. Not the least of his contributions was giving them a name that everyone could understand. By making black holes sound simple, Wheeler helped scientists and others to believe that they might be real.

formed if a very massive star ran out of energy and all its matter collapsed into a single tiny, incredibly dense point called a singularity. Wheeler initially thought the idea of a singularity was ridiculous and did not believe that a dying star would experience this kind of gravitational collapse. Wheeler began to study cold, dead stars to prove that Oppenheimer and Snyder's theory was wrong. The more he examined dead stars, however, the more evidence Wheeler found that a very massive star really would collapse in on itself when it died. By 1967 he had not only become an enthusiastic supporter of the singularity theory, he had also given John Michell's hypothetical object the name "black hole."

IMPACT

Throughout Wheeler's career he made significant contributions to areas of science including nuclear and particle physics, black holes and gravitation, and information theory studies, while also changing conceptions of general relativity. He developed the concept of wormholes and formulated geometrodynamics. In his quantum mechanics research he proposed what became known as Wheeler's delayed choice experiment, a thought experiment for detecting photons. His work with other researchers in the field of quantum mechanics also led to the development of the "many-worlds interpretation" of reality and conception of the universe.

As his career progressed, Wheeler continued to make important contributions to the development of research in many areas of physics, especially concerning the topics of black hole physics and quantum gravity. Wheeler's 1973 book *Gravitation* (coauthored with Charles S. Misner and Kip S. Thorne) is a landmark text on the subject of gravitation physics, general relativity,

space-time, and other subjects. In 1976 he accepted a position as professor of physics at the University of Texas at Austin, where he continued to teach and study until his retirement in 1986.

Wheeler was the recipient of the 1969 Franklin Medal, the 1970 National Medal of Science, and the 1988 Albert Einstein Medal. In 1997 he was honored with the prestigious Wolf Prize in Physics. Wheeler served as a president of the American Physical Society and as a member of organizations including the American Philosophical Society, the Royal Academy, the Accademia Nazionale dei Lincei, and the Royal Academy of Science. In the 1970s, he was appointed to the US General Advisory Committee on Arms Control and Disarmament. Wheeler died in 2008 at the age of ninety-six.

M. Lee

FURTHER READING

Ford, Kenneth W. "John Wheeler's Work on Particles, Nuclei, and Weapons." *Physics Today* 62.4 (2009): 29–33. Print. Describes the life and work of nuclear physicist John Wheeler. Discusses Wheeler's major career achievements.

Misner, Charles, Kip Thorne, and Wojciech Zurek. "John Wheeler, Relativity, and Quantum Information." *Physics Today* 62.4 (2009): 40–46. Print. Discusses Wheeler's work on relativity and quantum theory and describes his teaching and research methods.

Wheeler, John Archibald, and Kenneth Ford. *Geons, Black Holes, and Quantum Foam: A Life in Physics*. New York: Norton, 1998. Print. Autobiography of John Wheeler, documenting his life and his scientific career.

ERIC F. WIESCHAUS

American biologist

American molecular biologist Eric Francis Wieschaus has been involved in the study of genetics as a researcher and teacher since the 1960s. His collaborative experiments on the mutation of genes of fruit flies aided in understanding the process of embryonic development across the animal kingdom, and earned him a share of the Nobel Prize.

Born: June 8, 1947; South Bend, Indiana
Primary field: Biology

Specialties: Embryology; genetics; zoology; molecular biology

EARLY LIFE

Eric Francis Wieschaus was born into a Catholic family in South Bend, Indiana, on June 8, 1947. At the age of six, his family moved to Birmingham, Alabama. As a child, he enjoyed drawing. Wieschaus and his four siblings often roamed nearby woods, capturing frogs, turtles, and other creatures.

After attending Catholic grade school, Wieschaus entered John Carroll High School, the only Catholic high school in the city. In 1964, he participated in a National Science Foundation (NSF) program in Lawrence, Kansas, where he dissected a variety of animals for a zoology laboratory course. The following year, Wieschaus was invited back to the program's neurobiology lab, where he was put to work removing nerves from land tortoises and recording the effects of electrical stimulation on the tissue. By the end of his time in Kansas, Wieschaus had decided he would major in biology in college. He graduated from John Carroll High School in 1965.

Returning to the state of his birth, Wieschaus enrolled at the University of Notre Dame. As a sophomore, he was hired to prepare food for fruit flies (*Drosophilia melanoganster*) in the laboratory of Harvey A. Bender, professor of biological sciences and director of the human genetics program at Notre Dame. The experience piqued his interest in embryology. During his later years at the university, Wieschaus became an outspoken activist against the Vietnam War before graduating magna cum laude in 1969 with a bachelor of science degree in biology.

LIFE'S WORK

After graduating from Notre Dame, Wieschaus entered the postgraduate program at Yale University, where he studied under geneticists Donald Poulson and Walter Gehring. As part of his doctoral program, Wieschaus traveled to the University of Basel, Switzerland, where he met and befriended German biologist Christiane "Janni" Nÿsslein-Volhard and Swiss molecular biologist Gertrude "Trudi" Schÿpbach. He earned his PhD in biology in 1974—receiving the John Spangler Niclaus Prize for the outstanding dissertation in experimental embryology—and returned to Switzerland on a scholarship to continue postdoctoral studies at the University of Zurich.

In 1976, Wieschaus took time out from his research at the University of Zurich to work via fellowship at the Genetic Molecular Laboratory in Gif-sur-Yvette, France, becoming a visiting researcher in a laboratory at the Center of Pathobiology at the University of California, Irvine.

Wieschaus was hired in 1978 to be a group leader at the new European Molecular Biology Laboratory (EMBL), a multinational research organization headquartered in Heidelberg, Germany. At the state-of-the-art EMBL facility, he worked alongside fellow employee

Nÿsslein-Volhard, where for three years they performed groundbreaking experiments related to the mutation of genes in the development of embryos of fruit flies. In a painstaking screening process that required thousands of separate tests, the pair identified a number of genes essential for successful insect life. In the course of their research exploring embryonic mechanisms, Wieschaus and Nÿsslein-Volhard discovered three types of genetic sets and isolated specific genes responsible for the formation and placement of particular body parts. Fruit fly embryo cells are genetically programmed to form specific body parts, and during the normal course of development, change in shape, position, and pattern. After fertilization, *Drosophilia* embryos become segmented larvae containing cells of many different types and functions, including hairs, muscles, and organs. Certain cellular genes (called homeotic genes) control development by providing exact directions, dictating which parts go where and in what order.

The fruit fly genome—the complete molecular package of encoded hereditary information—consists of some fourteen thousand genes. Wieschaus and Nÿsslein-Volhard set themselves the enormous task of screening the genes in search of those vital to early development. To do that, the team produced nearly twenty-seven thousand chemically induced mutant flies. They then closely observed mutations via microscope at the moment of gastrulation (when single-layered cells convert to a three-layered structure), looking for differences in the usual patterns of embryonic development, indicated by changes in the shapes of the cells.

Two-thirds of the induced mutations prevented the fruit flies from surviving to maturity and proved lethal to the organism at various stages during its life cycle. Some individuals were missing parts, and others had parts where they did not belong: Eyes grew out of wings, legs sprouted out of heads. About one-quarter of the mutations kept the embryos from developing into larvae. These findings were considered significant because they were similar to the development patterns found in other organisms. Later research revealed that the Wieschaus/Nÿsslein-Volhard fruit fly studies were even relevant to the study of human genetics, once it became known that some diseases were the result of gene mutations.

Ultimately, less than six hundred viable mutated varieties, or phenotypes, were produced. From these, more than a hundred encoded genes essential to development were identified that related to specific cellular purposes, such as wing formation or muscle differentiation. These genes were given names according to their

Wieschaus, Nÿsslein-Volhard, and Lewis Study Fruit Fly Genetics

To scientists, fruit flies are allies in the effort to unravel the secrets of life and in the battle to combat disease. One species of fruit fly in particular, *Drosophilia melanogaster*, is considered an ideal model for conducting studies of genetics, developmental biology and morphology, embryology, and evolution—all of which can be applied to other species, including humans.

The advantages of using fruit flies in the laboratory are many and obvious. First and foremost, there are genetic and molecular similarities between flies and humans. The insect is small and easy to maintain with a simple diet, making it an inexpensive research subject. It has a well-defined life cycle (larva, pupa, adult) that occurs over a short time frame, so experiments can be performed relatively quickly. Mutations are easy to induce and observe. Females are prolific, producing large broods, which make large-scale studies feasible.

Moreover, ethics do not enter into the equation: Sensitive researchers, who might be uncomfortable with sacrificing mice, rabbits, rhesus monkeys, or other mammals to the cause of science, apparently do not have the same qualms about experimenting with flies. Similarly, the fruit fly's popular reputation as a nuisance means that animal rights activists have not campaigned against its use in scientific research.

Fruit flies were first introduced to the laboratory in 1909, when Thomas Hunt Morgan of Columbia University used the insects to study genetic development. Since then, *Drosophilia* has been at the center of numerous experiments, especially since the 1970s, when technological advances in molecular biology improved the ability of researchers to observe results on a microscopic scale. Significant breakthroughs occurred during the early 1980s. Nobel Prize winners Eric Wieschaus and Janni Nÿsslein-Volhard identified more than a hundred mutations affecting embryogenesis, and fellow prizewinner Edward B. Lewis independently used mutations of genes to produce bizarre creations, such as flies with no wings, with two pairs of wings, or with legs where their antennae should be.

In the late twentieth and early twenty-first centuries, fruit flies have been used to explore a bewildering range of ailments or phenomena that could have major repercussions for human welfare. Contemporary studies, for example, have shown that *Drosophilia* can acquire Alzheimer's disease, Parkinson's disease, and different forms of cancer. Mutations have caused epilepsy in flies. Experiments are now being conducted with fruit flies relating to heart disease, diabetes, muscular dystrophy, aging, and obesity. Other research concerns sleep research and visual perception of moving objects. Each of these studies carries great potential for the development of genetically based solutions to prevent, treat, or cure various human afflictions.

appearance under the microscope: armadillo, snail, hedgehog, twist, and so forth.

Wieschaus returned to the United States in 1981 to accept a position as teacher of molecular biology at Princeton University in New Jersey. In 1983, he married Trudi Schÿpbach, who also became a teacher at Princeton, and the couple eventually produced three daughters, Ingrid, Eleanor, and Laura. Wieschaus was later named Squibb Professor of Molecular Biology at Princeton. He also became an adjunct professor of biochemistry at the University of Medicine and Dentistry of New Jersey and an investigator at the Howard Hughes Medical Institute in Bethesda, Maryland.

In 1995, Wieschaus was awarded the Nobel Prize in Medicine/Physiology for his work on fruit flies. He shared the honor with colleague and collaborator Janni Nÿsslein-Volhard and with Edward B. Lewis (1918–2004) of the California Institute of Technology (Caltech), an independent fruit fly researcher who made related contributions to genetics.

Since winning the Nobel, Wieschaus has continued his research with *Drosophilia* embryos at Princeton. He has found new genes that control the fate of cells. His studies concentrate on refining the understanding of how genes are activated at various stages to cause changes in the shape and form of cells, particularly as such changes relate to developmental abnormalities in humans.

IMPACT

The massive Nobel Prize–winning fruit fly project that Wieschaus and Nÿsslein-Volhard undertook in the late 1970s and early 1980s—an extension of fellow award-winner Edward B. Lewis's experiments with *Drosophilia* in genetic mutations—had a significant impact on the history of genetics. The Wieschaus/Nÿsslein-Volhard experiments, though simple in concept, were sweeping in scope. The study, using the fruit fly as a model, explored the process of embryonic development and succeeded in unveiling the mechanism of how a whole organism is built from genetic instructions.

In the intervening years, other researchers have built upon the work of Wieschaus, Nÿsslein-Volhard, and Lewis. Scientists have discovered that genes similar to those identified in fruit flies exist in other animals, including humans, and they perform identical functions during the development of embryos. Likewise, mutations or defects in the genes—whether in *Drosophilia* or in other animals—can also adversely affect the health or survival of the mature organism. Once the origin and behavior of such defects or mutations is fully understood, it may be possible to make modifications during development stages that eliminate targeted abnormalities.

Jack Ewing

FURTHER READING

Badge, Peter. *Nobel Faces*. Weinheim: Wiley-VCH, 2008. Print. Includes photographs and short biographies of all Nobel Prize winners, including Wieschaus.

Creager, Angela N. H., Elizabeth Lunbeck, and M. Norton Wise. *Science without Laws: Model Systems, Cases, Exemplary Narratives*. Durham: Duke UP, 2007. Print. A collection of essays encompassing Wieschaus's Nobel Prize–winning studies of the fruit fly. Examines repeatable model systems in various scientific fields that, in the absence of provable universal laws, serve as points of reference or analyses of principles for researchers.

Hartl, Daniel L. *Essential Genetics: A Genomics Perspective*. 5th ed. Sudbury: Jones, 2011. Print. An illustrated edition of a popular text intended to introduce students to the subject. Covers molecular genetics, probability factors, and other key concepts.

EUGENE P. WIGNER

Hungarian American physicist

Wigner applied quantum theory to theoretical physics and focused on group theory in quantum mechanics. During World War II, he joined with other physicists in an effort to convince President Franklin D. Roosevelt of the need to develop nuclear weapons.

Born: November 17, 1902; Budapest, Hungary
Died: January 1, 1995; Princeton, New Jersey
Also known as: Jenő Pál Wigner
Primary field: Physics
Specialty: Quantum mechanics

EARLY LIFE

Jenő Pál Wigner was born on November 17, 1902, in Budapest, Hungary, the son of Antal and Erzsebet Einhorn Wigner. His father was the director of a leather tanning factory. In 1920, Wigner graduated from the Lutheran Gymnasium (high school) in Budapest, where one of his classmates was mathematician John von Neumann, a lifelong colleague and friend. After high school, Wigner studied for a year at the Budapest Institute of Technology before transferring to Berlin's Technische Hochschule (Technical School). He received his diploma in chemical engineering in 1924 and obtained his doctorate in engineering the next year. His doctoral dissertation, written under the direction of British Hungarian physical chemist and philosopher Michael Polanyi, discussed chemical reaction rates and the formation of molecules.

After a brief stint in his father's factory, Wigner returned to the Technische Hochschule as a research assistant. He then spent one year at the University of Göttingen as a research assistant and lecturer in physics. Quantum mechanics was a new science, and at Göttingen Wigner became acquainted with leading figures such as Max Born, James Franck, Pascual Jordan, Walter Heitler, and Victor Weisskopf. Under their influence, he decided to reconstruct theoretical physics according to quantum theory. In 1927, his paper on group theory in quantum mechanics predated Hermann Weyl's seminal work. Wigner also collaborated with some of his fellow theorists. He published three papers with John von Neumann on what came to be called the *law of conservation of parity*, which states that left and right cannot be identified in fundamental reactions. This research helped to explain what Wigner called "magic numbers." A magic number of either protons or neutrons in a nucleus makes the nucleus unusually stable and abundant. This work would prove helpful to physicists Maria Goeppert-Mayer and J. Hans D. Jensen, who researched the underlying source of magic numbers.

Returning to the Technische Hochschule as an instructor and temporary professor, Wigner became acquainted with physicists Léo Szilárd and Edward Teller, with whom he would build lifelong associations. Around this time, Wigner researched the rates of chemical reactions and worked on the theory of metallic cohesion. He studied the structure of atoms and nuclei and the characteristics of nuclear reactions.

LIFE'S WORK

In 1930, Wigner accepted a visiting lectureship at Princeton University. After a year, this appointment became a visiting professorship. In 1931, he published a study of group theory (a mathematical means of discussing symmetry) for physicists, *Group Theory and Its Application to Quantum Mechanics of Atomic Spectra*, which detailed the Wigner-Eckart theorem. This theorem was the result of the analysis of the SO(3) rotation group, and is constructed from representational theory and quantum mechanics in relation to various mathematical functions.

Wigner's research on the neutron—the elementary particle first discovered in 1933—showed that neutrons and protons are bound together only when the binding force is very close to the particles and unaffected by the electric force that attracts the electrons to the nucleus of the atom. Throughout the 1930s, Wigner published prolifically on numerous groundbreaking topics, including the Wigner-Seitz cellular method and wave functions (1933), the Wigner-Bardeen work function (1935), and the Breit-Wigner resonance formula (1936). Wigner also developed the theory of neutron absorption, or neutron capture, wherein a target nucleus absorbs a neutron and emits a slightly different form, or isotope, of the same element.

In 1936, Wigner married fellow physicist Amelia Ziporah Frank; however, she died the following year. That year, Wigner became a US citizen and accepted an appointment as professor of physics at the University of Wisconsin. Wigner returned to Princeton University in 1938 as the Thomas D. Jones Professor of Mathematical Physics. Except for war service and some visiting appointments, he would remain at Princeton until his retirement in 1971.

Wigner's friend and colleague von Neumann, who had come to Princeton in 1938, was the editor of the journal *Annals of Mathematics*. In 1939, von Neumann's

Wigner on Math in the Natural Sciences

Quantum physicists understand symmetry as relating to subatomic systems that are unchanging and continuous. The circular rotation of a particle, for instance, is considered an example of physical symmetry. Simultaneous transformations such as time and electric charge (positive or negative) are also classified as physical symmetries. Eugene Wigner's theorem on fundamental symmetry, or Wigner's theorem, laid a new foundation for the role of mathematics in the interpretation and explanation of various functions of quantum mechanics. The theorem posits that the symmetry of any quantum system must be unitary or antiunitary. Principles of symmetry are also helpful in predicting nuclear reactions.

Wigner discusses his thoughts on the relationship between physics and mathematics in his famed 1960 paper "The Unreasonable Effectiveness of Mathematics in the Natural Sciences," which would become a significant part of his legacy not only as a scientist but as one of the twentieth-century's most progressive minds. In the paper, Wigner lauded the effectiveness of mathematics with regard to observing and hypothesizing the laws of physics. Such use of mathematics was, according to Wigner, a potentially "wonderful gift."

Wigner wondered whether the use of mathematics in explicating the natural world in scientific terms was a mere coincidence or if it was so rational that it might reflect a more complex quality of nature as yet unknown to humanity.

An interest in the relationship between the natural world and humanity's attempt to understand it (in such sciences as mathematics) spanned Wigner's career, from his scientific research to his retirement. Wigner was one of the first scientists to pose questions about the fundamental nature of humanity's interpretation of the universe: Is humanity's interpretation innate or merely indicative of a previously undesignated natural order?

As the complexity of theories in quantum physics escalates, many scientists, educators, and even philosophers continue to draw upon Wigner's work. Wigner envisioned a future in which mathematics could be utilized to further investigate the phenomena of biology and psychology. Wigner noted that, given the appropriate tools for explanation, these systems may not be any less complex than the many scientific systems and theories that previously have been reduced to simple processes by talented minds.

journal published Wigner's "On Unitary Representation of the Inhomogeneous Lorentz Group." The paper presented new ideas in both mathematics and physics, defining an elementary particle as an irreducible representation of the inhomogeneous Lorentz group.

With the beginning of World War II, several immigrant scientists—including Wigner, Léo Szilárd, Albert Einstein, and Enrico Fermi—wanted to be sure that the United States would be protected from Hitler and his totalitarian reign. In 1938, Otto Hahn and Lise Meitner of Germany had discovered nuclear fission, and, in the summer of 1939, these naturalized citizens presented their case to President Franklin D. Roosevelt, arguing that the United States needed to develop nuclear weapons. Their efforts would eventually result in the development of an atomic bomb through the Manhattan Engineering District, more commonly known as the Manhattan Project.

In 1940, Wigner produced a seminal paper dealing with the reduction of Kronecker products. The paper, which discusses the algebra of angular momentum and recoupling, includes the famous three-j symbols, now known as Clebsch-Gordan or Wigner coefficients, and the six-j symbols, now known as Racah coefficients. As the paper was privately circulated over the next decades, friends having persuaded Wigner that it was too long and difficult to understand, other researchers later rediscovered some of the same results. The paper was finally published in 1965.

When the Manhattan Project was launched in 1942, Wigner was appointed head of the theoretical section of the Metallurgical Laboratory at the University of Chicago. Applying his abilities in areas from theory to mechanical engineering, Wigner developed many of the standard techniques used in constructing reactors. After Victory in Europe Day was proclaimed in May 1945, Wigner, along with Einstein, Szilárd, and others, asked President Harry S. Truman to refrain from using the atomic bomb. But, in early August 1945, atomic bombs were dropped on Hiroshima and Nagasaki, Japan. Wigner became director of research and development at the Clinton Laboratories of Oak Ridge National Laboratory in Tennessee; between 1945 and 1947, he received thirty-seven patents on nuclear reactors. Wigner recommended the type of parallel plate reactor that was used in the *Nautilus*, the world's first nuclear-powered submarine. His team also developed the isotope carbon-14.

From 1952 to 1957, and again from 1959 to 1964, Wigner was a member of the general advisory committee of the Atomic Energy Commission. He collaborated on two influential books, *Nuclear Structure* (1958) with Leonard Eisenbud, and *The Physical Theory of Neutron Chain Reactors* (1958) with Alvin M. Weinberg. In the early 1960s, Wigner also directed civil defense programs for the National Academy of Sciences and the Oak Ridge National Laboratory.

In 1963, Wigner was awarded the Nobel Prize in Physics for his systematic improvement, extension, and wide application of the methods of quantum mechanics. He shared the prize with Maria Goeppert-Mayer and J. Hans D. Jensen. The year after, Wigner published *Dispersion Relations and Their Connection with Causality*. In 1967, he published *Symmetries and Reflections*.

In 1977, Mary Annette Wheeler, Eugene Wigner's second wife, died. In 1979, he married Eileen C. P. Hamilton. He continued to serve the government in an advisory capacity on various projects and supported President Ronald Reagan's Strategic Defense Initiative. He also continued to write and focused on the philosophical implications and physical interpretation of quantum mechanics.

Wigner died at the age of ninety-two in Princeton, New Jersey, on January 1, 1995.

Impact

Physicist, nuclear engineer, and Nobel laureate Eugene P. Wigner is considered one of the most important figures in the history of theoretical physics. Wigner was a pioneer in the application of the principles of symmetry to predict invariances in physical processes; these symmetry principles can help predict which nuclear reactions are most likely to occur.

While mathematics had been utilized in the research and development of science, engineering, and technology, Wigner was the first to apply mathematical concepts such as group theory to quantum mechanics, the branch of physics pertaining to energy on the atomic and subatomic level.

As a member of the Manhattan Project, Wigner was responsible for applying knowledge of quantum energy toward national defense—an area to which Wigner would contribute throughout his career. In addition to his work at Princeton, Wigner served as a visiting professor at several universities in Europe. His honors include election to the National Academy of Sciences in 1945 and the vice presidency (1955) and presidency (1966) of the American Physical Society. He was presented with numerous medals and awards, including the Presidential Medal of Merit (1946).

Ellen Bailey

FURTHER READING

Hargittai, István. *The Martians of Science: Five Physicists Who Changed the Twentieth Century*. New York: Oxford UP, 2006. Print. Provides biographical information on Theodore von Kármán, Léo Szilárd, Eugene P. Wigner, John von Neumann, and Edward Teller. Recounts the events of their lives and describes their important scientific discoveries.

Vogt, Erich. "Eugene Paul Wigner: A Towering Figure of Modern Physics." *Physics Today* 48.12 (1995): 40–44. Print. Reviews the impact of Wigner's research on the field of quantum mechanics. Includes photographs, a table of major milestones in Wigner's career, and a list of references.

Weinberg, Alvin M. "Eugene Wigner, Nuclear Engineer." *Physics Today* 55.10 (2002): 42–46. Print. Discusses the contributions of Wigner to nuclear engineering, including the 1936 discovery of the Breit-Wigner formula.

Wightman, Arthur S., and J. Mehra, eds. *The Collected Works of Eugene Paul Wigner*. New York: Springer, 2001. Print. A collection of documents on Wigner's life and work. Compiles scientific, biographical, mathematical, and historical papers.

MAURICE VINCENT WILKES

British computer scientist

Maurice Wilkes designed and built the EDSAC computer, the first computer to combine mercury delay line memory with stored program instructions. He later developed WISP, one of the first high-level programming languages.

Born: June 26, 1913; Dudley, England
Died: November 29, 2010; Cambridge, England
Primary field: Computer science
Specialties: Logic; information theory; electromagnetism; atmospheric sciences

EARLY LIFE

Maurice Vincent Wilkes was born in the village of Dudley in Worcestershire, England, on June 26, 1913. His father worked as a clerk on the estates of the Earl of Dudley. One of his father's duties was to operate the private telephone switchboard, which at the time was considered advanced technology. Perhaps in consequence, Wilkes's childhood interests were mechanical toys, batteries, lights, and buzzers.

Wilkes attended the King Edward VI Grammar School in Stourbridge. After completing the junior course, he was promoted to the main school, where he began a four-year syllabus emphasizing mathematics and science, in addition to English and modern languages. As a young student, Wilkes became interested in radio and built several receivers. One of his teachers, the chemist J. Timbrell, was also a radio enthusiast and encouraged him to study for an amateur radio transmitting license. Wilkes succeeded and later built his own transmitting equipment.

In 1931, Wilkes applied to Cambridge University and was accepted. At Cambridge, Wilkes studied mathematics for three years while maintaining his interest in amateur radio. He graduated with first-class honors in June 1934.

As a result of his strong showing in his degree examinations, Wilkes received a research grant that allowed him to study the propagation of radio waves at the university's Cavendish Laboratory. The work combined his interest in mathematics with practical radio applications. In March 1936, while Wilkes was pursuing this research, he received a demonstration of a mechanical differential analyzer that had been using pieces of a metallic toy. This machine, which could produce analog solutions of simple differential equations, fascinated Wilkes. Its success resulted in a proposal to establish a mathematical laboratory at Cambridge. Wilkes accepted a post in the new laboratory in 1938.

LIFE'S WORK

Wilkes was working in Cambridge in September 1939, when World War II started. He had earned his PhD in October 1938 after presenting a thesis on long-wave radio propagation. Wilkes and many of his colleagues worked in support of the war effort after Britain declared war on Germany. Wilkes worked on developing radar technology. When the war broke out, Britain already had some radar apparatus in service. It used a wavelength of 1.5 meters. In radar, the shorter the wavelength the more precise the results. Wilkes was part of a group that developed and built radar sets with a wavelength of 50 centimeters. Later in the war, they

Wilkes Builds the EDSAC Computer

Maurice Wilkes's idea of computer architecture required what is now called "random-access memory" (RAM). RAM is needed to hold program instructions and the results of intermediate calculations. RAM differs from other forms of storage in that any particular memory cell can be accessed directly rather than serially. For example, punched paper tape and magnetic tape are serial devices. All the data have to be run past before the necessary place is found. However, at the time Wilkes was working on the design of EDSAC, no random access memory existed. A fast and reliable means of reading the computer's memory had to be devised.

Mercury delay lines were first used during World War II to help reduce ground clutter in radar sets. The delay line consists of a tube of mercury in which electrical impulses were turned into ultrasonic mechanical pulses by a piezoelectric crystal at one end of the line. The pulses move more quickly through mercury than, for example, through air; when they reach the end of the delay tube, the pulses are reconverted to electrical energy by another crystal. The content of the delay line is refreshed periodically at the starting end. In order to use this technology for computing, it is necessary to have very pure mercury that is uniformly warmed. In addition, exact timing and careful shielding of the signal is needed to prevent stray impulses from corrupting the data. Most of the engineering problems that corrupted the process were solved by Wilkes and his assistant, William Renwick, an experienced electronic engineer who had worked on radar at the British Admiralty during the war. In May 1947, Wilkes was able to give a demonstration of a mercury delay line, exhibiting the pulses on a cathode ray tube.

The tubes that were developed for the EDSAC computer could hold 512 35-bit words. Thirty-two delay lines were required. This memory, which was incredibly small by today's standards, nevertheless allowed EDSAC to be the first stored-program digital computer. On May 6, 1949, the EDSAC computer, programmed initially with a paper tape, began running a routine for computing a table of squares. Two days later, a program for computing prime numbers had been fed into the machine and was working satisfactorily. The results of these computations were printed out by a printer.

Although EDSAC had originally been considered an experimental machine, it worked so well that increased demands for its computational services were placed on Wilkes's laboratory. The machine had actually become a production machine and was used extensively for practical scientific applications for another nine years.

In January 2011, the Computer Conservation Society of the United Kingdom announced it would rebuild the EDSAC computer and place it on exhibit at the National Museum of Computing at Bletchley Park, the locus of British code-breaking efforts during World War II.

---

successfully built sets of 10- and 3-centimeter wavelengths. The resolution of the latter equipment was so fine that shell splashes in the water could be detected, thus making the equipment suitable for controlling naval gunnery. Beginning in 1943, Wilkes also worked on "operations research"—the application of mathematical statistics or game theory to practical military operations.

After World War II ended, Wilkes became interested in atmospheric oscillations. These oscillations occur as the result of tidal forces working on the atmosphere with the rise and fall of the moon. The necessary mathematical analyses required immense amounts of computation, far beyond any practical production with mechanical adding machines. This need spurred Wilkes to return to his earlier interest in the differential analyzer and other new forms of calculating machinery. In 1946, he read John von Neumann's famous 1945 paper "First Draft of a Report on the EDVAC," on the Electronic Discrete Variable Automatic Computer being developed in the United States. This paper set out the principles on which digital computers could be constructed. Wilkes later wrote, "I recognized this at once as the real thing, and from that time on never had any doubt as to the way computer development would go."

The Moore School of Electrical Engineering at the University of Pennsylvania in Philadelphia invited Wilkes to attend a course in electronic computers. Wilkes leaped at the opportunity, and sailed for the United States in August 1946. While in the United States, he met von Neumann and other American computer scientists and discussed computer architecture with them. While in Boston in September 1946, he began to sketch out the design of the machine that became EDSAC—the Electronic Delay Storage Automatic Calculator. Upon his return to England, Wilkes set to work on building EDSAC with his team at the Cambridge University

Mathematical Laboratory. Mercury delay lines were used as the machine's memory. Upon its completion in 1949, EDSAC was more advanced than its two giant American predecessors, ENIAC and EDVAC.

Once EDSAC was completed, Wilkes turned his attention to programming issues. He had come to believe that subroutines—subordinate computer programs completing discrete tasks within a larger program—could be developed for the use of the main computer program. Within two years, a library of subroutines for EDSAC had been written, which permitted the laboratory to solve complex problems in many disciplines. For example, Wilkes himself worked with the biologist Ronald Fisher to write a routine that solved an equation for Fisher's paper on gene frequencies. This effort represented the first application of computer technology to the science of biology.

Wilkes realized that general-purpose computer languages would be necessary, and some of his laboratory's staff set to work on devising them. Wilkes himself devised a programming language called WISP. This was a list processor, and was in vogue as a teaching tool for some time. It also had some practical applications.

When work surrounding the development of EDSAC became routine, Wilkes began work on a successor machine, EDSAC 2. This machine, more advanced than EDSAC, was used for production computing until 1956.

Repeatedly over the course of his career in computing, Wilkes visited the United States in order to keep up with American technological developments. Following his retirement from Cambridge University, he and his family moved to the United States, where he took up a post as a senior engineer and consultant on the staff of Digital Equipment Corporation (DEC), a large American computer firm. In 2002, he moved back to Cambridge.

Wilkes received many university and organizational honors in his lifetime, including an honorary doctor of science degree from Cambridge University. He was knighted in the 2000 New Year Honors List. Wilkes died on November 29, 2010, at the age of 97.

IMPACT

Wilkes lived to see his systems of computer architecture and programming widely implemented. Computer programs are written using Boolean logic, and all but the simplest use subroutines. These characteristics are all consistent with the architecture that Wilkes helped devise. Indeed, the extraordinary capabilities of solid state electronics—central processing units with billions of transistors and dynamic random access memories in the range of gigabytes—are proof of how sound Wilkes's architecture actually is. Any number of alternate designs could have supplanted those of Wilkes in the half-century that followed his work, but none have proven to be more effective, and, as Wilkes foresaw, computers have in that time become ubiquitous.

Robert Jacobs

FURTHER READING

Campbell-Kelly, Martin, and William Aspray. *Computer: A History of the Information Machine*, 2nd ed. Boulder, CO: Westview, 2004. Print. Traces the development of computing machinery from Charles Babbage to the present. Includes a discussion on the designs of ENIAC and EDVAC.

Goldstine, Herman H. *The Computer from Pascal to von Neumann*. Princeton: Princeton UP, 1980. Print. Covers the development of computers as both historian and participant. Maurice Wilkes's role is frequently discussed.

Wilkes, Maurice V. *Memoirs of a Computer Pioneer*. Cambridge, MA: MIT Press, 1985. Wilkes recounts his life and work. Includes a discussion of his associates and collaborates, and his other scientific interests.

MAURICE WILKINS

British biophysicist

Maurice Wilkins's X-ray diffraction studies were instrumental in determining the double-helical structure of DNA. He came to regard DNA's simplicity as symbolizing the underlying simplicity of all biological phenomena.

Born: December 15, 1916; Pongaroa, New Zealand
Died: October 5, 2004; London, England
Also known as: Maurice Hugh Frederick Wilkins
Primary fields: Physics; biology
Specialties: Genetics; biophysics

EARLY LIFE

Maurice Wilkins was born in Pongaroa, New Zealand, to Edgar Henry and Eveline Constance Jane Whittaker Wilkins, who both came from Dublin, Ireland. At the age of six, Wilkins was brought to England and educated at King Edward's School in Birmingham. He studied physics at St. John's College, Cambridge University, where he studied crystallography with John Desmond Bernal. He obtained his BA degree in 1938. Then he attended University of Birmingham, where he became research assistant to John T. Randall in the physics department. Together, they developed the electron-trap theory of phosphorescence and thermoluminescence. Wilkins received his PhD in 1940.

During World War II, Wilkins joined physicists under Mark Oliphant in their work using the mass spectrometer to separate uranium isotopes for the atom bomb. When nuclear research was transferred to the United States, Wilkins followed. He traveled to the University of California, Berkeley, to become part of the Manhattan Project. He continued to use the mass spectrograph to build up quantities of uranium-235 for the American atom bomb. As the war neared its end and the first atom bombs were dropped in Japan, Wilkins's interest in nuclear physics waned. He read *What Is Life?* (1944) by physicist Erwin Schrödinger and became eager to apply his understanding of physics to the complexities of living things.

In 1945, Wilkins returned to Great Britain and began a career in biophysics at University of St. Andrews in Scotland, where he again was under the direction of Randall. In 1946, Wilkins and Randall moved to King's College London.

LIFE'S WORK

By the time Wilkins went to King's College, scientists at the Rockefeller Institute in New York had proved that genes were made of deoxyribonucleic acid (DNA). Wilkins started doing research on DNA, at first indirectly, by trying to cause mutations in fruit flies with ultrasonic vibrations, and then directly, by developing a special microscope for studying the amount of DNA in cells. Eventually, Wilkins decided to leave the analysis of DNA in intact cells to the biologists; he believed that he could use his specialized skills more effectively to study the DNA molecule in isolation, outside the cell.

One of the techniques physicists had developed by then was the analysis of dichroism patterns. Wilkins placed a specimen of DNA under a microscope and then subjected it to two colors of light simultaneously: One color was transmitted directly and the other was reflected. From the contrast of the colors, some information about the structure of DNA could be inferred.

Wilkins next turned to analysis by X-ray diffraction, a technique that was still in its infancy. X-ray crystallography works by focusing a beam of X-rays on a crystalline structure. The scattered reflected beam is photographed. By rotating the substance under investigation, different diffraction patterns can be observed. The patterns can reveal the positions of the electrons within the substance, their density, and the chemical bonds that attach them to one another.

In 1951, there was considerable controversy in biophysics over the nature of genes. Many biologists believed that they were separate protein molecules within cells; others had come to suspect that the substance DNA, which appears in all living cells, was implicated. To show that DNA contained the genetic information that makes life possible, researchers had to determine not only the molecule's chemical structure but also how it could replicate itself and transmit genetic information. The DNA molecule, which is large and complex, turned out to be suitable for investigation using X-ray diffraction techniques, and Wilkins's laboratory began studying it in 1950. Rosalind Franklin, a skilled X-ray crystallographer, joined Wilkins's team in 1951 and became one of the chief investigators.

Wilkins's work, which established that DNA has a long crystalline structure, interested Francis Crick and James D. Watson of the Cavendish Laboratory at Cambridge University. However, research was hampered by complex interpersonal relations: Wilkins did not get along well with Franklin, and the two laboratories were both cooperating and competing with each other.

In 1953, Wilkins showed Watson an exceptionally clear photograph made by Franklin. From this picture Watson and Crick were able to hypothesize that the DNA molecule consisted of two identical chemical strands wound around one another helically. The molecule contains more than three billion chemical base pairs that contain genetic information. Crick and Watson published this discovery in April 1953.

Wilkins led much of the investigation and verification that remained to be done. The two laboratories had agreed to joint subsequent publication. After publications in *Nature* by the two groups in 1953, Wilkins proved that the Watson-Crick model was unique; no other model would give the same X-ray diffraction pattern. The data also allowed Wilkins to readjust and refine the Watson-Crick model. In 1962, Wilkins

Maurice Wilkins Investigates the Structure of DNA

After his World War II work on the atomic bomb, Maurice Wilkins turned to applications of physics to genetics. At the time, scientists were investigating the enigmatic molecule deoxyribonucleic acid (DNA) to determine whether it was responsible for genetic transmission.

Optical studies of DNA molecules convinced Wilkins that DNA fibers would be ideal material for X-ray diffraction studies. While examining DNA gels prepared for his dichroism work, Wilkins observed that each time he touched the gel with a glass rod and then removed it, a thin fiber of DNA was drawn out and suspended between the rod and the gel. The uniformity of the fibers suggested that the DNA molecules were arranged in some kind of regular pattern and therefore might be suitable material for analysis by X-ray diffraction.

The first diffraction patterns of DNA obtained with makeshift equipment were encouraging. By 1951, Wilkins and his colleagues had much sharper diffraction photographs. The sharpness showed that the DNA molecules were highly regular. Keeping the fibers moist was key to getting good diffraction patterns. In fact, when the material was dried, there was no pattern; when high humidity was restored, a detailed crossing pattern was apparent. A theory was developed to predict the absence and presence of certain reflections, which appeared as spots in the X-ray photographs. The precise location and intensity of these spots depended on the repeat distance and diameter of the helix. With this theory and improved images, Wilkins and his colleagues realized that DNA had helical characteristics.

Biophysicist Rosalind Franklin joined the group soon after, and a personality conflict arose. On Wilkins's return from a 1951 visit to Italy and the United States, he found that Franklin and Raymond Gosling, using more advanced X-ray equipment with even higher humidities, had made much progress. Collaboration was no longer possible, the work was divided, and Wilkins and Franklin studied different problems. Wilkins proved the existence of helical DNA in certain living cells. He also showed that DNAs from different biological sources were basically the same, providing important evidence for the generality of the DNA structure. Meanwhile, Franklin observed a less crystalline form of DNA, the B form, at high humidities; this was to be instrumental in elucidating DNA's structure.

During this period, Wilkins maintained personal contact with Francis Crick, a physicist in collaboration with James D. Watson at Cambridge University. After examining the research of Franklin and Wilkins, Watson and Crick were able to construct the famous double helix for the structure of DNA.

Wilkins subsequently demonstrated that the structure of DNA is not merely an artifact resulting from the manipulation of the material once it has been removed from the cell. He found that X-ray diffraction photographs taken of intact biological systems bore a close resemblance to the photographs obtained from purified DNA, thus proving that DNA is the same highly structured double-helical molecule both before and after isolation.

obtained the first clear X-ray diffraction patterns of ribonucleic acid (RNA), and he showed that it had a helical structure very similar to the Watson-Crick double helix.

Wilkins shared the 1962 Nobel Prize in Physiology or Medicine with Watson and Crick; Franklin had died of ovarian cancer in 1958 and her contribution was less recognized. After his Nobel Prize, Wilkins felt free to broaden his interests and to use his newly acquired prestige for the betterment of human life. Because of the Cuban Missile Crisis of 1962, he became deeply concerned about the dangers posed by biological and chemical weapons. His participation in the Cambridge Scientists' Anti-War Group helped to focus this interest.

Although his studies on DNA had effectively ended by 1967, his curiosity about basic biological problems continued. For example, he began studies on the structure of nerve membranes. Also, he became the president of the British Society for Social Responsibility in Science.

During the 1980s, Wilkins extended his humanistic efforts by signing a manifesto on poverty and starvation in the developing world, which was connected with his participation in Food and Disarmament International. He also became an important part of the Pugwash movement, which brought together internationally prominent scholars and scientists to discuss ways of reducing the likelihood of war. Though he and his wife avoided public demonstrations, they did undertake nonpolitical work for the Campaign for Nuclear Disarmament during the 1980s and 1990s.

Wilkins's autobiography, *The Third Man of the Double Helix* (2003), was largely devoted to his views on the discovery of DNA's three-dimensional structure and his critique of the earlier accounts of Watson and others. He died on October 5, 2004.

IMPACT

Despite the complications and human foibles surrounding the discovery of the double helix, the structure itself proved to be a simple and beautiful one. Wilkins was impressed by this simplicity, and he came to regard DNA's simplicity as symbolizing the underlying simplicity of all biological phenomena. In his later career, he believed that science's search for simple principles also could be used to resolve social conflicts.

For Wilkins, science represented rationality as well, and in the late twentieth and early twenty-first centuries, he warned of the growth of irrationality. Nonetheless, he recognized that objective thinking could reduce moral sensitivity. According to Wilkins, modern humans live with a dilemma: Science is the only way for human beings to avoid starvation, disease, and premature death, but science can be used to accelerate human annihilation. To reduce these dangers, he felt, science must be carefully interrelated with technology, politics, art, and the rest of society.

Robert J. Paradowski

FURTHER READING

Squires, G. L. "The Discovery of the Structure of DNA." *Contemporary Physics* 44.4 (2003): 289–305. Print. Describes the careers of Crick, Watson, Wilkins, and Franklin. Traces the events leading up to the discovery of the structure of DNA.

Watson, James, and Andrew Berry. *DNA: The Secret of Life*. New York: Knopf, 2003. Print. Written fifty years after the discovery of the double helix, this historical study emphasizes the transformative effect that the double helix's discovery has had on scientific, biotechnological, social, and ethical issues. Also includes Watson's reflections on the discovery itself, including the role that Wilkins played.

Wilkins, Maurice. *The Third Man of the Double Helix: The Autobiography of Maurice Wilkins*. New York: Oxford UP, 2003. Print. Written to commemorate the fiftieth anniversary of the discovery of the double helix. Contains Wilkins's reminiscences of the events and personalities of his early life and career as well as his own perspective on the DNA story and its aftermath. Includes photographs.

EDMUND BEECHER WILSON

American zoologist

American zoologist Edmund Beecher Wilson is considered one of most influential cell biologists in history. During a career that spanned the late nineteenth and early twentieth centuries, he conducted multiple studies on the cellular division of eggs in insects and marine creatures, and helped define the vital role of chromosomes in determining gender across the animal kingdom.

Born: October 19, 1856; Geneva, Illinois
Died: March 3, 1939; New York, New York
Primary field: Biology
Specialties: Cellular biology; zoology; genetics

EARLY LIFE

Edmund Beecher "Eddy" Wilson was descended from a New England family whose ancestors came to America from England on the *Mayflower*. His father, Isaac Grant Wilson, was a lawyer and judge. His mother's name was Caroline Louisa Clarke Wilson. Wilson's parents relocated from Massachusetts to Geneva, Illinois, in the early 1840s. One of five children, Wilson developed an interest in music and natural history at an early age, studying birds, reptiles, and insects.

At the age of sixteen, Wilson became a salaried teacher at a one-room schoolhouse in the village of Oswego, Illinois, just south of Geneva. He presided over twenty-five students, ranging in age from six to eighteen, instructing them in reading, writing, arithmetic, and history. In 1872, he took an entrance exam for West Point. Despite earning a top score, he was too young to be admitted. The following year, Wilson entered Antioch College in southern Ohio, where he took a challenging course of study that included Latin, Greek, zoology, botany, chemistry, geometry, and trigonometry. To help support himself, he worked as an assistant in a geographical survey of Lake Ontario and Lake Erie.

In 1875, Eddy transferred to Yale University. He worked the summer of 1877 with the US Commission of Fish and Fisheries (also known as the Fish Commission, established in 1871). Sailing out of Gloucester, Massachusetts, aboard the *Speedwell*, a naval steamship, he participated in dredging operations and collected marine animals. Wilson graduated from Yale in 1878, majoring in biology. That same year, he published the first of more than one hundred zoological papers. He stayed on for another year at Yale, taking graduate courses in embryology and heredity. Wilson was then granted a fellowship to study at Johns Hopkins University, where he remained for three years while conducting research at the university's marine station on Chesapeake Bay. He earned his PhD in 1881.

LIFE'S WORK

In 1882, Wilson traveled abroad to further his education. He first studied at Cambridge University, taking courses from some of the leading British scientists of the day, including zoologist and comparative anatomist Adam Sedgwick, physiologist and embryologist Walter Heape, zoologists William Hay Caldwell and William Bateson, and physiologist Michael Foster. He then moved to Germany, where he conducted laboratory research under zoologist Rudolf Leuckart and took classes from physiologist and comparative anatomist Carl F. W. Ludwig at the University of Leipzig. Wilson then worked for a year with German scientist Anton Dohrn, founder and director of the Zoological Station in Naples, Italy, conducting experiments and making observations of marine animals. At the station, Wilson also worked alongside marine biologist Hugo Eisig and comparative invertebrate anatomist Arnold Lang.

Wilson returned to the United States in 1883 to teach biology at Williams College. After spending a year as lecturer at the Massachusetts Institute of Technology (MIT), he took a position at Bryn Mawr College, where he served as head of the biology department for six years.

Following another year abroad in Munich, Naples, and Sicily, Wilson was appointed to a post at Columbia University, where he helped establish the school's new department of zoology. He began spending summers researching at the Marine Biological Laboratory in Woods Hole, Massachusetts.

Wilson remained at Columbia for the rest of his professional career, teaching biology and zoology, including specialized courses on heredity, cytology, chromosomes, variation, and evolution. Under Wilson's influence, Columbia's department of zoology became internationally renowned as a leading institution in the study of modern genetics. Many of Wilson's students became leaders in the fields of biology and zoology. His students Thomas Hunt Morgan and Hermann Muller later won Nobel Prizes.

Throughout his time at Columbia, Wilson conducted extensive research on cell organization, structure, and function, with a particular emphasis on studies of eggs through every stage of development. In the course of his research, he became an expert in the use of microscopes and was known for his proficiency in tissue sectioning and slide staining.

While at Columbia, Wilson published numerous papers based on his research related to chromosomes, spermatogenesis, and experimental embryology that helped to refine existing concepts of evolution. During his tenure, he published an authoritative book, *The Cell in Development and Inheritance* (1896), which became a standard college text and went through second (1915) and third (1925) editions before advancements in the field rendered it obsolete. Part of the work's long popularity was due to the clarity of the illustrations that Wilson, an excellent draftsman, had included.

In 1904, Wilson married Anne Maynard Kidder of Washington, DC, whose family was associated with the US Fish Commission and with the Marine Biological Station. The couple had a daughter, Nancy, who became a professional cellist. In 1906, the couple took a long working vacation, traveling through Arizona, Wyoming, and California to collect insects for Wilson's investigations into chromosomes.

The first decade of the twentieth century was a productive time for Wilson. Between 1905 and 1912—during a revival in interest in the genetic studies of late Austrian scientist Gregor Mendel—he conducted extensive research into heredity, chromosomes, and cell division. Inducted into the American Academy of Arts and Sciences in 1902 and into the American Association for the Advancement of Science in 1913, Wilson continued his work until the end of his life. He published his final paper in 1937, nine years after retiring as a professor at Columbia. Wilson died in 1939 at age eighty-two.

IMPACT

During his four decades of teaching, Wilson influenced numerous students who worked to advance scientific understanding of biology. Morgan (Nobel Prize, 1933) and Muller (Nobel Prize, 1946) are perhaps the best known

Wilson's Key Genetic Discovery: XX and XY Chromosomes

Edmund Beecher Wilson began his scientific investigations as a traditional biologist, following the conventional precept of "ontogeny recapitulates phylogeny." The theory, since discredited, was concocted by influential German biologist-naturalist Ernst Haeckel, who hypothesized that animals in the process of embryonic development (ontogeny) pass through or recapture stages that reflect the evolution of ancient ancestors (phylogeny).

Wilson's early research centered on observation and examination of the structure and activity of the hydra, a fresh-water animal with tentacles that has the ability to regenerate missing limbs. He later studied annelids (earthworms) and platyhelminthes (flatworms), which can also recreate lost segments and are self-propagating hermaphrodites. Wilson's investigations led him to concentrate on embryology, with a particular focus on cytology—defined as the study of the structure, function and chemistry of cells—especially as related to the cellular division that occurs in fertilized eggs.

In the late 1880s and early 1890s, in the process of attempting to draw connections between heredity and cellular development, he conducted research at the Marine Biological Laboratory and elsewhere. Wilson experimented with the cell division in the eggs of marine worms (*Nereis*), studied germination in mollusks (*Dentalium*), compared cleavage stages and cellular organization in the eggs of sea snails (*Patella*), and induced artificial parthenogenesis—reproduction without fertilization—in the eggs of sea urchins (*Echinoidea*). By the end of the nineteenth century, Wilson had concluded that chromosomes, packages of genes found in the nuclei of cells, were the primary carriers of hereditary information in any organism.

To further develop his idea, Wilson focused his research on the embryology of insects, paying particular attention to chromosomes. Using the fruit fly (Drosophilidae) as his initial subject of study, and later extending his research with investigation of arachnids (Scorpi-

ones), Wilson painstakingly separated and counted the chromosomes within fertilized eggs. Among the pairs of chromosomes contained in cell nuclei—half contributed by the male, half by the female of the species—that provide an organism's genetic blueprint (now termed the genome), he sometimes found an additional set of chromosomes. Through careful observation, Wilson noticed that the extra pair of chromosomes was present only in germ cells produced by the male. Furthermore, when the fertilized egg began to divide, the extra chromosome was found in only one of the two new cells. When the cell divided again, two of the four cells contained the extra chromosome; this process continued throughout cell division.

On the basis of his research, Wilson concluded that—unlike the other chromosomes, called autosomes, which govern other characteristics of the offspring—the extra chromosome was solely concerned with determining the sex of the new individual. Females always contribute an XX chromosome to the sexual development of an egg. Males, however, can either contribute the usual XX or an extra XY chromosome. When both male and female contribute XX chromosomes, the result is female. When the male contributes the extra XY chromosome, the progeny is male.

Wilson's discovery, which could be applied to other species, including humans—had far-reaching implications, particularly in animal breeding, and was highly influential in the further development of genetics as a specialized science. Later research conducted by other scientists would reveal anomalies within the X-Y chromosome system, and slightly different systems in certain organisms—butterflies, frogs, and some fish—for determining sex. Remarkably, one of Wilson's former students, Nettie Stevens, simultaneously conducted similar research and independently reached the same conclusions at the same time as Wilson, and today both Wilson and Stevens are jointly credited with the discovery of the XX and XY sex-determinant chromosome system.

of Wilson's former students, but his classes also inspired other such leading evolutionary biologists and geneticists as Nettie Stevens, Gary N. Calkins, James McGregor, Alfred Henry Sturtevant, and Marcella O'Grady Boveri.

Considered America's first cytologist (cell biologist), Wilson also pioneered the disciplines of embryology, heredity, and genetics through his research on

marine animals and insects. Among his many contributions to the study of evolution was his coining of the term "stem cell" in 1896, and his discovery of the XX and XY chromosomes.

Wilson received many honors and awards for his work, both during his lifetime and posthumously. In 1925, the National Academy of Sciences presented him with the Daniel Giraud Elliot Medal for his contributions to zoology. In 1928, he received the Gold Medal of the Linnean Society of London. In 1936, he garnered the US National Academy of Sciences John J. Carty Medal and Award. Over the years, he collected honorary degrees from numerous universities. In his memory, the American Society for Cell Biology established the E. B. Wilson Medal and Lecture as its highest honor for accomplishments in the field.

Jack Ewing

FURTHER READING

Carlson, Elof Axel. *Mutation: The History of an Idea from Darwin to Genomics*. Long Island: Cold Spring Harbor Lab P, 2011. Print. Discusses the birth and development of mutation, a key concept in the theory of evolution that has occupied geneticists—including Edmund Beecher Wilson—for more than 150 years.

Laubichler, Manfred D., and Jane Maienschein, eds. *From Embryology to Evo-Devo: A History of Developmental Evolution*. Cambridge: MIT P, 2007. Print. Presents an overview of the modern field of evolutionary developmental biology, which has grown out of earlier research into embryology, heredity, and genetics.

Wilson, Edmund Beecher. *The Supernumerary Chromosomes and their Relation to the Odd or Accessory Chromosome*. Whitefish: Kessinger, 2010. Print. Reprint of Wilson's groundbreaking 1909 work on chromosomes as determinants of sex.

EDWARD WITTEN

American physicist and mathematician

Sometimes called the successor to Albert Einstein, Edward Witten has developed numerous theories in advanced mathematics, often borrowing concepts from biology, physics, and other branches of science. He is best known for proposing superstring theory, which seeks to reconcile Einsteinian relativity with Newtonian gravitation.

Born: August 26, 1951; Baltimore, Maryland
Primary fields: Mathematics; physics
Specialties: Theoretical physics

EARLY LIFE

Edward Witten was born in 1951 to Lorraine and Louis W. Witten, a physicist and expert on the theory of general relativity propounded by Albert Einstein. As a precocious boy, Witten discussed physics with his father. He became an avid bridge player within weeks of learning the game as a ten-year-old. Two years later, essays he wrote about the Vietnam War were published in the *Baltimore Sun*.

In 1971, Witten earned a bachelor's degree in history, with a minor in linguistics, at Brandeis University. During his undergraduate career, he published a few articles related to politics in the *New Republic* and the *Nation*. His work as an aide on George McGovern's presidential campaign in 1972 convinced him not to pursue his initial plans to enter politics or journalism.

Witten began a graduate program at Princeton in applied mathematics but later switched to the physics department. He received a master's degree in 1974 and a PhD two years later. He then went on to postdoctoral work at Harvard in 1976 and 1977, becoming a junior fellow of the Society of Fellows in 1977. Following that, he rejoined Princeton as a tenured faculty member in 1980; seven years later he was made Charles Simonyi Professor at the School of Natural Sciences of the Institute for Advanced Study, a position that did not include teaching responsibilities.

His wife, particle theorist Chiara Nappi, is also a member of the Institute for Advanced Study at Princeton. The couple has two daughters and a son.

LIFE'S WORK

In 1990, Witten became the first physicist to win the Fields Medal, awarded to mathematicians under the age of forty and is sometimes called the Nobel Prize in mathematics. At the ceremony in Kyoto, he was lauded for achievements in four aspects of mathematics, including index theory, knot theory, Morse theory, and rigidity theory. Although Witten himself did not always provide the mathematical proofs to his theories and insights, others were later able to supply the proofs. The Fields Medal was in part a recognition of Witten's ability to inspire new directions in mathematics. His work on Morse theory and supersymmetry, for example, has become key in differential geometry.

Witten has collaborated with several other scientists and mathematicians. The Seiberg–Witten equations, for example, involve a simplified approach to classifying four-dimensional manifolds using partial differential equations. Other joint efforts have produced Gromov–Witten invariants, the Dirac–Witten operator, Chern-Simons–Witten graphs, and Witten–Sander aggregates, each of them related to higher mathematics.

On a 1995 flight from Boston to Princeton, Witten developed superstring theory—sometimes called M-theory—which posits eleven dimensions rather than the more familiar four (height, length, depth, and time). He has continued to work on that theory and on related areas.

Witten worked on knot theory, a branch of mathematics that molecular biologists use to study polymers, including the structure of deoxyribonucleic acid (DNA). He developed an idea set forth by Michael Atiyah, a professor at Oxford University, that the Jones polynomial could be used not only to distinguish one knot from another but could also be applied to subatomic particles. As a result, mathematicians could begin studying knots in more than the usual three dimensions. Langlands's program, an idea that Canadian mathematician Robert

Langlands expounded in 1967, is another area in which Witten has worked. Like knot theory, it has implications for quantum field theory and superstring theory.

Witten's interests include attempts to locate the Higgs particle, named for Peter Higgs, who in 1964 theorized it to be one of nature's most basic building materials. This particle, then, would be similar to protons and electrons. Attempts to discover the Higgs particle—also known as the Higgs boson or the "God particle"—involve work done at supercollider sites such as the European Organization for Nuclear Research (CERN). Particles that have been accelerated are then made to collide, after which the actual results of the collisions are compared to the predicted results. The standard theory regarding the Higgs has resulted in discoveries such as the neutrino, particles W and Z, and the top quark, which scientists had sought for two decades. The Higgs particle also is interwoven with string theory. In 2012, scientists from the Tevatron particle collider at the Fermi National Accelerator Laboratory (Fermilab) outside Chicago announced the clearest evidence of the particle to date.

Edward Witten Develops Superstring Theory

String theory was popular in the 1960s and 1970s as an explanation that unified quantum mechanics and the theory of relativity. No one had been able to prove it, however, and many scientists moved on to other concerns. In 1995, during a flight home to Princeton, American physicist Edward Witten thought that several competing string theories could be united under one umbrella. Thus, superstring theory was born.

Instead of being composed of very small particles, according to superstring theory, the universe is made up of strings—perhaps as many as eleven different dimensions of time and space, only four of them currently known. These strings, made of some unknown material, vibrate, and it is their vibrations that create the mass, charge, spin, and other properties of all particles. Electrons, protons, or quarks may result from the vibration. One analogy is that these strings are like the strings of a violin, creating different sounds depending on how they are played. The strings move in various ways, such as curling or rolling. Because they are so small, humans have not yet seen them.

The four known forces of nature are gravity, electromagnetism, the strong force (binding neutrons and protons), and the weak force (causing radioactive decay). Gravity creates a problem for anyone seeking a unified theory; the other three forces can be explained, but calculations involving gravity have failed. Superstring theory accounts for all four forces. The superstring theory, called M-theory when it posits eleven dimensions, resolves the conflicts between Einstein's theories and quantum mechanics.

Superstring theory also resolves problems such as Hawking radiation and the entropy of black holes. The same techniques used in superstring theory have also been used to solve problems in entirely different branches of physics, such as quantum chromodynamics, which deals with quarks.

Witten has continued to work on ideas related to M-theory. He suggests various meanings for M: mystery, matrix, magic, or murky. The 1999 discovery that neutrinos, which are elementary particles without an electrical charge, have mass is one piece of evidence that seems to confirm superstring theory. However, because M-theory cannot be empirically tested or observed, some scientists doubt that it will ever be validated. Witten himself has indicated that doing so may require decades of further work, possibly done in the supercollider at CERN. Other, similar attempts at what some have called the theory of everything include twistor theory and loop quantum gravity (LQG).

In 2009, Witten was at the CERN particle physics laboratory near Geneva, Switzerland, on sabbatical. He arrived the day the Large Hadron Collider (LHC) was turned on; however, nine days later, the machine malfunctioned and had to be shut down for a year. Witten's hope had been that the LHC would find theorized heavier particles corresponding to known particles. Doing so would confirm the idea of supersymmetry, an enhancement of Einstein's theory of special relativity.

Witten has been a prolific writer, with more than three hundred articles published. He has also contributed to books such as *Current Algebra and Anomalies*, published in 1985, and *Superstring Theory*, published in 1987.

Witten's numerous awards include a MacArthur Foundation fellowship in 1982, the Dirac Medal from the International Centre for Theoretical Physics in 1985, and the Poincaré Prize from the International Association of Mathematical Physics in 2006. He also shared the Crafoord Prize in Mathematics in 2008 with Maxim Kontsevich for their contributions to mathematics based on theoretical physics. He received the Isaac Newton medal in 2010. He has received several honorary doctorates, including those from Columbia University in 1996 and from Johns Hopkins University and Harvard University in 2005.

IMPACT

In 1995, Witten suggested that various existing understandings of superstring theory were all variations on a theme. Superstring theory is one attempt to find what Einstein called a *unified field theory*. It tries to reconcile ideas of quantum mechanics and Newtonian gravity. Although nothing has been definitively proven, work on superstring theory has led to solving problems in the fields of pure geometry, quantum mechanics, quark confinement, and black holes. Because this has been the case, scientists such as Witten believe that string theory must be moving in the right direction.

Witten also has worked with Princeton astrophysicist Jeremiah P. Ostriker on the possible application of string theory to the universe at large. Ostriker had noted that galaxies are prone to group at the edge of voids, making the universe appear "lumpy." Witten has posited that cosmic strings, resulting from the cooling process after the big bang, are the answer to this clustering. Vibrating at low frequencies, they pushed the dust and gases that eventually coalesced into galaxies and planets.

Witten attempted to influence the US government to support the Large Hadron Collider at CERN, after Congress cut funding for a superconducting supercollider in 1993. In articles in national newspapers, he has stressed that "big science" projects would have to be international; competing funds for each nation to develop its own program would dilute efforts.

Witten has also sought to encourage peace in the Middle East. He has visited Israel frequently. In recognition of these efforts, he received the Shalom Award from the group Americans for Peace Now in 2002.

Judy A. Johnson

FURTHER READING

Chalmers, Matthew. "Journey to the Heart of the Universe." *New Scientist* (11 Apr. 2009): 24–25. Print. An article based on an interview with Witten during his sabbatical at CERN, summarizing the contributions to string theory.

Greene, Brian. *The Hidden Reality: Parallel Universes and the Deep Laws of the Cosmos.* New York: Knopf, 2011. Print. Includes discussion on string theory and Witten, along with notes, an index, some black-and-white illustrations, and charts.

Witten, Edward. "Unravelling String Theory." *Nature* 22 (Dec. 2005): 1085. Print. A brief article that explains what string theory is and why scientists have hopes for it being the unified field Einstein was seeking. Includes a few references and an illustration.

FRIEDRICH WÖHLER

German chemist

In synthesizing urea, Wöhler was the first scientist to demonstrate that organic materials—which had previously been believed to possess a vital force—need not be made exclusively within living organisms. He also isolated aluminum metal and discovered the elements beryllium and yttrium.

Born: July 31, 1800; Eschersheim, Germany
Died: September 23, 1882; Göttingen, Germany
Primary field: Chemistry
Specialty: Organic chemistry

EARLY LIFE

Friedrich Wöhler was the son of Anton August Wöhler and Anna Katharina Schröder. He received his early education from his father. As a child Wöhler pursued both mineralogy and chemistry as hobbies and, in addition to public school, received tutoring in Latin, French, and music.

Wöhler showed an early interest in science, as he built voltaic piles from zinc plates and some old Russian coins and experimented with the reactive elements phosphorus and chlorine. Between 1814 and 1820, Wöhler attended the gymnasium to prepare himself for the University of Marburg, where he began to study medicine and won a prize for his work on the transformation of waste substances into urine. It became obvious to him, at this early stage of his career, that his interests lay more in chemistry than in medicine, and thus he went to Heidelberg, where he studied under chemist Leopold Gmelin. At Heidelberg University, Wöhler earned his medical degree in 1823 and received permission to work in Stockholm, Sweden, with Jöns Jakob Berzelius, perhaps the greatest figure in chemistry of the day.

It was in Stockholm that Wöhler gained the scientific and technical skills that were crucial to his future career, as he was carefully trained in exact chemical analysis using such simple tools as a platinum crucible, a balance, and a blow pipe. This expertise, coupled with his interest in cyanic acid and the cyanates, ultimately led to investigations that transformed the fundamental nature of modern chemistry.

LIFE'S WORK

At the beginning of the nineteenth century, organic chemistry was generally associated with the extraction, isolation, and identification of animal and vegetable matter for medicinal purposes. Scientists believed that organic molecules could only be synthesized and form organized bodies in plants and animals. The presence of a vital force was attributed to this unique chemistry found only in living systems.

Organic chemistry was a science concerned primarily with understanding the nature of life and creation—not merely a study of isolated reactions of carbon-containing compounds. The concept of vitalism discouraged the use of the theory of chemical affinities that was associated with mineral or inorganic chemistry in explanations related to the organic branch of the discipline. Accordingly, Berzelius wrote in 1819 that his electrochemical theory could not be applied to organic matter, because—in his opinion—the influence of a vital force led to entirely different electrochemical properties. Wöhler's research would subsequently refute this idea and thus unify the animal and mineral branches of chemistry.

Upon returning from Berzelius's laboratory in 1825, Wöhler began his teaching career at an industrial school in Berlin. He soon began communicating with University of Giessen professor Justus von Liebig. For some time, Liebig had been working on explosive fulminates and, during the course of these investigations, he prepared a compound that was similar in composition to silver cyanate, a compound Wöhler had prepared in 1823. Despite the fact that silver cyanate and silver fulminate had the same empirical formula ($AgCNO$) they had different chemical and physical properties. In 1930 Berzelius called this new phenomenon isomerism.

Wöhler's studies on the cyanates directed him to reexamine reactions that he had initially undertaken while a student in Berzelius's laboratory, thus setting the stage for his artificial synthesis of urea, which stands as a milestone in the history of science. Wöhler prepared urea by first reacting lead cyanate with ammonia. White crystals appeared that, when treated with nitric acid, were transformed into flakes of a substance he quickly recognized as urea. In February of 1828, Wöhler told Berzelius that he had prepared urea without the kidney of a human or a dog.

Wöhler's synthesis marked the beginning of a new chemistry in which distinctions between inorganic and organic fields were blurred. Wöhler left Berlin in 1831 for Kassel, where he held a similar position. In 1832 his first wife, Franziska Wöhler, died and Wöhler went to Liebig's laboratory, where they collaborated on an important paper dealing with oil of bitter almonds (benzaldehyde). In their investigations they demonstrated that a group of atoms remained unchanged through a series of chemical operations, and to this fundamental unit they gave the name benzoyl. This discovery played a major role in debates of the 1830s dealing with radical theory.

Liebig and Wöhler continued to work together during the 1830s, even though Wöhler returned to Kassel, where he remarried. In 1836, Wöhler began working at the University of Göttingen and remained there for almost half a century until his death in 1882. Although Wöhler worked on various problems related to organic chemistry during his first few years at Göttingen, by 1840 he increasingly turned to the study of inorganic and mineralogical chemistry. Wöhler's background in inorganic and mineralogical chemistry was a solid one, the result of his studies with his former mentor

Friedrich Wöhler and the Urea Accident

Although there is a clear delineation between living and nonliving matter, it is understood that all matter—organic or inorganic—is composed of the same chemicals, the same molecules, and the same atoms. The difference between organic and inorganic is merely one of arrangement. While this is implicit in the twenty-first century, it was not until German chemist Friedrich Wöhler's work in the late 1800s that it was accepted in the field.

The concept of vitalism—the belief that stuff of living things possesses some "vital quality" that makes it distinct from inorganic materials—was customary in the nineteenth century. This meant that living things were seen as fundamentally distinct from nonliving things, and that their "life" came from a different, undefined force. Chemists, thus, saw a barrier indicating that living and nonliving materials could not be crossed in their work; according to principles of vitalism, rules and theories in one branch of chemistry would not apply to the other branch. If a chemist wanted an organic compound, urea from urine, for example, he would need a living kidney to produce it instead of creating it synthetically.

In 1828, Wöhler succeeded in creating an organic compound from inorganic reactants when he (accidentally) synthesized crystals of urea as part of an attempt to create ammonium cyanate. When he combined silver cyanate with ammonium chloride, he ended up with white crystals with none of the properties of cyanates. Wöhler tried another approach, combining lead cyanate and ammonium hydroxide, and got white crystals with organic properties. When Wöhler tested these crystals against those of urea, isolated using the best techniques available, he found them to be identical. The ammonium cyanate—an inorganic compound—had rearranged to form urea—a decidedly organic compound. Wöhler had thus artificially prepared an organic substance outside of a living system.

The revolutionary aspect of Wöhler's unexpected result (which became known as the Wöhler synthesis) may have been slightly inflated in the history of science. Yet the fact remains that the Wöhler synthesis is still indicated by many texts as the starting point for modern organic chemistry. Indeed, the Wöhler synthesis is still performed as an undergraduate laboratory exercise today.

Although Wöhler's work did not immediately break down vitalism's wall between organic and inorganic, it certainly paved the way for dispelling the notion of a vital force and accepting the true composition of compounds. Upon making his discovery, Wöhler wrote a letter to his colleague and mentor, renown vitalist and chemist Jöns Jakob Berzelius, about his work. Wöhler announced that he could make urea without a kidney; indeed, without any living thing at all.

Berzelius on silicon, selenium, and zirconium. Indeed, in 1827 Wöhler had been the first scientist to isolate metallic aluminum through a process that required reaction of a small quantity of potassium with an excess of aluminum chloride. By 1850, Wöhler was active in preparing a large number of metallic salts, and later in 1862 he was the first to synthesize calcium carbide from acetylene. Other important contributions included the preparation of silicon hydride, silicon chloroform, iodoform, and bromoform.

IMPACT

The importance of Wöhler's investigation lay not in his refutation of the concept of vitalism, but in the development of ideas related to structural chemistry. His demonstration of the isomeric relationship between urea and ammonium cyanate further exposed previously little-known chemical complexities that could be best understood in terms of molecular structure. For chemists such as Wöhler, Berzelius, and Liebig, the vital force apparently remained a scientific concept even after 1828.

The experimental synthesis of acetic acid by Hermann Kolbe in 1844 and the synthesis of methane and acetylene by Marcelin Berthelot in 1855 and 1856 contributed to the decline in popularity of the vitalistic theory. More significant, however, is that vitalism's importance in organic chemistry declined by the mid-nineteenth century, when the life sciences became increasingly specialized. Organic chemistry dealt with compounds of carbon atoms and physiology focused on organic functions, but neither subdiscipline examined the creation of life. Thus, for the organic chemist, vitalism was no longer a necessary concept.

John A. Heitmann

FURTHER READING

Buckingham, John. *Chasing the Molecule*. Stroud: Sutton, 2004. Print. Describes how scientists during the mid-nineteenth century made significant discoveries about molecules. Includes information about Wöhler's synthesis of an organic from an inorganic compound, and how this accomplishment challenged previous theories of vitalism.

Ihde, Aaron. *The Development of Modern Chemistry*. New York: Harper, 1964. Print. This general survey in the history of chemistry includes a thorough discussion of Wöhler's chief contributions to both organic and inorganic chemistry.

Keen, Robin. "Friedrich Wöhler and His Lifelong Interest in the Platinum Metals." *Platinum Metals Review* 29 (1985): 81–85. Provides an overview of Wöhler's life and professional career. Also focuses upon his work in the isolation of aluminum and the separation of iridium and osmium. Links the careers of two of Wöhler's students, Wilhelm Carl Heraeus and Heinrich Rössler, to the development of the platinum industry.

---. *The Life and Work of Friedrich Wöhler (1800–1882)*. Ed. Johannes Bütner. Nordhausen: Verlag Traugott Bautz, 2005. Print. A scientific biography of Wöhler, covering his life from early childhood and providing biographical information and details of his research efforts.

Lipman, Timothy O. "Wöhler's Preparation of Urea and the Fate of Vitalism." *Journal of Chemical Education* 41 (1964): 452–58. Print. An essay on vitalism and Wöhler that provides a model of careful research and critical thinking for scholars working in the field of the history of chemistry. Attempts to settle the issue of whether Wöhler's 1828 synthesis of urea overturned vitalistic notions in organic chemistry.

FLOSSIE WONG-STAAL

Chinese American biologist and virologist

Molecular biologist Flossie Wong-Staal conducted important research into retroviruses while working at the National Cancer Institute and was part of a team that discovered a link between HIV and AIDS. Considered a leading authority on HIV, she headed America's first university-affiliated department established to research AIDS and founded a cutting-edge pharmaceutical company.

Born: August 27, 1947; Guangzhou, China
Also known as: Yee Ching Wong; Flossie Wong
Primary field: Biology
Specialties: Virology; molecular biology

EARLY LIFE

Flossie Wong-Staal was born Yee Ching Wong on August 27, 1947, in Guangzhou, China. The daughter of businessman Sueh-fung Wang and his homemaker wife, her family relocated from Communist China to the free city of Hong Kong (then under British control) when she was five years old. In Hong Kong, young Wong was enrolled in an all-girls Catholic school. As a student, she gravitated towards literature, with a particular interest in poetry. However, her teachers encouraged her to pursue scientific subjects. Although she was at first reluctant, Wong grew to enjoy mathematics and biology in particular.

When it came time for Wong to pursue higher education, her teachers suggested to her parents that they choose a more Western-sounding name. Her father selected Flossie, after the name of a typhoon that had struck Asia in August 1958.

After graduating high school in 1965, Wong left Hong Kong for the United States to enroll at the University of California, Los Angeles (UCLA). Majoring in biology, she graduated magna cum laude three years later. In 1971, while undertaking a graduate degree at UCLA, she married Stephen Staal and affixed his surname to her own; the couple had two daughters before later divorcing. Wong-Staal earned her PhD in molecular biology in 1972.

LIFE'S WORK

After leaving UCLA, Wong-Staal continued her postgraduate studies at the University of California, San Diego (UCSD). In 1973, she accepted a position in Bethesda, Maryland, at the National Cancer Institute, part of the National Institutes of Health (NIH) and an agency of the US Department of Health and Human Services. Working under biomedical researcher Robert Gallo as a section chief of the laboratory of tumor cell biology and later as head of the molecular biology group, she led research into retroviruses. Retroviruses are viruses that contain ribonucleic acid (RNA) as genetic material and produce deoxyribonucleic acid (DNA) for incorporation into the genetic structure, or genome, of an organism. The purpose of the research was to determine the relationship between retroviruses and human diseases.

Wong-Staal Discovers HTLV and HIV

Flossie Wong-Staal was among the first wave of molecular biologists at the National Cancer Institute. In graduate school, she concentrated on retroviruses—particularly RNA tumor viruses that cause certain forms of cancer in animals, such as feline leukemia—and became fascinated by the way some viruses cloned a cancer-causing gene that infected cells. Wong-Staal became interested in proving or disproving the scientific notion that retroviruses were unrelated to human diseases and only caused cancer in chickens, cats, mice, and cattle.

In the late 1970s, under the direction of Robert Gallo, Wong-Staal and her group discovered the first human retrovirus, HTLV, which causes a type of leukemia that attacks white T-cells (also known as lymphocytes) in the bloodstream. T-cells, which originate in bone marrow, are vital blood components because they secrete proteins that regulate or assist in human immune responses, such as destroying infections. Further studies revealed that HTLV was different from other retroviruses: It was self-activating and did not need to depend on cellular proteins to begin its destructive work.

When what became known as AIDS began to make a deadly impact on human health in the early 1980s, Wong-Staal and her group immediately began investigating the disease. While it was quickly learned that AIDS attacks the immune system, the causative agent remained unknown. Wong-Staal and her colleagues speculated that a retrovirus might be responsible. Scientists noticed that AIDS and the newly discovered leukemia-causing HTLV have several similarities. Both attack T-cells—though HTLV causes T-cells to multiply, while AIDS causes the number of T-cells to diminish.

Both diseases can be transmitted by bodily fluids, such as blood, and from a mother to an unborn child.

Those like Wong-Staal and her group, who thought the likely cause of AIDS was a virus, formed an international coalition to exchange tissue and blood samples and research. Within three years, Wong-Staal and her group at the National Cancer Institute in the United States and Luc Montagnier and his group at the Institut Pasteur in France had isolated the human immunodeficiency virus (HIV).

Since the discovery of HIV, Wong-Staal, through her academic and corporate research, has joined numerous other entities in the long, drawn-out—and potentially lucrative—process to create an appropriate vaccine to conquer AIDS.

The progress of vaccine development has been complicated by the nature of the disease. As a retrovirus, HIV has the sinister ability to incorporate its genetic data into human DNA. When patients receive drug treatment, blood tests seem to indicate the virus has vanished, but when drug treatment is discontinued, the virus can reappear. Since HIV affects the immune system, any tampering is highly risky: Drugs that stimulate the immune system could also stimulate the virus, while a medical treatment that depresses the immune system could leave the body vulnerable to the ravages of AIDS.

Medical researchers now think that there may be no way to create a method of completely preventing HIV. Most efforts focus on developing a vaccine that reduces the strength of the virus so it becomes too weak to cause disease or to be transmitted from one person to another. Wong-Staal, still in the forefront of research, continues her work in the fight against HIV/AIDS.

During the 1970s, Wong-Staal and her team discovered the first human retrovirus, human T-cell leukemia virus (HTLV). The research proved significant in the early 1980s, when a strange new epidemic with a high rate of fatality broke out. In 1983, Wong-Staal and colleagues independently discovered human immunodeficiency virus (HIV)—the cause of acquired immunodeficiency syndrome (AIDS); at the same time virologist Luc Montagnier was making the same discovery at the Institut Pasteur in France.

In 1985, Wong-Staal became the first scientist to clone HIV, an important step in drawing a genetic map of the virus, which in turn led to the creation of tests to

determine the presence of HIV in blood and the development of drugs to combat the disease. Late in the decade, Wong-Staal unraveled the structure of HIV enough to learn that regulatory genes such as tat (transactivating transcriptional regulation) and rev (regulator of virion) released protein into the blood to adversely affect uninfected cells and that they were largely responsible for the initiation of Kaposi's sarcoma, a type of cancer usually associated with AIDS.

After more than sixteen years at the National Cancer Institute, in 1990, Wong-Staal accepted the Florence Seeley Riford Chair for Acquired Immune Deficiency Syndrome Research at UCSD and remained in the post until her retirement in 2002, when she became professor emerita. In 1994, she was named head of the NIH-funded AIDS Research Center at the university.

In 1992, Wong-Staal cofounded Immunsol and served as its chief scientific officer and executive vice president of genomics. She was named director of genomics in 2002. Based in San Diego, the privately held Immusol (renamed itherX in 2008) was established to develop drugs to treat cancer, hepatitis C, viral infections, and metabolic and ophthalmologic diseases. In 1995, after serving as a consultant, she also became a director with United Biomedical Inc., headquartered in Hauppauge, New York. United Biomedical Inc. is a multinational biopharmaceutical company that develops peptide and antibody-based vaccines and immunotherapies to prevent or treat a variety of chronic diseases.

Wong-Staal, in addition to her multiple duties at itherX, has served in numerous medically oriented organizations. A member of the National Task Force on AIDS Drug Development, she has served as a member of the Board on Health Sciences Policy of the Institute of Medicine, the Science Board to the Food and Drug Administration, and the Board of Scientific Counselors for the National Institute of Allergy and Infectious Diseases.

IMPACT

In conjunction with Gallo, Wong-Staal earned considerable recognition at the National Cancer Institute for the independent discovery of the AIDS-causing virus, HIV. While Montagnier and a colleague in France were later awarded the Nobel Prize in Medicine/Physiology for their simultaneous discovery, Gallo and Wong-Staal were passed over. Many in the scientific community believed Wong-Staal and Gallo should have shared in the Nobel honor.

Wong-Staal meanwhile furthered her academic and professional careers. For her contributions in advancing knowledge of the structure and behavior of HIV, the Institute for Scientific Information recognized Wong-Staal

as the most important female scientist for the decade of the 1980s. She was also named as one of the top-ranking scientists under the age of forty-five and was selected for membership into the American Society of Clinical Investigation.

Known for her dynamic personality, Wong-Staal was keynote speaker at the National Institute of Health's May 2011 celebration of Asian American Pacific Islander Heritage Month. For her significant work in both public and private sectors, she was included in *Discover* magazine's 50 Most Important Women in Science list in 2002. The British *Daily Telegraph* newspaper profiled Wong-Staal as one of the Top 100 Living Geniuses in 2007.

Jack Ewing

FURTHER READING

Friedman, Theodore, and John Rossi, eds. *Gene Transfer: Delivery and Expression of DNA and RNA, a Laboratory Manual*. Cold Spring Harbor: Cold Spring Harbor Lab P, 2006. Print. Illustrated textbook that provides detailed technical information on various protocols for clinical and laboratory research into the types of genetic studies Wong-Staal conducted in the process of introducing nucleic acids into the cells of organisms and testing the results.

Levine, Aaron D. *Cloning: A Beginner's Guide*. London: Oneworld, 2007. Print. Discusses the scientific and ethical issues related to cloning, the process by which Wong-Staal became the first to reproduce HIV, a vital step in demonstrating that HIV causes AIDS.

Wong-Staal, Flossie, and Robert Gallo, eds. *AIDS Vaccine Research*. New York: Dekker, 2002. Print. Discusses the nature of HIV as well as the major challenges researchers face in their attempts to develop a useful vaccine for the prevention of HIV/AIDS. Contains a preface written by Wong-Staal and Gallo, who were key American players in the simultaneous discovery of HIV.

CHIEN-SHIUNG WU

Chinese American physicist

Nuclear physicist Chien-Shiung Wu disproved the principle of conservation of parity and proved the law of vector current in beta decay. Wu was the first woman elected president of the American Physical Society and honored with Israel's Wolf Prize.

Born: May 31, 1912; Liu Ho, China
Died: February 16, 1997; New York, New York
Primary field: Physics
Specialties: Nuclear physics; atomic and molecular physics; quantum mechanics

EARLY LIFE

Chien-Shiung Wu was born in Liu Ho, China, near Shanghai, on May 31, 1912. At this time, Chinese girls were educated at home, if at all, but Wu's father, Wu Zhong-Yi, was progressive. With Wu's mother, he operated a local school for girls, the first school of its kind in China. Wu attended this institution until she was nine years old. When Wu had completed her studies at the girls' primary school, her father encouraged her to go to Suzhou to attend a private high school. Studying under leading scholar Hu Shi, Wu learned English and became politically active. She graduated as valedictorian of her class.

Wu decided she wanted to become a physicist, and with the encouragement of Hu Shi, she entered the National Central University in Nanjing in 1930. By this time, it was not unusual for women to study science. Although Wu was studying during the early years of the Sino-Japanese War, and Japan had invaded China, she managed to complete her degree in physics in four years.

In 1936, Wu traveled to the United States, where she pursued her graduate work in physics at the University of California at Berkeley. One of her most influential professors was Ernest O. Lawrence, winner of the Nobel Prize in Physics in 1939 for inventing the particle accelerator known as the cyclotron. Wu was inducted into the Phi Beta Kappa academic honor society in recognition of her outstanding work as a graduate student.

Wu received her PhD in 1940, and accepted a job as a research assistant at Berkeley. During the early years of World War II, she taught at Smith College in Northampton, Massachusetts, and then Princeton University in New Jersey, where she was the first woman to teach in the Physics Department. In 1942, she married Luke Chia-Liu Yuan, also a physicist.

LIFE'S WORK

In the early 1940s, Wu began conducting experiments to test Enrico Fermi's 1934 theory of beta decay, the radioactive transformation of an atom from one atomic number to another, caused by the emission of beta particles from the nucleus. In March 1944, Wu joined Columbia University in New York City, where she would remain until her retirement. Her first position was on the scientific staff of the Division of War Research. This group was working on the Manhattan Project to develop the atomic bomb. Specifically, Wu worked on radiation detection. In this capacity, she developed a gaseous diffusion process for separating radioactive uranium-235

from common uranium-238. She also helped to develop a more sensitive Geiger counter. After the war, Wu stayed on at Columbia as a research associate and teacher. Her son, Vincent, was born in 1948. In 1952, she was made associate professor of physics.

In the 1950s, theoretical physicists Chen Ning Yang and Tsung-Dao Lee were looking for an experimental physicist to conduct research that would disprove the principle of conservation of parity. Lee was a colleague of Wu's on the Columbia faculty, so he knew of her expertise in beta decay, and asked for her help.

It had long been known that physical properties of particles—such as mass, energy, momentum, and electrical charge—remain unchanged after a nuclear reaction. *Parity* refers to the property of symmetry of the physical laws. Parity, like other physical properties, had been believed since 1924 to be conserved in nuclear reactions. In other words, particles emitted during a nuclear reaction should be emitted in all directions equally. However, in 1956, Yang and Lee found theoretical evidence that parity is not always conserved in nuclear reactions, specifically in certain weak interactions, such as those occurring in beta decay. But they needed experimental results to prove their hypothesis.

Wu's team consisted of a group of top scientists from the National Bureau of Standards. In 1957, the team tested Yang and Lee's hypothesis with the radioactive material cobalt-60. First, they cooled the cobalt to 0.01 degree above absolute zero, approximately −459 degrees Fahrenheit. This was to minimize any random thermal movements of the nuclei, so that the scientists could record the disintegration of the radioactive atoms without the interference of other effects. When the electrons emitted during the cobalt's decay moved in the direction opposite that of the magnetic field that Wu had set up, they contravened the law of parity.

Worldwide recognition followed for Wu, Lee, and Yang. Scientists at Columbia and the University of Chicago conducted similar experiments utilizing other weak reactions, and their results confirmed Wu's research. This disproved forever the law of conservation of parity. When Yang and Lee received the Nobel Prize in Physics in 1957 for disproving the conservation of parity, many scientists were disappointed that Wu was not included in the award.

Wu did, however, receive numerous other awards and honors. For instance, in 1957, Wu was named a full professor at Columbia University. She was made a member of the National Academy of Sciences in 1958; at that time, she was only the seventh woman so honored and was also the first Chinese American to be made a member. Also in 1958, Wu became the first woman to receive the Research Corporation Award, given annually to outstanding scientists. In her acceptance speech, Wu remarked on the uniqueness of winning the award for destroying a law rather than for establishing one. Also that year, Wu received an honorary doctorate of science degree from Princeton University. She was the first woman to receive this honor from Princeton.

While continuing to research and teach, Wu and her husband edited the book *Nuclear Physics* (1961). In 1963, Wu's experiments provided evidence to confirm the theoretical law of vector current in beta decay. This theory had been proposed in 1958 by physicists Murray Gell-Mann and Richard P. Feynman. Wu's research culminated in her publication of *Beta Decay* in 1965. The text became a standard reference for physicists. That same year, she was awarded the Chi-Tsin Achievement Award from Taiwan's Chi-Tsin Culture Foundation.

Wu also performed experiments to confirm the theory that electromagnetic radiation is emitted when an electron and a positron collide. Her success in measuring low-energy electrons emitted by beta decay supported Fermi's theory of weak interactions. Later, Wu conducted research in ultra-low-temperature physics, muonic and pionic X-rays, and spectroscopic examinations of hemoglobin. She coedited, with Vernon W. Hughes, a three-volume text called *Muon Physics* (1975–1977).

The honors that Wu received for her research included a number of firsts. In 1975, the American Physical Society honored Wu with the National Medal of Science, the Tom Bonner Prize, and election to the presidency of the society. Wu was the first woman appointed to this role and the first woman honored with Israel's Wolf Prize in 1978. She was also the first scientist to receive the Wolf Prize in the category of physics. An asteroid was named for Wu in 1990; she was the first living scientist to receive that honor.

Wu retired from her position at Columbia University in 1981, after thirty-seven years, and was named professor emeritus. She died of a stroke on February 16, 1997, in New York City.

Wu Proves the Law of Conservation of Vector Current in Beta Decay

The theory of conservation of vector current in beta decay was first proposed by Murray Gell-Mann and Richard P. Feynman in 1958. The theory originated from Enrico Fermi's experiments in beta decay in the 1930s, in which he initiated a theory of weak interactions. He described the weak interaction of beta decay as an electron and a neutrino interacting with a current operator that converts a neutron into a proton or a proton into a neutron. Analogous to electromagnetism, Fermi described this current as a vector current, like an electric current. Though Fermi's theory accounted for the spectrum shape of the beta decay in the fastest beta decays, it did not fit particularly well with all known beta decays. When this became clear to scientists, it was decided that something other than vector currents could be at work. For a long time, physicists favored the theory that scalar and tensor currents are responsible for the interaction; but this did not support Fermi's analogy to electromagnetism, which has a vector current.

Despite intermittent experiments, the scalar and tensor theory, though flawed, was widely accepted and mostly overlooked as an area of study. Chien-Shiung Wu's discovery disproving the law of conservation of parity, however, renewed interest in the subject of beta decay. In 1958, George Sudarshan and Robert Marshak proposed, in the name of universality, that the currents are indeed vector and axial vector. Experiments proved this theory correct. The importance of this discovery was the restored analogy to electromagnetism. Feynman and Gell-Mann further suggested that the vector current in beta decay is conserved in the manner of an electromagnetic current; this means that the rate of change of its time component, plus the divergence of its space, equals zero. It was a good theory, but once again, as with the law of parity, Wu decided to see if she could prove law quantitatively.

To test the conservation of vector current, Wu and her collaborators performed an experiment that had been done earlier but with inconclusive results. Wu and her team compared symmetric and asymmetric states of protons and neutrons; *isospin* is the term for their relating symmetry. An isospin singlet is in an asymmetric state and an isospin triplet is in a symmetric state. The experiment was completed in 1963 and successfully demonstrated the conservation of weak vector current. Not only had Wu proved a new law of nature, but her discovery also marked the crucial first step toward the unification of weak and electromagnetic interaction.

IMPACT

Though Wu never won a Nobel Prize, she was considered one of the foremost female physicists during her lifetime. She is remembered primarily for her research in nuclear forces and structure, which helped disprove the principle of conservation of parity. Until 1957, the conservation of parity, related to symmetry, was considered a basic law of nuclear physics. Wu showed that although parity might be conserved in strong, electromagnetic interactions, the same does not necessarily hold true in weak interactions of subatomic particles. The discovery of this lack of symmetry in parity was hugely influential to the scientific community, since the idea of symmetry has been tied to the laws of physics for centuries.

Wu's findings in nuclear physics led to further research by other influential physicists, including Feynman, Gell-Mann, Robert Marshak, and George Sudarshan. While Wu's work disproved the law of conservation of parity, it did not explain why this was so. Feynman and Gell-Mann were later able to explain it with the V-A theory of weak interactions.

Ellen Bailey

FURTHER READING

Bertulani, Carlos A. *Nuclear Physics in a Nutshell*. Princeton: Princeton UP, 2007. Print. Discusses the atomic nucleus and explains the theories of the physicists who have studied it. Includes Wu's disproving of the principle of conservation of parity.

Cooperman, Stephanie H. *Chien-Shiung Wu: Pioneering Physicist and Atomic Researcher*. New York: Rosen, 2004. Print. Describes Wu's life, career, and legacy.

Garwin, Richard L., and Tsung-Dao Lee. "Chien-Shiung Wu." *Physics Today* 50.10 (1997): 120–21. Print. An obituary for Chien-Shiung Wu, with biographical data and information regarding her scientific career.

Rosalyn Yalow

American physicist

Yalow helped develop the radioimmunoassay technique for the measurement of minute quantities of biological materials in blood. This technique was established after her research determined that people who had received injections of the polypeptide hormone insulin for conditions such as diabetes developed antibodies against the hormone. For her work, Yalow was awarded a Nobel Prize in Physiology or Medicine in 1977.

Born: July 19, 1921; Bronx, New York
Died: May 30, 2011; Bronx, New York
Primary field: Physics
Specialty: Nuclear physics

EARLY LIFE

Rosalyn Yalow (YAH-loh) was born Rosalyn Sussman in the New York City borough of the South Bronx. She was the second child, and first daughter, of Simon Sussman and Clara Zipper Sussman. Neither of her parents had any significant level of formal education. Simon, a Russian American Jew born on the Lower East Side, never finished grade school. He earned a living with a paper and twine business. Yalow's mother, Clara, had emigrated from Germany at the age of four.

Rosalyn was described by one of her biographers as a "precocious, stubborn, and determined child." Along with her brother, she made frequent trips to the local library, and she learned to read before entering kindergarten. Her formal schooling set the stage for her later work. Attending local public schools, she developed a strong interest in mathematics by the seventh grade, and in chemistry while attending Walton High School.

While enrolled at Hunter College, Yalow read the recently published biography of Marie Curie written by Eve Curie, the daughter of the great scientist. Yalow later recommended the book to women interested in careers in science. A colloquium on nuclear fission sponsored by Enrico Fermi and strong support from her professors convinced Yalow that she should consider a career in physics. In 1941, she became the first graduate with a degree in physics from Hunter College.

Despite the reluctance of graduate schools to accept and support women in physics, Yalow was offered a teaching assistantship at the University of Illinois at Urbana-Champaign. She was the only woman among four hundred students and the first woman within that college since 1917. On the first day of school, she met a physics student named Aaron Yalow, whom she would marry in June, 1943. She received her PhD degree in physics in 1945.

LIFE'S WORK

Yalow's graduate career in nuclear physics was strongly influenced by her adviser, Maurice Goldhaber, and his wife, Gertrude, who was also a physicist. Under their direction, Yalow became competent in the safe handling of radioisotopes and in the use of apparatuses for their measurement. Yalow's first job following her graduation was as an assistant engineer at the Federal Telecommunications Laboratory (FTL) in New York. She was the only female engineer at FTL at the time. Since Aaron Yalow had not yet completed the work for his thesis, Roslyn returned to New York alone. Aaron joined her in late 1945 on the staff at Montefiore Medical Center as a medical physicist.

In 1946, with the closing of FTL, Yalow returned to Hunter College as a physics instructor for veterans returning from the war. During this period, Yalow also began developing an interest in medical research. Through her husband's contacts, Yalow met Edith Quimby, a medical researcher at New York's Columbia University College of Physicians and Surgeons. Since Quimby was interested in the application of physics to medical research, Yalow volunteered to work in Quimby's laboratory, gaining experience in the use of radioisotopes for such research.

During the early postwar period, Yalow's expanding knowledge and experience in the field of physics was a rare commodity. In December 1946, she was hired as a part-time consultant in the newly opened Radioisotope Section of the Bronx Veterans Administration (VA) Hospital, a place that Yalow considered to be the first organization to "recognize the importance of radioisotopes in medicine." The facilities at the hospital were crude, to say the least. One portion of the facilities was located in a converted janitor's closet. Of necessity, Yalow was forced to design and build much of the equipment for the laboratory. Yalow's research at the VA Hospital focused on the application of nuclear materials to medical diagnosis and therapy. She was highly successful in this endeavor, producing numerous publications and receiving official support and recognition from the Veterans Administration.

By 1950, Yalow had resigned her position at Hunter College to become a full-time member of the VA staff. That same year, a thirty-two-year-old resident at the VA Hospital, Solomon Berson, was appointed to Yalow's group, becoming chief of the service four years later. Berson and Yalow began an extensive collaboration, each supporting the other: Yalow provided the experience in mathematics and nuclear medicine, and Berson provided the necessary clinical expertise. Their collaboration continued for more than two decades, ending only with Berson's sudden death in 1972.

Yalow and Berson began their collaboration by attempting to improve the application of radioisotopes in the clinical diagnosis of disease. Specifically, they developed a method for measuring the rate at which a radioactive

Rosalyn Yalow Develops Radioimmunoassay

The development of a radioimmunoassay (RIA) procedure by Rosalyn Yalow and Solomon Berson at the Bronx Veterans Administration Hospital began largely by accident. It was believed that adult-onset diabetes, now called Type II diabetes, might result from the degradation of serum insulin by the enzyme insulinase. To test the hypothesis, Yalow and Berson injected radioactive insulin into both diabetic and nondiabetic subjects. They observed that the radioactive insulin actually decreased more slowly in the diabetic subjects. They suspected that this was the result of antibodies in the blood that were binding to the injected insulin. The idea was not surprising given the source of insulin at the time was from the pancreases of cattle or sheep. However the existing methods for measurement of the antibody were not sensitive enough to test their hypothesis. Nor were other scientists receptive to the idea that small molecules like insulin could produce an antibody response. To continue their research, Yalow and Berson would have to develop their own technique for measuring antibodies.

Yalow and Berson's RIA technique for measuring insulin was based on their assumption that in a mixture of serum insulin, radioactive insulin, and antibodies, both types of insulin would compete to bind with the antibodies. RIA consisted of adding a known quantity of radioactive insulin to a solution consisting of anti-insulin antibody mixed with a serum sample containing an unknown quantity of insulin. The level of competition would reveal the previously unknown concentration of serum insulin.

Yalow and Berson's RIA had several advantages. First it could be carried out entirely in a test tube; the radioactive substance would not have to be injected into the patient. Second, the assay was extremely sensitive, capable of measuring minute amounts of whatever protein was being monitored. Yalow and Berson first published their work in 1956. Within a decade most clinical laboratories had the expertise to carry out the procedure.

After developing RIA to measure insulin, Yalow and Berson used their technique to measure hormones such as human growth hormone, as well as other substances in human blood serum, including vitamins and viral proteins. Applications of RIA in clinical medicine allowed in theory the measurement of any serum protein.

For the work she did with Berson to develop the RIA, Yalow was awarded the Nobel Prize in Physiology or Medicine in 1977. Unfortunately, Berson died suddenly from a heart attack in 1972. Yalow said that had he lived, her longtime colleague surely would have shared the prize with her.

isotope of iodine (Iodine-131) is metabolized. When their first publication on the subject appeared in 1952, it was hailed as an important contribution to the use of diagnostic tracers in medicine. Shortly thereafter, Yalow and Berson began applying their techniques to the analysis of proteins in blood serum, focusing on the metabolism of insulin. Through their research, they developed the technique of radioimmunoassay (RIA) for the measurement of insulin. In the early 1960s, Yalow and Berson extended their research to the study of other hormones within the body. The RIA procedures they had developed proved to be applicable to a wide variety of studies. Meanwhile, Berson became more involved with administrative work, leaving the research area to Yalow. In 1967, the Veterans Administration Hospital became associated with Mt. Sinai School of Medicine. Berson became chair of the Department of Medicine, and Yalow eventually became chief of Nuclear Medicine Service, formerly the Radioisotope Section. Yalow was also appointed research professor at Mt. Sinai, and in 1974, she became a distinguished research professor at the medical school.

In 1972, Berson's unexpected death ended years of joint study. That same year, Yalow became the first woman appointed senior medical investigator at the VA Hospital. At Yalow's request, her laboratory was renamed the Solomon Berson Research Laboratory.

Numerous awards followed. Yalow was elected to the National Academy of Sciences in 1975 and the American Academy of Arts and Sciences in 1978. In 1976, she became the first woman to receive the Albert Lasker Award for basic medical research. Yalow also received many other honorary doctorates and awards. In 1977, she was awarded the Nobel Prize in Physiology or Medicine for the development of radioimmunoassays. Subsequently, Yalow served on a wide range of advisory committees and prestigious boards and as a consultant for numerous national and international organizations.

IMPACT

Yalow was among the first scientists to wed the emerging field of nuclear physics to diagnostic medicine, and her success is an example of how far women have progressed in science. Yalow's parents, though strong supporters of her education, initially pressured her to go into the "standard" female profession of education. It was to Yalow's credit that she overcame this and more overt discrimination to settle and succeed in what was an overwhelmingly male scientific field at the time.

The methodology that Yalow and Berson developed had benefits and applications far beyond the initial area of diabetic research. The RIA technique has subsequently been applied to measurements of most serum proteins, vitamins, drugs, and hundreds of other substances. There had been no technique that could measure minute changes in concentrations of these substances during various biological states.

Richard Adler

FURTHER READING

Blumenthal, Stanley. "The Insulin Immunoassay after 50 Years." *Perspectives in Biology and Medicine* 52.3 (2009): 343–54. Print. Reviews the ideas that were current in the medical research community when Berson and Yalow began the work that led to the development of radioimmunoassay.

Magill, Frank N., ed. "Rosalyn S. Yalow." *The Nobel Prize Winners: Physiology or Medicine*. Vol. 3. Pasadena: Salem, 1991. Print. Provides a synopsis of Yalow's work and information on her personal life and career. Includes a list of Yalow's important publications.

Straus, Eugene. *Rosalyn Yalow, Nobel Laureate: Her Life and Work in Medicine*. Cambridge, MA: Perseus, 1999. Print. A comprehensive biography detailing Yalow's life and work, including her work with Sol Berson on blood volume, the thyroid, insulin, and the development of radioimmunoassay.

Tang, Joyce. *Scientific Pioneers: Women Succeeding in Science*. Lanham, MD: UP of America, 2006. Print. Analyzes the political, cultural, personal, and economic influences of ten outstanding women scientists, including Yalow.

CHEN NING YANG

Chinese American physicist

Chinese-born American physicist Chen Ning Yang was awarded the Nobel Prize in Physics in 1957 together with Tsung Dao Lee for their research into universal parity conservation. Yang is also known for his work on the Yang–Mills theory and Yang–Baxter equation.

Born: October 1, 1922; Hefei, China
Primary field: Physics
Specialties: Statistical mechanics; theoretical physics

EARLY LIFE

Chen Ning Yang, sometimes known as Franklin, was born in Hefei, China, on October 1, 1922. His birthday was wrongly given as September 22, 1922, on his 1945 passport. To avoid bureaucratic complications, Yang has used this incorrect date since. Yang's father, Ko Chuen Yang, taught mathematics, and his mother, Meng Hwa Loh, was a homemaker.

In 1923, Yang's father won a scholarship to study in the United States. Until his father's return to China in 1928, Yang was educated at home. In 1929, Yang's father became a professor of mathematics at Beijing's Tsinghua University. The family moved to Beijing, where Yang attended elementary school and later became a boarding student at Chong De Middle School. When Japan invaded China in July 1937, the Yangs returned to Hefei and then evacuated to the southwestern town of Kunming. There, three evacuated universities were combined into one institution known as National Southwest Associated University. In the summer of 1938, Yang passed the entrance examinations and enrolled in the university, where his father taught.

Yang earned his bachelor's degree in 1942, and in 1944, he graduated with a master's degree from Tsinghua University. That year, Yang won a scholarship to study in the United States, but he delayed his travel until the end of World War II. In early 1946, Yang enrolled in the University of Chicago to pursue graduate studies with physicist Enrico Fermi.

As a noncitizen, Yang lacked clearance to work with Fermi at the University of Chicago's Argonne National Laboratory. Instead, he joined a group of graduate students who tried unsuccessfully to build a Cockcroft-Walton accelerator. Encouraged by physicist Edward Teller, Yang turned to theoretical physics. He also developed a friendship and professional relationship with fellow student Tsung Dao Lee during this period. In 1948, Yang earned his PhD in physics with the thesis "On the Angular Distribution in Nuclear Reactions and Coincidence Measurements," for which Teller was his adviser.

LIFE'S WORK

Yang taught at the University of Chicago for a year before accepting a postdoctoral appointment at the Institute for Advanced Study in Princeton, New Jersey, in 1949. Along with Lee and physicist Marshall Nicholas Rosenbluth, Yang developed a theory about the strength of various weak nuclear force interactions. Yang designed with Fermi what became known as the Fermi–Yang model, affirming the question of their paper "Are Mesons Elementary Particles?" On August 26, 1950, Yang married Chih-Li Tu, who had come to the United States to study. They later had three children.

In the early 1950s, Yang carried out work in particle physics and statistical mechanics in collaboration with Lee, who worked at the institute in Princeton from 1951 to 1953 and thereafter at Columbia University. In 1952, Yang published his solution for computing spontaneous magnetization for the two-dimensional Ising model, a mathematical model of magnetism. Building on the Ising model, Yang and Lee published two papers setting up a theory to describe the mechanism of liquid-gas phase transitions.

In 1953, Yang visited Brookhaven National Laboratory. There, with physicist Robert Mills, Yang developed what would become known as the Yang-Mills theory. They published their theory in *Physical Review* in 1954. Yang's accomplishments led to his appointment as full professor at the Institute for Advanced Study in 1955. The discovery of the antiproton by physicists at the University of California, Berkeley in 1955 sent Yang and Lee on a quest to develop a new quantum number. They described their new quantum number in the paper "Charge Conjugation, a New Quantum Number G, and Selection Rules Concerning a Nucleon-Antinucleon System," published in the journal *Il Nuovo Cimento* in 1956.

In the spring of 1956, Yang and Lee developed the idea that one of the fundamental principles in physics, parity conservation, may not apply at the level of weak nuclear force interactions. To prove their theory, they proposed a series of experiments and published their proposal, "Question of Parity Conservation in Weak Interactions," in *Physical Review*. When physicist Chien-Shiung Wu performed one of the proposed experiments, she determined that parity is not always conserved in weak nuclear force interactions, confirming Yang and Lee's theory. In recognition of their work, Yang and Lee were awarded the Nobel Prize in Physics in 1957.

Yang and Lee used their discovery to propose a two-component theory for the neutrino in 1957, and they published "Theoretical Discussions on Possible High-Energy Neutrino Experiments" in *Physical Review Letters* in 1960. Yang and Lee also studied the intermediate boson, also known as the W particle. In 1961 and 1962, Yang's theoretical work extended to superconductivity. In an influential paper written with physicist Nina Byers, Yang

937

Yang and Tsung Dao Lee Challenge the Principle of Universal Parity Conservation

Prior to the 1950s, physicists thought that natural laws should apply regardless of the direction of a reaction— a principle known as parity conservation. A reaction of a right-handed particle, for example, should yield the same result as the same reaction of a left-handed particle. By the late 1920s, the law of parity was thought to apply to the four fundamental physical forces: gravitation, electromagnetism, weak interaction (weak nuclear force), and strong interaction (strong nuclear force). However, early in the 1950s, Australian physicist Richard Dalitz and Italian physicist Elio Fabri independently showed what became known as the theta-tau puzzle. For the beta decay of the K mesons, discovered in 1947, Dalitz and Fabri showed that a so-called theta meson decayed into two pions with even parity, and a so-called tau meson decayed into three pions with odd parity. Because of these two different parities, physicists expected the theta meson to be different from the tau meson. However, experimental data showed that both theta and tau meson had the same mass and lifetime, indicating they were actually the same meson.

In the spring of 1956, Chen Ning Yang and Tsung Dao Lee developed the idea that parity conservation is not universal and is sometimes violated in the case of the weak nuclear force interaction of the beta decay of

the K meson. Thus, the theta meson and the tau meson are actually the same, but the decay process leads to two different possible outcomes. The two theoretical physicists devised a number of possible experiments that could prove, or disprove, parity conservation in this case. In June 1956, they published their ideas in *Physical Review*.

Many physicists, most notably Austrian physicist Wolfgang Pauli, rejected this idea of parity violation. However, Lee persuaded physicist Chien-Shiung Wu, a colleague at Columbia University and an expert in beta decay, to perform one of the proposed experiments. In early 1957, Wu took a sample of radioactive cobalt 60 material to the facilities of the National Bureau of Standards. There, together with a team of several other physicists, Wu cooled the cobalt 60 to cryogenic temperatures. As predicted by Yang and Lee, the beta decay of cobalt 60 was asymmetrical. This proved a massive violation of the principle of parity conservation in the case of the weak nuclear force.

The impact of this experimental proof of Yang and Lee's theory was monumental in the physicist community. A principle held to be universal had been disproven for a particular case. For their work, Yang and Lee were awarded the Nobel Prize in Physics for 1957.

---

looked at quantization of the magnetic flux in superconductors. He also developed the concept of off-diagonal long-range order on the basis of explaining superfluidity of helium. In 1964, Yang became a naturalized citizen of the United States.

In 1966, Yang turned down the offer of directorship of the Institute for Advanced Study and instead took the position of Albert Einstein Professor of Physics at the State University of New York at Stony Brook. In 1967, Yang published two papers solving a one-dimensional quantum many-body problem. Australian physicist Rodney James Baxter also worked on the problem, and the equation he and Yang independently developed became known as Yang-Baxter equation in 1981.

In 1971, Yang visited China for the first time since leaving the country in 1945. Following this visit, Yang became active in promoting Chinese-American interchange in the field of theoretical physics. Throughout the 1970s and 1980s, Yang continued research in particle physics, particularly in areas such as symmetry violation and global formulation of gauge fields. In this

research, he collaborated with physicist Tai Tsun Wu. In 1983, Yang proposed an experiment in superconducting shielding that was performed successfully in 1986. That year, Yang received the National Medal of Science. He also joined the Chinese University of Hong Kong as distinguished professor at large.

In 1998, Yang became a professor at Tsinghua University. He retired from Stony Brook the following year, taking on the title of Albert Einstein Professor of Physics Emeritus. Yang's wife Chih-Li died in 2003, and in December 2004, Yang married Weng Fan. Although largely retired, Yang has continued to contribute to the field of physics, serving as honorary director of the Institute for Advanced Study at Tsinghua University and publishing papers on a variety of topics.

IMPACT

Yang has made a number of significant contributions to the fields of theoretical physics and mathematics. The Yang–Mills theory, developed to explicate strong nuclear force interaction, has been an enduring area of study among researchers such as Nobel Prize–winning physicist Yoichiro Nambu. Yang and Lee's proposal of parity nonconservation in weak nuclear force interaction, proven to be correct, not only won Yang and Lee the Nobel Prize but also prompted physicists working in the field to think about elementary particles in new ways. The Yang–Baxter equation proved itself invaluable in quantum mechanics, field theory, and higher mathematics.

Yang is particularly known for considering challenges in theoretical physics that were created by specific observations of reality and proposing theoretical solutions to explain the behavior of observed phenomena. While Yang is not an experimental physicist, he has excelled in mentally devising experiments that would prove or disprove his proposed theories. Over the course of his career, Yang has drawn inspiration and intellectual strength from collaborating with fellow physicists.

As scientist, Yang has embraced his Chinese American identity, considering himself to be a mediator between the two cultures. He promoted access for Chinese scientists to the global scientific community and also bridged the gaps between scientists in the People's Republic of China (mainland China), the Republic of China (Taiwan), and Hong Kong. Yang holds honorary doctoral degrees from all three of these political entities.

R. C. Lutz

FURTHER READING

Ge, Mo-Lin, et al., eds. *Statistical Physics, High Energy, Condensed Matter and Mathematical Physics: Proceedings of the Conference in Honor of C. N. Yang's 85th Birthday.* Singapore: World Scientific, 2008. Print. Introduces Yang and his scientific accomplishments, offers a personal portrait written by one of Yang's former students, and collects scientific papers related to Yang's areas of study.

Liu, C. S., and Shing-Tung Yau, eds. *Chen Ning Yang: A Great Physicist of the Twentieth Century.* Cambridge: International, 1992. Print. Collects biographical essays, personal recollections of Yang by his former students and his colleagues, and scientific articles presented at a conference in honor of Yang's seventieth birthday.

Roy, Amit. "Discovery of Parity Violation: Breakdown of a Symmetry Principle." *Resonance* 10 (2005): 164–75. Print. Chronicles the achievement of Yang, Lee, and Wu in proposing and proving parity violation for weak nuclear force.

ADA E. YONATH

Israeli biochemist

In 2009, Israeli biochemist Ada E. Yonath became the first woman from her country to win a Nobel Prize for her work on ribosome structure and function. Yonath pioneered the use of cryo-biocrystallography, which she used to determine the ribosome's complex structure. Her work has implications for the development of antibiotics and the search for the origin of life in the universe.

Born: June 22, 1939; Jerusalem, Palestine
Primary field: Chemistry
Specialty: Biochemistry

EARLY LIFE

Ada E. Yonath was born in 1939 to Hillel and Esther Livshitz, who had emigrated from Poland in 1933 to what was then known as Palestine, and which became Israel in 1948. Her father was a third-generation rabbi and grocery store owner who endured frequent hospitalizations and surgeries. The family was poor; they shared a four-room apartment with two other families. Both parents valued education, however, making sure that their older daughter received a good primary education.

From her earliest years, Yonath was interested in science and conducted experiments. She revered Marie Curie, the first woman to receive the Nobel Prize in chemistry. Her father's illnesses gave her an interest in medicine. When Ada was only eleven, her father died. By that time, she was already teaching younger students and earning money. She continued to work after her mother relocated her two daughters to Tel Aviv to be nearer her family. Yonath attended Tichon Hadash, a well-respected high school. Although it was the most expensive school in the nation, she attended without charge in exchange for work done there.

Military service was compulsory for both young men and women in Israel. Yonath served in the Medical Forces, strengthening her interest in medicine. She enrolled at the Hebrew University of Jerusalem, where she was one of only fifty students admitted to the chemistry program, due to limited laboratory space. She earned a bachelor's degree in chemistry in 1962, then went on to earn a master's degree in biochemistry two years later. After completing doctoral work in X-ray crystallography at the Weizmann Institute of Science, she went to the United States for postdoctoral studies at Pittsburg's Carnegie Mellon University, working on muscle research in 1969. The following year at the Massachusetts Institute of Technology in Cambridge, she was finally able to begin research on protein crystallography. During the 1970s, Yonath began to research the structure of the ribosome.

LIFE'S WORK

In 1970, Yonath returned to the Weizmann Institute in Israel to work in the Chemistry Department, where she began her own protein crystallography laboratory. Her career advanced at Weizmann as she was promoted to senior scientist (1974–83), associate professor (1984–88), chairperson of the structural chemistry department (1989–90), chair of structural biology (1992–94), and director of the Mazer Center for Structural Biology (1988–2004). She has been a professor in Weizmann's structural biology department since 1988 and director of the institute's Kimmelman Center for Biomolecular Structure and Assembly since 1989. During her tenure at Weizmann, she also headed the Max Planck Research Unit for Ribosomal Structure in Germany, from 1986 to 2004.

Yonath's goal was to understand biosynthesis, the method whereby cells use code from the nucleic acids to produce proteins. She focused her study on ribosomes, which are found in all living cells, and which make protein. Higher organisms such as mammals have more complex ribosomes than bacteria and other simpler organisms. The complexity allows the body to respond to problems that prokaryotes (single-cell organisms without membrane-bound nuclei) do not experience, such as heart problems.

When Yonath began her research, many scientists, including Nobel Prize winners Frances Crick and James Watson, had already attempted to crystallize ribosomes from *E. coli* and other bacteria, but without success. Yonath made the first ribosome crystals in 1980, using bacteria that were both salt-loving (halophilic) and heat-loving (thermophilic). To avoid the damage that intense X-rays caused, Yonath also pioneered the technique of flash-freezing the crystals. *Cryo-biocrystallography*, as

the technique is called, sharpens the image seen under the microscope.

In 2000, after two decades of work, Yonath and her team unveiled a three-dimensional structure of the ribosome. Two years later, they were confident of an internal two-fold symmetry of ribosomes near the site where the transfer RNA arrives with the amino acid. This symmetry went against the findings of other scientists, and the scientific community required time to replicate and verify the team's work. After the team's findings were verified, Yonath was coawarded the 2009 Nobel Prize in Chemistry for her work, becoming the first Israeli woman to receive a Nobel and the fourth woman to win the prize for chemistry. She shared the prize with Thomas Steitz of Yale and Venkatraman Ramakrishnan of the Medical Research Council Laboratory of Molecular Biology at Cambridge.

Yonath has also worked with the US National Aeronautics and Space Administration (NASA) Astrobiology Institute in its efforts to determine the origins of life in the universe. She was the first Israeli biologist to send research material into space, and has collaborated on twelve NASA missions. She has also presented lectures at conferences held by the institute.

Yonath's many awards in addition to the Nobel Prize include the Weizmann Institute's Martin A. Kimmel Professorial Chair, which she has held since 1989; the Israel Prize for Chemical Research (2002); the first European Crystallography Prize (2000); and the Wolf Prize in Chemistry, given annually since 1978 by the Israel-based Wolf Foundation. In 2008, Yonath received the Albert Einstein World Award of Science and an honorary doctorate from Oxford University. That same year, the United Nations Educational, Scientific and Cultural Organization (UNESCO) presented her with the L'Oréal-UNESCO Award for Women in Science.

Yonath is a member of several influential scholarly organizations, such as the International Academy of Astronautics, the American Academy of Arts and Sciences, the European Academy of Sciences and Art, the European Molecular Biology Organization, the Israeli Academy of Sciences and Humanities, and the United States National Academy of Sciences. She has also participated in extensive national and international committee work for the RNA Institute of Albany, New York; the Center of Excellence (I-CORE) in Israel; and the International Committee for Synchotron Radiation, among many others.

Yonath has one daughter, Hagith Yonath, who is a medical doctor, and a granddaughter, Noa.

Ada Yonath Reveals the Structure of the Ribosome

Prior to Ada Yonath's research on ribosome structure, many scientists had attempted to understand the structure of the ribosome because of its importance in transmitting the genetic code. At the Max Planck Institute for Molecular Genetics in Berlin, where she was a visiting professor, Yonath began her research on ribosomes with the support of Heinz Günter Wittmann. At the same time, she worked at the Weizmann Institute, where she led a multinational team of investigators.

Ribosomes possess a complex spatial structure, with more than fifty proteins and an even greater number of ribonucleic acids (RNA). Ribosomes, however, do not have an internal symmetry, and they are composed of both RNA chains and proteins. In addition, ribosomes are not stable and are very flexible. All of these challenges made crystallizing a difficult task.

While recuperating from a bicycle accident, Yonath read an article on the hibernation of polar bears that suggested that collecting the ribosomes along the cells' membranes just before hibernation kept the cells together over several months while allowing the cells to retain the possibility of functioning. She also read about extremophiles, bacteria living in extreme temperatures. Yonath's reading led her to use organisms living in extreme conditions for her research. Thus, she and her team chose heat-seeking (thermophilic) cells, using bacteria from the Dead Sea, atomic piles, and hot springs. At the lab in Berlin, Wittmann had a collection of crystals that he put at her disposal.

In 1980, Yonath presented her first, blurry images at a conference and discussed the quest to map the ribosome. Her ideas were largely dismissed by members of the scientific community. Wittmann, however, and a few key people such as Nobel laureate John Kendrew, continued to support her work.

To keep the crystals from disintegrating under the microscope, in the mid-1980s Yonath developed the technique of cryo-biocrystallography. She froze the crystals, using liquid nitrogen to ensure their stability. Thus, after more than a decade of experimentation, Yonath was able to produce the first high-resolution images. Other research groups began to replicate the efforts Yonath and her team had made.

In 2000 and 2001, Yonath's research resulted in publication of the first three-dimensional structures of bacterial ribosomes. However, other researchers had been able to produce high-resolution images before she could do so. Thus, she shared the 2009 Nobel Prize in Chemistry with Tom Steitz and Venkatraman Ramakrishan.

IMPACT

Yonath's work on cells applies not only to human cells but also to those of bacteria. Her research is critical, because antibiotics often work by blocking action in bacterial ribosomes and greater knowledge about ribosomes may lead to both antibiotics and improvement in existing drugs. Such an advance could in turn bring about a decline in antiobiotic resistance.

Ribosomes, which are organelles composed of proteins and RNA, follow the instructions of the genetic code given by the messenger RNA (mRNA). Amino acids come to the ribosome from transfer RNA (tRNA), which decodes the message. Yonath's work on ribosome structure is one of the keys for solving the mysteries of cell communication, as well as the most basic mystery of life's origins on Earth and in the universe.

Outside of her research, Yonath has used her stature to take on controversial issues such as the detaining of Palestinians in Israeli prisons. She supports the construction of a major research laboratory in Jordan, which will bring together scientists from a number of surrounding Arab nations. Less controversial is her work to further the advancement of women in science. At the time of Yonath's Nobel Prize award, only about thirty percent of European women worked in the field of chemistry. To encourage young women to study science, she has invited groups to tour the laboratory at the Weizmann Institute.

Judy A. Johnson

FURTHER READING

Berisio, Rita, David Baram, and Ehud Keinan. "Nobel Prize in Chemistry 2009: When Biology Turns into Chemistry." *Israel Journal of Chemistry* 50.1 (2010): 24–26. Print. Technical article explaining research on ribosome structure and discussing the work of all three 2009 Nobel laureates in chemistry.

Di Domenico, Kelly. *Women Scientists Who Changed the World*. New York: Rosen, 2012. Print. This very accessible book includes a chapter on Yonath with photographs. Includes glossary, plus sites for more information and further reading, mainly about women in science generally, and an index.

Hargittai, István, and Magdolna Hargittai. *Candid Science VI: More Conversations with Famous Scientists.* London: Imperial College P, 2006. Print. A chapter in

the work is devoted to Yonath, with a question-and-answer format covering both personal and professional topics. Includes photographs and index.

ROGER ARLINER YOUNG

American biologist

An African American woman, Roger Arliner Young rose from poverty to become a respected biologist and zoologist. The first black female in the United States to earn a doctoral degree in zoology, she began her career as a researcher, but spent most of her adult life teaching at historically black colleges and universities.

Born: August 20, 1899; Clifton Forge, Virginia
Died: November 9, 1964; New Orleans, Louisiana
Primary field: Biology
Specialties: Zoology; marine biology; embryology

EARLY LIFE

Roger Arliner Young was born on August 20, 1899. An only child, she was the daughter of a poor African American couple living in Clifton Forge, Virginia, a small town in the Allegheny Mountains near the border of West Virginia. Her family relocated to Burgettstown, Pennsylvania, a village west of Pittsburgh, when she was a young girl. Young faced significant challenges as a female minority in a white community during an era of endemic racial discrimination and gender prejudice. Because little schooling was provided for black children, Young was largely self-educated. In addition, she was required from an early age to work part-time jobs in order to support her family. Her mother was a woman of fragile physical constitution, and was often sick. Perhaps because of the difficulties of her early years, Young suffered from bouts of depression throughout her life.

After passing her college entrance examination, Young was accepted at Howard University in Washington, DC, in 1916. A part-time student who had to work to support herself, Young began with a concentration in music. She was active in the glee club, in the Young Women's Christian Association, and in the Howard University Players, a student drama group.

By 1921, her fifth year as a part-time student at Howard, Young had accumulated enough credits to be classified as a junior. Still undecided about what career to pursue, she registered for a general science class.

LIFE'S WORK

Young's science course at Howard brought her into contact with a person who would exert tremendous influence on her life, Ernest Everett Just (1883–1941), the head of Howard's Zoology Department. In 1915, Just was named the first recipient of the National Association for the Advancement of Colored People's (NAACP) Spingarn Medal for outstanding achievement, and was the first African American in the United States to earn a PhD in zoology (1916). He was well known in the scientific community for his groundbreaking research in embryology.

Though Young's performance was lackluster—she earned a C in science—she nonetheless caught Just's attention. She was one of only three women students who enrolled in Just's courses during the 1920s. (The others were Marguerite Thomas Williams, the first African American to earn a doctorate in geology, and Lillian Burwell Lewis, the first black woman to earn a natural science doctorate at the University of Chicago.) Just encouraged Young to pursue a career in science, as most of his male students were focused on careers in medicine, as opposed to research. Young blossomed under Just's mentorship, talking courses in vertebrate and invertebrate biology.

In 1923, Young earned a bachelor of science degree from Howard. She was hired as assistant professor of zoology, and Just helped her acquire funding to attend graduate school. In the summer of 1924, Young became a part-time student at the University of Chicago, where Just had earned his doctorate. At the same time, she conducted research connected with Just's studies, and later that year published a brief article in *Science* magazine on her findings.

Young, balancing her graduate studies with her teaching assignments at Howard, was awarded her master's degree in 1926. The following summer, Just invited her to the Marine Biological Laboratory at Woods Hole, Massachusetts, as his research assistant. The first black woman admitted to the lab, Young would spend ten seasons at Woods Hole conducting research.

Young's Studies of Marine Life

Roger Arliner Young's research was conducted between the time she earned her bachelor's degree at Howard (1923) and her doctorate at the University of Pennsylvania (1940). Though her early work unfolded in the laboratory at Howard, where she taught, from 1927 through the late 1930s the bulk of her research was undertaken at the Marine Biological Laboratory (MBL) at Woods Hole in Massachusetts.

At MBL, Young worked alongside and collaborated with embryologist Frank R. Lillie, MBL director (1908–1939), founder and president (1930–1939) of the Woods Hole Oceanographic Institution, and longtime chairman of the Department of Zoology at the University of Chicago, where he had mentored Ernest Just. Young also researched with zoologists Lewis V. Heilbrunn from the University of Pennsylvania and Donald P. Costello from the University of North Carolina.

Most of Young's research was related to that of Just, who was interested in exploring the biochemical process of fertilization, specifically as exhibited in the eggs of marine life. Young's first subject for study was the paramecium, a protozoan. Her paper on the paramecium's excretory system, published in the 1920s, anticipated the later work of Russian cell scientist Dimitri Nasconov.

Young's later studies concentrated on the development of eggs in particular forms of marine life. Most of her work involved subjecting particular species of annelid sandworms and tubeworms (*Nereis*, *Platynereis*, and *Chaetopterus*), and sea urchins (*Arbacia*), to X-rays and ultraviolet rays to observe the effects on their eggs. The experiments formed the basis for several papers Young published during the 1930s in collaboration with fellow researchers, and served as the topic of her PhD dissertation, "The Indirect Effects of Roentgen Rays on Certain Marine Eggs." The radiation employed in the experiments not only affected sea life, it also affected Young's life as well: Her eyes were permanently damaged, and after 1940, she was never again able to conduct research.

From 1929 onward, however, Young worked in Massachusetts without Just. After procuring funding from fellowships and grants, he began spending much of his time traveling, lecturing, and researching in Europe. During his prolonged absences, Young added Just's teaching load to her own. She also took over his duties as head of the zoology department, which rankled the all-male teaching staff.

In 1930, an overburdened and underprepared Young took qualifying exams for the doctoral program at the University of Chicago. She failed the tests. Undeterred, she returned to teach at Howard, and continued her yearly research at Woods Hole. During the 1930s, she authored or coauthored several papers on different aspects of marine biology.

By mid-decade, Young's tenure at Howard University was drawing to a close. Her original sponsor, Just, was no longer enamored with his protégé, and chose a man, Hyman Y. Chase, as his successor as head of the Zoology Department in 1936. Young was dismissed. Soon afterward, one of her colleagues at Woods Hole, biologist Lewis V. Heilbrunn, suggested she enter the doctoral program at the University of Pennsylvania, and helped her secure a grant to fund her studies. Young took him up on the offer, and in 1940 earned her PhD, becoming the first African American woman to earn a doctorate in zoology.

Despite earning her doctorate, Young struggled to advance her career. She could only find work to support herself and her mother at a succession of historically black colleges and universities. In the early 1940s, she was an assistant professor at North Carolina College for Negroes (later North Carolina Central University). A few years later, she headed the Biology Department at Shaw University in Raleigh, North Carolina. She afterward taught briefly at Paul Quinn College in Waco, Texas, before moving on to Jackson College for Negro Teachers (later Jackson State University) in Mississippi.

Young was at Jackson in 1953 when her sickly mother died, an event that plunged her into a deep depression. Her psychological health deteriorated to the point that she voluntarily checked into the Mississippi Mental Asylum (later Mississippi State Hospital). For most of the next decade, she was a resident at the then-segregated 350-acre facility.

Discharged in 1962, Young relocated to New Orleans, Louisiana, where she was a visiting lecturer in biology at Southern University. She died two years later, never having married.

IMPACT

As a poor African American woman born in the racially segregated American south, Young faced numerous obstacles throughout her life. However, she used her talent and determination to flourish for a time in a hostile, prejudiced academic environment.

Her association with Just was both a blessing and a curse to her career. His early sponsorship allowed her to become a pioneer of her race and gender in education and research, and brought her into contact with others beneficial to her growth. Her academic work in the master's degree program at the University of Chicago led to her acceptance into Sigma Xi, a national science society honor normally reserved for doctoral students.

However, Just's role in Young's life was not an unmixed blessing. To keep grant money flowing, he convinced her to reject a 1931 job offer from Spelman College and stay at Howard. Embittered over the disparity between European and American racial attitudes, he spent considerable time in the laboratories of Germany, Italy, and France, leaving Young to fill in for him as department head during her last five years at Howard. Just did not attempt to quiet stories that he and Young had been romantically involved, and he fueled rumors of infidelity by divorcing his wife; in 1939 he married a German woman. Just demonstrated little appreciation of Young's taking on his many responsibilities at Howard. In the end, he diminished her reputation by firing her for seemingly petty reasons, denying her the departmental head position for which she seemed well prepared.

While Young's research of the 1920s and 1930s largely represents an extension of the innovative work of Just, her legacy to science probably lies in education. A science instructor for over four decades, she led by example, and inspired countless young black students to follow her into the field by introducing them to zoology.

Jack Ewing

FURTHER READING

Carey, Charles W., Jr. *African Americans in Science: An Encyclopedia of People and Progress*. Santa Barbara: ABC-CLIO, 2008. Print. An illustrated two-volume reference that explores the full range of personal experiences of African Americans attempting to make their marks within scientific communities.

Manning, Kenneth R. *Black Apollo of Science: The Life of Ernest Everett Just*. New York: Oxford UP, 1985. Print. A Pulitzer Prize–nominated biography of the brilliant but controversial zoologist who initially inspired Roger Arliner Young to pursue a career as a biology researcher.

Warren, Wini. *Black Women Scientists in the United States*. Bloomington: Indiana UP, 2000. Print. Presents a collection of brief, annotated biographies of African American women—many of them, like Young, virtually unknown to the general population—who made significant contributions across a wide range of scientific disciplines.

Williams, Zachery R. *In Search of the Talented Tenth: Howard University Public Intellectuals and the Dilemmas of Race, 1926–1970*. Columbia: U of Missouri P, 2009. Print. Discusses the intellectually stimulating and culture-changing environment that prevailed at Howard in the years when Young and her mentor Just were active, leading up to the civil rights movement of the 1960s and 1970s.

THOMAS YOUNG

British physicist

British scientist Thomas Young is known for his contributions to the fields of physics, optics, and medicine. He proposed a wave theory of light, challenging the particle theory of earlier scientist Isaac Newton.

Born: June 13, 1773; Milverton, England
Died: May 10, 1829; London, England
Primary field: Physics
Specialties: Theoretical physics; optics; physiology

EARLY LIFE

Thomas Young was born in 1773 in Milverton, England, to Thomas and Sarah Young. By the age of two, Young had learned to read. By the age of fourteen, he had mastered multiple languages, including Greek, Latin, French, Italian, Hebrew, Arabic, and Farsi.

Young completed his education quickly and soon began to prepare for a career in medicine. He enrolled at the University of Edinburgh but completed his studies at the prestigious University of Göttingen in the Holy Roman Empire (now Germany). In 1793, he lectured before the Royal Society on the eye and its muscular structure. On the basis of his paper "Observations on Vision," he was elected to the Royal Society at the age of twenty-one. He later became the society's secretary.

With the completion of his medical studies in 1796, Young continued his scholarly work at Emmanuel College, Cambridge. That year, he inherited the fortune of his granduncle, physician Richard Brocklesby, which allowed him to be financially independent. Thus, at a very young age, Young had the freedom to pursue inquiries in whatever field interested him. He later moved to London and established a medical practice there.

LIFE'S WORK

While experimenting at Cambridge, Young became increasingly interested in optics and the perception of colors. Drawing on his earlier observations of the eye, Young advanced a theory on colors. He assumed there are three basic colors (red, green, and violet) and that the retina of the eye contains groups of receptors, later determined to be cone cells, that are sensitive to one of these three colors. For example, a red light stimulates a receptor sensitive to red colors, a violet light stimulates a receptor sensitive to violet colors, and so on. Young proposed that other colors are seen when different combinations of receptors are stimulated. For instance, a yellow color is seen when both violet and green receptors are stimulated at the same time.

Young published variations on this theory at several points in his career, eventually including elements of it in his article on chromatics for the *Encyclopedia Britannica*. Later, German scientist Hermann von Helmholtz developed Young's theory further, and it became known as the Young-Helmholtz theory. In the 1950s, new technology demonstrated conclusively that the Young-Helmholtz theory is largely correct and that the cone cells in the retina function according to Young's description.

From his initial forays into optics, Young began to experiment with the nature of light. Having previously investigated the transmission of sound, which he proposed traveled in waves, as well as the movement of waves in water, Young theorized that light travels in a similar manner. In 1802, he invented a simple experiment to prove this theory and demonstrated conclusively that light does indeed travel in waves. As he developed his wave theory of light, Young found that many English physicists were unreceptive to his findings because they contradicted the particle theory of light developed by Isaac Newton more than a century earlier. However, French physicists Augustin Jean Fresnel and François Arago tested Young's theory, and their experiments helped confirm that Young was correct in his findings.

On the basis of his experiments, in 1801, Young was appointed professor of natural philosophy, the field that later became known as physics, at the Royal Institution. Over the next two years, Young delivered lectures on nearly every subject then studied in physics. Young resigned his professorship in 1803, explaining that it was interfering with his medical duties. The following year, he married Eliza Maxwell.

Although he had resigned his professorship, Young continued to conduct experiments in physics. He made an important contribution to the theory of elasticity known as Young's modulus, a ratio used to measure the stiffness of elastic materials. In 1818, working with the Board of Longitude and the Royal Navy, he helped supervise the publication of a nautical almanac. In addition, Young made significant contributions to the field of medicine. Young was the first physician to describe astigmatism in the eye accurately. In recognition of his medical work, he was made a fellow at the College of Physicians in Cambridge. He was often invited to lecture on medical matters, and throughout his life, he practiced at St. George's Hospital in London.

Young applied himself to other areas of study as well. In 1799, French soldiers had discovered a stone buried outside the town of Rosetta, Egypt, on which was carved a proclamation in Greek, hieroglyphics, and a third, unknown language that later became known as demotic. While Egyptian hieroglyphics were present on many monuments, scholars had been unable to decode what they meant. However, the Rosetta Stone placed a known language, Greek, alongside the hieroglyphics, allowing them to be translated. Young began to study the Rosetta Stone and discovered that the third language (demotic) was a mixture of phonetic and hieroglyphic signs. Thus, he was able to trace the demotic writing back to hieroglyphics and decode names and words from the ancient symbols.

Young spent his later years practicing medicine and contributing articles to the *Encyclopedia Britannica*. He died in London on May 10, 1829.

IMPACT

Young's work in the field of physics greatly influenced the development of scientific thought. His work on the wave theory of light not only served to displace the longstanding particle theory of Newton but also led to a variety of advances in the study of light. Early in the twentieth century, scientists determined that light behaves as both a wave and a particle, indicating that Newton and Young were both partially correct. This discovery, in turn, allowed scientists to make important contributions to the developing field of quantum physics. Young's research regarding how the eye recognizes and interprets different colors also proved to be influential, serving as the foundation for further study in that area.

Although Young is perhaps best known as a scientist, he was also a significant figure in the field of linguistics. He studied and compared the vocabulary and

Thomas Young Determines That Light Is a Wave

In the early eighteenth century, British scientist Isaac Newton published his influential work on light, postulating that light consists of particles that he called "corpuscles." Over the following decades, Newton came to be considered an expert on the nature of light, and his particle theory found almost no opposition. Nearly a century after Newton articulated his theory of light, British scientist Thomas Young challenged the theory, arguing that light behaves as a wave.

Young initially formulated his theory after observing the patterns caused by waves on water from a single source. When another source of waves was added, the two sets of waves would interfere with each other in predictable ways. Young set out to test the wave theory of light using these observations as a basis for constructing a simple experiment.

In order to control the light source as much as possible, he placed a card with a very narrow slit in front of a small opening of a blacked-out window in bright sunlight. Only a little of the strong sunlight was allowed through the window, and even less made it through the slit. Another card with two smaller slits only a fraction of an inch apart was placed in front of the first card, and a screen was set up to receive whatever light was left.

Young anticipated that the pattern of light formed on the screen would be similar to the pattern formed by two interfering waves. If he was correct, the screen should show a pattern of bands of light and darkness that would be more intense in the middle of the screen and fade as it approached the edges. If light behaved as Newton had suggested, the particles of light would fall in a uniform random pattern on the screen with no bands of darkness. When Young performed the experiment, it produced the results he had anticipated. The characteristic pattern was visible on the screen, indicating that light behaves as a wave.

In 1803, Young presented his findings to the Royal Society of London, of which he was a member. His results were controversial, as Newton and his particle theory of light had greatly shaped the development of European scientific thought. However, Young's experiment was simple to reproduce, and a number of scientists built upon his findings in their own research. The wave theory eventually became the dominant theory for understanding light and remained so until the twentieth century, when scientists discovered that light can behave as both a particle and a wave depending on the experiment and the circumstances. This wave-particle duality remained a major area of research in physics, particularly after scientists suggested that matter such as electrons can behave as both a particle and a wave as well.

grammar of over four hundred languages, publishing his findings in a series of articles in the *Encyclopedia Britannica*. Finding similarities along a wide spectrum of languages, Young coined the term "Indo-European" to describe the family of European languages that includes Greek, Latin, Sanskrit, and many other modern languages. Young's articles and work on the Rosetta Stone were of great help to Egyptologist Jean Francois Champollion, who ultimately translated the Egyptian hieroglyphics on the stone in the 1820s.

Jeffrey Bowman

FURTHER READING

Atchison, David A., and W. Neil Charman. "Thomas Young's Contributions to Geometrical Optics." *Clinical and Experimental Optometry* 94.4 (2011): 333–40. Print. Describes Young's contributions to the fields of optical instrumentation, physical optics, and geometrical optics and discusses Young's theorems regarding paraxial refraction and astigmatism and image curvature.

Robinson, Andrew. *The Last Man Who Knew Everything: Thomas Young, the Anonymous Polymath Who Proved Newton Wrong, Explained How We See, Cured the Sick, and Deciphered the Rosetta Stone, among Other Feats of Genius*. New York: Pi, 2005. Print. Provides a thorough biography of Young, drawing on Young's writings and letters. Discusses Young's early life, his optics research and theory of color vision, the translation of the Rosetta Stone, his medical practice, his contributions to the *Encyclopedia Britannica*, and his many other accomplishments.

Wood, Alexander, and Frank Oldham. *Thomas Young: Natural Philosopher, 1773–1829*. 1954. Cambridge: Cambridge UP, 2011. Print. Chronicles Young's life and career and includes excerpts from his writings as well as diagrams explaining his experiments and discoveries.

HIDEKI YUKAWA

Japanese physicist

When Hideki Yukawa won the 1949 Nobel Prize in Physics, he became the first Japanese person to win a Nobel Prize. Though he was often regarded as soft-spoken and shy, his ideas about the nature of atoms spoke loudly, forming the foundation for modern particle studies.

Born: January 23, 1907; Tokyo, Japan
Died: September 8, 1981; Kyoto, Japan
Primary field: Physics
Specialties: Theoretical physics; atomic and molecular physics

EARLY LIFE

Hideki Yukawa was born Hideki Ogawa on January 23, 1907, in Tokyo, Japan. He was the fifth of seven children in a well-educated family. His grandparents were professors and scholars, and his father, Takuji Ogawa, became a professor of geology at Kyoto Imperial University (now Kyoto University) in 1908. Three of his brothers also became professors.

Though Yukawa mainly studied mathematics and literature as a young student, he quickly became interested in the sciences when he entered Kyoto Imperial University. He eventually decided to study theoretical physics, partly due to his stated inability to work in more experimental fields. He credited two of his professors, Yoshio Nishina and K. Tamaki, with encouraging him to study theoretical physics.

When he graduated from Kyoto Imperial University in 1929, Yukawa stayed on at the school as an unpaid assistant, working on solving the so-called divergence problems of quantum electrodynamics. Yukawa failed to make any headway with these problems, so he began looking into nuclear forces.

The next few years proved both fruitful and rewarding for Yukawa. While continuing to lecture at Kyoto Imperial University, he married Sumiko Yukawa, and was adopted by her family (taking the name Yukawa), in 1932. The couple's first son, Harumi, was born in 1933, and their second son, Takaki, was born in 1935.

In 1933, Yukawa was awarded an assistant professorship at Osaka Imperial University. In 1934, at the age of twenty-seven, he began the work that would later earn him the Nobel Prize in Physics. He successfully predicted the existence of a particle called a *meson*—the subatomic particle responsible for the force that holds all atoms together.

LIFE'S WORK

In 1935, Yukawa published his theory of mesons in the paper "On the Interaction of Elementary Particles. I." Just three years earlier, Werner Karl Heisenberg had updated the standard model of the atomic nucleus. Heisenberg correctly proposed that the nucleus is comprised of protons and neutrons, rather than protons and electrons as had been previously assumed.

This new theory posed a further problem: Since protons are positively charged, and neutrons have no charge, the protons in the nucleus should repel each other; this would break up the nucleus and, by extension, the atom. This mystery of atomic force intrigued Yukawa and eventually led him to his meson theory.

Working with Eugene Paul Wigner, another future Nobel laureate, Yukawa proposed the existence of a force that keeps protons from repelling each other. Existing experimental data gave him two important clues in his investigation. The first clue was that the atomic force must have a very short range in order to not interfere with the electrons orbiting the nucleus. Yukawa used an electromagnetic field as a model for his theoretical force and adapted it to produce short-range forces. The second clue was that any field must be associated with a particle. Therefore, Yukawa determined, there had to be a previously unknown particle in the nucleus of an atom that acted to hold the nucleus together.

Yukawa found there was a relationship between the range of a force and the mass of the particles associated with that force. Based on the assumed range of atomic forces, he estimated the particle's mass at about two hundred times the mass of an electron. These particles, he theorized, are constantly being exchanged between the protons and the neutrons (collectively known as *nucleons*) in an atomic nucleus.

Each nucleon, Yukawa deduced, has a cloud of particles orbiting around it, and each nucleon shares its cloud with neighboring nucleons, much in the same way that molecules are formed from the shared electrons in the outer layers of atoms. Yukawa thought these new particles were too unstable to exist outside of an atomic nucleus but that they were likely to appear in cosmic radiation, which comes from outer space.

Though Yukawa's theory did not receive a lot of attention at the time, it eventually became the basis for modern particle physics. Two years after Yukawa

947

published his theory, scientists Carl David Anderson and Seth Neddermeyer discovered what they thought were mesons. Though the particles (called *mu-mesons* or *muons*) had a mass roughly two hundred times that of electrons and appeared in cosmic rays, they did not interact with nucleons in the way that Yukawa had predicted. They turned out to be a type of particle created when mesons decay.

In 1947, a scientist named Cecil Powell discovered actual mesons, which he labeled *pi-mesons*, or *pions*. These pions perfectly fit all the specifications of Yukawa's theory. Interestingly, Powell also found that mesons lose mass during decay and that the lost mass then turns into energy, which illustrates Albert Einstein's theory of the relationship between mass and energy.

The discovery of the meson, thirteen years after the idea was first introduced, finally confirmed Yukawa's theory. He was awarded the Nobel Prize in Physics in 1949 for his prediction of such a crucial elementary particle.

Meanwhile, Yukawa had developed another important theory about atoms. His theory put forth that sometimes the nucleus of an atom will "capture" one of the electrons from the innermost shell of electrons, called the *K-shell*. He predicted that this process—called *K-capture*—would alter the charge of the atom and make

Yukawa Proposes the Existence of Mesons

Werner Heisenberg's suggestion that neutrons and protons (collectively called *nucleons*) were held together in the nucleus by electrons troubled Japanese theoretical physicist Hideki Yukawa, so he worked to solve the nuclear puzzle by using Paul Dirac's theory of electrical forces.

Dirac described electrical forces as exchanges of virtual photons. Virtual particles are particles that are created for only a short time, and as long as they exist, they violate the law of conservation of energy. The law of conservation of energy says that the total amount of energy in a closed system (a system that does not take in or give off energy) is constant. If a particle is suddenly created within a closed system, its energy is added to the total energy of the system, thereby breaking the law of conservation of energy. Classical physics does not admit that virtual particles exist; such particles indicate the existence of the uncertainty principle. The uncertainty principle says that a system can violate the law of conservation of energy for a short time. A photon has no rest mass (mass that could, theoretically, be measured by someone who was traveling with the photon); therefore, the uncertainty principle says that it has an infinite lifetime, can travel at the speed of light, and has an infinite range.

In October 1934, Yukawa realized that the attraction nucleons have for one another is caused by the exchange of virtual particles. Virtual photons, which have zero rest mass, have an infinite range. Yukawa recognized that the range of a particle with a rest mass that was not zero would decrease as its rest mass increased. By using the diameter of a small nucleus as the range, he calculated that such a virtual particle—

which he called the *heavy quantum*, or *U-quantum*—would need to have about two hundred times the mass of an electron (200 electronic masses). Yukawa discussed this virtual particle in a scientific research paper he published in 1935.

At first, the international physics community did not see the importance of Yukawa's work, but that changed in 1937 when Carl Anderson discovered a new particle whose mass was about two hundred times that of an electron. Yukawa and others soon suggested that the new particle was the particle that he had proposed. In 1939, Homi Bhabha coined the name that stuck to Yukawa's particle: the meson. Bhabha also proposed a method of calculating the lifetime of the meson, and Yukawa and a team of theoreticians refined and used this method. By then, the lifetime of Anderson's particle had been measured, and it was found that Anderson's particle was not Yukawa's meson. The puzzle was still unsolved.

During World War II, Yukawa continued exploring meson physics. In 1942, two members of Yukawa's group, Shoichi Sakata and T. Inoue, proposed the two-meson theory, which suggested that Yukawa's particle decayed quickly, becoming Anderson's particle. Investigations conducted by Cecil Powell fully supported this theory, and in 1947, Powell and his coworkers published photographs of the tracks of both mesons. Each meson had a mass of more than two hundred electron masses, but one was about 20 percent heavier. Yukawa's meson, which was the heavier of the two, became known as a pi-meson, or pion. Anderson's particle, the pion's decay product, was called a mu-meson, or muon. In 1949, Yukawa was awarded the Nobel Prize in Physics for his work; he was the first Japanese to be awarded a Nobel Prize.

it unstable. As with his theory of mesons, Yukawa's K-capture theory was also confirmed several years later.

Hideki Yukawa had a special relationship with the city of Kyoto and with Kyoto University, always returning there after periods of teaching at other schools. In 1938, he went back to study at his alma mater to earn his doctorate. The next year, he became a full professor in the school's theoretical physics department. In 1953, after teaching overseas at the Institute for Advanced Study in Princeton, New Jersey, and at Columbia University in New York City, Yukawa again returned to Kyoto to become the director of an interuniversity research institute for fundamental physics founded in his honor. *Progress of Theoretical Physics*, the monthly journal he founded in 1946, continues to be published by the research institute, which was renamed the Yukawa Institute for Theoretical Physics.

Later in life, Yukawa was an active protestor of the use of atomic weapons. He was only two hundred miles from Hiroshima when the United States dropped an atom bomb on the city in 1945 at the end of World War II. A few days later, the United States dropped another atom bomb on the Japanese city of Nagasaki. The two events resulted in the deaths of more than 100,000 Japanese citizens.

IMPACT

Although Yukawa recognized the extraordinary scientific achievement that atomic weapons represented, he denounced their use. He kept his feelings about atomic weaponry quiet for several years, but in 1954, he finally spoke publicly and said that the use of atomic energy for defensive purposes would be harmful to all of humankind. In 1955, Yukawa joined with ten other prominent scientists, including Albert Einstein, to sign a document called the Russell-Einstein Manifesto. The document urged the world to find peaceful means to resolve disputes rather than resorting to nuclear weapons.

Yukawa retired from his position at Kyoto University in 1970. On September 8, 1981, he died of pneumonia in Kyoto at the age of seventy-four. Many of his notes, manuscripts, and letters were discovered after his death. They are preserved in the Yukawa Hall Archival Library at Kyoto University.

Alex K. Rich

FURTHER READING

Brown, Laurie M. "Hideki Yukawa and the Meson Theory." *Physics Today* 39.12 (1986): 55–62. Print. Explains Yukawa's meson theory, the development of the theory, and its impact on particle physics.

Nambu, Yoichiro. "The Legacies of Yukawa and His Disciples." *Nuclear Physics A* 805.1–4 (2008): 90c–97c. Print. Discusses the impact of Yukawa's work in developing the field of particle physics and examines the influence he had on his students.

Sato, Humitaka. "Biography of Hideki Yukawa." *Nuclear Physics A* 805.1–4 (2008): 21c–28c. Print. Presents biographical information on Hideki Yukawa and another Japanese physicist, Sin-Itiro Tomonaga.

Pieter Zeeman

Dutch physicist

Pieter Zeeman shared the Nobel Prize in Physics in 1902 with Hendrik A. Lorentz. Zeeman is remembered for discovering that spectral lines could be split when placed in a magnetic field. This "Zeeman effect" aided in the discovery of the electron and helped lead to the development of magnetic resonance imaging, among many other advances.

Born: May 25, 1865; Zonnemarie, Netherlands
Died: October 9, 1943; Amsterdam, Netherlands
Primary Field: Physics
Specialty: Optics

Early Life

Pieter Zeeman was born May 25, 1865, in the small town of Zonnemarie in the Netherlands. Zonnemarie is in the Zeeland province on the island of Schouwen, in the southeastern part of the country. Zeeman's parents, Catharinus Farandinus Zeeman and Wilhelmina Worst, had six children: four sons and two daughters. Catharinus was a Lutheran minister. Wilhelmina home-schooled Zeeman and his siblings through elementary school. Zeeman then attended secondary school in Zierikzee, the island's major city. Zeeman was still in high school on November 17, 1882, when a massive geomagnetic storm disrupted telegraphs and created auroras worldwide. He observed and sketched the aurora as a pale green arch that formed in the eastern sky. Zeeman sent letters with his description and drawings to the journal *Nature*, and they were published in 1883. After graduating, he attended school in Delft for two years, studying classical languages and reading papers by leading scientists. While there, Zeeman met physicist H. Kamerlingh Onnes, who was a pioneer in refrigeration technology and later discovered superconductivity.

Life's Work

After passing his qualifying exams, Zeeman enrolled at the University of Leiden in 1885. Zeeman began studying physics under Onnes and theoretical physicist Hendrik A. Lorentz. Under Lorentz, Zeeman studied electromagnetism, mechanics, thermodynamics, and light. In 1890, Zeeman began working as an assistant to Lorentz in Leiden's physics department. He was responsible for setting up the demonstrations and experiments that Lorentz used in his introductory physics courses. He also helped Lorentz with his research on the Kerr effect. The Kerr effect, discovered by Scottish physicist John Kerr, describes changes in the index of refraction of a material within an electric field. Zeeman's paper "Mesures relatives du phénomène de Kerr" (Relative measurements of the Kerr effect) was published in 1892, and was awarded a gold medal from the Dutch Society of Sciences. Zeeman later wrote his doctoral thesis on the Kerr effect in 1893. He spent the next term at F. Kohlrausch's institute in Strasbourg (then part of the German Empire, today in France), studying the propagation and absorption of electrical waves in fluids. Zeeman then returned to Leiden, where he became a lecturer of mathematics and physics. On March 25, 1895, he married Johanna Elisabeth Lebret in Dordrecht.

Zeeman continued to study optics, and began investigating the effect of magnetism on visible light. In

The Zeeman Effect

Pieter Zeeman's work on light and magnetism was built on that of the nineteenth-century British scientist Michael Faraday, whose groundbreaking work in electromagnetism made possible the development of electric motors. Faraday's work centered on electricity, but he also believed there was an underlying connection between light and magnetism, although he was never able to prove it experimentally. His main attempt came in 1862, when he used a spectroscope—an instrument for dispersing light and analyzing its spectrum—to try to identify changes in the spectral lines of light from a flame subjected to a magnetic field; the experiment failed. However, more than three decades later, Zeeman had the idea to try again with improved equipment—remarking in his notebook, "Experiments, with negative outcome, performed by great scientists from the past, using worse instruments than are currently available, are worth being repeated."

Therefore, on September 2, 1896, Zeeman took a piece of asbestos soaked in a solution of table salt (sodium) and placed it in a flame situated between the poles of a magnet. The resulting light seen through Zeeman's spectroscope produced the spectral lines—sharp lines appearing at various points in the familiar rainbow of the visible light spectrum—characteristic of sodium. When the magnet was turned on, these lines thickened significantly—an effect that had never been observed before. When the experiment was repeated later, using a stronger magnet, the lines split into multiple lines. This phenomenon was dubbed the Zeeman effect, and was provided with a theoretical explanation by another Dutch physicist, Hendrik Lorentz, with whom Zeeman shared the 1902 Nobel Prize in Physics for the discovery.

The implications and applications of the Zeeman effect were manifold. It helped confirm Lorentz's theory that atoms were in fact constructed of smaller, subatomic particles with electrical charges, and which were responsible for the emission of light. Thus, the Zeeman effect was important in helping establish the structure of the atom.

Zeeman's later results showed that the magnetic splitting of the lines was more complex than initially believed. Lorentz had predicted that the Zeeman effect would produce a splitting into three components or multiplets, but scientists soon found that most elements in fact split into four, six, or more lines. The theoretical three-component result became known as the "normal Zeeman effect"; those that do not fit the prediction are known as the "anomalous Zeeman effect." Ironically, however, it has been determined that most elements and conditions produce "anomalous" results, not "normal" ones. Experimentation also found that the larger the atom, the more complex the splitting of its spectral lines when within a magnetic field. Stronger magnetic fields were also found to increase the distance between the component lines. The Zeeman effect is now known to be caused by alterations of the energy states of electrons in magnetic fields. It is best described by electron spin, a topic in the field of quantum mechanics.

1896, he discovered that the spectral line of burning salt (sodium) divided when the flame was placed within the magnetic field created by a powerful electromagnet. The emitted radiation lines were split into lines with different wavelengths, frequencies, and polarizations. Zeeman observed and photographed the phenomenon using a concave grating with a ten-foot radius. Zeeman unveiled the results of his work on October 31, 1896, at a meeting of the Academy of Science in Amsterdam. Lorentz had predicted what happened during the experiment: that the lines would have circular polarization at the ends. Zeeman found that by reversing the magnet's polarity, he could view both edges of the line and that they were in fact "circularly polarized" in opposite directions. Zeeman always referred to his discovery as "the magnetic splitting of the spectral lines," though it became known as the Zeeman effect. He later published his notes in *Researches in Magneto-Optics* in 1913. In 1902, Zeeman and Lorentz received the Nobel Prize in Physics for their work in optics.

In 1897, Zeeman became a lecturer of physics at the University of Amsterdam. He was promoted to full professor in 1908 when he also became the director of the Physics Institute. In 1923, a new laboratory was built for Zeeman to continue his research into the magnetic splitting of spectral lines. The building was designed with temperature control and a dark room with a zig-zag entrance, which aided in improving the quality of photographic results. The lab was also designed with higher-quality grating spectrographs. The laboratory was later named for Zeeman in 1940.

Zeeman also studied the optical Doppler effect. The Doppler effect causes the wavelength of light to be shifted. For example, in astronomy, light waves from a distant galaxy moving toward the Earth will be shortened, or shifted toward the blue part of the spectrum. The light from galaxies moving away will have increased wavelengths and appear redshifted. Zeeman also investigated the propagation of light through moving media, like water, glass, and quartz. Along with one of his students, he also discovered a number of new isotopes, including argon-38 and nickel-64. Zeeman retired when he turned seventy in 1935. He and his wife had three daughters: Wilhelmina, Elisabeth, and Johanna, and one son, Jan. He died October 9, 1943, in Amsterdam.

IMPACT

The Zeeman effect has had a wide-ranging impact on physics and medical technology. It helped scientists better understand the mechanics of light radiation, the structure of the atom, and the behavior of the electron. Zeeman's discovery lead to J. J. Thomson's experiment that proved the existence of the electron. The Zeeman effect has also played an important role in various fields of spectroscopy, including electron spin resonance, atomic absorption, Mössbauer spectroscopy, and nuclear magnetic resonance (NMR) spectroscopy. Magnetic resonance imaging (MRI), the most common tool used by radiologists and doctors, would not be possible without the Zeeman effect. Other biological and medical applications include determining the presence of various chemicals like zinc, lead, cadmium, copper, and iron in blood, plasma, and urine. In addition to the Nobel Prize, Zeeman received various other awards throughout his career, including the Henry Draper Medal (from the National Academy of Sciences, 1921) and the Franklin Medal (from the Franklin Institute,

1925). He was a member of the Royal Netherlands Academy of Arts and Sciences, and held the position of secretary for eight years. He also was a member of many foreign science academies and received a number of honorary degrees.

Jennifer L. Campbell

FURTHER READING

Hunt, Bruce. *Pursuing Power and Light: Technology and Physics from James Watt to Albert Einstein.* Baltimore: Johns Hopkins UP, 2010. Print. Investigates the connection between nineteenth-century technology and advancements in modern physics. Discusses Zeeman, his discovery, and its impact.

Tipler, Paul A., and Ralph Llewellyn. *Modern Physics.* 6th ed. New York: Freeman, 2012. Print. Modern physics textbook designed for undergraduates. Covers the Zeeman effect in detail in mathematical and theoretical terms.

Velthuys-Bechthold, P. J. M. *Inventory of the Papers of Pieter Zeeman (1865–1943), Physicist and Nobel Prize Winner: C. 1877–1946.* Haarlem: Rijksarchief in Noord-Holland, 1993. Print. Inventory of the Zeeman's papers. Includes a review of documents donated to the North Holland Archives in Haarlem.

Zeeman, Pieter. *Researches in Magneto-Optics: With Special Reference to the Magnetic Resolution of Spectrum Lines.* London: Macmillan, 1913. Print. Zeeman's collection of works in magneto-optics, first published in 1913, written as a narrative. Includes chapters on spectroscope technology at the time, the effect bearing his name, issues with resolutions, circular polarization, Hale's sunspot discovery, and Thomson's discovery of the electron. .

NORTON DAVID ZINDER

American virologist

As a graduate student, twentieth-century American virologist Norton Zinder discovered transduction, the process by which genetic material is transferred between bacteria by bacteriophage (bacterial viruses). Later in his career, he discovered the first bacteriophage in which RNA was the genetic material.

Born: November 7, 1928; New York, New York

Died: February 3, 2012; New York, New York
Primary field: Biology
Specialties: Genetics; virology; microbiology

EARLY LIFE

Norton David Zinder was born November 7, 1928. He was the first of two sons of Harry Zinder, a local manufacturer, and Jean Gottesman Zinder. Following his early education in the New York public school system, he attended the Bronx High School of Science, founded in 1938 to provide education for gifted students in science and mathematics. He graduated in 1944 at the age of fifteen.

Zinder enrolled at Columbia University in New York City. He received his bachelor's degree in biology at the age of eighteen in 1947. While an undergraduate at Columbia, Zinder spent time in the zoology laboratory of biologist Francis J. Ryan. Among Ryan's former students was molecular biologist Joshua Lederberg, who by then was on the faculty at the University of Wisconsin, and it was Ryan who helped Lederberg apply techniques while working with the bread mold *Neurospora* to a system utilizing *Escherichia coli*. Ryan encouraged Zinder to pursue his postgraduate work at the University of Wisconsin in order to work with Lederberg.

LIFE'S WORK

Zinder joined Lederberg's laboratory in 1948. Lederberg had recently completed his graduate work with geneticist Edward Tatum and had codiscovered bacterial conjugation, the transfer of genetic material between cells. Lederberg had carried out this work using the bacterium *Escherichia coli* (*E. coli*), and was interested in determining whether the process could also take place among other species of bacteria.

Zinder began this work with the bacterium *Salmonella*, chosen in part because of the large number of available mutants. The experimental method was similar to that previously used by Lederberg for *E. coli*, crossing two different strains that had different amino acid nutritional requirements and observing whether recombinants were produced that were capable of synthesizing those amino acids. In the process of conjugation, it was thought that the bacteria must come into contact with each other for the genetic information to pass. However, Zinder found in his experiments that contact was not necessary; the two different strains could even be kept separate using a filter between them. Zinder's interpretation was that something physical was passing through the filter from one cell to another. The agent was shortly identified as a bacteriophage, a bacterial virus that was incorporating fragments of DNA from one strain and passing them to the second strain upon infection. Lederberg termed the process *transduction*. The same phenomenon was subsequently demonstrated in other species of bacteria.

In December 1949, Zinder married Marilyn Estreicher. Their fifty-five year marriage lasted until her death in 2004. The couple had two sons.

After receiving his PhD at Wisconsin in Medical Microbiology in 1952, Zinder accepted an offer as Assistant Professor at the Rockefeller Institute in New York, where he remained for the rest of his professional career. In 1960, Timothy Loeb joined Zinder's laboratory as a graduate student. Loeb was interested in whether bacteriophage existed that were "male" specific and were capable of infecting the pilus on *E. coli* bacteria, the means by which conjugation took place. Since *E.coli* was found in sewage, a logical place to search for such bacteriophage was at the sewage plant in New York. Loeb quickly found seven types of such phage, which he and Zinder termed f1 (for fertility) through f7. F1 was found to contain single-stranded DNA as its genetic material, but f2 through f7 all contained RNA as genetic material, the first such bacteriophage demonstrated to contain RNA. Zinder found that the viral RNA was not only the genome, but that it served as its own messenger RNA, associating with ribosomes for translation into proteins.

In 1964, Zinder was promoted to professor of genetics at the institute, and a decade later he was promoted to John D. Rockefeller, Jr. Professor of Molecular Genetics. That same year saw his appointment as chair of the committee for evaluation of the Virus Cancer Program. The Zinder Report's recommendation for altering the funding process resulted in a significant reorganization of the cancer program. In 1974, Zinder was also among those expressing concern about hazards associated with the new technology of recombinant DNA. The 1975 Asilomar Conference provided guidelines for such work.

During the late 1980s, scientists began work on what became known as the Human Genome Project, the goal of which was to sequence the entire human genome. Two figures stood at the forefront of the proposed project: James Watson, Nobel laureate for his role in determining the structure of DNA, and J. Craig Venter, biochemist and physiologist who entered the project as a private entrepreneur. The concern among many scientists was that if the project was publicly funded through research grants, the funding would occur at the expense of other equally worthwhile projects. At the time it was believed that relatively little of the human genome was relevant and that most consisted of unread sequences considered "junk." Zinder repeatedly pushed for serious

Zinder Discoveries Transduction, the Transfer of Genetic Information by Bacteriophage

In 1948, Norton Zinder joined Joshua Lederberg's laboratory as a first-year graduate student. Two years earlier Lederberg and Edward Tatum had discovered recombination as a means of transferring genetic material among strains of the bacterium *Escherichia coli.* Zinder planned to study the same phenomenon among a different species of bacteria, *Salmonella typhimurium.* The choice of *Salmonella* was not fortuitous. It was a known pathogen—certain strains were the etiological agents of typhoid fever—and a large number of mutant strains were already available in the Lederberg laboratory. The existence of so many strains suggested they might be useful in applying the recombination studies previously used for *E. coli.*

Zinder began by refining the procedure routinely used in creating auxotrophs (mutants), the addition of mutagens to the bacterial growth media, followed by screening for bacteria that had become the desired mutants. The challenge was the difficulty in the selection of mutants against the background of wild-type (normal) bacteria. Zinder correctly assumed that if penicillin was added to media that lacked the nutrient the mutant required, any (wild-type) bacteria that grew would be killed, leaving only mutants to be removed, washed, and isolated.

The initial experiments carried out by Zinder in which various combinations (crosses) of nutritional mutant auxotrophs were incubated together proved negative; he found no evidence for conjugation. Finally, after trying over one hundred combinations of crosses, he observed the presence of some recombinants. One explanation was these could potentially represent spontaneous reversion to the wild-type

rather than the result of conjugation. The problem was addressed by using individual auxotrophs with combinations of mutations, making spontaneous reversion of several genes simultaneously unlikely.

Conjugation between bacteria required direct contact. However, when Zinder placed the two different strains on opposite sides of a filter he again observed recombination, making conjugation unlikely to have been the explanation. Since the agent that caused the recombination must have passed through the filter, Zinder and Lederberg referred to it as a "filterable agent." Identification of the agent as a virus began with elimination of what it was not. Since it was not affected by the enzyme DNase, it was not likely free DNA, as would be the case with transformation. Its sensitivity to heat also ruled out DNA and pointed to a protein component. When the agent was observed with an electron microscope, it was identified as a bacteriophage. The biologic characteristics of the agent, such as the limitations in the quantities of the agent that could infect bacteria, also helped identify the agent as a bacteriophage. The timing of the discovery also played a role: Several years earlier Andre Lwoff had discovered lysogeny, the ability of bacteriophage to integrate into the bacterial genome.

The term *transduction* ("to lead across") in defining the role of bacteriophage as vector was coined by Lederberg at a scientific meeting in 1951. Lederberg applied the term in a more general sense, in part because he was not convinced of the unique role played by bacteriophage. Zinder, however, used the term in the sense in which it was subsequently defined, the view being widely accepted by the mid-1950s.

consideration by funding committees and was ultimately successful. The presence of Venter as a private citizen duplicating the work that Watson hoped to lead was also a concern. In 2000, Zinder negotiated an understanding between the different parties that allowed the project to continue.

Zinder died February 3, 2012 in New York at the age of eighty-three.

IMPACT

Zinder's discovery of transduction represented the third mechanism of transfer of genetic information between bacteria. As noted by other scientists in the

field of genetics, several aspects common to each of these mechanisms involving movement of genetic elements in bacteria set them apart from genetic recombination in eukaryotic organisms. First, recombination did not involve the entire genome but only portions of the DNA. The discovery of transduction altered the thinking applied to the role of viruses. In addition to possibly killing the bacterial cells they infect, viruses could also serve as vectors for the transfer of genetic material.

Within several years, two forms of transduction were shown to take place. Generalized transduction, as first described by Zinder, involved the transfer of random fragments of DNA, largely anything that was packaged during bacteriophage assembly. The discovery of lysogeny in bacteria, the integration of bacteriophage into the host genome usually at nonrandom sites, allowed for what became known as specialized transduction, the transfer of only those genes adjacent to the site of integration in the host.

The discovery of transduction provided one more technique for fine-structure genetic mapping of bacteria. By determining which genes co-transduced in the same fragment, it became possible to observe which particular genetic markers were adjacent to each other in the bacterial genome. Among the first of these discoveries was that genes that regulate specific metabolic pathways or regulate the expression of genes within a pathway are often closely linked to each other on the bacterial genome in an area that became known as the operon. For example, in the early 1960s, French molecular biologists François Jacob and Jacques Monod produced their model of regulation of the *lactose operon* by means of transducing specific genes within the operons of *Escherichia coli* and *Shigella*. The model

they produced became the basis for Jacob and Monod being awarded Nobel Prizes in Physiology or Medicine in 1965.

Richard Adler

FURTHER READING

Brock, Thomas. *The Emergence of Bacterial Genetics*. Woodbury, New York: Cold Spring Harbor Lab. P, 1990. Print. Reviews the history behind understanding bacterial genetics. Zinder's role in the discovery of transduction is discussed.

Crotty, Shane. *Ahead of the Curve: David Baltimore's Life in Science*. Berkeley: U of California P, 2001. Print. Biography of Nobel laureate David Baltimore. Addresses the significance of Zinder's role in the discovery of RNA phage.

Witkowski, Jan. *The Inside Story: DNA to RNA to Protein*. Woodbury, New York: Cold Spring Harbor Lab. P, 2005. Print. Includes a discussion of Zinder's discovery of RNA phage, which was among the first indications RNA could also serve as genetic material.

FRITZ ZWICKY

Swiss American astronomer

Astronomer and physicist Fritz Zwicky observed and named the supernova phenomenon. He also theorized the existence of neutron stars and dark matter, and patented numerous inventions related to jet propulsion.

Born: February 14, 1898; Varna, Bulgaria
Died: February 8, 1974; Pasadena, California
Primary fields: Astronomy; physics
Specialties: Astrophysics; theoretical astronomy; observational astronomy; condensed-matter (solid state) physics

EARLY LIFE

Fritz Zwicky was born on February 14, 1898, in Varna, Bulgaria. He was the eldest of the three children of wealthy Swiss merchant and longtime Bulgarian resident Fridolin Zwicky and his Czech wife, Franziska Wrcek Zwicky. When he was six years old, Zwicky was sent to Glarus, Switzerland, where his father's family had originated. He lived with his grandparents and enrolled at a boarding school in the village of Mollis. During his early education, when he demonstrated skills

in scientific subjects, Zwicky became an avid skier and mountain climber; he would retain a strong interest in sports throughout his life.

At the age of sixteen, Zwicky moved to Zurich. In 1916, he entered the Swiss Federal Institute of Technology, initially intending to follow his father into the world of business. However, he decided to pursue science and, with his father's permission, switched his focus to physics and mathematics. After taking courses from such teachers as physicist Albert Einstein, mathematician Herman Weyl, physicist Auguste Piccard, chemist Peter Debye, and physicist Paul Scherrer, Zwicky graduated with a bachelor's degree in 1920. He subsequently earned his PhD in physics in 1922 and remained at the institute for the next three years as a teacher of the subject.

In 1925, Robert A. Millikan, winner of the 1923 Nobel Prize in Physics, invited Zwicky to become a physics professor at the California Institute of Technology (Caltech). Zwicky accepted and relocated to Pasadena, where, for two years after assuming his teaching duties, he conducted research on the quantum theory of solids and liquids under a Rockefeller Fellowship provided by the International Education Board.

LIFE'S WORK

During Zwicky's years as an assistant professor of physics at Caltech, (1925–29) and associate professor (1929–42), he became known as a brilliant but quirky scientist. Recognized for his studies and publications on crystals, solid-state physics, ionization, and thermodynamics, Zwicky also earned a reputation for his peculiar sense of humor and his arrogance. In 1932, he married Dorothy Vernon Gates, the daughter of a wealthy California businessman; they divorced in 1941.

In the early 1930s, Zwicky's interests drifted toward astrophysics, with a focus on cosmic rays. He began working with German astronomer Walter Baade at the Mount Wilson and Palomar Observatories in southern California. During that decade, the two scientists concentrated their attention on distant galaxies, particularly infrequent extra-large stellar nuclear explosions, for which they coined the term "supernovae," because the event is considerably more energetic—more than one hundred million times brighter than the sun—than an ordinary nova. Zwicky theorized that supernovae create great bursts of cosmic rays in the process of becoming small-scale, extremely dense neutron stars. His hypotheses would not be proven for more than thirty years.

In the mid-1930s, Zwicky and Baade convinced Caltech to fund the installation of a wide-angle, low-distortion eighteen-inch Schmidt telescope at Mount Palomar, the first such instrument in North America. With the new telescope, Zwicky and numerous collaborators began scanning the skies for supernovae. Their search yielded most of the known supernovae—Zwicky himself discovered more than 120—and resulted in the 1960s in a six-volume catalog of some thirty thousand galaxies and galaxy clusters where the majority of supernovae occur. The *Catalogue of Galaxies and of Clusters of Galaxies* (1961–68) became a standard reference for the study of galaxies.

It was also during the 1930s that Zwicky suggested the existence of dark matter. In 1933, while studying the Coma Cluster of galaxies, he found that the galaxies have dispersed velocities. This indicated that a large, invisible mass has to be holding the cluster together. He called the unknown mass "dunkle materie," or dark matter. After estimating the mass of the Coma Cluster, first by measurements of galactic luminosities and then by measurements based on galactic velocities, he found the cluster's velocity-based mass to be four hundred times larger than his estimate based on luminosity. This, he postulated, means that the Coma Cluster is mostly composed of dark matter; by extension, most of the universe must be composed of dark matter.

In 1942, Zwicky became Caltech's first full professor of astrophysics, a position he retained until his retirement more than twenty-five years later. He specialized in teaching graduate-level courses in analytical mechanics and advanced seminars in astronomy.

That same year, Zwicky became a founder—along with Clark B. Millikan, Caltech aeronautics professor and son of Robert A. Millikan, and Hungarian-born aerospace engineer-physicist Theodore von Kármán—of Aerojet Engineering Corporation in Azusa, California. The company, formed during World War II, was initially established to create rocket engines to assist the launch of heavily laden bombers. Zwicky served as director of research at Aerojet (later a subsidiary of GenCorp) from 1943 to 1946, and was associated with the company as a technical adviser until the late 1950s.

After the end of the war, Zwicky traveled to Germany and Japan to visit secret weapons facilities, where he gained ideas that helped Aerojet develop high-energy fuels later used in solid-fuel rocket boosters. During his tenure at Aerojet, Zwicky patented dozens of concepts and pieces of high-tech equipment related to jet propulsion. In 1946, he used reconstituted German V-2 rocket to launch an artificial meteor to study the behavior of genuine meteors. In 1957, Zwicky experimented with the Aerobee rocket, a type of sounding rocket created by Aerojet to test and push the limits of traveling through Earth's atmosphere. The rocket reached an altitude of fifty-four miles above the southwestern United States, when high explosives blew it up. The blast launched streams of metal into space, and it is believed that one stream escaped from Earth's gravity to become the first man-made object to achieve orbit around the sun.

In 1947, Zwicky, by then a dual American-Swiss citizen, married Swiss native Anna Margaritha Zuercher. The couple would have three daughters: Margarit, Franziska, and Barbarina. A member of the American Astronautical Society, Zwicky also served as vice president of the International Academy of Astronautics. In 1949, US president Harry S. Truman awarded Zwicky the Medal of Freedom. He received the Royal Astronomical Society Gold Medal in 1972.

Throughout the 1950s and 1960s, Zwicky continued to teach, conduct astronomical research, and publish extensively; he wrote more than three hundred papers and books during his lifetime. Zwicky formally

Zwicky and Baade Propose the Existence of Neutron Stars

By the 1930s, studies of novas—stars that produce nuclear explosions—suggested that novas are not a simple class of stars. Some novas are bright and rare, while others are much fainter and more common. Astronomers Fritz Zwicky and Walter Baade recognized in 1934 that a division was necessary and renamed the brighter novas "supernovas."

Stars originate from collapsing clouds of gas and dust. As they become older, the interior pressure and temperature increase, producing chemical reactions in which hydrogen fuses into helium. Energy is released from this reaction in the form of light and other electromagnetic radiation. The length of a star's life cycle is determined by its mass. Low-mass stars such as the sun fuse the hydrogen slowly and have lifetimes of tens of billions of years. The most massive stars have lifetimes of tens of millions of years. As a star dies, it can do so in one of several ways. A low-mass star depletes its hydrogen supply, grows in size to become a "red giant," and then collapses to a "white dwarf" phase. It shines by its stored heat until eventually it cools and reaches the "black dwarf" stage. A star the size of the sun will shrink to the size of Earth.

A binary star system is a pair of stars that orbit a common center of gravity. A binary star system whose stars are near the end of their life cycles is the common source of nova explosions. Material from one of the stars is pulled onto the surface of the other star. When enough of it accumulates, it fuses to create helium and produce the brightening that can be seen as a nova.

A supernova, however, is the rapid explosion of a massive star near the end of its life cycle. When a massive star depletes its supply of hydrogen, it collapses and its internal heat and pressure increase until helium is converted to carbon. Elements with increasingly higher atomic numbers are formed as the collapse continues. Once the core becomes the element iron, the process cannot continue until more energy is added. At this point, the collapse continues because of gravity; in the last stages, the star's outer layers hit the core and bounce. The star explodes, sending a large part of its mass into space. The remainder of the supernova collapses to become a neutron star or a black hole, depending on its mass.

The existence of neutron stars was postulated jointly by Zwicky and Baade and independently by physicist Lev Davidovich Landau. They theorized that, after a supernova explosion, the pressure of the star's collapse overcomes the atoms' electrical forces and fuses protons and electrons into neutrons—thus creating a small, dense neutron star. This explanation was not verified experimentally until British astrophysicist Jocelyn Bell discovered the first pulsar in 1967. A pulsar is a neutron star that spins very rapidly, emitting radio waves from its rotating magnetic field. The discovered existence of pulsars provided the first observational evidence of Baade and Zwicky's theory.

retired from Caltech, becoming professor emeritus, in 1968. He died of a heart attack on February 8, 1974.

IMPACT

Zwicky was one of the most influential astronomer-astrophysicists in the United States during the twentieth century. Though the scientific community dismissed many of Zwicky's theories at the time of their publication—concerning supernovae, star clusters, galaxy masses and distances, neutron stars, cosmic rays, and blue, quasar-like stars—his theories were later shown to be accurate once technology had advanced sufficiently to confirm them. Zwicky's hypothesis that most of the universe is composed of dark matter has become widely accepted as true, and studies of dark matter continue in an attempt to unravel and understand those mysterious forces. In addition, the confirmed existence of neutron stars and supernovae has helped scientists understand the formation of galaxies in the universe.

Despite his sometimes arrogant personality, Zwicky had a large humanitarian streak. After World War II, he restocked many European scientific libraries destroyed in the conflagration and was a driving force in helping set up institutions for war orphans. Recognized both during and after his lifetime for his scientific and charitable achievements, Zwicky was inducted posthumously into the International Space Hall of Fame in 1976. An asteroid, a lunar crater, and a galaxy have been named in his honor. The Fritz Zwicky Foundation and Zwicky Museum, which houses his scientific papers and preserves his legacy, was established in Glarus, Switzerland, where he is buried.

Jack Ewing

FURTHER READING

Bartusiak, Marcia, ed. *Archives of the Universe: 100 Discoveries that Transformed Our Understanding of the Cosmos*. New York: Vintage, 2006. Print. A collection of essays and excerpts from scientific papers—including samples of Zwicky's groundbreaking writings—encompassing the study of the cosmos.

Gates, Evalyn. *Einstein's Telescope: The Hunt for Dark Matter and Dark Energy in the Universe*. New York: Norton, 2010. Print. An illustrated discussion of Einstein's theory of gravitational lensing, which Zwicky used in his theory about dark matter.

Impey, Chris. *How It Began: A Time-Traveler's Guide to the Universe*. New York: Norton, 2012. Print. An overview of significant milestones achieved in the scientific examination of the universe, including Zwicky's observations of distant galaxies.

Appendixes

CHRONOLOGICAL LIST OF ENTRIES

All people appearing in this list are the subjects of articles in Great Lives from History: Scientists and Science. *The names of the people are listed chronologically based on their date of birth.*

Ancient Times

Pythagoras (c. 580 BCE)
Anaxagoras (c. 500 BCE)
Democritus (c. 460 BCE)
Hippocrates (c. 460 BCE)
Eudoxus (c. 390 BCE)
Aristotle (c. 384 BCE)
Theophrastus (c. 372 BCE)
Euclid (c. 330 BCE)
Herophilus (c. 330 BCE)

Erasistratus (c. 304 BCE)
Archimedes (c. 287 BCE)
Eratosthenes of Cyrene (c. 276 BCE)
Apollonius of Perga (c. 262 BCE)
Hipparchus (c. 190 BCE)
Hero of Alexandria (c. 10)
Galen (of Pergamum) (c. 129)
Diophantus (c. 210)

Medieval Times

al-Khwarizmi (c. 780)
Alhazen (c. 965)

Leonardo of Pisa (Fibonacci) (c. 1170)

1401–1600

Leonardo da Vinci (April 15, 1452)
Nicolaus Copernicus (February 19, 1473)
Georgius Agricola (March, 24, 1494)
Andreas Vesalius (December 31, 1514)
Conrad Gesner (March 26, 1516)
Hieronymus Fabricius (May 20, 1537)
William Gilbert (May 24, 1544)
Giordano Bruno (c. 1548)

John Napier (c. 1550)
Sophia Brahe (August 24, 1556)
Johannes Kepler (December 27, 1571)
William Harvey (April 1, 1578)
Jan Baptista van Helmont (c. 1579)
Johannes Fabricius (January 8, 1587)
René Descartes (March 31, 1596)

1601–1700

Blaise Pascal (June 19, 1623)
Giovanni Domenico Cassini (June 8, 1625)
Robert Boyle (January 25, 1627)
John Ray (November 29, 1627)
Antoni van Leeuwenhoek (October 24, 1632)
Robert Hooke (July 18, 1635)
Nicolaus Steno (January 11, 1638)

Ole Christensen Rømer (September 25, 1644)
Gottfried Wilhelm Leibniz (July 1, 1646)
Elisabeth Hevelius (January 17, 1647)
Edmond Halley (November 8, 1656)
René-Antoine Ferchault de Réaumur (February 28, 1683)
Daniel Bernoulli (February 8, 1700)

1701–1800

Anders Celsius (November 27, 1701)
Leonhard Euler (April 15, 1707)
Carolus Linnaeus (May 23, 1707)
Georges-Louis Leclerc, Comte de Buffon (September 7, 1707)

Mikhail Vasilyevich Lomonosov (November 19, 1711)
Maria Gaetana Agnesi (May 16, 1718)
James Hutton (June 3, 1726)
Joseph Black (April 16, 1728)
Lazzaro Spallanzani (January 12, 1729)

Jan Ingenhousz (December 8, 1730)
Henry Cavendish (October 10, 1731)
Joseph-Louis Lagrange (January 25, 1736)
Charles-Augustin de Coulomb (June 14, 1736)
Luigi Galvani (September 9, 1737)
William Herschel (November 15, 1738)
Antoine-Laurent Lavoisier (August 26, 1743)
Jean-Baptiste Lamarck (August 1, 1744)
Giovanni Battista Venturi (March 15, 1746)
Jacques Charles (November 12, 1746)
Johann Elert Bode (January 19, 1747)
Pierre-Simon Laplace (March 23, 1749)
Joseph Louis Proust (September 26, 1754)
John Dalton (September 6, 1766)
Joseph Fourier (March 21, 1768)
Georges Cuvier (August 23, 1769)
Alexander von Humboldt (September 14, 1769)
Friedrich Mohs (January 29, 1773)
Thomas Young (June 13, 1773)
Robert Brown (December 21, 1773)

Jean-Baptiste Biot (April 21, 1774)
André-Marie Ampère (January 22, 1775)
Amedeo Avogadro (August 9, 1776)
Carl Friedrich Gauss (April 30, 1777)
Hans Christian Ørsted (August 14, 1777)
Jöns Jacob Berzelius (August 20, 1779)
Mary Somerville (December 26, 1780)
Siméon Denis Poisson (June 21, 1781)
David Brewster (December 11, 1781)
John James Audubon (April 26, 1785)
Georg Simon Ohm (March 16, 1789)
August Ferdinand Möbius (November 17, 1790)
Michael Faraday (September 22, 1791)
Charles Babbage (December 26, 1791)
Karl Ernst von Baer (February 29, 1792)
Gaspard-Gustave Coriolis (May 21, 1792)
Charles Lyell (November 14, 1797)
Mary Anning (May 21, 1799)
Friedrich Wöhler (July 31, 1800)

1801–1850

Germain Henri Hess (August 7, 1802)
Justus von Liebig (May 12, 1803)
Christian Doppler (November 29, 1803)
Matthias Jakob Schleiden (April 5, 1804)
Richard Owen (July 20, 1804)
Louis Agassiz (May 28, 1807)
Charles Darwin (February 12, 1809)
Theodor Schwann (December 7, 1810)
Johann Gottfried Galle (June 9, 1812)
Claude Bernard (July 12, 1813)
Karl Weierstrass (October 31, 1815)
George Boole (November 2, 1815)
Ada Lovelace (December 10, 1815)
Maria Mitchell (August 1, 1818)
James Prescott Joule (December 24, 1818)
Rudolf Virchow (October 13, 1821)
Rudolf Clausius (January 2, 1822)
Francis Galton (February 16, 1822)
Gregor Mendel (July 22, 1822)
Alfred Russel Wallace (January 8, 1823)
Gustav Robert Kirchhoff (March 12, 1824)
Lord Kelvin (June 26, 1824)
Henry Walter Bates (February 8, 1825)

Johann Jakob Balmer (May 1, 1825)
Emil Erlenmeyer (June 28, 1825)
Bernhard Riemann (September 17, 1826)
James Clerk Maxwell (June 13, 1831)
Othniel Charles Marsh (October 29, 1831)
August Weismann (January 17, 1834)
Dmitry Ivanovich Mendeleyev (February 8, 1834)
Johannes Diderik van der Waals (November 23, 1837)
Ernst Mach (February 18, 1838)
Josiah Willard Gibbs (February 11, 1839)
Edward Drinker Cope (July 28, 1840)
Ellen Swallow Richards (December 3, 1842)
Camillo Golgi (July 7, 1843)
Robert Koch (December 11, 1843)
Ludwig Boltzmann (February 20, 1844)
Wilhelm Conrad Röntgen (March 27, 1845)
Edwin Ray Lankester (May 15, 1847)
Hugo de Vries (February 16, 1848)
Margaret Lindsay Huggins (August 14, 1848)
Felix Klein (April 25, 1849)

Ivan Pavlov (September 26, 1849)
Henri Louis Le Chatelier (October 8, 1850)

1851–1860

Antoine Henri Becquerel (December 15, 1852)
Albert A. Michelson (December 19, 1852)
Hendrik Lorentz (July 18, 1853)
Johannes Robert Rydberg (November 8, 1854)
Edmund Beecher Wilson (October 19, 1856)
J. J. Thomson (December 18, 1856)
Andrija Mohorovičić (January 23, 1857)
Heinrich Rudolf Hertz (February 22, 1857)

Williamina Paton Stevens Fleming (May 15, 1857)
Edward Emerson Barnard (December 16, 1857)
Max Planck (April 23, 1858)
Jagadish Chandra Bose (November 30, 1858)
Svante August Arrhenius (February 19, 1859)
Pierre Curie (May 15, 1859)
William Maddock Bayliss (May 2, 1860)

1861–1870

William Bateson (August 8, 1861)
Vilhelm Bjerknes (March 14, 1862)
Annie Jump Cannon (December 11, 1863)
Walther Nernst (June 25, 1864)
Pieter Zeeman (May 25, 1865)
Ernest Henry Starling (April 17, 1866)
Thomas Hunt Morgan (September 25, 1866)

Marie Curie (November 7, 1867)
Robert Andrews Millikan (March 22, 1868)
Karl Landsteiner (June 14, 1868)
George Ellery Hale (June 29, 1868)
Henrietta Swan Leavitt (July 4, 1868)
Hans Spemann (June 27, 1869)

1871–1880

Ernest Rutherford (August 30, 1871)
Florence R. Sabin (November 9, 1871)
Karl Schwarzschild (October 9, 1873)
Johannes Stark (April 15, 1874)
Ludwig Prandtl (February 4, 1875)
Robert E. Horton (May 18, 1875)
Gilbert N. Lewis (October 23, 1875)
John J. R. Macleod (September 6, 1876)
G. H. Hardy (February 7, 1877)
Frederick Soddy (September 2, 1877)

Oswald Theodore Avery (October 21, 1877)
Henry Norris Russell (October 25, 1877)
Richard Goldschmidt (April 12, 1878)
Lise Meitner (November 7, 1878)
Johannes Nicolaus Brønsted (February 22, 1879)
Otto Hahn (March 8, 1879)
Albert Einstein (March 14, 1879)
Milutin Milankovitch (May 28, 1879)
Max von Laue (October 9, 1879)
Alfred Wegener (November 1, 1880)

1881–1890

Alexander Fleming (August 6, 1881)
Emmy Noether (March 23, 1882)
Percy Williams Bridgman (April 21, 1882)
Max Born (December 11, 1882)
Arthur Stanley Eddington (December 28, 1882)
Victor Francis Hess (June 24, 1883)
Peter Debye (March 24, 1884)
Niels Bohr (October 7, 1885)
Karl von Frisch (November 20, 1886)

Erwin Schrödinger (August 12, 1887)
James B. Sumner (November 19, 1887)
Henry Gwyn Jeffreys Moseley (November 23, 1887)
Srinivasa Ramanujan (December 22, 1887)
Chandrasekhara Venkata Raman (November 7, 1888)
Edwin Powell Hubble (November 20, 1889)
William Lawrence Bragg (March 31, 1890)
Hermann Joseph Müller (December 21, 1890)

1891–1900

James Chadwick (October 20, 1891)
J. B. S. Haldane (c. 1892)

Louis de Broglie (August 15, 1892)
Edward Victor Appleton (September 6, 1892)

Arthur Holly Compton (September 10, 1892)
Raymond Dart (February 4, 1893)
Harold C. Urey (April 29, 1893)
Marietta Blau (April 29, 1894)
Georges Lemaître (July 17, 1894)
Yellapragada SubbaRow (January 12, 1895)
Gerty Cori (August 15, 1896)
Carl F. Cori (December 5, 1896)
Fritz Zwicky (February 14, 1898)
Isidor Isaac Rabi (July 29, 1898)

Roger Arliner Young (August 20, 1899)
Albert Claude (August 24, 1899)
Theodosius Dobzhansky (January 25, 1900)
Frédéric Joliot-Curie (March 19, 1900)
Irène Joliot-Curie (September 12, 1897)
Wolfgang Pauli (April 25, 1900)
Jan Hendrik Oort (April 28, 1900)
Cecilia Payne-Gaposchkin (May 10, 1900)
Hans Adolf Krebs (August 25, 1900)

1901–1910

Henry Eyring (February 20, 1901)
Linus Pauling (February 28, 1901)
Werner Heisenberg (December 5, 1901)
Barbara McClintock (June 16, 1902)
Paul Dirac (August 8, 1902)
Eugene P. Wigner (November 17, 1902)
Louis S. B. Leakey (August 7, 1903)
George Wells Beadle (October 22, 1903)
Konrad Lorenz (November 7, 1903)
George D. Snell (December 19, 1903)
John von Neumann (December 28, 1903)
George Gamow (March 4, 1904)
J. Robert Oppenheimer (April 22, 1904)
Louis Néel (November 22, 1904)
Erwin Chargaff (August 11, 1905)
Carl David Anderson (September 3, 1905)
Severo Ochoa (September 24, 1905)
Karl Guthe Jansky (October 22, 1905)

Felix Bloch (October 23, 1905)
Gerard Peter Kuiper (December 7, 1905)
Clyde W. Tombaugh (February 4, 1906)
Kurt Gödel (April 28, 1906)
Harry Hammond Hess (May 24, 1906)
Maria Goeppert-Mayer (June 28, 1906)
Hans Albrecht Bethe (July 2, 1906)
Grace Murray Hopper (December 9, 1906)
Hideki Yukawa (January 23, 1907)
Rachel Carson (May 27, 1907)
J. Hans D. Jensen (June 25, 1907)
Edwin Mattison McMillan (September 18, 1907)
Lev Davidovich Landau (January 22, 1908)
Rita Levi-Montalcini (April 22, 1909)
Edward Tatum (December 14, 1909)
Jacques-Yves Cousteau (June 11, 1910)
Subrahmanyan Chandrasekhar (October 19, 1910)

1911–1920

Melvin Calvin (April 8, 1911)
John Archibald Wheeler (July 9, 1911)
Wernher von Braun (March 23, 1912)
Chien-Shiung Wu (May 31, 1912)
Alan Turing (June 23, 1912)
Mary Leakey (February 6, 1913)
Paul Erdös (March 26, 1913)
Maurice Vincent Wilkes (June 26, 1913)
Mildred Cohn (July 12, 1913)
Norman Borlaug (March 25, 1914)
Max Perutz (May 19, 1914)
James Van Allen (September 7, 1914)
Robert Hofstadter (February 5, 1915)

Fred Hoyle (June 24, 1915)
Norman F. Ramsey (August 27, 1915)
Claude Shannon (April 30, 1916)
Francis Crick (June 8, 1916)
Jean Dausset (October 19, 1916)
Maurice Wilkins (December 15, 1916)
Richard Feynman (May 11, 1918)
Edward B. Lewis (May 20, 1918)
Frederick Sanger (August 13, 1918)
Kenichi Fukui (October 4, 1918)
David Blackwell (April 24, 1919)
E. Margaret Burbidge (August 12, 1919)
Rosalind Franklin (July 25, 1920)

1921–1930

Yoichiro Nambu (January 18, 1921)
Rosalyn Yalow (July 19, 1921)
Leon M. Lederman (July 15, 1922)
Chen Ning Yang (October 1, 1922)
Joshua Lederberg (May 23, 1925)
Emmett Chappelle (October 25, 1925)
Abdus Salam (January 29, 1926)
Paul Berg (June 30, 1926)
F. Sherwood Rowland (June 28, 1927)
Martha Chase (November 30, 1927)

James D. Watson (April 6, 1928)
Eugene M. Shoemaker (April 28, 1928)
Norton David Zinder (November 7, 1928)
Peter Higgs (May 29, 1929)
Werner Arber (June 3, 1929)
Carolyn Shoemaker (June 24, 1929)
Murray Gell-Mann (September 15, 1929)
Maarten Schmidt (December 28, 1929)
Stanley Miller (March 7, 1930)

1931–1940

Dian Fossey (January 16, 1932)
Paul R. Ehrlich (May 29, 1932)
Luc Montagnier (August 18, 1932)
Steven Weinberg (May 3, 1933)
Jane Goodall (April 3, 1934)
Leonard Kleinrock (June 13, 1934)
Carl Sagan (November 9, 1934)
Howard Martin Temin (December 10, 1934)
Samuel C. C. Ting (January 27, 1936)

J. Michael Bishop (February 22, 1936)
Hiroo Kanamori (October 17, 1936)
Roald Hoffmann (July 18, 1937)
Lynn Margulis (March 5, 1938)
David Baltimore (March 7, 1938)
Ivan Sutherland (May 16, 1938)
Ada E. Yonath (June 22, 1939)
Harold E. Varmus (December 18, 1939)
Joseph L. Goldstein (April 18, 1940)

1941–1950

Richard Dawkins (March 26, 1941)
Stephen Jay Gould (September 10, 1941)
Stephen Hawking (January 8, 1942)
Christiane Nüsslein-Volhard (October 20, 1942)
Mario Molina (March 19, 1943)
Jocelyn Bell Burnell (July 15, 1943)
Kary Mullis (December 28, 1944)
Biruté Galdikas (May 10, 1946)
Shirley Ann Jackson (August 5, 1946)
J. Craig Venter (October 14, 1946)

Michio Kaku (January 24, 1947)
Eric F. Wieschaus (June 8, 1947)
Françoise Barré-Sinoussi (July 30, 1947)
France Anne Córdova (August 5, 1947)
Flossie Wong-Staal (August 27, 1947)
Margaret Geller (December 8, 1947)
Steven Chu (February 28, 1948)
Elizabeth Blackburn (November 26, 1948)
Francis S. Collins (April 14, 1950)

1951–1980

Edward Witten (August 26, 1951)
Venkatraman Ramakrishnan (c. 1952)
Jack W. Szostak (November 9, 1952)
Adriana Ocampo Uria (January 5, 1955)
Freda Porter-Locklear (October 14, 1957)

Andrew Z. Fire (April 27, 1959)
Craig Mello (October 18, 1960)
Carol W. Greider (April 15, 1961)
Jane X. Luu (c. 1963)
Terence Tao (July 17, 1975)

TIMELINE

The more than 750 events below represent milestones in the major sciences, theoretical and applied, from ancient times to 2012.

DATE	MILESTONE
585 BCE	Thales of Miletus, a Greek philosopher, predicts a solar eclipse. About the same time he theorizes that water is the fundamental element for all substances. He also records the first description of electric and magnetic attraction.
c. 550 BCE	Greek philosopher and astronomer Anaximander proposes a theory of biological evolution. Around the same time he offers the first proposal that Earth is suspended in space.
c. 530 BCE	Greek mathematician and philosopher Pythagoras invents the Pythagorean theorem. He also argues that Earth is a sphere and that the sun, stars, and other planets revolve around it.
c. 500 BCE	The Greek physician and scientist Alcmaeon of Croton makes the first known dissections of dead human bodies.
5th cent. BCE	Greek philosopher Anaxagoras writes *On Nature*, arguing that the mind exists and that matter is composed of an infinite number of atomic elements. He also explains the phases and eclipses of the moon.
c. 430 BCE	Death of Greek philosopher Empedocles, who held that all matter is made of four elements: water, fire, air, and earth.
c. 400 BCE	Greek philosopher Philolaus is the first known person to argue that Earth moves along with the sun around a speculated "Central Fire."
c. 370 BCE	Death of Greek physician Hippocrates, author of many books with detailed case histories and proposed physical explanations for diseases. The Hippocratic Oath, which appears later, represents his principles.
c. 325 BCE	Greek physician Praxagoras of Cos discovers the value of measuring the pulse when diagnosing diseases.
c. 323 BCE	Aristotle theorizes about the nature of species, reproduction, and hybrids.
c. 320 BCE	Theophrastus initiates the study of botany.
c. 300 BCE	Greek mathematician Euclid of Egypt writes *Elements*, which includes a summary of plane and solid geometry.
c. 300 BCE	The Yellow Emperor's *Classic of Internal Medicine*, a compilation attributed to Chinese emperor Huangdi, contains references to the function of the heart and the circulation of the blood.

DATE	MILESTONE
Early 3rd cent. BCE	Greek astronomer Aristarchus of Samos writes *On the Size and Distance of the Sun and the Moon*, arguing that the Earth revolves around the sun.
c. 250 BCE	Greek scientist Archimedes becomes the first to discuss the principle of buoyancy for floating objects, later known as Archimedes's principle.
240 BCE	Chinese astronomers make the first known observation of Halley's comet.
240 BCE	Eratosthenes of Cyrene, librarian of Alexandria, Egypt, correctly calculates the circumference of Earth at about 25,000 miles.
200 BCE	The Greeks invent the astrolabe to determine the positions of the stars.
165 BCE	The Chinese make the first known observations of sunspots.
150 BCE	Greek astronomer Hipparchus of Nicaea calculates that the moon is about 240,000 miles from Earth.
c. 100 BCE	Greek philosopher Poseidonius shows correlation between tides and the lunar cycle.
7 BCE	Greek philosopher Strabo summarizes geographical knowledge in his *Geography*.
77	Roman natural philosopher Pliny the Elder publishes *Natural History*, which will serve as a standard scientific handbook until the Renaissance.
c. 10	Chinese inventor Cai Lun makes paper out of wood, rags, or other materials containing cellulose.
c. 150	Alexandrian scientist Ptolemy argues that all heavenly bodies move around a fixed Earth on epicycle paths.
c. 157–201	Greek physician and anatomist Galen proves that the arteries carry blood but incorrectly explains how the blood passes through the heart.
595–665	Invention of decimals and negative numbers.
619	Europeans begin to use tidal mills.
7th–8th cent.	The Maya build an astronomical observatory at Palenque.
c. 803	Abu-Musa Jabir ibn Hayyan becomes the first chemist to produce sulfuric acid, as well as many other chemicals and instruments.
833	Al-Farghânî, known as Alfraganus, publishes *Elements of Astronomy*, detailing celestial motions, and providing a study on the science of stars.
Mid-9th cent.	Invention of firearms using gunpowder.

DATE	MILESTONE
c. 920	Al-Uqlidisi, an Arab mathematician, modifies the Hindu number system; it is noted that he may have been the first to use decimals.
c. 953–1029	Al-Karaji becomes the first person to free algebra from geometrical operations.
c. 1093–1162	Ibn Zuhr successfully performs a tracheotomy on a goat, proving it safe for humans.
c. 1118	Omar Khayyam discovers a geometrical method of solving cubic equations by intersecting a parabola with a circle. He also discovers that cubic equations can have more than one solution.
c. 1135	Sharafeddin Tusi writes a treatise on cubic equations, beginning the study of algebraic geometry.
c.1213–1288	Ibn Al-Nafis becomes the first to correctly describe pulmonary circulation.
c.1224–1248	Ibn al-Baitar contributes his *Book of Simple Drugs and Food*, which becomes one of the great treatises of botany, used until the eighteenth century.
c. 1259	Gilbert the Englishman describes the loss of sensation of the skin as one of the early stages of leprosy, which becomes one of the best early diagnostic symptoms.
1266	Hugh and Theodoric Borgognoni advocate the use of narcotic-filled sponges to put patients to sleep prior to surgery. They also recommend cleaning wounds with wine and stitching together deep cuts so that they can heal better.
1268	Roger Bacon comments on the use of lenses for optical purposes, they become introduced by Alessandro di Spina in Italy.
1275	Invention of the first mechanical clock.
Late 13th cent.	Bethlehem Royal Hospital, later simply Bedlam, is built in London and eventually specialized for mental patients.
1316	Mondino of Luzzi publishes *Anatomia*; he also introduces the practice of public dissections as a teaching method.
c. 1323	William Ockham publishes *Quaestiones super quatuor libros senteniarum*, which introduces the distinction between dynamic motion and kinematic motion.
1328	Thomas Bradwardine's *Treatise on Proportions* begins a period of intense investigation at Merton College, Oxford, into what would later be called the laws of physics.
1341	Gentile da Foligno performs the first anatomical dissection in Padua.
Before 1361	Nicole Oresme invents coordinate geometry; he also is the first to use a fractional exponent.

DATE	MILESTONE
1423	Venice sets up its first lazaretto, or quarantine station, on an island outside the city, which becomes the model for other European countries and the basis for widespread quarantine control for many centuries.
1424	Al-Kashi makes his famous calculation of pi to sixteen decimal places, which does not get eclipsed for some two hundred years.
1437	Ulugh Beg publishes *Catalogue of the Stars*, which contains the positions of 992 stars, as well as calendar calculations and important results in trigonometry, including tables of sines and tangents given at 1 degree intervals to a high degree of accuracy.
1462	Regiomontanus (Johann Müller) completes the *Epitome of Ptolemy's Almagest*. His work forms the basis of trigonometry in Western Europe as handed down from the Arab world.
c. 1478–1519	Leonardo da Vinci compiles his notebooks.
1490–1492	Martin Behaim builds the first world globe.
1517	Fracastoro develops his theory of fossils.
1530s–1540s	Paracelsus presents his theory of disease.
1543	Copernicus publishes *De revolutionibus*, articulating his heliocentric view of the universe.
1543	Vesalius publishes *On the Fabric of the Human Body*, which will be used for human anatomical studies for generations.
1546	Fracastoro discovers that contagion spreads disease.
1550s	Tartaglia publishes *The New Science*.
1553	Michael Servetus describes pulmonary circulation of the blood.
1572–1574	Tycho Brahe observes a supernova and conducts astronomical observations and measurements on which Johannes Kepler will base much of his work.
1580s–1590s	Galileo conducts his early experiments in motion and falling bodies.
1600	William Gilbert publishes *De Magnete*, pioneering the study of magnetism and Earth's magnetic field.
1601–1672	Rise of European scientific societies, which join great mathematical and scientific minds with official approval and institutionalized support.
Sept. 1608	Hans Lippershey invents a simple telescope, credited as the first.
1609–1619	Johannes Kepler develops his laws of planetary motion.

DATE	MILESTONE
1610	Galileo confirms the heliocentric model of solar system.
1612	Sanctorius (Santorio) invents the clinical thermometer.
1615–1696	Sir Isaac Newton and Gottfried Wilhelm Leibniz independently invent the calculus.
1620	Sir Francis Bacon publishes *Novum Organum*, in which he advocates an inductive, empirical scientific method.
1623–1674	Appearance of the earliest calculators.
1628	William Harvey publishes *Exercitatio Anatomica de Motu Cordis et Sanguinis*, which describes general circulation of the blood.
1632	Galileo publishes *Dialogue Concerning the Two Chief World Systems*, Ptolemaic and Copernican.
1637	René Descartes publishes *Discourse on Method*, articulating the Cartesian scientific method.
1643	Evangelista Torricelli measures atmospheric pressure.
1651	William Harvey suggests that all living things must originate in an egg.
1655–1663	Francesco Grimaldi discovers the principle of light diffraction.
Feb. 1656	Christiaan Huygens identifies the rings of Saturn.
1660s–1700	Antoni van Leeuwenhoek and others conduct the first observations using microscopes.
1660–1692	The "father of modern chemistry," Robert Boyle, discovers the inverse relationship between the pressure and volume of a gas and uses a corpuscular (atomic) theory of matter to explain his experimental results.
1664	Thomas Willis identifies the basal ganglia.
1665	Gian Domenico Cassini discovers Jupiter's Great Red Spot.
1669	Nicholas Steno, the "father of stratigraphy," presents his theories of fossils and dynamic geology.
c. 1670	First widespread smallpox inoculations using a method imported from the Ottoman Empire, variolation.
Dec. 1671	Sir Isaac Newton builds the first reflecting telescope.
Dec. 7, 1676	Ole Rømer calculates the speed of light.
1677	Antoni van Leeuwenhoek describes sperm and eggs and collects evidence that helps disprove the theory of spontaneous generation.

DATE	MILESTONE
1686	Edmond Halley develops the first weather map.
Summer 1687	Sir Isaac Newton publishes his *Principia*, the most important scientific treatise of the century, in which he presents his theory of universal gravitation.
1691–1694	German botanist Rudolph Jacob Camerarius establishes the existence of sex in plants.
July 25, 1698	Thomas Savery patents the first successful steam engine.
1704	Sir Isaac Newton publishes Opticks.
1705–1712	Thomas Newcomen develops the steam engine.
1709	Abraham Darby invents coke-smelting of iron ore.
1714	Henry Mill patents the typewriter.
1714	Daniel Fahrenheit develops the mercury thermometer.
1714–1735	The quest for a means of determining longitude at sea leads John Harrison to develop his chronometer.
1718	Publication of Daniel Bernoulli's *Calculus of Variations*.
1722	René-Antoine Réaumur discovers carbon's role in hardening steel.
1722–1733	Abraham de Moivre describes the bell-shaped curve.
1725	John Flamsteed issues the first comprehensive star catalog, *Historia Coelistis Britannica*.
1729	Stephen Gray discovers the principles of electric conduction.
1733	Charles Du Fay describes positive and negative electric charge.
1735	George Hadley describes atmospheric circulation.
1735	Carl Linnaeus creates the binomial system of classification of plants and animals.
1735–1743	Charles La Condamine measures a meridional arc at the equator and explores the Amazon River basin.
1738	Daniel Bernoulli proposes the kinetic theory of gases.
1742	Anders Celsius proposes an international fixed temperature scale.
1743–1744	Jean le Rond d'Alembert develops his axioms of motion.
1745	Invention of the Leyden jar.

DATE	MILESTONE
1746	John Roebuck develops the lead-chamber process.
1748	James Bradley discovers the nutation of Earth's axis.
1748	Jean-Antoine Nollet discovers osmosis.
1748	Maria Agnesi publishes *Analytical Institutions*, a two-volume textbook on calculus that offers a complete synthesis of the mathematical methods developed in the scientific revolution.
1748	Leonhard Euler develops integral calculus.
1749–1789	Georges Leclerc publishes *Natural History*, the first comprehensive examination of the natural world.
1751	Pierre Louis de Maupertuis postulates "hereditary particles" as the basis for inherited traits.
1752	Benjamin Franklin demonstrates the electrical nature of lightning.
1752	Johann Tobias Mayer's lunar tables enable mariners to determine longitude at sea.
1753	James Lind identifies citrus fruit as a preventive for scurvy.
1755	Joseph Black identifies carbon dioxide.
1757	Alexander Monro distinguishes between lymphatic and blood systems.
1759	Franz Aepinus publishes *Theory of Electricity and Magnetism*.
1764	The Reverend Thomas Bayes issues his "Essay Towards Solving a Problem in the Doctrine of Chances," on inverse probability.
1765–1769	James Watt develops his steam engine.
1766	Albrecht von Haller publishes *Elements of Human Physiology*.
1767–1768	Lazzaro Spallanzani refutes the theory of spontaneous generation.
1771	Discovery of picric acid and its explosive properties.
1772–1789	Antoine-Laurent Lavoisier devises the modern system of chemical nomenclature.
c. 1773	Sir William Herschel builds his reflecting telescope.
1774	Joseph Priestley discovers oxygen.
1777	Jan Ingenhousz discovers photosynthesis.
1783	Nicolas Leblanc develops a process for producing soda from common salt.

Date	Milestone
1784	Adrien-Marie Legendre introduces polynomials.
1784–1785	Henry Cavendish discovers the composition of water.
1785–1788	James Hutton proposes the uniformitarian theory of the history of Earth and geologic change.
1796	Pierre-Simon Laplace articulates his nebular hypothesis.
1796–1798	Edward Jenner develops smallpox vaccination.
1799	Discovery of the earliest anesthetics.
1799	Joseph Louis Proust establishes law of definite proportions, thus effectively distinguishing between chemical elements and chemical compounds.
1800	Alessandro Volta invents the battery.
1801	Astronomers make the first discovery of an asteroid, Ceres.
1803–1807	John Dalton formulates the atomic theory of matter.
1804	Nicolas de Saussure publishes *Chemical Research in Vegetation*.
c. 1805	William H. Wollaston develops principles of modern metallurgy and later discovers the dark lines in the solar spectrum.
1809	Jean-Baptiste Lamarck publishes *Zoological Philosophy*, in which he sets forth his law of acquired characteristics.
1814	Joseph Fraunhofer invents the spectroscope.
1816	René Laennec invents the stethoscope.
1820s	André Ampère reveals magnetism's relationship to electricity.
1830	Sir Charles Lyell publishes *Principles of Geology*.
1831	Michael Faraday converts magnetic force into electricity.
1835	Charles Babbage invents a mechanical calculator.
1838	G. J. Mulder precipitates a fibrous material from cells, which he calls "protein."
1838–1839	Matthias Schleiden and Theodor Schwann's cell theory becomes the foundation of modern biology.
1839	Louis Daguerre and Joseph Niepce invent daguerreotype photography.

DATE	MILESTONE
1840	Justus von Liebig invents artificial fertilizers.
1846	First demonstration of surgical anesthesia by ether inhalation.
1847	Ignaz Philipp Semmelweis recognizes that puerperal fever is spreading within his hospital by transmission from doctors, nurses, and medical students and advances antiseptic practices by insisting on hand washing.
1847	George Boole publishes *Mathematical Analysis of Logic*, establishing the field of mathematical logic.
1850	Rudolf Clausius formulates second law of thermodynamics.
1850	Theodore Schwann, Matthias Schleiden, and Rudolf Virchow recognize that tissues are made up of cells.
1855	Alfred Russel Wallace publishes *On the Law Which Has Regulated the Introduction of New Species*, in which he develops the theory of natural selection around the same time as Charles Darwin.
1855–1859	Sir Henry Bessemer develops new methods for processing steel.
1856	Louis Pasteur begins research into fermentation, later developing his "pasteurization" process.
1858	Étienne Lenoir invents the internal combustion engine.
1859	Charles Darwin publishes *On the Origin of Species by Means of Natural Selection*, in which he sets forth his theory of natural selection, the mechanism of evolution.
1861	The oldest bird fossil, Archaeopteryx, is discovered at Solnhofen.
1864–1867	Joseph Lister promotes antiseptic surgery.
1866	Alfred Nobel invents dynamite.
1866	Ernst Haeckel develops the hypothesis that hereditary information is transmitted by the cell nucleus.
1866	Gregor Mendel, an Austrian monk, publishes a paper introducing his ideas of the mechanisms of heredity, including dominant and recessive traits.
1868	The bones of a Cro-Magnon skeleton, thought to be the earliest modern human being, are discovered in France.
1868	Christopher Latham Sholes patents a practical typewriter.
1869	George Westinghouse patents air brakes.

Date	Milestone
1869	Friedrich Miescher isolates "nuclein" from the nuclei of white blood cells, which is later found to be the nucleic acids DNA and RNA.
1869	Dmitry Mendeleyev develops the periodic table of elements.
1871	Charles Darwin publishes *The Descent of Man and Selection in Relation to Sex*.
1875	Oskar Hertwig demonstrates the fertilization of an ovum in a sea urchin, establishing the principle of sexual reproduction: the union of egg and sperm cells.
1876	Alexander Graham Bell invents the telephone.
1876	Nikolaus Otto invents a practical internal combustion engine.
1877	Thomas Alva Edison patents the cylinder phonograph.
1879	Thomas Alva Edison demonstrates the incandescent lamp, an early form of the lightbulb.
1880	Walter Fleming first describes mitosis.
1882	The first birth control clinic is established in Amsterdam.
1882–1884	Robert Koch isolates microorganisms that cause tuberculosis and cholera.
1883	Wilhelm Roux theorizes that mitosis must result in equal sharing of all chromosomal particles.
1883	Francis Galton founds the field of eugenics.
1885	Karl Benz develops the first practical automobile.
1887	Hannibal Williston Goodwin develops celluloid film.
1887–1890	Theodor Boveri notes that chromosomes are preserved through cell division and that sperm and egg contribute equal numbers of chromosomes.
1888–1906	Santiago Ramón y Cajal establishes the neuron as the functional unit of the nervous system.
1890–1901	Emil von Behring discovers the diphtheria antitoxin.
1893	Rudolf Diesel patents the diesel engine.
1895	Wilhelm Röntgen discovers X-rays.
1896	Guglielmo Marconi patents the telegraph.
1897	Felix Hoffman invents aspirin.
1897	Sir Ronald Ross discovers the malaria bacillus.

DATE	MILESTONE
1897–1901	John Jacob Abel and Jokichi Takamine independently isolate adrenaline.
1898	Martinus Beijerinck discovers viruses.
1898–1902	Teisserenc de Bort discovers the stratosphere and the troposphere.
Sept. 1898–July 1900	David Hilbert develops a model for Euclidean geometry in arithmetic.
Early 1900s	Willem Einthoven develops the forerunner of the electrocardiogram.
1900	Sir Frederick Hopkins discovers tryptophan, an essential amino acid.
1900	Emil Wiechert invents the inverted pendulum seismography.
1900–1901	Karl Landsteiner discovers human blood groups.
June 1900–Feb. 1901	Walter Reed establishes that yellow fever is transmitted by mosquitoes.
July 2, 1900	Ferdinand von Zeppelin constructs the first dirigible that flies.
Dec. 14, 1900	Max Planck announces his quantum theory.
1901	Julius Elster and Hans Friedrich Geitel demonstrate radioactivity in rocks, springs, and air.
1901	The first synthetic vat dye, indanthrene blue, is synthesized.
1901	Gerrit Grijns proposes that beriberi is caused by a nutritional deficiency.
1901	Ilya Ivanov develops artificial insemination.
Dec. 12, 1901	Guglielmo Marconi receives the first transatlantic telegraphic radio transmission.
1902	Beppo Levi recognizes the axiom of choice in set theory.
1902	Clarence McClung plays a role in the discovery of the sex chromosome.
1902	Walter S. Sutton states that chromosomes are paired and could be carriers of hereditary traits.
1902	Alexis Carrel develops a technique for rejoining severed blood vessels.
1902	Richard Zsigmondy invents the ultramicroscope.
1902	Arthur Edwin Kennelly and Oliver Heaviside propose the existence of the ionosphere.
June 1902	William Maddock Bayliss and Ernest Henry Starling discover secretin and establish the role of hormones.
1903	Konstantin Tsiolkovsky proposes that liquid oxygen be used for space travel.

DATE	MILESTONE
Sept. 10, 1903	Marie Curie, along with her husband, Pierre Curie, and Henri Becquerel, is awarded the Nobel Prize in Physics for her role in the discovery of natural radioactivity. She becomes the first woman to win a Nobel Prize.
Dec. 17, 1903	The Wright brothers launch the first successful airplane.
1904–1907	L. E. J. Brouwer develops intuitionist foundations of mathematics.
1904–1908	Ernst Zermelo undertakes the first comprehensive axiomatization of set theory.
1904	Julius Elster and Hans Friedrich Geitel devise the first practical photoelectric cell.
1904	Johannes Franz Hartmann discovers the first evidence of interstellar matter.
1904	Jacobus Cornelis Kapteyn discovers two star streams in the galaxy.
May 1904	Sir Charles Scott Sherrington delivers the lectures that would form *The Integrative Action of the Nervous System.*
Nov. 16, 1904	Sir John Ambrose Fleming files a patent for the first vacuum tube.
1905	George Washington Crile performs the first direct blood transfusion.
1905	Albert Einstein develops his theory of the photoelectric effect.
1905–1907	Bertram Boltwood uses radioactivity to obtain the age of rocks.
1905	Ejnar Hertzsprung notes the relationship between color and luminosity of stars.
1905	Reginald Punnett's Mendelism presents his diagrams showing how hereditary traits are passed from one generation to the next.
Aug. 1905	Percival Lowell predicts the existence of Pluto.
1906	Frederick Gardner Cottrell invents the electrostatic precipitation process.
1906	Sir Frederick Hopkins suggests that food contains vitamins essential to life.
1906	Charles Glover Barkla discovers the characteristic X-rays of the elements.
1906	Andrey Markov discovers the theory of linked probabilities.
1906–1910	Richard D. Oldham and Andrija Mohorovicic determine the structure of Earth's interior.
1906–1913	Richard Willstätter discovers the composition of chlorophyll.
Dec. 1906	J. J. Thomson wins the Nobel Prize for the discovery of the electron.

DATE	MILESTONE
Dec. 24, 1906	Reginald Aubrey Fessenden perfects radio by transmitting music and voice.
1907	Louis and Auguste Lumière develop color photography.
1907	John Scott Haldane develops stage decompression for deep-sea divers.
1907	Ejnar Hertzsprung describes giant and dwarf stellar divisions.
Spring 1907	Ross Granville Harrison observes the development of nerve fibers in the laboratory.
1908	Fritz Haber develops a process for extracting nitrogen from the air.
1908	G. H. Hardy and Wilhelm Weinberg present a model of population genetics.
1908	Charles Proteus Steinmetz warns of pollution in *The Future of Electricity.*
1908–1915	Thomas Hunt Morgan develops the gene-chromosome theory.
Feb. 11, 1908	Hans Geiger and Ernest Rutherford develop the Geiger counter.
June 26, 1908	George Ellery Hale discovers strong magnetic fields in sunspots.
Nov. 1908	Paul Ehrlich and Élie Metchnikoff conduct pioneering research in immunology.
Dec. 1908	Marcellin Boule reconstructs the first Neanderthal skeleton.
1910	Peyton Rous discovers that some cancers are caused by viruses.
1910	Bertrand Russell and Alfred North Whitehead's *Principia Mathematica* develops the logistic movement in mathematics.
1910	J. J. Thomson confirms the possibility of isotopes.
Apr. 1910	Paul Ehrlich introduces Salvarsan as a cure for syphilis.
Fall 1911	Alfred H. Sturtevant produces the first chromosome map.
1912	Henrietta Swan Leavitt's study of variable stars unlocks galactic distances.
1912	Vesto Slipher obtains the spectrum of a distant galaxy.
1912–1913	Niels Bohr writes a trilogy on atomic and molecular structure.
1912–1914	John Jacob Abel develops the first artificial kidney.
1912–1915	X-ray crystallography is developed by William Henry and Lawrence Bragg.
Jan. 1912	Alfred Lothar Wegener proposes the theory of continental drift.

DATE	MILESTONE
Mar. 7, 1912	Ernest Rutherford presents his theory of the atom.
Aug. 7 and 12, 1912	Victor Franz Hess discovers cosmic rays through high-altitude ionizations.
1913	Thomas Alva Edison introduces the kinetophone to show the first talking pictures.
1913	Henry Ford produces automobiles on a moving assembly line.
1913	Ejnar Hertzsprung uses cepheid variables to calculate the distances to stars.
1913	Geothermal power is produced for the first time.
1913	Beno Gutenberg discovers the mantle-outer core boundary of Earth's core.
1913	Albert Salomon develops mammography.
1913	Béla Schick introduces the Schick test for diphtheria.
Jan. 17, 1913	Charles Fabry quantifies ozone in the upper atmosphere.
Dec. 1913	Henry Norris Russell announces his theory of stellar evolution.
1914	Ernest Rutherford discovers the proton.
Oct. 1915	Transatlantic radiotelephony is first demonstrated.
Oct. 1915–Mar. 1917	Paul Langevin develops active sonar for submarine detection and fathometry.
Nov. 25, 1915	Albert Einstein completes his theory of general relativity.
1916	Karl Schwarzschild develops a solution to the equations of general relativity.
1917	Insecticide use intensifies when arsenic proves effective against the boll weevil.
Jan. 8, 1918	Harlow Shapley proves the sun is distant from the center of our galaxy.
1919	Francis William Aston builds the first mass spectrograph and discovers isotopes.
1919	Richard von Mises develops the frequency theory of probability.
1919	The principles of shortwave radio communication are discovered.
1919–1921	Vilhelm Bjerknes discovers fronts in atmospheric circulation.
Nov. 6, 1919	Albert Einstein's theory of gravitation is confirmed.
Early 1920s	Vesto Slipher presents evidence of redshifts in galactic spectra.

DATE	MILESTONE
1920–1930	Robert Andrews Millikan names cosmic rays and investigates their absorption.
1921	John A. Larson constructs the first modern polygraph.
1921	Albert Calmette and Camille Guérin develop the tuberculosis vaccine BCG.
1921	Emmy Noether publishes the theory of ideals in rings.
1921–1923	William Grant Banting and J. J. R. Macleod win the Nobel Prize for the discovery of insulin.
1922	Elmer McCollum names vitamin D and pioneers its use against rickets.
1923	Arthur Holly Compton discovers the wavelength change of scattered X-rays.
1923	Roy Chapman Andrews discovers the first fossilized dinosaur eggs.
1923	Louis de Broglie introduces the theory of wave-particle duality.
1923–1951	Reuben Leon Kahn develops a modified syphilis test and the universal serologic test.
Summer 1923	Otto Zdansky discovers Peking man.
1924	Harry Steenbock discovers that sunlight increases vitamin D in food.
1924	Theodor Svedberg develops the ultracentrifuge.
Mar. 1924	Arthur Stanley Eddington formulates the mass-luminosity law for stars.
Summer 1924	Raymond Arthur Dart discovers the first recognized australopithecine fossil.
Dec. 1924	Edwin Powell Hubble determines the distance to the Andromeda nebula and demonstrates that other galaxies are independent systems.
1925	Fred Whipple finds iron to be an important constituent of red blood cells.
Spring 1925	Wolfgang Pauli formulates the exclusion principle.
Apr. 1925–May 1927	The German Meteor expedition discovers the Mid-Atlantic Ridge.
Mar. 16, 1926	Robert Goddard launches the first liquid fuel propelled rocket.
July 1926	Arthur Stanley Eddington publishes *The Internal Constitution of the Stars*.
1927	Georges Lemaître proposes the big bang theory.
1927	Jan Hendrik Oort proves the spiral structure of the Milky Way.
Feb.–Mar. 1927	Werner Heisenberg articulates the uncertainty principle.

Date	Milestone
1928	Vannevar Bush builds the first differential analyzer.
1928	George Gamow explains radioactive alpha-decay with quantum tunneling.
1928–1932	Albert Szent-Györgyi discovers vitamin C.
Jan. 1928	George N. Papanicolaou develops the Pap test for diagnosing uterine cancer.
Sept. 1928	Alexander Fleming discovers penicillin in molds.
1929	Edwin Powell Hubble confirms the expanding universe.
Apr. 22, 1929	Hans Berger develops the electroencephalogram (EEG).
July 1929	Philip Drinker and Louis Shaw develop an iron lung mechanical respirator.
July 1929–July 1931	Kurt Gödel proves incompleteness-inconsistency for formal systems, including arithmetic.
1930	Thomas Midgley introduces dichlorodifluoromethane as a refrigerant gas.
1930	Hans Zinsser develops an immunization against typhus.
1930	Bernard Lyot builds the coronagraph for telescopically observing the sun's outer atmosphere.
1930–1931	Linus Pauling develops his theory of the chemical bond.
1930–1932	Karl G. Jansky's experiments lead to the founding of radio astronomy.
1930–1935	Edwin H. Armstrong perfects FM radio.
Feb. 18, 1930	Clyde Tombaugh discovers Pluto.
Jan. 2, 1931	Ernest Orlando Lawrence develops the cyclotron.
Apr. 1931	Ernst Ruska creates the first electron microscope.
May 27, 1931	Auguste Piccard travels to the stratosphere by balloon.
Feb. 1932	James Chadwick discovers the neutron.
Apr. 1932	John Douglas Cockcroft and Ernest Walton split the atom with a particle accelerator.
Sept. 1932	Carl David Anderson discovers the positron.
1932–1935	Gerhard Domagk discovers that antibacterial sulfonamides can save lives.
Nov. 1933	Enrico Fermi proposes the neutrino theory of beta decay.

DATE	MILESTONE
1933–1934	Frédéric Joliot and Irène Joliot-Curie develop the first artificial radioactive element.
1934	Pavel Cherenkov discovers the Cherenkov effect.
1934	Fritz Zwicky and Walter Baade propose their theory of neutron stars.
Fall 1934	John H. Gibbon develops the heart-lung machine.
1934–1935	Hideki Yukawa proposes the existence of mesons.
1935	Robert Alexander Watson-Watt and associates develop the first radar.
1935	Sydney Chapman determines the lunar atmospheric tide at moderate latitudes.
Jan. 1935	Charles F. Richter develops a scale for measuring earthquake strength.
Nov.–Dec. 1935	Antonio Egas Moniz develops prefrontal lobotomy.
1936	Inge Lehmann discovers Earth's inner core.
1936	Erwin Wilhelm Müller invents the field emission microscope.
Nov. 23, 1936	Fluorescent lighting is introduced.
1937	Max Theiler introduces a vaccine against yellow fever.
1937	Ugo Cerletti and Lucino Bini develop electroconvulsive therapy for treating schizophrenia.
Jan.–Sept. 1937	Emilio Segrè identifies the first artificial element, technetium.
Mar. 1937	Hans Adolf Krebs describes the citric acid cycle.
June–Sept. 1937	Grote Reber builds the first radio telescope.
1938	George S. Callendar connects industry with increased atmospheric carbon dioxide.
1938	Albert Hofmann synthesizes the potent psychedelic drug LSD-25.
1938	Peter Kapitsa explains superfluidity.
Dec. 1938	Otto Hahn splits an atom of uranium.
1939	The Bourbaki group publishes *Éléments de mathématique*.
1939	Paul Hermann Müller discovers that DDT is a potent insecticide.
Feb. 15, 1939	J. Robert Oppenheimer calculates the nature of black holes.

DATE	MILESTONE
Early 1940s	A secret English team develops the Colossus computer.
Late 1940s	Willard F. Libby introduces the carbon-14 method of dating ancient objects.
May 1940	Baron Florey and Ernst Boris Chain develop penicillin as an antibiotic.
Feb. 23, 1941	Glenn Seaborg and Edwin McMillan make element 94, plutonium.
May 15, 1941	The first jet plane using Frank Whittle's engine is flown.
1942–1947	Grote Reber makes the first radio maps of the universe.
Dec. 2, 1942	Enrico Fermi creates the first controlled nuclear fission chain reaction.
1943–1944	Oswald Avery, Colin Macleod, and Maclyn McCarty determine that DNA carries hereditary information.
1943–1944	Carl Friedrich von Weizsäcker finalizes his quantitative theory of planetary formation.
1943–1946	John Presper Eckert and John William Mauchly develop the ENIAC computer.
Spring 1943	Jacques Cousteau and Émile Gagnan develop the Aqua-Lung.
Nov. 4, 1943	The world's first nuclear reactor is activated.
Jan. 1944	Gerard Peter Kuiper discovers that Saturn's largest moon, Titan, has an atmosphere.
1944–1949	Dorothy Crowfoot Hodgkin solves the structure of penicillin.
1944–1952	Sir Martin Ryle's radio telescope locates the first known radio galaxy.
1945	Benjamin Minge Duggar discovers aureomycin, the first of the tetracyclines.
July 16, 1945	The first atomic bomb is detonated.
July 25, 1946	Vincent Joseph Schaefer performs cloud seeding by using dry ice.
Nov. 1946	University of California physicists develop the first synchrocyclotron.
1947	Dennis Gabor develops the basic concept of holography.
1947	Willis Eugene Lamb Jr. and Robert C. Retherford discover the lambshift.
Nov.–Dec. 1947	William Shockley, John Bardeen, and Walter Brattain discover the transistor.
1948	George Gamow and associates develop the big bang theory.
Nov. 26, 1948	Edwin Herbert Land invents a camera/film system that develops instant pictures.

DATE	MILESTONE
1949	X-rays from a synchrotron are first used in medical diagnosis and treatment.
Aug. 1949	BINAC, the first electronic stored-program computer, is completed.
1950s	Robert Wallace Wilkins discovers Reserpine, the first tranquilizer.
1950s	Choh Hao Li isolates the human growth hormone.
Mid-1950s	Severo Ochoa creates synthetic RNA.
1951	Robert Hofstadter discovers that protons and neutrons each have a structure.
1951	UNIVAC I becomes the first commercial electronic computer and the first to use magnetic tape.
1951–1952	Edward Teller and Stanislaw Ulam develop the first hydrogen bomb.
1951–1953	James Watson and Francis Crick develop the double-helix model for DNA.
1951–1954	Jan Hendrik Oort postulates the existence of the Oort Cloud.
Dec. 20, 1951	The world's first breeder reactor produces electricity while generating new fuel.
1952	Eugene Aserinsky discovers rapid eye movement (REM) in sleep and dreams.
Feb. 23, 1952	Douglas Bevis describes amniocentesis as a method for disclosing fetal genetic traits.
July 2, 1952	Jonas Salk develops a polio vaccine.
Aug. 1952	Walter Baade corrects an error in the cepheid luminosity scale.
1952–1956	Erwin Wilhelm Müller develops the field ion microscope.
1953	Vincent du Vigneaud synthesizes oxytocin, the first peptide hormone.
1953	Stanley Miller reports the synthesis of amino acids.
1953–1959	The liquid bubble chamber is developed.
1954–1957	John Backus's IBM team develops the FORTRAN computer language.
Apr. 30, 1954	Elso Barghoorn and Stanley Tyler discover two-billion-year-old microfossils.
May 1954	Bell Telephone scientists develop the photovoltaic cell.
1955	Kenneth Franklin and Bernard Burke discover radio emissions from Jupiter.
1955	Sir Martin Ryle constructs the first radio interferometer.

DATE	MILESTONE
1956	Bruce Heezen and Maurice Ewing discover the midoceanic ridge.
Apr.–Dec. 1956	Birth control pills are tested in Puerto Rico.
1957	Albert Bruce Sabin develops an oral polio vaccine.
1957	Alick Isaacs and Jean Lindenmann discover interferons.
1957	Sony develops the pocket-sized transistor radio.
Feb. 7, 1957	John Bardeen, Leon N. Cooper, and John Robert Schrieffer explain superconductivity.
Aug. 1957	The Jodrell Bank radio telescope is completed.
Oct. 4, 1957	The Soviet Union launches the first artificial satellite, Sputnik.
Oct. 11, 1957	Leo Esaki demonstrates electron tunneling in semiconductors.
Dec. 2, 1957	The United States opens the first commercial nuclear power plant.
1958	James Van Allen discovers Earth's radiation belts.
1958	Ian Donald is the first to use ultrasound to examine unborn children.
Jan. 2, 1958	Eugene N. Parker predicts the existence of the solar wind.
Jan. 31, 1958	The United States launches its first orbiting satellite, Explorer 1.
1959	A radio astronomy team sends and receives radar signals to and from the sun.
July 17, 1959	Louis and Mary Leakey find a 1.75-million-year-old fossil hominid.
Sept. 13, 1959	Luna 2 becomes the first human-made object to land on the moon.
Early 1960s	The plastic IUD is introduced for birth control.
Early 1960s	Roger Sperry discovers that each side of the brain can function independently.
1960–1962	Harry Hammond Hess concludes the debate on continental drift.
1960–1969	A vaccine is developed for German measles.
Apr. 1–June 14, 1960	Tiros 1 becomes the first experimental weather reconnaissance satellite.
July 1960	The first laser is developed in the United States.
Aug. 12, 1960	Echo, the first passive communications satellite, is launched.

| 1961 | Frank L. Horsfall announces that cancer develops from alterations in the DNA of cells. |

1961	Marshall Nirenberg invents an experimental technique that cracks the genetic code.
Date	**Milestone**
May 5, 1961	Alan Shepard is the first United States astronaut in space.
Dec. 1961	Melvin Calvin identifies the chemical pathway of photosynthesis.
1962	Lasers are used in eye surgery for the first time.
1962	Riccardo Giacconi and associates discover the first known X-ray source outside the solar system.
July 10, 1962	Telstar, the first commercial communications satellite, relays live transatlantic television pictures.
Aug. 1962–Jan. 1963	Mariner 2 becomes the first spacecraft to study Venus.
1963	Maarten Schmidt makes what constitutes the first recognition of a quasar.
1963–1965	Arno Penzias and Robert Wilson discover cosmic microwave background radiation.
1964	Quarks are postulated by Murray Gell-Mann and George Zweig.
1964–1965	John G. Kemeny and Thomas E. Kurtz develop the BASIC computer language.
1964–1965	Richard Rayman Doell and Brent Dalrymple discover the magnetic reversals of Earth's poles.
1965	The Sealab 2 expedition concludes.
Mar. 18, 1965	The first spacewalk is conducted from Voskhod 2.
1965–1966	Venera 3 is the first spacecraft to impact on another planet.
Dec. 1965	The orbital rendezvous of Gemini 6 and 7 succeeds.
Jan. 1966	Elwyn L. Simons identifies a thirty-million-year-old primate skull.
Jan. 31–Feb. 8, 1966	The Soviet Luna 9 makes the first successful lunar soft landing.
Aug.–Oct. 1966	The Lunar Orbiter 1 sends photographs of the moon's surface.
1967	Rene Favaloro develops the coronary artery bypass operation.
1967	Syurkuro Manabe and Richard Wetherald warn of the greenhouse effect and global warming.
1967	Raymond Davis constructs a solar neutrino detector.

DATE	MILESTONE
1967–1968	Elso Barghoorn and coworkers find amino acids in three-billion-year-old rocks.
Aug.–Sept. 1967	Arthur Kornberg and coworkers synthesize biologically active DNA.
1967–1968	Jocelyn Bell discovers pulsars, the key to neutron stars.
Dec. 1967	Christiaan Barnard performs the first human heart transplant.
1968	Jerome I. Friedman, Henry W. Kendell, and Richard E. Taylor discover quarks.
1968	The Glomar Challenger obtains thousands of ocean floor samples.
1968	John Archibald Wheeler names the phenomenon "black holes."
July 20, 1969	Neil Armstrong and Edwin "Buzz" Aldrin land on the moon.
Dec. 10, 1969	Derek H. R. Barton and Odd Hassel share the Nobel Prize for determining the three-dimensional shapes of organic compounds.
1970	The floppy disk is introduced for storing data used by computers.
1970	Lunokhod 1 lands on the moon.
1971	The microprocessor "computer on a chip" is introduced.
1971–1972	Mariner 9 is the first known spacecraft to orbit another planet.
1971–1972	Mars 2 is the first spacecraft to impact on Mars.
Apr. 1972	Godfrey Hounsfield introduces a computed tomography (CT) scanner that can see clearly into the body.
Sept. 1972	Murray Gell-Mann formulates the theory of quantum chromodynamics (qcd).
Sept. 1972	Texas Instruments introduces the first commercial pocket calculator.
Sept. 23, 1972	David Janowsky publishes a cholinergic-adrenergic hypothesis of mania and depression.
Dec. 31, 1972	The United States government bans DDT use to protect the environment.
1973	Stanley Cohen and Herbert Boyer develop recombinant DNA technology.
1973–1974	Organic molecules are discovered in Comet Kohoutek.
1973–1974	Skylab inaugurates a new era of space research.
1973–1975	Mariner 10 is the first mission to use the gravitational pull of one planet to help it reach another.

DATE	MILESTONE
1973–1974	F. Sherwood Rowland and Mario J. Molina theorize that ozone depletion is caused by Freon.
Feb. 1974	Howard Georgi and Sheldon Glashow develop the first grand unified theory.
Apr. 1974	Optical pulses shorter than one-trillionth of a second are produced.
Aug.–Sept. 1974	The J/psi subatomic particle is discovered.
Nov. 1974	Donald Johansen and Tim White discover "Lucy," an early hominid skeleton.
Oct. 22, 1975	Soviet Venera spacecraft transmit the first pictures from the surface of Venus.
1976	Thomas Kibble proposes the theory of cosmic strings.
1977	Alan J. Heeger and Alan G. MacDiarmid discover that iodine-doped polyacetylene conducts electricity.
1977	Deep-sea hydrothermal vents and new life forms are discovered.
Mar. 10–11, 1977	Astronomers discover the rings of the planet Uranus.
Apr. 1977	Apple II becomes the first successful preassembled personal computer.
May 1977	The first commercial test of fiber-optic telecommunications is conducted.
Sept. 16, 1977	Andreas Gruentzig uses percutaneous transluminal angioplasty, via a balloon catheter, to unclog diseased arteries.
1977–1989	Voyager 1 and Voyager 2 explore the planets.
July 25, 1978	Louise Brown gives birth to the first "test-tube" baby.
1978–1981	Heinrich Rohrer and Gerd Binnig invent the scanning tunneling microscope.
Mar. 4–7, 1979	The first ring around Jupiter is discovered.
1980	Paul Berg, Walter Gilbert, and Frederick Sanger develop techniques for genetic engineering.
1980	Evidence is found of a worldwide catastrophe at the end of the Cretaceous period.
1980	The inflationary theory solves long-standing problems with the big bang theory.
Feb. 5, 1980	Klaus von Klitzing discovers the quantized Hall effect.
May 1980	Pluto is found to possess a thin atmosphere.

Date	Milestone
1981	The US Centers for Disease Control recognizes acquired immune deficiency syndrome (AIDS) for the first time.
1981–1982	A human growth hormone gene transferred to a mouse creates giant mice.
June 1981	Joseph Patrick Cassinelli and associates discover R136a, the most massive star known at the time.
Sept. 1981	William H. Clewell corrects hydrocephalus by surgery on a fetus.
Nov. 12–14, 1981	Columbia's second flight proves the practicality of the space shuttle.
1982	Thomas Cech and Sidney Altman demonstrate that RNA can act as an enzyme.
1982	William Castle Devries implants the first Jarvik-7 artificial heart.
1982	Étienne-Émile Baulieu develops RU-486, a pill that induces abortion.
1982–1983	Fernand Daffos uses blood taken through the umbilical cord to diagnose fetal disease.
1982–1989	Astronomers discover an unusual ring system of the planet Neptune.
Apr. 1982	Solar One, the prototype power tower, begins operation.
May 14, 1982	The first commercial genetic engineering product, Humulin, is marketed by Eli Lilly.
1983	Carlo Rubbia and Simon van der Meer isolate the intermediate vector bosons.
1983	The first successful human embryo transfer is performed.
Mar. 8, 1983	IBM introduces a personal computer with a standard hard disk drive.
Apr. 4, 1983	The first tracking and data-relay satellite system opens a new era in space communications.
Sept. 1983	Andrew Murray and Jack Szostak create the first artificial chromosome.
Nov. 28, 1983	Spacelab 1 is launched aboard the space shuttle.
1984	Charles Gald Sibley and Jon Ahlquist discover a close human and chimpanzee genetic relationship.
1984	Steen M. Willadsen clones sheep using a simple technique.
1985	The British Antarctic Survey confirms the first known hole in the ozone layer.
1985	Construction of the world's largest land-based telescope, the Keck, begins in Hawaii.

DATE	MILESTONE
Mar. 6, 1985	Alec Jeffreys discovers the technique of genetic fingerprinting.
Oct. 1985	The Tevatron particle accelerator begins operation at Fermilab.
1986–1987	R. Brent Tully discovers the Pisces-Cetus supercluster complex.
Jan. 1986	J. Georg Bednorz and Karl Alexander Müller discover high-temperature superconductivity.
Feb. 20, 1986	The first permanently manned space station is launched.
July 1986	A genetically engineered vaccine for hepatitis B is approved for use.
Oct. 1986	A gene that can suppress the cancer retinoblastoma is discovered.
Dec. 14–23, 1986	Burt Rutan and Chuck Yeager pilot the Voyager around the world without refueling.
Feb. 23, 1987	Supernova 1987a corroborates the theories of star formation.
Sept. 1987	Wade Miller discovers a dinosaur egg containing the oldest known embryo.
1987–1988	Scientists date a Homo sapiens fossil at ninety-two thousand years.
1988	Henry Erlich develops DNA fingerprinting from a single hair.
April 24, 1990	NASA launches the Hubble Space Telescope.
1990s–2002	Particle physicists demonstrate that neutrinos—atomic particles long thought to be without mass—do indeed have mass and that they can change "flavor."
1993	Andrew Wiles presents his proof of the "Last Theorem" of Pierre de Fermat, which had defied solution by mathematicians for more than three centuries.
1993	In the most dramatic report of ozone depletion since the phenomenon was first reported, the World Meteorological Organization announces a rapid decline in ozone levels in the Northern Hemisphere.
1994	Astronomers use the Hubble Space Telescope to find evidence for the existence of a black hole in the center of galaxy M87.
1994	The Hubble Space Telescope provides astronomers with clear images of distant objects in the universe.
1995	National and international health organizations react quickly to contain an outbreak of the deadly Ebola virus in Kikwit, Zaire.
1995	Two teams of physicists announce the discovery of the top quark, the last of six such subatomic particles predicted by scientific theory.

DATE	MILESTONE
1995	US astronauts aboard the shuttle Atlantis dock with the space station Mir on a mission that sets the stage for future rendezvous and construction of an international space station.
Aug. 24, 1995	The first copy of Microsoft Windows 95 is sold. Windows 95, which makes using an Intel personal computer easy and intuitive, becomes the operating system of choice for personal computers and one of the most successful software products ever developed.
1995	The second assessment report of the Intergovernmental Panel on Climate Change (IPCC) projects a rise in global mean surface temperatures. The rise would constitute the fastest rate of change since the end of the last Ice Age.
1996	Dolly the sheep, is born. She is the first vertebrate cloned from the cell of an adult vertebrate.
1996	NASA scientists find traces of life processes and possible microscopic fossils in a meteorite believed to have come from Mars.
1997	Physicists at the Massachusetts Institute of Technology announce the success of an elementary version of a laser that produces a beam of atoms rather than a beam of light.
1997	After a six-year journey through interplanetary space, the Galileo spacecraft passes within 370 miles of Jupiter's moon Europa, revealing an ice-enshrouded world whose surface characteristics suggest an underlying planetary ocean that may harbor extraterrestrial life.
1997	Anthropologists discover the fossil skull of a boy who lived in Spain nearly 800,000 years ago. His skull combines features of both modern humans and earlier human species.
1997	A spacecraft that was launched from the Kennedy Space Center in Florida on December 4, 1996, lands safely on Mars after a flight lasting seven months.
1998	Scientists announce that preliminary findings from the Lunar Prospector mission suggest the presence of water ice in the shadowed craters near the moon's poles.
1998	The Monahans meteorite is the first extraterrestrial object to provide a sample of liquid water from an asteroid. The water, trapped in salt crystals, demonstrates that liquid water existed early in the history of the solar system, and the association of water with salt crystals suggests that brine evaporated on or near the surface of the asteroid.
1998	Developed by a team of scientists of the Pfizer Company, Viagra is the first anti-impotence drug to be approved by the US Food and Drug Administration.
1998	The annual ozone hole extends a record 10.5 million square miles (27.3 million square kilometers).
1999	A team of surgeons perform a successful hand transplant operation in Louisville, Kentucky, enabling the recipient to perform twisting and gripping functions and to feel sensation in the hand.

DATE	MILESTONE
1999	Scientists trace HIV, the virus that causes AIDS, to chimpanzees.
1999	In an effort to produce alternative sources of clean energy, researchers generate nuclear energy on a tabletop by both fusion and fission.
1999	Careful analysis of light from Upsilon Andromedae reveals the first known multiple-planet system orbiting a normal star.
1999	A team of scientists at the Lawrence Berkeley Laboratory Nuclear Science Division detect the formation of two new elements, with atomic numbers 116 and 118, as the result of bombarding lead targets with krypton ions in a cyclotron.
1999	Physicists produce nickel-48, the most proton-rich nucleus, an international breakthrough in nuclear physics.
1999	Researchers announce the identification of an enzyme that plays a key role in the development of Alzheimer's disease.
1999	A team of scientists at Brown University present topographical measurements that indicate that an ocean once existed on Mars.
Oct. 12, 1999	According to United Nations data, the world's six-billionth person is born.
2000	Imaging radar aboard the space shuttle Endeavour captures data to assemble the most comprehensive topographic map of Earth, covering 80 percent of its land surface.
2000	Scholars from two research institutions announce the discovery of at least nine planets around stars other than the sun, bringing the total number of known extrasolar planets to at least fifty; by 2005, the number of known extrasolar planets exceeded one hundred.
2000	The Food and Drug Administration approves medical abortions using mifepristone (RU-486) as an alternative to surgical abortion.
2000	The gas-electric "hybrid" automobile is brought to market.
2000	With the aid of computers, geneticists are rapidly sequencing the genomes of many organisms, culminating in the year's sequencing of the complete genome Drosophila melanogaster, the fruit fly.
Feb. 14, 2000	The Near Earth Asteroid Rendezvous (NEAR) spacecraft begins a yearlong orbit of the asteroid Eros, gathering data on its chemical composition, mineralogy, shape, and structure.
2001	Scientists advance a new area of applied science, nanoelectronics, by assembling molecules into basic circuits.
Feb. 10, 2001	The human genome is completely sequenced, opening a new era of medical promise; the event marks the most important breakthrough in genetics since the discovery of the double-helical structure of DNA in 1953.

DATE	MILESTONE
2002	A variety of small RNA molecules are discovered to be capable of altering gene expression and even the genome itself.
2003	Biophysicists experiment with "quantum dots," tiny semiconductor nanocrystals that glow in the presence of laser light, to enhance biological imaging techniques.
2003	Biologists discover that mouse stem cells can develop into both sperm and egg cells in vitro, raising the question of whether the same is possible with human stem cells.
2003	Physicists confirm the existence of "left-handed" materials, which have a negative refractive index (they bend light at a negative angle when it passes into them from a different medium) as well as other odd and potentially useful properties.
2003	The combination of conventional chemotherapy and new antiangiogenesis drugs—which starve cancer tumors of their blood supply by preventing them from growing blood vessels—proves effective with colon cancer patients.
2003	The Wilkinson Anisotropy Microwave Probe maps the universe showing the cosmic background radiation, the "afterglow" of the big bang, and pinpoints the age of the universe at 13.7 billion years.
Jan. 2004	The Mars Exploration Rovers, Spirit and Opportunity, land at different locations on the Martian surface and return unprecedented photographs of topographic features as well as geological data.
Jan. 27, 2005	Oxford University's ClimatePrediction.net project announces evidence of a long-term increase in Earth's surface temperature in the range of 2 to 11 degrees Celsius as a result of global warming.
Feb. 17, 2005	Two human skulls discovered in Ethiopia by Richard Leakey in 1967 are redated to 195,000 years old, the oldest known remains of modern human beings.
July 4, 2005	The Deep Impact spacecraft reaches Comet Tempel 1 and launches a 372-kilogram copper projectile into the comet's icy surface to collect data.
July–Sept. 2005	Xena, a body beyond Pluto that orbits the sun, is discovered by astronomers at the University of Hawaii's Keck Observatory in July and its moon Gabrielle is discovered in September. The question of Xena's planetary status—like those of several other trans-Neptunian objects discovered since 1995—is debated by astronomers.
Sept. 2005	The US National Snow and Ice Data Center and the National Aeronautics and Space Administration report "a stunning reduction" in Arctic sea ice, 20 percent below the mean average during September from 1978 to 2001.
Jan. 15, 2006	NASA's Stardust spacecraft capsule was recovered with the first-ever samples of comet particles and interstellar dust, collected near Comet Wild-2. Analysis by more than one hundred scientists is giving new information about the origins of the solar system.

DATE	MILESTONE
Apr. 2006	Paleontologists announced the discovery in the Nunavut territory of Canada of a 375-million-year-old "fishapod" (Tiktaalik roseae), which is a new transitional species bridging the gap between fish and tetrapod (four-legged vertebrate).
Apr. 2006	Geologists of the Integrated Ocean Drilling Program (IODP) reported the first intact sample of all the crustal layers including the igneous rock of the deepest layers called gabbro, drilling more than a kilometer into the ocean's crust off the west coast of Costa Rica.
Apr. 1, 2007	Hendrik Clausen and colleagues from the University of Copenhagen published a method of using enzymes to convert any kind of blood into type O, which can be used with most trans-fusion recipients.
Apr. 2007	Stéphane Udry and colleagues from the University of Geneva announced the discovery of two planets orbiting the red dwarf star Gliese 581, one slightly larger than Earth.
Apr. 13, 2007	John Asara and colleagues reported their analysis of soft tissue found in the well-preserved leg bone of a Tyrannosaurus rex from Montana, concluding that it had proteins similar to those of chickens.
Nov. 2007	A group led by Shinya Yamanaka of Kyoto University used a virus to reprogram human skin cells to form stem cells for growing tumor-free muscle, fat, heart, and nerve tissues without having to destroy human embryos.
Jan. 14, 2008	NASA's MESSENGER spacecraft made its first flyby of Mercury on its way to orbiting the planet, providing evidence for past volcanic activity on the surface, and a large amount of water in the outer atmosphere.
May–Nov. 2008	NASA's Phoenix Lander was the first to land on the north polar region of Mars, documenting water and finding small amounts of nutrients for life and perchlorate salts that are dangerous for life.
Sept. 10–19, 2008	The Large Hadron Collider (LHC) made its first successful run before a super-conducting magnet breakdown delayed its probe of the most basic structure of matter.
Nov. 2008	Penn State biochemist Stevan Schuster announced the reconstruction of 80 percent of the genome of an ancient wooly mammoth from clumps of hair in excavated remains.
Nov. 2008	A small dinosaur's fossilized nest was analyzed by Darla Zelenitsky of the University of Calgary, identifying several dinosaur eggs that add to their link with birds.
2009	Four teams of biologists demonstrated the first safe gene therapies applied to blindness, brain disorders, skin problems, and weak immune systems in a variety of approaches.
2009	Several pharmaceutical teams confirmed that the drug Rapamycin extended the life of mice by the equivalent of thirteen extra years, the first drug-based extension of mammalian life.

DATE	MILESTONE
July 2009	Three teams of geneticists reported on their genome studies of fifty thousand schizophrenia patients, finding some ten thousand genetic variants rather than a clear disease pattern.
Oct. 2009	Joseph Ecker and his team at the Salk Institute in La Jolla, California, announced the complete mapping of the human epigenome, which is a record of chemical changes to the DNA.
Oct. 2009	Paleontologists announced their discovery in Ethiopia of four-million year old Ardipithecus ramidus, called Ardi, an upright-walking primate a million years older than Lucy.
Nov. 12, 2009	NASA announced the discovery of water on the moon after it found at least 25 gallons of water vapor and ice in the plume formed by crashing the Lunar Crater Observation and Sensing Satellite (LCROSS) into a lunar crater.
Apr. 9, 2010	A joint Russian-American team announced the detection of six atoms of the artificial super-heavy chemical element 117 by combining berkelium and calcium isotopes.
May 2010	Biologists at the J. Craig Venter Institute announced the construction of the first synthetic self-replicating bacterial cell by inserting a modified genome into a living cell.
July 20, 2010	Fermilab researchers reported a violation of matter-antimatter symmetry in the decay of B-mesons, yielding about 1 percent more matter than antimatter.
Sept. 29, 2010	Astronomers with the Lick-Carnegie Exoplanet Survey announced the discovery of an extrasolar planet in the habitable zone of the red dwarf star Gliese 581 with a mass three to four times that of Earth.
Dec. 2, 2010	Scientists from NASA's Astrobiology Institute in Menlo Park, California, announced the formation of arsenic-based life by replacing phosphate with arsenate in a bacterial culture.
May 12, 2011	The HIV Prevention Trials Network (HPTN) reported that their multinational clinical study (HPTN 052) demonstrated a 96 percent reduction in HIV transmission from HIV infected persons who take antiretroviral drugs.
June 6, 2011	Scientists at the CERN laboratory in Geneva, Switzerland, announced that they had trapped antimatter hydrogen atoms (positrons bound to antiprotons) for several minutes in a magnetic field for the first time.
July 2011	Genetic evidence was published linking Homo sapiens with Neanderthals, with most inbreeding taking place as modern humans migrated from Africa.
Oct. 18, 2011	Oxford University scientists announced that they had developed the first successful malaria vaccine, reducing the risk of infection by 50 percent in clinical tests.
Dec. 5, 2011	NASA announced that its Kepler Space Telescope discovered the first transiting planet in the habitable zone of a sun-like star, Kepler-22b, about 2.4 times Earth's radius.

DATE	MILESTONE
Dec. 2011	Scientists at the Large Hadron Collider (LHC) in Geneva reported evidence for the existence of the Higgs particle, which theory requires to account for particle masses.
Jan. 11, 2012	NASA announced that its Hubble Space Telescope detected the most distant stellar explosion for measuring the rate of expansion of the universe, a Type Ia supernova remnant that exploded 9 billion years ago.
Feb. 14, 2012	Paleontologists in Australia announced their discovery of the oldest known animal fossils with a skeleton, designated Coronacollina acula, it is a few millimeters in size and dated at about 550 million years old.
Mar. 8 2012	The Daya Bay Reactor Neutrino Experiment in the south of China reported the discovery of a new type of neutrino oscillation, a last link in explaining neutrino behavior.
July 4, 2012	Researchers at CERN announce the discovery of a subatomic particle with energy levels and other properties consistent with those expected in Higgs boson, as predicted by the Standard Model of particle physics.

BIOGRAPHICAL DIRECTORY OF SCIENTISTS

The following list of 800 scientists briefly summarizes the achievements of not only the 354 scientists covered in this publication (starred with an asterisk *) but hundreds of other noted scientific figures and inventors as well.

A

Abul Wefa: Abul Wefa played a major role in mathematics by developing sines and cosines as they apply to the field of trigonometry and used them to correct astronomical calculations carried forward from classical into Islamic times.

Edward Goodrich Acheson: A former assistant to Thomas Alva Edison, in 1891 Acheson synthesized carborundum, an industrial abrasive. Later, by heating it further, he produced pure graphite, a substance useful in lubricants and electrodes.

Elizabeth Cabot Agassiz: One of the founders and the first president of Radcliffe College, Agassiz was an influential pioneer in higher education for women and was also noted for her writings on natural history and her work with her husband, naturalist Louis Agassiz.

Louis Agassiz*: Nineteenth-century Swiss-born naturalist Louis Agassiz promoted the study of natural history in the United States with his founding of the Museum of Comparative Zoology at Harvard University. He was a pioneer in making science an integral part of the curriculum in American higher education and is particularly well known for his work on glaciers.

Maria Gaetana Agnesi*: In her youth, Maria Agnesi advocated education for young women, in part by demonstrating her own impressive intellectual abilities. Her two-volume textbook on calculus provided a complete synthesis of the mathematical methods developed during the scientific revolution. In her later years, she devoted herself to charitable work for the sick, poor, and aged.

Georgius Agricola*: Sixteenth-century German physician and geoscientist Georgius Agricola is regarded as the founder of mineralogy and physical geology. Agricola's exhaustive study of all subjects related to mining led to new developments in mining technology and engineering, as well as the fields of metallurgy, structural geology, and paleontology.

Howard Aiken: With Grace Hopper, Aiken designed the first of the electromechanical Mark series of computers, built in 1944. The U.S. Navy used it to calculate trajectories for projectiles.

Saint Albertus Magnus: Albertus expanded scientific knowledge through experimentation and observation. As an Aristotelian, he reconciled reason with revelation.

George Edward Alcorn: American physicist George Alcorn designed innovative semiconductors and X-ray detection devices that were incorporated in numerous scientific, technological, and industrial applications. He also advanced aerospace, physics, and engineering technology through his roles as educator and administrator.

Ernst Alexanderson: Alexanderson, a pioneering telecommunications engineer, received more than 345 patents. His fame rests on his 1906 invention of the high-frequency alternator for long-wave transmissions.

Hans Alfvén: Alfvén developed magnetohydrodynamics, a branch of physics that studies the propagation of currents and electromagnetic waves through fluids, and studied its applications to plasmas, leading to his description of the physics of the aurora, radiation belts around planets having magnetic fields, and other astrophysical phenomena.

Alhazen*: Alhazen's *Book of Optics*, in which he deftly used experiments and advanced mathematics to understand the relationship of light and vision, exerted a profound influence on many Islamic and European scientists and natural philosophers.

Paul Allen: Paul Allen was one of the pioneers of the personal computer industry, creating software and operating systems that would eventually be used by millions of people worldwide. He is also a generous philanthropist. For example, in 2003, he gave $100 million to the Allen Institute for Brain Science.

Sidney Altman: Altman won the 1989 Nobel Prize in Chemistry, with Thomas R. Cech. Working independently Altman and Cech discovered that RNA, like proteins, can act as a catalyst; moreover, they found that when ribosomal RNA participates in translation of messenger RNA (mRNA) and the synthesis of polypeptides, it acts as a catalyst in some steps.

Luis W. Alvarez: A Nobel Prize-winning physicist with diverse interests, Alvarez discovered the radioactive isotope tritium and worked on the atomic bomb. He was aboard the plane that dropped the bomb on Hiroshima, Japan, during World War II. Like many atomic scientists, he believed nuclear weapons would discourage war. After his retirement, he and his son theorized that a meteor impact caused the extinction of the dinosaurs, a theory that has since become widely accepted.

Viktor A. Ambartsumian: Ambartsumian developed the astrophysics of stars and stellar origins and was instrumental in the theory of gigantic catastrophe formation in galaxies related to the evolution of stars and galaxies. He was the founder of the major school of theoretical astrophysics in the Soviet Union.

André-Marie Ampère*: André-Marie Ampère was a major French scientist of the early nineteenth century who, through extensive experimentation with electric currents, discovered the relationship between electricity and magnetism and established an early form of electrodynamics.

Anaxagoras*: Anaxagoras devised a way to explain the origins and nature of matter that overcame the paradoxes and inconsistencies of earlier philosophies. His work, preserved in the fragments of his book, *Nature*, provided a bridge between the pre-Socratic philosophy and such philosophers as Plato and Aristotle in the golden age of ancient Greece.

Anaximander: Anaximander invented the scientific use of models and maps. He also realized, contrary to the prevailing thought of his day, that the original substance of matter must be an eternal, unlimited reservoir of qualities and change.

Carl David Anderson*: At the age of thirty-one, American physicist C. D. Anderson was the second youngest person ever awarded a Nobel Prize. He received the honor for his discovery of the positron, a particle that helped explain the nature of matter and antimatter. Anderson's discovery was instrumental in founding the field of particle physics, which has unlocked many of the mysteries of the universe.

Marc Andreessen: Andreessen, along with Eric Bina, created Mosaic (released in 1993), the first Internet browser to present graphics and text together. He also developed Netscape Navigator.

Christian B. Anfinsen: Anfinsen won the 1972 Nobel Prize in Chemistry. Studying the three-dimensional structure of the enzyme ribonuclease, he proved that its conformation was determined by the sequence of its amino acids and that to construct a complete enzyme molecule no separate structural information was passed on from the DNA in the cell's nucleus.

Mary Anning*: Working as a paleontologist during a period in history when men dominated the scientific community, Mary Anning's discoveries and contributions greatly expanded scientists' understanding of the history of the Earth and helped paleontology become a respected scientific field.

Apollonius of Perga*: A geometer of Ancient Greece, Apollonius of Perga systematized the theory of conic sections. His study of circular motion established the foundation for Greek geometric astronomy.

Edward Victor Appleton*: Nobel Prize–winning physicist Edward Victor Appleton is credited with confirming the existence of the ionosphere (a layer of Earth's upper atmosphere) and the E layer within it, as well as with discovering the F layer, also known as the Appleton layer. Appleton's findings directly led to the discovery of radar technology.

Werner Arber*: Werner Arber received the Nobel Prize in Physiology or Medicine in 1978 for his discovery and exploration of restriction enzymes in DNA molecules. His scholarship proved an important contribution to the emerging field of genetics.

Archimedes*: Ancient Greek mathematician Archimedes made his most important contributions to the field of geometry and also founded the disciplines of statics and hydrostatics.

Aristarchus: Aristarchus of Samos showed by the use of observations and of plane geometry that the sun was some three hundred times larger than Earth. Aristarchus went on to deduce that the sun, apparently because it was so much larger than Earth, must itself be the unmoving center of the cosmos, with Earth and the other planets revolving about it in circles, the Moon about Earth, and Earth rotating on its axis.

Aristotle*: Building on Plato's dialogical approach, Aristotle developed what is known as the scientific method. In addition, he founded the Lyceum, which housed the first research library.

Svante August Arrhenius*: Arrhenius was a pioneer in the interdisciplinary science of physical chemistry. He also helped establish the international reputation of the Nobel Prizes, clarified the physical effects of light pressure from the sun, and developed the concept of "panspermia," which holds that life was introduced on Earth by particles from space.

Lev Andreevich Artsimovich: A leading Soviet physicist, Artsimovich led the team of scientists that built the first tokamak in the 1950s, a device that creates a doughnut-shaped electromagnetic field in order to sustain a controlled fusion reaction.

al-Ashraf: About 1282, Sultan al-Ashraf, Umar ibn Yusuf, wrote an astronomical treatise in which he described an early mariner's compass: a bowl of water in which a magnetized compass floats.

Francis William Aston: In 1919, Aston discovered how to separate two isotopes of neon—in a focused electromagnetic field, which moved the small-mass isotope, achieving separation. Thus was born the mass spectrograph, which helped earn him the 1922 Nobel Prize in Chemistry.

John Vincent Atanasoff: A mathematics professor, Atanasoff conceived the idea for a digital computer with electronics as the medium, base-two numbers, condensers for memory, and direct logical action for computation. He built the first prototype in 1939.

John James Audubon*: Nineteenth-century French American ornithologist, naturalist, and painter, John James Audubon observed and documented nature, especially birds. His work, which merged art and science, helped to change the public's perception of the natural world and humanity's role in it.

Charlotte Auerbach: German-born geneticist Auerbach fled to England following the rise of the Nazi Party. She demonstrated that the mutations produced by mustard gases and other chemicals in Drosophila (fruit flies) were similar to those induced by X-rays, suggesting a common mechanism.

Avicenna: Avicenna was the first Islamic thinker to synthesize the philosophy of Aristotle and Plato with Islamic traditions. His writings on medicine were studied in Europe as late as the seventeenth century. According to some scholars, Avicenna's insistence on observation and experimentation helped to turn Western thought in the direction of the modern scientific revolution.

Oswald Theodore Avery*: Along with fellow scientists Colin MacLeod and Maclyn McCarty, Oswald Theodore Avery is credited with discovering in 1944 that deoxyribonucleic acid (DNA) is the material that forms the basis for the composition of chromosomes and genes.

Amedeo Avogadro*: A pioneer in atomic theory, Avogadro was the first scientist to distinguish between atoms and molecules. Avogadro's law, a hypothesis that relates the volume of a gas to the number of particles present, greatly advanced the understanding of chemical reactions and resolved many chemical problems.

Richard Axel: A pioneer in the field of molecular neurobiology, Axel discovered a method for inserting foreign genes into deoxyribonucleic acid (DNA), and he won a Nobel Prize for his research into how the brain recognizes a smell.

B

Charles Babbage*: Charles Babbage is best remembered for developing an early steam-driven mechanical calculator known as the difference engine, as well as for a later design similar to the modern programmable computer that he called the analytical engine. Although neither device directly influenced eventual electronic computer designs, Babbage is often called the "father of computing."

John Warner Backus: In the 1950s, Backus developed the computer programming language Fortran. An acronym for "formula translation," it allows direct entry of commands into computers with English-like words and algebraic symbols.

Francis Bacon: Although fuel cells date from the mid-nineteenth century, Bacon developed the first practical hydrogen-oxygen cell. The Bacon Cell, introduced in 1959, could generate five kilowatts.

Roger Bacon: Franciscan friar Bacon, among the first people to rely on experimentation to study nature, improved the understanding of optics, astronomy, and chemistry, including the manufacture of gunpowder.

Karl Ernst von Baer*: Karl Ernst von Baer gained his greatest fame early in his career through his discovery of the mammalian egg and his contributions to the understanding of embryological development. In his later years, Baer would turn his attention to anthropological investigations, including the state of primitiveness of various races, and to geological studies, especially in Russia.

Jean-Sylvain Bailly: Bailly, a renowned astronomer and historian of science, was elected president of the Third Estate in 1789. In the same year, he became the first mayor of Paris under the New Republic. He soon fell out of favor, however, and was later guillotined by the Revolutionary Tribunal of Paris.

John Logie Baird: A Scottish electrical engineer and inventor, Baird successfully transmitted black-and-white (in 1925) and color (in 1928) moving television images, and the BBC used his transmitters to broadcast television from 1929 to 1937. He had more than 175 patents for such far-ranging and forward-thinking concepts as big-screen and stereo TV sets, pay television, fiber optics, radar, video recording, and thermal socks. Plagued with ill health and a chronic lack of financial backing, Baird was unable to develop his innovative ideas, which others later perfected and profited from.

Ibn al-Baitar: One of the greatest botanists of the Middle Ages, Ibn al-Baitar is credited with creating the first herbal drug treatment for cancer, using hindiba (chicory).

Abi Bakr of Isfahan: In 1235, Persian astronomer Bakr invented an astrolabe (an instrument for finding stars) that had a mechanical calendar to calculate the date. The astrolabe survives and is the oldest complete mechanical geared machine in existence.

Robert D. Ballard: As a pioneering undersea explorer, Ballard made several remarkable discoveries, including the resting place of the Titanic and other ships, new life-forms along hot spots in the undersea Earth crust, and evidence supporting the theory of plate tectonics.

Johann Jakob Balmer*: Nineteenth-century Swiss mathematician Johann Balmer deduced a formula that predicted the wavelengths of the Balmer series, which are spectral lines emitted by hydrogen atoms. The formula, now known as the Balmer formula, proved a key contribution to the later development of atomic theory.

David Baltimore*: Molecular biologist and Nobel laureate David Baltimore has achieved great influence as a researcher, scientific policymaker, and leader of academic institutions. He is most celebrated for his molecular virology discoveries in recombinant DNA research.

Joseph Banks: Combining his knowledge of botany and an inherited fortune, Banks led the scientific group on Captain James Cook's expedition in the Endeavour and, for forty-one years, as president of the Royal Society, supported and encouraged various scientific activities.

Benjamin Banneker: In 1791, Banneker, a self-taught African American mathematician and astronomer, published his first almanac, providing information about eclipses, star and lunar positions, and weather based on his calculations.

Frederick Grant Banting: In 1922, Banting and Charles Herbert Best developed a method to produce insulin for treating diabetes. For this work, he received the 1923 Nobel Prize in Physiology or Medicine.

John Bardeen: Bardeen is the only person to win two Nobel Prizes in Physics, one for his part in inventing the transistor (1956) and the other for his explanation of superconductivity (1972).

Edward Emerson Barnard*: In 1916, Edward Emerson Barnard discovered Barnard's Star, which is the second-nearest star to our solar system and the fourth-closest known star to the sun. Although Barnard was not the first to observe the star, he was the first to accurately measure its proper motion of 10.3 arc seconds per year by using photographic images taken several years apart, in order to track the star's movement.

Murray Llewellyn Barr: Canadian geneticist Murray Llewellyn Barr discovered the existence of the Barr (Barr's) body, an inactive X chromosome found in cells from a female. The existence or absence of the body has been used in determining the sex of the individual from whom the cell originated.

Françoise Barré-Sinoussi*: French virologist Françoise Barré-Sinoussi received the 2008 Nobel Prize in Physiology or Medicine for her codiscovery, with Luc Montagnier, of the human immunodeficiency virus (HIV), the retrovirus that causes acquired immune deficiency syndrome (AIDS).

Nikolay Gennadiyevich Basov: Basov played a key role in the invention of quantum microwave amplification devices (masers) and light amplifiers that operate on the principle of stimulated emission of radiation (lasers). He collaborated with Aleksandr Prokhorov, with whom he shared the 1964 Nobel Prize in Physics, to produce the first Soviet maser and did pioneering work on the use of semiconductors in lasers.

Henry Walter Bates*: Nineteenth-century British naturalist and explorer Henry Walter Bates traveled the Amazon River basin for eleven years. He collected over fourteen thousand insect specimens, more than half of which were previously unknown, making a lasting contribution to the theory of evolution.

William Bateson*: Often called the father of genetics, William Bateson was a British evolutionary biologist who founded the study of genetics. An early proponent of the rediscovered Mendelian principles, his work provided the base for a modern understanding of heredity as it applies to evolution.

al-Battānī: Among the most illustrious of early astronomers, al-Battānī introduced trigonometry to astronomical calculation, laying the groundwork for spherical trigonometry.

William Maddock Bayliss*: William Bayliss made major discoveries in the field of physiology, most notably in terms of the heart and in biochemistry relating to lymph flow, hormones and their actions, principles of enzyme action, and properties of colloidal biological systems.

George Wells Beadle*: American geneticist George Wells Beadle is best remembered for his Nobel Prize–winning collaboration with Edward Tatum on the one gene-one enzyme hypothesis. Their work revealed that DNA encodes individual proteins and that mutations, or changes in DNA, lead to changes in proteins. Beadle and Tatum laid the foundations for the field of genetic engineering. In 1958, they were awarded the Nobel Prize in Physiology or Medicine.

Johann Joachim Becher: Becher developed ideas on the nature of physical substances that led to a new theory of chemistry. Also, his theory of the three "earths" argued that minerals grew from seeds in Earth's "bowels." As a businessperson, he would seek to capitalize financially on his ideas and inventions.

Jonathan R. Beckwith: Beckwith determined the role of specific genes in regulating bacterial cell division. During the 1960s, he was among the first to isolate a specific gene. Beckwith is also known as a social activist in his arguments for the use of science for improvement of society.

Antoine Henri Becquerel*: In his experiments with uranium, French physicist and Nobel laureate Antoine Henri Becquerel discovered a source of incredible energy that required no human interaction to produce: radioactivity. His discovery opened up a new field of science called nuclear physics.

Georg J. Bednorz: Bednorz, with Karl Alexander Müller, discovered high-temperature superconductivity in a new class of ceramic materials, starting a worldwide effort to develop superconductor technology.

Ulugh Beg: Beg built the largest astronomical observatory of its day and stocked it with instruments of his own design, notably a large Fakhri sextant that enabled him to take highly accurate measurements.

Georg von Békésy: Békésy's discovery of the mechanics and physiology of hearing brought him the 1961 Nobel Prize in Physiology or Medicine.

Alexander Graham Bell: Before inventing the telephone in 1876, Bell taught at a school for the deaf, where he became fascinated by the nature of sound. He later produced innovations in aviation and hydrofoils and was the first president of the National Geographic Society.

Pierre Belon: Pierre Belon wrote monographs on birds, trees, and marine life, contributing to the advancement of botany and zoology. His studies of dolphin embryos and bird skeletons signal the founding of modern embryology and comparative anatomy.

Baruj Benacerraf: While studying the ability of inbred strains of animals to respond to certain foreign proteins or antigens, Benacerraf discovered a series of genes that regulated the interactions of immune cells. Benacerraf termed these the immune response (Ir) genes, and the discovery earned him a Nobel Prize.

Carl Benz: A German engineer and designer born illegitimately as Karl Vaillant, Benz designed bridges before setting up his own foundry and mechanical workshop. In 1888, he invented, built, and patented a gas-powered, engine-driven, three-wheeled horseless carriage named the Benz Motorwagen, which was the first automobile available for purchase. In 1895, he built the first trucks and buses and introduced many technical innovations still found in modern automobiles. The Benz Company merged with Daimler in the 1920s and introduced the famous Mercedes-Benz in 1926.

Seymour Benzer: A pioneer in the field of neurogenetics, Benzer used viruses to map genes, showing the connection between molecular biology and genetics. His research with the Drosophila fly showed how genes control behavior.

Paul Berg*: Paul Berg won the Nobel Prize in Chemistry in 1980 for his pioneering technique of splicing together deoxyribonucleic acid (DNA) from different types of organisms, which revolutionized the study of viral chromosomes and launched the field of genetic engineering.

Friedrich Bergius: Bergius discovered how to obtain liquid hydrocarbon fuels by hydrogenation of coal and how to obtain synthetic sugar from wood cellulose. The fuels made by his processes aided Germany during World War II, and Bergius's methods form the basis for the modern synthetic fuels industry.

Claude Bernard*: French physiologist Claude Bernard was the first to articulate the concept of "milieu intérieur," or homeostasis. He also discovered that the liver produces glucose and was a proponent for the use of the scientific method in the field of medicine.

Tim Berners-Lee: In 1989 Berners-Lee propounded his conception of a global hypertext project and wrote the first server and client for what became known as the World Wide Web.

Daniel Bernoulli*: Eighteenth-century Swiss mathematician Daniel Bernoulli is best known for his work in the field of fluid dynamics, particularly the Bernoulli equation. His book *Hydrodynamica* gave the field its original name. Bernoulli also worked in the fields of physics and acoustics.

Clifford Berry: Berry's contributions to the Atanasoff-Berry Computer (ABC, 1942) were its design details and construction; thereby, he proved that an electronic digital computer would work.

Marcellin Berthelot: The first chemist to synthesize hydrocarbons, in 1866 Berthelot was also the first to prepare polystyrene from ethylene and benzene.

Alphonse Bertillon: Best known for his pioneering work applying science to criminal identification; the Bertillon system, also known as bertillonage, later lost favor for identification because it was often impractical for use in identifying suspects at crime scenes, measurements were inconsistently recorded, and it was useless to describe the measurements of twins and other skeletally similar criminals—such persons could be distinguished from one another only through fingerprinting.

Jöns Jacob Berzelius*: Born in the eighteenth century and working in the nineteenth, Jöns Jacob Berzelius was a Swedish chemist best known for his work in chemical notation and atomic weights. He was also an early investigator in the field of organic chemistry.

Henry Bessemer: Bessemer advanced the field of metallurgy by developing the Bessemer process for purifying molten iron. This process cut in half the cost of steel, made possible a great increase in production, and ushered in the "Age of Steel."

Hans Albrecht Bethe*: Hans Albrecht Bethe's work in theoretical nuclear physics explained how stars convert mass to energy and broadened the scientific understanding of subatomic events. Long an influential advocate for restraint in the proliferation of nuclear weapons, Bethe laid the theoretical groundwork for the explosion of the first atom bomb.

Gerd Binnig: With Heinrich Rohrer, Binnig developed the scanning tunneling microscope, capable of imaging a single atom. They shared the 1986 Nobel Prize in Physics for their work.

Jean-Baptiste Biot*: Jean-Baptiste Biot's research helped define the fields of modern physics and mathematics. He contributed significantly to the current understanding of meteorites, optics, and the physics of light. Biot worked with numerous prominent physicists and other scientists in nineteenth-century France and contributed his scientific understanding to numerous pivotal discoveries.

Clarence Birdseye: The naturalist, inventor, and entrepreneur was born in Brooklyn, New York. He began experimenting in the early 1920s with flash-freezing fish. Using a patented process, he was eventually successful in freezing meats, poultry, vegetables, and fruits, and in so doing changed consumers' eating habits. Birdseye sold his process to the company that later became General Foods Corporation, for whom he continued to work in developing frozen-food technology. His surname— split in two for easy recognition—became a major brand name that is still familiar.

al-Bīrūnī: One of the greatest scholars of medieval Islam, al-Bīrūnī was both a singular compiler of the knowledge and scientific traditions of ancient cultures and a leading innovator in Islamic science.

J. Michael Bishop*: Oncogenes, genes which when mutated transform a normal cell into a malignant one, had been discovered in tumor viruses during the early 1970s. J. Michael Bishop isolated the first known human oncogene and demonstrated its origin in the human genome.

Vilhelm Bjerknes*: Nineteenth-century Norwegian geophysicist and meteorologist Vilhelm Bjerknes is considered a founder of modern meteorology. Bjerknes developed a mathematical theory of fronts and their effects, as well as an influential procedure for numerical weather forecasting, although the computing technology necessary to put his theories to really practical use

would not appear until the second half of the twentieth century.

Joseph Black*: A pioneer in quantitative experimental chemistry, Joseph Black discovered carbon dioxide, the first gas to be isolated and have its properties systematically identified. He also proposed the theories of latent and specific heats and, as a gifted lecturer, raised the profile of chemistry to that of a philosophical and public science.

Elizabeth Blackburn*: Molecular biologist Elizabeth Blackburn discovered the molecular nature of telomeres, the repeat units of nucleotide bases on the tips of chromosomes in DNA. She also discovered telomerase, the enzyme that synthesizes the telomeres.

David Blackwell*: Twentieth-century African American mathematician David Blackwell's research encompassed several areas, including probability theory, statistical theory, and game theory. He published more than ninety papers and several textbooks in various areas of mathematics and received international recognition for his work. Blackwell was the first African American mathematician elected to the National Academy of Science.

Marietta Blau*: Austrian physicist Marietta Blau advanced the field of particle physics by developing the photographic method of studying nuclear emulsions. Despite this breakthrough, she remains relatively unknown, although followers of her work have earned worldwide recognition.

Felix Bloch*: Twentieth-century Swiss-born physicist Felix Bloch shared the Nobel Prize in Physics in 1952 with Edward Purcell. Bloch's experiments led him to determine the magnetic moments in nuclei, which in turn led to the discoveries of nuclear magnetic resonance (NMR) and magnetic resonance imaging (MRI).

Katharine Burr Blodgett: The first woman to become a research scientist for General Electric, Blodgett invented nonreflecting glass in 1938 by coating regular glass with many layers of a fatty acid film, each one molecule thick.

Baruch S. Blumberg: In 1976, Blumberg was co-winner of the Nobel Prize in Physiology or Medicine with D. Carleton Gajdusek for developing a diagnostic test for hepatitis and a vaccine.

Johann Elert Bode*: Known as "the Berlin astronomer," Johann Elert Bode popularized astronomy and stargazing in Germany in the late eighteenth century. His lavishly produced series of celestial maps capped the European tradition of depicting the constellations of the starry sky.

Niels Bohr*: Twentieth-century Danish physicist Niels Bohr received the Nobel Prize in Physics in 1922 for his work on creating a model of atomic structure. His theory that electrons orbit an atom's nucleus formed the foundation of quantum mechanics. The chemical element bohrium is named for him.

Ludwig Boltzmann*: Austrian physicist Ludwig Boltzmann is best remembered for inventing the field of physics now known as statistical mechanics. Boltzmann's discoveries in thermodynamics and electromagnetism were important contributions to the later development of quantum mechanics. He was particularly interested in the relationship between heat and entropy (a concept that he helped to define) and of particles in gases.

Roberta Bondar: Dr. Bondar's research into space medicine and the neurological effects of spaceflight for NASA led to her serving on the space shuttle Discovery mission STS-42 in 1992, becoming the first Canadian woman and the first neurologist in space.

George Boole*: Nineteenth-century British mathematician and logician George Boole is best known for developing the concept of modern symbolic logic and the creation of what is now known as Boolean algebra. Prior to Boole, logic was considered part of philosophy, not mathematics. His linguistic algebra, consisting of three basic operations (AND, OR, and NOT), has formed the basis of modern computer languages, systems, and circuits.

Giovanni Alfonso Borelli: Borelli, a scientist with wide-ranging accomplishments, founded the field of biophysics (iatrophysics) with his pioneering work on the mechanical basis of muscular motions, respiration, and circulation in animals. He made significant contributions to mathematics, astronomy, physics, mechanics, hydraulics, medicine, epidemiology, and physiology.

Norman Borlaug*: Twentieth-century American humanitarian and scientist, Borlaug received the 1970 Nobel Peace Prize for his genetic modifications of wheat and other crops, which produced large yields in developing countries. His biotechnological work adapting plants to resist diseases and survive in varied climates enabled the Green Revolution, providing practical ways to ease hunger and malnutrition by consistently growing substantial quantities of nutritious food to feed expanding populations.

Max Born*: Max Born's work in quantum mechanics earned him the Nobel Prize in Physics in 1954. He taught numerous other physicists who eventually won the Nobel Prize, many of whom were instrumental in the development of atomic fission. Like his close friend Albert Einstein and other Jewish scientists, he fled from Germany's Nazi regime in the early 1930s.

Carl Bosch: Bosch adapted the high-pressure synthesis of ammonia for large-scale commercial production, a key step in the creation of cheap nitrogen fertilizers. For this he shared the 1931 Nobel Prize in Chemistry.

Amar Bose: Amar Bose made fundamental advances in the science of psychoacoustics and nonlinear systems and the technology of stereo loudspeakers, headphones, two-state amplifier-modulators, and auto-suspension systems.

Jagadish Chandra Bose*: An Indian polymath whose work focused on physics, physiology, and education, Jagadish Chandra Bose flourished between the 1890s and the 1930s. He researched electromagnetism and created devices that advanced the development of radio and pioneered biophysics by exploring the reactions of plants, animals, and inorganic materials to various stimuli.

Walter Bothe: Bothe was awarded the Nobel Prize in Physics for his invention of the coincidence counting technique and for discoveries made using it, including the nature of cosmic rays and the fashion in which X-rays interact with electrons. He was one of Germany's leading atomic scientists and constructed its first cyclotron.

Robert W. Bower: In 1969, Bower patented his Self-Aligned Gate MOSFET (metal-oxide semiconductor field-effect transmitter), a basic component of integrated circuits.

Herbert Wayne Boyer: With Stanley Norman Cohen in 1973, Boyer created the first viable deoxyribonucleic acid (DNA) cloned from different types of bacteria—recombinant DNA, now a basic technique in genetic engineering.

Robert Boyle*: Boyle discovered Boyle's law of ideal gases, which describes the relationship between air pressure and volume. He promoted the experimental method in scientific study, especially in the field of chemistry.

William Henry Bragg: With his son William Lawrence, Bragg shared the 1915 Nobel Prize in Physics for founding a new branch of science, the analysis of crystal structure by X-ray diffraction.

William Lawrence Bragg*: Bragg used X-ray diffraction to determine the arrangement of atoms in many crystals and helped establish the field of X-ray crystallography. With his father, also a physicist, he won the Nobel Prize in Physics in 1915.

Sophia Brahe*: Sophia Brahe assisted her brother, noted astronomer and alchemist Tycho Brahe, in making and recording astrological observations, including the lunar eclipse of 1573. Most historians consider her greater lifetime contributions to be in the fields of genealogy and horticulture as she produced a substantial manuscript recording the genealogy of sixty Danish noble families and was well known for the magnificent gardens she designed and the rare plants she grew to produce medicinal products.

Tycho Brahe: A nobleman born of Danish heritage in what is modern-day Sweden, Brahe became interested in astronomy while studying at the University of Copenhagen. He made improvements to the primitive observational instruments of the day but never had access to the telescope. Nonetheless, he was able to study the positions of stars and planets accurately and produced useful catalogs of celestial bodies, particularly for the planet Mars, which helped Johannes Kepler (1571–1630) to formulate the laws of planetary motion. Craters on the Moon and on Mars are named in Brahe's memory.

Brahmagupta: Brahmagupta wrote Brahma Sphuta Siddhanta, a book in verse expounding a complex system of astronomy and containing two chapters on arithmetic, algebra, and geometry. His work on indeterminate equations and the introduction of negative numbers greatly influenced the development of science in both India and Arabia.

Walter H. Brattain: Brattain shared the 1956 Nobel Prize in Physics with John Bardeen and William

Shockley for their invention of the transistor. His part was to test Shockley's arrangements of semiconductors.

Karl Ferdinand Braun: For his 1897 invention of the oscilloscope, a precursor to the television, and other electronics devices, Braun shared the 1909 Nobel Prize in Physics with Guglielmo Marconi.

Wernher von Braun*: A pioneer in German rocketry and a visionary of spaceflight, Wernher von Braun dominated the early American space program by directing construction of the Saturn rocket that propelled the first astronauts to the moon.

Sydney Brenner: Molecular geneticist Sydney Brenner's observations of mutations in nematodes (long, unsegmented worms) helped in understanding the design of the nervous system. Brenner was among the first to clone specific genes. He was awarded the Nobel Prize in Physiology or Medicine in 2002.

David Brewster*: Nineteenth-century physicist David Brewster spent his life studying the behavior of light, making significant advances in the understanding of polarization and refraction through crystal. He is also remembered as the inventor of the kaleidoscope.

Percy Williams Bridgman*: Bridgman vastly extended the range of high-pressure physics. Through his development of the philosophical notion of operational analysis, he aided his colleagues in coping with the new ideas of twentieth-century physics. His work contributed significantly to the coming of age of physics as a field of science in the United States.

Louis de Broglie*: Through his theory of the wave-particle duality of matter, Louis de Broglie introduced a major and necessary component to quantum theory. For his contributions to the field, de Broglie was awarded the Nobel Prize in Physics in 1929.

Johannes Nicolaus Brønsted*: Twentieth-century physical chemist Johannes Nicolaus Brønsted was born in Denmark and studied at the University of Copenhagen. He is known for revising the definition of acids and bases, focusing on the chemical reactions themselves.

Michael S. Brown: Brown discovered the means by which cells regulate cholesterol biosynthesis and provided the biochemical foundations for the invention of cholesterol-lowering medicines.

Robert Brown*: Nineteenth-century Scottish botanist Robert Brown collected and classified thousands of previously undocumented plant species during a government-funded scientific and geographical expedition to Australia. He made several important contributions to biology, including the discovery of the phenomenon named for him, Brownian motion.

Giordano Bruno*: Philosopher, scientist, and mystic, Giordano Bruno anticipated several ideas integral to the modern era. During his relatively short life, he wrote on a variety of topics while traveling throughout Europe. Because his ideas challenged the rigid belief systems of his day, he often ran afoul of the authorities and was eventually put to death for heresy. Though time has obscured his achievements to some degree, many philosophers and scientists have given him credit for significant advances in human thought, while others view him as a free thinker and martyr.

Georges-Louis Leclerc, Comte de Buffon*: French aristocrat Georges-Louis Leclerc, comte de Buffon, was one of the eighteenth-century's leading naturalists. Although Buffon began his career as a mathematician, he is best known for his thirty-six-volume Histoire naturelle, a survey of most of what was known about the natural world.

Robert Wilhelm Bunsen: Bunsen's burner, first described in 1860 and built by Peter Desaga, provides a high-temperature, non-luminous flame and quickly became a standard piece of laboratory equipment.

Luther Burbank: Despite having only an elementary-school education, the Massachusetts-born botanist and horticulturist was a pioneer in the field of agricultural science. Working from a greenhouse and experimental fields in Santa Rosa, California, Burbank developed more than 800 varieties of plants, including new strains of flowers, peaches, plums, nectarines, cherries, peaches, berries, nuts, and vegetables, as well as new cross-bred products such as the plumcot. One of his most useful creations, the Russet Burbank, became the potato of choice in food processing, particularly for French fries.

E. Margaret Burbidge*: E. Margaret Burbidge has been keeping an eye on the universe for more than seventy years. An observer by nature, she has made some of the most important astronomical discoveries of the twentieth century, and her work is characterized by a determination to unlock the mysteries of the cosmos.

Jean Buridan: A distinguished natural philosopher, Buridan wrote critical commentaries on the works of Aristotle, laid the foundations of the modern science of mechanics, and defined objectives and a methodology that separate science from philosophy and theology, making him a major figure in the development of modern science.

Jocelyn Bell Burnell*: As a graduate student in radio astronomy at Cambridge University, Burnell helped construct a large radio telescope array. Using this telescope in 1967, she found an unexpected series of rapid radio pulses from outer space, leading to the discovery of rotating neutron stars called pulsars.

Frank Macfarlane Burnet: Burnet proposed a theory of clonal selection to explain regulation of the immune response. He was awarded the 1960 Nobel Prize in Physiology or Medicine.

Vannevar Bush: Bush pioneered the design and construction of electromechanical analog computers and was the first to describe the idea of hypertext.

C

Melvin Calvin*: American biochemist Melvin Calvin was among the first modern scientists to use a truly interdisciplinary approach in his research, blending techniques from the fields of chemistry and biology. In 1961, he won the Nobel Prize in Chemistry for his research concerning the chemical reactions that take place during photosynthesis.

Annie Jump Cannon*: Twentieth-century American astronomer Annie Jump Cannon created a system for stellar classification that was adopted by the International Astronomical Union. Cannon also catalogued nearly 400,000 stars. Her work, published as the Henry Draper Catalogue, became an important reference for astronomers.

Manuel Cardona: One of the leading solid-state physicists in the world, Cardona made fundamental discoveries across a range of areas, particularly those related to semiconductors and superconductors. He was for twenty-eight years an able founding administrator of the Max Planck Institute for Solid State Research.

Chester F. Carlson: Carlson first tested his process for electrophotography, or xerography, in 1938, making the first photocopy.

Sadi Carnot: A French physicist and military engineer, Carnot was an army officer before becoming a scientific researcher, specializing in the theory of heat as produced by the steam engine. His *Reflections on the Motive Power of Fire* focused on the relationship between heat and mechanical energy and provided the foundation for the second law of thermodynamics. His work greatly influenced scientists such as James Prescott Joule (1818–1889), William Thomson (Lord Kelvin, 1824–1907), and Rudolf Diesel (1858–1913) and made possible more practically and efficiently designed engines later in the nineteenth century. Carnot's career was cut short by his death from cholera.

Wallace Hume Carothers: Working for Dupont, Carothers, a chemist, led a research team that synthesized nylon and neoprene, the first artificial polymer-based products that were comparable to natural materials.

George R. Carruthers: A space scientist and physicist, Carruthers invented ultraviolet imaging devices—a camera and a spectrograph—that detect pollutants in Earth's atmosphere. A camera of his design took photographs of the moon during the Apollo 16 mission in 1972.

Rachel Carson*: A marine biologist and conservationist, Rachel Carson is most remembered for her 1962 book *Silent Spring*, an exhaustively researched exposé that sparked a national furor over the use of pesticides in the United States.

George Washington Carver: Born a slave, Carver became a leading agricultural researcher, inventing a multitude of useful products from such plants as the peanut, sweet potato, and soybean while at the Tuskegee Institute in Alabama.

Giovanni Domenico Cassini*: Giovanni Domenico Cassini was a seventeenth-century Italian astronomer.

He was a professor of astronomy at the University of Bologna when Louis XIV of France invited him to Paris to become the founding director of the new Paris Observatory, a position he held for the rest of his life, during which he made several important first-time observations of Saturn and its moons, among other achievements.

Henry Cavendish*: Henry Cavendish, a reclusive character, made significant advances in the chemistry of gases and contributed to the study of electrical phenomena. He is noted for discovering hydrogen and for measuring the Earth's density.

Thomas R. Cech: Cech won the 1989 Nobel Prize in Chemistry, with Sidney Altman. Working independently, Cech and Altman discovered that RNA, like proteins, can act as a catalyst; moreover, Cech found that when ribosomal RNA participates in translation of mRNA and the synthesis of polypeptides, it acts as a catalyst in some steps.

Anders Celsius*: Anders Celsius was an eighteenth-century Swedish astronomer who made significant observations about the North Pole. He is best remembered for inventing the temperature scale that bears his name.

Vinton Gray Cerf: Cerf codesigned the packet network interconnection protocols (TCP/IP) that became the groundwork for the Internet.

Andrea Cesalpino: Cesalpino systematized botanical classification, wrote the first true textbook on the subject of botany, and founded the taxonomical movement, which reached its apex in the work of Linnaeus. Cesalpino's speculation into the anatomy and physiology of the heart anticipated William Harvey's conclusions about the circulation of the blood.

James Chadwick*: Nobel laureate James Chadwick is best known for his discovery of the neutron in 1932. This discovery led to the creation of the atomic bomb, but on a more elemental level, the neutron was the last major piece in the puzzle of atomic structure.

Subrahmanyan Chandrasekhar*: Twentieth-century Indian American astrophysicist Subrahmanyan Chandrasekhar studied the evolution of stars throughout their life spans. Chandrasekhar predicted which stars would become white dwarfs and determined that larger stars would eventually collapse into small areas of extreme gravity called black holes.

M. C. Chang: As a reproductive biologist specializing in the process of mammalian fertilization, M. C. Chang is best known for his work developing an oral contraceptive, otherwise known as birth-control pills. He also helped pioneer the assisted reproductive technology known as in vitro fertilization.

Franklin Ramón Chang-Díaz: One of the first Latin Americans to fly in space, Chang-Diaz developed technology for energy generation by nuclear fusion and applied those techniques to an advanced rocket engine.

Daryl Chapin: With Calvin Fuller and Gerald Pearson, in 1954 Chapin demonstrated their Bell Solar Battery, which directly converts sunlight into electricity.

Emmett Chappelle*: African American biochemist and astrochemist Emmett Chappelle is primarily known for his work in bioluminescence. His methods of making bacteria glow have been used in searching for life on other planets, in monitoring the health of human urine, and in studying plants.

Erwin Chargaff*: Twentieth-century Ukrainian American biochemist Erwin Chargaff was a pioneer in the field of genetics. The discoveries he made about the base ratios of DNA, which became known as Chargaff's rules, led to the determination of the structure of DNA.

Jacques Charles*: A French mathematician and physicist who flourished during the end of the Enlightenment, Jacques Charles invented or improved several scientific instruments and formulated a law governing the behavior of gases. He is best remembered for designing and piloting the first hydrogen-filled hot air balloon.

Martha Chase*: A new college graduate working at Cold Spring Harbor, Martha Chase aided geneticist Alfred Hershey in discovering that viruses replicate through DNA (deoxyribonucleic acid). The work led to Watson and Crick's helix model of DNA less than a year later.

Steven Chu*: Steven Chu's method to slow, cool, and capture atoms using laser light made him one of three winners of the 1997 Nobel Prize in Physics. As the twelfth US secretary of energy, Chu promoted both renewable fuels and nuclear power as alternatives to hydrocarbons and their climate impact.

Albert Claude*: Albert Claude developed many of the modern procedures used in cell fractionation and separation critical for identification and analysis of cellular components. His isolation of mitochondria was critical in understanding their function.

Carl von Clausewitz: As a Prussian-born soldier and military scientist, Clausewitz participated in numerous campaigns, beginning in the early 1790s, and fought in the Napoleonic Wars. After his appointment in 1818 to major general, he taught at the Prussian military academy and helped reform the state army. His principal written work, *On War*, unfinished at the time of his death from cholera, is still considered relevant and continues to influence military thinking via its practical approach to command policies, instruction for soldiers, and methods of planning for strategists.

Rudolf Clausius*: German physicist Rudolf Clausius is credited with developing the concept of entropy and helping to develop the field of thermodynamics. Clausius's research also advanced understanding of the kinetic theory of gases and the theory of electrolysis. His work assisted in establishing a general acceptance of theoretical physics within the scientific community.

Adam Cohen: Cohen's anti-Brownian Electrokinetic trap (ABEL trap) isolates and manipulates individual fluorescent molecules in solution at room temperature. It is a tool for analyzing complex molecules.

Stanley Norman Cohen: Cohen, with Herbert Wayne Boyer, was the first scientist to synthesize a functional recombinant DNA molecule, a basic advance for genetic engineering.

Ferdinand Julius Cohn: Cohn is considered one of the founders of modern bacteriology. As a botanist, he contributed to understanding the evolutionary position of many microscopic plantlike organisms by elucidating their life histories.

Mildred Cohn*: Cohn spent her scientific career in the study of molecules and their roles in metabolic reactions. Her research into magnetic forces played a significant role in the development of medical instrumentation and applications in new techniques, such as magnetic resonance imaging (MRI).

Francis S. Collins*: A pioneer in the field of human genetics, physician Francis Collins served as the director of the National Human Genome Research Institute at the National Institutes of Health (NIH) in Washington, DC, for fifteen years. His groundbreaking work on mapping the complete human genome led to his being named director of the NIH by US president Barack Obama in 2009.

Frank B. Colton: A research chemist, Colton invented Enovid. First used to treat menstrual disorders, it was introduced in 1960 as an oral contraceptive.

Arthur Holly Compton*: American physicist Arthur Holly Compton described the particle nature of light and measured the change in wavelength of a quantum of radiation as it collides with an electron. This discovery, known as the Compton effect, earned him the Nobel Prize in Physics in 1927.

James Cook: With his inspired seamanship and his practical grasp of scientific method, Cook added greatly to world knowledge of geography and oceanography. His voyages led to British colonialism in the Pacific.

William Fothergill Cooke: From the joining of Cooke's entrepreneurial skills and Charles Wheatstone's scientific knowledge came the world's first commercial telegraph network. (In addition to his pioneering telegraph work with Cooke, Wheatstone also made valuable contributions to later developments in telegraph as well as dynamo technology, electrical engineering, and the physics of sound, light, and electricity.)

Edward Drinker Cope*: Pioneering paleontologist Edward Drinker Cope published more than 1,300 papers during his lifetime and helped discover more than 600 extinct species. Cope was a major contributor to the growth of American paleontology in the nineteenth century and one of the most prolific fossil hunters in history.

Nicolaus Copernicus*: Copernicus dismissed the Ptolemaic model of the universe and introduced the theory that the planets, including Earth, revolve around the sun. He defended the rights of the educated to discuss scientific theories, even when those theories contradicted currently accepted beliefs and religious dogma.

France Anne Córdova*: American astrophysicist France Anne Córdova was the first female chief scientist at NASA, as well as the youngest. In addition to her research on multiwavelength observational astronomy, Córdova is known for her university administration and for promoting scientific awareness to the nonscientific community.

Carl F. Cori*: Carl Cori and his wife, Gerty Cori, were Czech American biochemists who discovered the eponymous Cori cycle, the mechanism by which lactic acid produced during metabolism is converted to glucose in the liver.

Gerty Cori*: Biochemist Gerty Cori and her husband, Carl Cori, shared the 1947 Nobel Prize in Physiology or Medicine for their discovery of the eponymous Cori cycle, the catalytic conversion of glycogen in the body.

Gaspard-Gustave Coriolis*: Eighteenth-century French mathematician, engineer, and physicist Gaspard-Gustave Coriolis defined the concepts of work and kinetic energy for the physical sciences. Coriolis is most famous for his discovery of the Coriolis force, which helped physicists to better understand wind currents and weather patterns.

Carl Erich Correns: German botanist Carl Erich Correns, confirmed Gregor Mendel's laws through his own work on the garden pea. Correns was one of several geneticists who rediscovered Mendel's work in the early 1900s.

Charles-Augustin de Coulomb*: Eighteenth-century French engineer and physicist Charles-Augustin de Coulomb investigated aspects of structure and applied mechanics while building military forts. He later conducted research into multiple areas of physics, including friction, torsion, electricity, magnetism, and hydraulics.

Jacques-Yves Cousteau*: French oceanographer Jacques-Yves Cousteau popularized undersea exploration. Cousteau coinvented with Émile Gagnan the Aqua-Lung, the first generation of what would come to be known as scuba gear. He also spearheaded the invention of the Turbosail and the engineering of several underwater human habitats. He shared his underwater explorations through films, books, and television.

Seymour Cray: By densely packing together hundreds of thousands of computer chips, in 1963 Cray built the first supercomputer, the CDC 6600. The supercomputer proved invaluable to scientific research, weather forecasting, and engineering.

Francis Crick*: In 1953, while still a graduate student, British molecular biologist Francis Crick helped discover the double-helix structure of DNA and the process of replication responsible for heredity. For this discovery, he and James Watson, along with biophysicist Maurice Wilkins, were awarded the 1962 Nobel Prize in Physiology or Medicine.

William Crookes: A great experimenter, Crookes discovered thallium and invented the radiometer, the spinthariscope for detecting alpha particles, and the Crookes tube, a vacuum tube that produces cathode rays (electrons).

William Cumberland Cruikshank: A chemist and anatomist, Cruikshank identified carbon monoxide as a compound that contains both oxygen and carbon and introduced chlorination to make water safe to drink.

William Cullen: A medical chemist, Cullen is credited with creating the first workable design for a refrigerator (1748). His was a proof-of-concept device and never saw practical use.

Marie Curie*: Polish physicist and chemist Marie Curie conducted pioneering research into radioactivity. She and her husband, Pierre Curie, discovered the radioactive elements radium and polonium. Curie was the first woman awarded the Nobel Prize, which she received in both 1903 and 1911.

Pierre Curie*: Nobel Prize–winning French physicist Pierre Curie spent his early career as a crystallographer, during which time he and his brother, Jacques Curie, discovered piezoelectricity. Curie and his wife, Marie Curie, discovered the radioactive elements polonium and radium, thus pioneering the study of radiation.

Georges Cuvier*: The early nineteenth-century French naturalist Georges Cuvier helped found the field of paleontology and established the principles of comparative anatomy. He also made significant contributions to zoology, including the invention of a new animal classification system.

D

Nils Gustaf Dalén: Dalén invented a fuel-saving, reliable acetylene gas lighting system for lighthouses and buoys, a boon to seafarers. He received the 1912 Nobel Prize in Physics for this invention.

John Dalton*: As the developer of atomic theory, Dalton's law, and an early version of the periodic table of elements, chemist John Dalton is considered one of the pioneers of modern science. He also conducted important research in the field of meteorology and investigated the cause of color blindness.

André-Louis Danjon: Danjon primarily worked to increase the precision of astronomical instruments in observing stars. The invention of the prismatic 60-degree astrolabe, or the Danjon astrolabe, is his crowning achievement. Toward the end of his career, in the 1950s, he also investigated irregularities in Earth's rotation.

Cyril Darlington: British geneticist Cyril Darlington demonstrated changes in chromosomal patterns that occur during meiosis, leading to an understanding of chromosomal distribution during the process. He also described a role played by crossing over, or genetic exchange, in changes of patterns.

Raymond Dart*: Twentieth-century Australian anatomist and anthropologist Raymond Dart spent most of his working career in South Africa. He discovered the remains of a hominid, Australopithecus, that provided an important evolutionary link between humans and apes and that contradicted the belief that human evolution began in Asia or Europe.

Charles Darwin*: Charles Darwin is best remembered for his theory of natural selection, which explains the evolution of animals and humans. His most famous written work, *On the Origin of Species* (1859), remains a landmark in the field of natural history.

Jean Dausset*: Twentieth-century French immunologist Jean Dausset shared the 1980 Nobel Prize in Medicine for his research in genetics related to hematology. His investigations into human blood types and transfusions increased the accuracy of disease susceptibility diagnoses and reduced the rejection rate of transplant recipients.

Donald Davies: The Internet depends upon packet switching, a means of communication between computers that Davies, a computer scientist, conceived in 1965.

Edmund Davy: A professor of chemistry, in 1836, Davy created acetylene by heating potassium carbonate to high temperatures and letting it react with water.

Humphry Davy: A renowned chemist, Davy is known for his discoveries of chemical elements and also invented the miner's safety lamp, which made it possible for coal miners to work in methane-laden air.

Richard Dawkins*: Prominent evolutionary biologist Richard Dawkins is recognized as one of the world's leading theorists in neo-Darwinian theory and has become a leading science writer whose essays and books on various aspects of evolutionary theory introduce the core concepts of evolution by natural selection to popular audiences. Dawkins has also become a prominent proponent of atheist philosophy and a leading opponent of political attempts to teach creationism in academic environments.

Mark Dean: A computer scientist, Dean, along with Dennis Moeller, designed the Industry Standard Architecture (ISA) bus that enables users to hook up peripheral devices to their personal computers.

Peter Debye*: Dutch American scientist Peter Debye made significant contributions to chemistry, including his pioneering work on electrolytic disassociation, now known as the Debye–Hückel theory. Debye's research also led to the calculation of the molecular dipole moment. The unit of the dipole has been termed the Debye in his honor. Debye was awarded the 1936 Nobel Prize for his various contributions to molecular chemistry and physics.

John Dee: Arguably the most influential astrologer in Renaissance England, Dee had an extensive education in continental Europe that enabled him to bring to England developments in cartography, navigation, mathematics, astronomy, and cryptography. His practice with alchemy and astrology made him a regular consultant to Queen Elizabeth I, even as these same interests exposed him to charges of necromancy.

Melvin De Groote: An industrial chemist, De Groote synthesized demulsifiers for purifying crude oil of salt, sulfur, and water.

Max Delbrück: Max Delbrück was a leading figure in the application of genetics to bacteriophage research, and later, with Phycomyces, a fungal organism. His bacteriophage course, taught for decades at Cold Spring Harbor,

New York, provided training for a generation of biologists. He was awarded the 1969 Nobel Prize in Physiology or Medicine.

Milislav Demerec: Croatian-born geneticist Milislav Demerec was among the scientists who brought the United States to the forefront of genetics research. Demerec's experiments, based on the genetics of corn, addressed the question of what a gene represents. His work with bacteria included the determination of mechanisms of antibiotic resistance, as well as the existence of operons, closely linked genes that are coordinately regulated. Demerec was director of the biological laboratories in Cold Spring Harbor, New York, for many years among the most important sites of genetic research.

Democritus*: Democritus developed a theory of atomism that he applied to science, metaphysics, and ethics. His view that the world is made up of changing combinations of unchanging atoms addressed one of the central questions of his age: how change was possible. Democritus provided a model of reasoning that was mechanistic, materialist, and nonsupernatural.

René Descartes*: Descartes extended the mathematical method, or the erasure of doubt by reaching certainty, to all fields of knowledge. He argued that "I think, therefore I am" is the only undoubtedly true statement that can be made. His radical distinction between mind and body and his revolutionary method of metaphysical inquiry have had a profound effect on the history of philosophy.

James Dewar: Among Dewar's wide-ranging achievements as a chemist was his invention of the double-walled flask in 1872, later marketed to the public as the Thermos.

Otto Paul Hermann Diels: Diels made two fundamental contributions to classical organic chemistry: the selenium dehydrogenation and the diene reaction. The selenium reaction made it possible to establish the structure of a large number of important natural materials, notably the steroids. The diene reaction is unique in its variety, durability, and quality. Diels was awarded the Nobel Prize in Chemistry with Kurt Alder in 1950.

Diophantus*: Diophantus of Alexandria wrote a treatise on arithmetic that represents the most complete collection of determinate and indeterminate equations and solutions dating from Greek times. This work was the basis of much medieval Arabic and European Renaissance algebra.

Paul Dirac*: British born theoretical physicist Paul Dirac made invaluable contributions to quantum mechanics, the branch of physics that deals with atoms and atomic particles. Among his most important achievements was his application of Albert Einstein's theory of special relativity to quantum mechanics and his resulting discovery of the antielectron, the first evidence of antimatter. He received the Nobel Prize in Physics in 1933.

Carl Djerassi: Chemist Carl Djerassi, with Luis Miramontes and George Rosenkranz, produced an oral contraceptive pill containing norethisterone synthesized from progesterone, which inhibits ovulation.

Theodosius Dobzhansky*: Twentieth-century evolutionary biologist Theodosius Dobzhansky demonstrated through his experiments with fruit flies that genetics are the mechanism driving natural selection. He established the field of evolutionary genetics and introduced the modern synthesis of evolution, combining genetics and evolutionary biology.

Gerhard Domagk: Domagk was awarded the Nobel Prize in Physiology or Medicine in 1939 (he accepted the award in 1947) for his discovery that a synthesized dye, prontosil, was an effective treatment for streptococcal infections in mice. This discovery led to the development of sulfa drugs, the first successful chemical means for dealing with bacterial infections.

Christian Doppler*: Nineteenth-century physicist and mathematician Christian Doppler began his career as a professor of mathematics. At the age of thirty-nine, he published a paper on the color of binary stars, in which he first described the Doppler effect.

Herbert Henry Dow: Dow's method for extracting bromine cheaply from brine by electrolysis set the stage for a great expansion in the American chemical industry, particularly through Dow Chemical Company, founded in 1895.

Renato Dulbecco: Dulbecco was among the first to study the genetics of tumor viruses. He was awarded the 1975 Nobel Prize in Physiology or Medicine.

E

Arthur Stanley Eddington*: Twentieth-century English astrophysicist Arthur Stanley Eddington was knighted in 1930 for his foundational contributions to astrophysics—particularly our understanding of the structure of stars—and for his work assisting Albert Einstein with his theory of general relativity.

Gerald M. Edelman: By sequencing the 1,330 amino acids that make up the structure of antibody molecules, Edelman determined the overall structure of the molecules and provided an understanding of how antibodies function in the immune response.

Thomas Edison: Edison was perhaps the greatest inventor in world history. His incandescent electric lights transformed electrical technology; his myriad other inventions included a stock ticker, duplex and quadraplex telegraphs, the phonograph, a telephone transmitter, the motion-picture camera, and the storage battery. He symbolized the ingenious, prolific, heroic, and professional American inventor in an age of invention, innovation, and industrialization.

Paul R. Ehrlich*: Paul R. Ehrlich, a distinguished biologist and entomologist specializing in butterflies, is best known as a prolific writer whose compelling books about the environment helped shape public policy in the twentieth century and raised awareness about overpopulation.

Albert Einstein*: Regarded as the most important scientist of the twentieth century, German physicist Albert Einstein received the Nobel Prize in Physics in 1921. While he made many contributions to the fields of physics, quantum mechanics, and statistics, he is best known for his theory of relativity.

Willem Einthoven: Accomplished in several areas of physiology, physics, and medicine, Einthoven elaborated techniques for measuring minute electrical currents in the human heart. His string galvanometer—best known in its later form as an electrocardiogram, or EKG—became the basis for modern electrocardiography and made possible great advances in combating heart disease. He was awarded the Nobel Prize in Physiology or Medicine in 1924.

Gertrude B. Elion: A biochemist and pharmacologist, Elion synthesized a purine-based compound that checks the growth of leukemia cells, for which she shared the 1988 Nobel Prize in Physiology or Medicine.

Empedocles: Empedocles was one of the earliest of the Greek philosophers to provide a unified theory of the nature of the world and the cosmos. In many ways, Empedocles influenced medieval and Renaissance conceptions of science and anticipated modern theories. For example, despite some criticism, Plato and Aristotle adopted his biological theories; his conception of the four elements, probably derived from the work of Hippocrates, thus had influence until the scientific revolution in the seventeenth century. Galen considered him the founder of the medical arts.

Douglas Engelbart: Internet pioneer Douglas Engelbart revolutionized the human-computer interface with his invention of the computer mouse, hypertext, and groupware.

Erasistratus*: The third-century BCE physician Erasistratus helped establish a scientific basis for studies of human anatomy and physiology. Together with the anatomist Herophilus, Erasistratus carried out the first recorded systematic dissections of the human body, which yielded information that undermined many misconceptions of the body.

Eratosthenes of Cyrene*: Ancient Greek scholar Eratosthenes helped make the Library of Alexandria the greatest repository of learning in the Mediterranean world. The first geographer, he calculated the Earth's circumference and invented latitude and longitude. He also invented the chronological concept of leap years.

Paul Erdös*: Hungarian mathematician Paul Erdös published over 1,500 papers on number theory, graph theory, combinatorics, and other topics in pure mathematics. He worked with hundreds of coauthors. His contributions to mathematics include the first elementary proof of the prime number theorem, and the development of the field of probabilistic number theory.

Emil Erlenmeyer*: Scientist, editor, and professor, Emil Erlenmeyer contributed to the great advances of organic chemistry in the second half of the nineteenth century. He discovered the Erlenmeyer Rule that hydrocarbon compounds will not form alcohols if the hydroxyl group is attached directly to double-bonded carbon atoms. The conical and iconic Erlenmeyer flask that he invented is still standard laboratory equipment.

Edgard O. Espinoza: An innovator in wildlife forensic science, with colleague Mary-Jacque Mann, Espinoza determined how to evaluate Schreger lines in ivory to aid customs agents in distinguishing banned elephant ivory imports from legal ivory sources. Espinoza also developed a technique using mass spectrometry to analyze minute amounts of blood evidence to identify the animal species from which the blood came according to the hemoglobin proteins present.

Euclid*: Euclid took the geometry known in his day and presented it in a logical system. His work on geometry became the standard textbook on the subject down to modern times.

Eudoxus*: Eudoxus and his disciples resolved classical difficulties in the fields of geometry and geometric astronomy. Their approach became definitive for later research in these fields.

Leonhard Euler*: Euler had a tremendous impact on almost all fields of mathematics, opening new and more fruitful courses of inquiry. One of the most prolific mathematical writers ever, his founding of the field of analysis was particularly important, and his notations remain in common use in mathematics.

Henry Eyring*: Twentieth-century chemist Henry Eyring helped develop the transition state theory of chemical reactions, an important contribution in the field of chemical kinetics, which deals with the speed of chemical reactions.

F

Hieronymus Fabricius*: Sixteenth-century surgeon and anatomist Hieronymus Fabricius is most famous for his discovery of valves in veins and for influencing English physician William Harvey, who used Fabricius's findings to become the first to describe the systemic circulation of the cardiovascular system. Fabricius also significantly advanced the fields of anatomy, anatomical illustration, embryology, and surgery.

Johannes Fabricius*: Seventeenth-century German amateur observational astronomer Johannes Fabricius was one of the first scientists to use a telescope to study the sun. He was the first person to publish a study of sunspots and the first to present written evidence suggesting the sun rotates rather than remaining stationary in the sky.

Daniel Gabriel Fahrenheit: Fahrenheit invented the mercury thermometer in 1714 and the temperature scale that bears his name.

Michael Faraday*: In the 1820s, British physicist and chemist Michael Faraday sprinkled iron filings on a piece of paper and guided an electromagnet beneath it to illustrate lines of magnetic force. Since then, generations of students have learned about the principle of magnetic fields and other basics of electromagnetism from repeating this simple exercise. Faraday's discovery of magnetic fields remains one of the most significant contributions to science and provided the foundation for the development of the telegraph and other important innovations.

Philo Farnsworth: An inventor born in Utah, Farnsworth became interested in electronics and mechanics as a child. He experimented with television during the 1920s, and late in the decade he demonstrated an electronic, nonmechanical scanning system for image transmissions. During the early 1930s, he worked for Philco but left to carry out his own research. In addition to significant contributions to television, Farnsworth held more than 300 patents and devised a milk-sterilizing process, developed fog lights, an infrared telescope, a prototype of an air traffic control system, and a fusion reaction tube.

Gustav Theodor Fechner: Fechner is widely regarded as both the founder of psychophysics—the science of the mind-body relation—and a pioneer in experimental psychology. His most important contributions are a number of quantitative methods for measuring absolute and differential thresholds that are still employed by psychologists to study sensitivity to stimulation.

Enrico Fermi: As well as his foundational work in radiation physics, for which he received the 1938 Nobel Prize in Physics, Fermi designed and oversaw the construction of the first nuclear reactor in 1942.

Richard Feynman*: Nobel Prize winner Richard Feynman was a groundbreaking physicist who helped to combine classical electrodynamics and quantum physics into a theory that guided the formation of modern physics.

Andrew Z. Fire*: American molecular biologist and geneticist Andrew Z. Fire received the 2006 Nobel Prize in Physiology or Medicine along with Craig. C. Mello for their work in elucidating the process behind RNA interference, which changed scientists' understanding of RNA's role in transcription.

Ronald Fisher: British biologist Ronald Fisher's application of statistics provided a means by which use of small sampling size could be applied to larger interpretations. Fisher's breeding of small animals led to an understanding of genetic dominance. He later applied his work to the study of inheritance of blood types in humans.

Edith M. Flanigen: Beginning in 1956, chemist Edith M. Flanigen developed numerous synthetic molecular sieves from zeolites. They are used in the chemical and petroleum industries for producing products such as gasoline and oxygen and cleaning up nuclear waste.

Alexander Fleming*: Scottish biologist Sir Alexander Fleming is best known for his role in the discovery of penicillin, the world's first cheap, effective antibiotic. Although he insisted that his discovery was merely the result of luck and a keen eye, he shared the 1945 Nobel Prize in Physiology or Medicine for his achievement.

Williamina Paton Stevens Fleming*: Scottish American astronomer Williamina Paton Stevens Fleming pioneered the analysis of stellar spectra and discovered more than three hundred variable stars and ten exploding stars (novas). Her work made her the leading female astronomer of her time.

Baron Florey: A wide-ranging intellect, extensive training in the sciences on which medicine has become progressively more dependent, and the capacity for organizing resources and directing efforts effectively made it possible for Florey to unlock the fundamental scientific secrets of Alexander Fleming's discoveries of lysozyme and penicillin and to make antibiotic therapy a cornerstone of the practice of modern medicine. His isolation of the active antimicrobial ingredient in Penicillium notatum made it readily available to physicians and stands as one of the more significant scientific achievements of the twentieth century.

Jay Wright Forrester: An engineer, teacher, and computer scientist born in Nebraska, Forrester built a wind-powered electrical system while in his teens. Associated with the Massachusetts Institute of Technology as a researcher and professor for many years, he developed servomechanisms for military use, designed aircraft flight simulators, and air defense systems. He founded the field of system dynamics to produce computer-generated mathematical models for such tasks as determining water flow, fluid turbulence, and a variety of mechanical movements.

Dian Fossey*: American primatologist Dian Fossey gained international recognition for her groundbreaking studies of mountain gorillas in central Africa. She spent eighteen years living among the gorillas, dispelling myths of their aggressiveness and ferocity, and spurring conservation efforts to protect the endangered species.

Léon Foucault: A brilliant experimental physicist, Foucault fabricated the first gyroscope in 1852 in order to demonstrate that the Earth rotates.

Joseph Fourier*: In deriving and solving equations representing the flow of heat in bodies, French mathematician and physicist Joseph Fourier developed analytical methods that became useful in the fields of pure mathematics, applied mathematics, theoretical physics, and thermodynamics.

Girolamo Fracastoro: Fracastoro's prophetic hypotheses on the causes of diseases foreshadowed by centuries the modern understanding of microbial infections. He believed infection could be spread through direct or indirect contact by tiny, even insensible, particles. He also believed that poetry was the ideal means to convey knowledge.

Benjamin Franklin: A noted scientist and Founding Father, Franklin is also well known for inventing the Franklin stove, bifocals, the lightning rod, and the odometer.

Rosalind Franklin*: Best known as a key figure in discovering the structure of DNA, Rosalind Franklin also made significant contributions to understanding the structure of viruses and elemental carbon. Despite the sexism she faced in a male-dominated profession, Franklin's foundational place in the field of genetics has been reestablished in the twenty-first century.

Augustin-Jean Fresnel: Drawing from his wave theory of light, French physicist Augustin-Jean Fresnel invented the Fresnel lens, a lightweight design with large aperture and short focal length that became widely used in lighthouses.

Karl von Frisch*: Austrian zoologist and ethologist Karl von Frisch was awarded the 1973 Nobel Prize in Physiology or Medicine for his achievements in ethology. He focused in particular on the social life of bees and the sensory capabilities of fish.

Leonhard Fuchs: Fuchs wrote the first significant botanical text of the Renaissance era, a massive illustrated work prized for its beauty, accuracy, and originality and considered foundational to the development of natural history. He also wrote or cowrote dozens of texts in the fields of medicine and pharmacology.

Ted Fujita: Highly respected as an observer and researcher, Japanese American Ted Fujita greatly advanced the science of meteorology in both his native and his adopted countries. He meticulously studied atmospheric systems and made many discoveries regarding tornadoes and hurricanes that have aided weather forecasting.

Kenichi Fukui*: Kenichi Fukui was a pioneer in the field of theoretical chemistry. His theory of frontier orbitals, a term he coined in the early 1950s, explains why different types of molecules demonstrate varying levels of chemical reactivity.

Calvin Fuller: A physical chemist employed at AT&T Bell Laboratories, Fuller was among the coinventors of the first efficient silicon solar cell.

Casimir Funk: A biochemist, Funk discovered that a deficiency of amines led to certain diseases, such as scurvy and rickets. He called these vital amines "vitamines," later shortened to vitamins.

G

Dennis Gabor: Gabor received the 1971 Nobel Prize in Physics for his invention of holography—three-dimensional, lensless imaging.

Biruté Galdikas*: For more than forty years, Biruté Galdikas has studied orangutans in their natural environment. During that time, she has also waged a fierce battle against encroachments destroying the habitat of an endangered animal that is one of humankind's closest relatives.

Galen (of Pergamum)*: Although he dabbled in philosophy and psychology, second-century physician Galen made his greatest contributions to scientific history in medicine, where he left one of the best repositories of anatomical knowledge in the ancient world. His theories and practices remained dominant until the end of the Middle Ages.

Galileo: Many scholars believe that Galileo established the modern form of scientific experimentation, but he also invented practical devices, such as the water thermometer in 1593 and a horse-powered pump in 1594.

Boris Borisovich Galitzine: Galitzine built the first electromagnetic seismograph in 1906 and was a founder of the scientific discipline seismology.

Johann Gottfried Galle*: Nineteenth-century German astronomer Johann Gottfried Galle discovered several new comets and one of Saturn's rings, but he is best remembered as the person who used another scientist's calculations to find and view Neptune—the first planet to be discovered based on mathematical prediction.

Francis Galton*: Francis Galton is credited with developing modern statistical methods that have made immense contributions in all areas of science. He also played a role in the development of modern psychology and the eugenics movement.

Luigi Galvani*: Late eighteenth-century Italian physician and anatomist Luigi Galvani made pioneering discoveries about the relationship between electricity and biology. Through a series of experiments in which he used electricity to stimulate muscular contractions in frog legs, Galvani demonstrated conclusively the presence of electric currents in organic tissue.

George Gamow*: Ukrainian American physicist George Gamow helped develop quantum theory and apply it to nuclear physics. Additionally, Gamow promoted the big bang theory, made various advances in cosmology, created a method for analyzing DNA, and wrote popular science books.

Archibald Garrod: Applying his work on alkaptonuria, Garrod proposed that some human diseases result from a lack of specific enzymes. His theory of inborn errors of metabolism, published in 1908, established the genetic basis for certain hereditary diseases.

Pierre Gassendi: Although best known for his Christianization of Epicurean atomism, Gassendi also advanced science through his discoveries in physics and astronomy, and he promoted Catholicism through his pastoral and administrative work.

Bill Gates: Gates cofounded the Microsoft Corporation, the world's largest PC software company, and he helped develop the Windows operating system, word processors, and spreadsheets. He also cofounded the largest charitable organization in the world, the Bill and Melinda Gates Foundation.

Carl Friedrich Gauss*: Nineteenth-century German mathematician Carl Friedrich Gauss made significant contributions to many branches of mathematics and science. He is known for his work on number theory, geometry, probability theory, geodesy, and theoretical astronomy.

Joseph-Louis Gay-Lussac: Gay-Lussac made significant advances in industrial and analytic chemistry and invented techniques and apparatuses for the production and study of chemicals.

Hans Geiger: Geiger's achievement, the counter (1908), detects the alpha particles (positive ions) emitted during radioactive decay. It was widely used by prospectors searching for uranium ore.

Heinrich Geissler: Geissler's achievement, the tube, invented in 1857, contains low-pressure gas that glows when high voltage is applied to the electrodes on either end.

Margaret Geller*: American astrophysicist Margaret Geller's research into the structure of galaxies has yielded a new understanding of their shape and distribution. With colleague John Huchra, Geller discovered and named the Great Wall, a superstructure cluster of galaxies.

Murray Gell-Mann*: Twentieth-century American physicist Murray Gell-Mann is famous for his discovery of the subatomic particles known as quarks and for developing the theory of elementary particles. In 1969, he was awarded the Nobel Prize in Physics.

Sophie Germain: Germain overcame the limits of a haphazard education and a variety of social and institutional impediments to make fundamental advances in the proof of Fermat's last theorem and in the physics of elasticity. Those achievements represent the most original and significant contribution to mathematics by any woman before the end of the nineteenth century.

Edmund Germer: German scientist Edmund Germer improved the efficiency of lighting with his inventions of the fluorescent lamp (patented in 1926 with Friedrich Meyer and Hans Spanner) and the high-pressure mercury-vapor lamp.

Conrad Gesner*: Conrad Gesner collected, studied, and published the works of earlier literary, medical, and natural history authorities. He also compiled encyclopedic surveys of earlier scholarship in these fields. Equally important, however, were Gesner's extension of knowledge and systematic classifications in the field of natural history.

William Francis Giauque: Giauque received the 1949 Nobel Prize in Chemistry for his experiments in ultra-low temperatures using adiabatic demagnetization refrigeration.

Josiah Willard Gibbs*: Josiah Willard Gibbs established the theoretical basis for modern physical chemistry by quantifying the second law of thermodynamics and developing heterogeneous thermodynamics. Gibbs also made significant contributions to the areas of statistical mechanics and vector analysis.

Eloise Giblett: Eloise Giblett was the discoverer of numerous genetic markers useful in defining blood groups and serum proteins. In the 1970s, Giblett discovered that certain immunodeficiency diseases result from the absence of certain enzymes necessary for immune cell development.

Walter Gilbert: Gilbert developed a method of sequencing DNA. With Paul Berg and Frederick Sanger, he was awarded the 1980 Nobel Prize in Chemistry.

William Gilbert*: English physician and physicist William Gilbert was one of the first scientists to make conclusions based on verifiable experimental data. He is credited with inventing the term "electricity" and is considered the founder of studies in magnetism.

Alfred G. Gilman: Gilman discovered the role of "G" proteins in regulating signal transduction in eukaryotic cells. With Martin Rodbell, won the Nobel Prize in Physiology or Medicine for 1994.

Donald A. Glaser: Glaser's ether-filled bubble chamber, for which he received the 1960 Nobel Prize in Physics, revolutionized nuclear physics, enabling scientists to detect short-lived subatomic particles.

Sheldon L. Glashow: A Nobel Prize-winning physicist famous for his work on the unification of electromagnetic and weak nuclear forces, Glashow predicted the charm quark's existence and searched for "grand unified theories."

Robert H. Goddard: Widely held to be the father of rocket science, Goddard launched the first liquid-fuel rocket in 1923.

William Goddard: In 1955, Goddard, John Lynott, and Louis Stevens developed a computer memory system of stacked magnetized disks on a rotating shaft with detached read-write heads: a magnetic disk drive.

Kurt Gödel*: Kurt Gödel did fundamental work in many areas of mathematical logic and made several contributions to philosophy and physics. His most famous achievement was the enunciation and proof of the incompleteness theorems of arithmetic, the consequences of which cut across all branches of mathematics and gave rise to results in computer science as well. Mathematical logic assumed a more central position in mathematics following Gödel's career.

Maria Goeppert-Mayer*: Twentieth-century German American physicist Maria Goeppert-Mayer shared the Nobel Prize in Physics in 1963 for discoveries related to the structure of the nuclear shell. She was the first woman to win the Nobel Prize for theoretical physics.

Maurice Goldhaber: Goldhaber, a physicist who worked primarily in research on the atomic and subatomic level, was responsible for several major findings about neutrons, protons, and neutrinos.

Richard Goldschmidt*: German-born geneticist Richard Goldschmidt provoked significant debate within the fields of evolutionary biology and genetics with his theory of "hopeful monsters." His controversial 1940 book, *The Material Basis of Evolution* argues that macromutations provide an explanation for large evolutionary changes.

Joseph L. Goldstein*: Joseph L. Goldstein is best known for discovering the role played by lipid receptors in the liver in regulating cholesterol levels in the blood. His work has proved critical in understanding the relationship between elevated lipids and heart disease.

Camillo Golgi*: Nineteenth-century physician and histologist Camillo Golgi was the first Italian scientist to be awarded the Nobel Prize. He is best known for his work on the human nervous system, including the discovery of a tendon sensory organ called the Golgi receptor. He is also known for formulating a method of staining nerve cells and tissues in order to observe their behavior.

Jane Goodall*: British primatologist and ethnologist Jane Goodall is best known for her groundbreaking work observing chimpanzee behavior in the wild. She has made significant contributions to the study of animal behavior, as well as to causes related to conservation and animal welfare.

Gordon Gould: Physicist Gordon Gould coined "laser" as an acronym for "light amplification by stimulated emission of radiation," a process he formulated independently of Theodore Harold Maiman, who built the first device.

Stephen Jay Gould*: Stephen Jay Gould was one of the most popular scientists of the twentieth century. He is remembered among evolutionary biologists for his modification of certain tenets of Charles Darwin's theory of evolution. Among the general public, Gould is best known for his award-winning books and essays that made science accessible to the layperson.

Meredith C. Gourdine: Engineer and physicist Meredith C. Gourdine was a pioneer in electrogasdynamics—the action of charged particles through a gas—and applied it in practical inventions for energy conversion, spraying systems, and pollution control.

Temple Grandin: An animal scientist born in Massachusetts, Grandin was diagnosed with autism as a child. As an adult she earned advanced degrees before receiving a doctorate from the University of Illinois in 1989. A professor at Colorado State University, an author, and an autism advocate, she has made numerous humane improvements to the design of livestock-handling facilities that have been incorporated into meat-processing plants worldwide to reduce or eliminate animal stress, pain, and fear.

Bernard Greenberg: Considered a founder of forensic entomology, Greenberg consulted and testified regarding forensic evidence involving insects and cadavers, particularly the use of insect evidence to determine time since death, establishing the scientific basis for forensic entomology.

Paul Greengard: Greengard researched signal transduction in neurons and the role of neurotransmitters in the brain. He won the Nobel Prize in 2000 for his research on dopamine. His discoveries help scientists understand how the brain functions and disorders such as Parkinson's disease.

James Gregory: Astronomer and mathematician James Gregory designed the first practical reflecting telescope.

Carol W. Greider*: Carol Greider was awarded the Nobel Prize in Physiology or Medicine in 2009 for her work in discovering the enzyme telomerase and identifying the role of telomeres in the maintenance of linear chromosomes.

Frederick Griffith: In 1928, British microbiologist Frederick Griffith reported the existence of a "transforming principle," an unknown substance that could change the genetic properties of bacteria. In 1944, Oswald Avery determined the substance to be DNA, three years after Griffith was killed during the German bombing of London.

Francesco Maria Grimaldi: Grimaldi is best known for his experiments with light, being the first to describe its diffraction. Light diffraction is a phenomenon that indicates that light consists of waves, and is not, as previously thought, corpuscular in nature. He also detailed and named prominent features on the moon's surface.

David Gross: A renowned physicist, Gross is a string theorist who won the Nobel Prize for his collaborative research with Frank Wilczek and David Politzer. He has also been the recipient of many honors in the scientific community, including the MacArthur Foundation Fellowship Prize in 1987.

William Robert Grove: Although trained as a lawyer, physicist William Robert Grove invented the electric cell that bears his name. He also discovered and popularized the conservation of energy principle and helped to reform the Royal Society of London.

Otto von Guericke: German scientist Otto von Guericke investigated the nature of atmospheric pressure and invented a vacuum pump.

Charles-Édouard Guillaume: Measurements, and the standards on which they are based, are the foundation of the physical sciences. Guillaume, during his long tenure as assistant director and director of the International Bureau of Weights and Measures at Sèvres, was indefatigable as researcher and administrator in refining instruments and methods of measurement to the greatest possible precision, and in publishing to the world the current status of metricization and metric standards. For his efforts, he received the Nobel Prize in Physics in 1920.

Robert Gundlach: As a research scientist for the Haloid Company (later Xerox Corporation), Gundlach made innovations to the photocopier that made it more versatile and easier and cheaper to use.

H

Fritz Haber: Haber received the 1918 Nobel Prize in Chemistry for developing artificial nitrogen-bearing fertilizers, which expanded global agricultural production.

Robert Abbott Hadfield: Hadfield's discovery of manganese steel ushered in the age of alloy steels, which have proven to be essential to the development of modern industrial technology and weapons.

Ernst Heinrich Haeckel: German zoologist Ernst Haeckel's writings were instrumental in the dissemination of Charles Darwin's theories. Haeckel's "biogenetic law," since discarded, stated that "ontogeny repeats phylogeny," suggesting that embryonic development mirrors the evolutionary relationship of organisms.

Otto Hahn*: A pioneer in radioactivity, Hahn and his colleagues Fritz Strassmann and Lise Meitner are credited with having discovered nuclear fission as well as certain radioactive isotopes and elements. Hahn was awarded the 1944 Nobel Prize in Chemistry and played a major role in reestablishing German science after World War II.

J. B. S. Haldane*: A key contributor to the field of population genetics, J. B. S. Haldane combined Charles Darwin's evolutionary theories with the hereditary laws discovered by Gregor Mendel into one synthesized theory of evolution. His popular writings influenced the cultural climate of the day and provided inspiration for novelist Aldous Huxley's vision of a genetically engineered future in *Brave New World*.

George Ellery Hale*: In the early twentieth century, American astronomer George Ellery Hale constructed the world's largest telescopes. He also discovered solar vortices and learned that sunspots are associated with intense magnetic fields, which proved key to understanding solar activity.

Lloyd Hall: Chemist Lloyd Augustus Hall developed an improved process for curing and preserving foods with salts in 1925 and later a way to sterilize foods with ethylene oxide gas.

Robert N. Hall : An applied physicist and electrical engineer, Hall built the first semiconductor injection laser in 1962, now widely used in compact disc (CD) players, printers, and optical fiber communications.

Edmond Halley*: English astronomer and natural scientist Edmond Halley accurately predicted the orbit of what became known as Halley's comet. Halley also made a number of observations concerning the Earth and thus is considered a founder of the field of geophysics.

William Hamilton: A leading mathematical physicist of the nineteenth century, Hamilton is best known for introducing quaternions in 1843, a number system used in calculations involving three-dimensional rotations.

Hidesaburo Hanafusa: Japanese-born scientist Hidesaburo Hanafusa played a key role in elucidating the role of oncogenes found among the RNA tumor viruses in transforming mammalian cells.

James E. Hansen: As a prominent climate scientist and activist, Hansen has been an important contributor to increased public awareness of global warming.

G. H. Hardy*: English mathematician G. H. Hardy made advances in number theory, mathematical analysis, and statistical analysis, though he focused primarily on pure mathematics. Hardy also wrote mathematics textbooks and is sometimes credited as the founder of population genetics analysis.

William Harvey*: Sixteenth-century English physician William Harvey pioneered the application of modern scientific methodology to biological questions. His greatest accomplishment was his discovery of the circulatory system, and his accurate descriptions of the mechanics of blood flow provided the foundation for the development of cardiovascular medicine.

Herbert A. Hauptman: Hauptman's work in mathematics and X-ray crystallography led to his development of a mathematical formula for determining the three-dimensional atomic structure of molecules from two-dimensional X-rays.

Stephen Hawking*: Astrophysicist Stephen Hawking's work in theoretical physics has helped shape the field of cosmology. A best-selling author, he has helped introduce the field to a wider audience, entering questions about the origins of the universe into the public consciousness.

Oliver Heaviside: An innovative mathematical physicist, Heaviside also invented the distortionless transmission line for telegraph and telephone cables.

Werner Heisenberg*: Twentieth-century German theoretical physicist Werner Heisenberg won the Nobel Prize in Physics in 1932 and is best remembered as one of the founders of quantum mechanics. His most important contribution to quantum mechanical ideas is the Heisenberg uncertainty principle, which has become a cornerstone of modern physics.

Hermann von Helmholtz: Helmholtz invented the ophthalmoscope for seeing into the eye and the ophthalmometer for measuring its curvature.

Jan Baptista van Helmont*: Jan Baptista van Helmont is best remembered for his discovery of gases and for his contributions to medicine. He was one of the founders of the modern theory of disease, arguing that diseases were caused by external forces rather than internal imbalance. Van Helmont is also remembered for his

interest in natural philosophy, alchemy, and the occult.

Joseph Henry: As the first secretary of the Smithsonian Institution, president of the National Academy of Sciences, and a leading experimental physicist, Henry was one of the most important molders of t American professional scientific community of the nineteenth century.

Hero of Alexandria*: Hero is known as the most important ancient authority on mechanical devices. Some of the inventions Hero described, including a rudimentary steam engine and a windmill, were his own. He also investigated mathematics, where his most noted contribution was a method for approximating square roots.

Herophilus*: The Alexandrian physician, researcher, and teacher known as Herophilus lived during a period of scientific flourishing in ancient Greece and Egypt. He is considered one of the first serious anatomists and physiologists in history. Herophilus was able to make his discoveries through the systematic scientific dissection of both humans and animals.

Caroline Lucretia Herschel: Herschel was an astronomer and mathematician who spent years assisting her better-known brother William Herschel in his astronomical observations. However, she also independently scanned the sky for new objects, discovering two galaxies, several open star clusters, and eight comets. After her brother's death, she completed the Herschel catalog of twenty-five hundred nebulae, which was included in her nephew John Herschel's *General Catalogue*.

William Herschel*: Astronomer William Herschel discovered the planet Uranus, two of its moons, and two of Saturn's moons. Herschel also identified star clusters, double stars, and nebulae, created the first map of the Milky Way Galaxy, and discovered infrared radiation.

Mayo D. Hersey: A mechanical engineer born in Rhode Island, Hersey was a preeminent expert on tribology, the study of the relationship between interacting solid surfaces in motion, the adverse effects of wear, and the ameliorating effects of lubrication. He worked as a physicist at the National Institute of Standards and Technology (1910–1920) and the U.S. Bureau of Mines (1922–1926) and taught at the Massachusetts Institute of Technology (1910–1922). He was a consultant to the Manhattan Project and won numerous awards for his contributions to lubrication science.

Alfred Day Hershey: Molecular biologist Alfred Day Hershey played a key role in understanding the replication and genetic structure of viruses. His experiments with Martha Chase confirmed that DNA carried the genetic information in some viruses. Hershey was awarded the 1969 Nobel Prize in Physiology or Medicine.

Heinrich Rudolf Hertz*: Heinrich Rudolf Hertz was a nineteenth-century German physicist. He is remembered for sending and receiving the first radio waves. Using the mathematical equations and the theoretical framework developed by Scottish physicist James Clerk Maxwell, Hertz proved that electromagnetic waves and radio waves behave in the same way as light waves.

Gerhard Herzberg: Herzberg became the leading researcher in the spectroscopy of atoms and molecules at a time when rapid development of the quantum theory made it possible to explain the observed spectra in terms of the behavior of the electrons and nuclei involved. Over the course of a productive career, Herzberg made many measurements of significance for chemistry and astronomy.

Germain Henri Hess*: Early nineteenth-century chemist Germain Henri Hess discovered the law of constant heat summation, which is a key ancestor of the first law of thermodynamics. Hess also investigated minerals, and contributed to education and research in chemistry in Russia.

Harry Hammond Hess*: American geologist Harry Hammond Hess developed the theory of seafloor spreading. This helped scientists come to a consensus about plate tectonic theory and changed the way people understood the formation of the Earth.

Victor Francis Hess*: Physicist Victor Francis Hess discovered the existence of cosmic rays in 1912, earning him the Nobel Prize and advancing the study of nuclear physics.

Elisabeth Hevelius*: One of the first modern female astronomers, Elisabeth Hevelius capped a lifetime of celestial observations with the publication of her and her late husband's work in 1690, consisting of a comprehensive star catalogue and star atlas.

George de Hevesy: As well as codiscovering the element hafnium, de Hevesy received the 1943 Nobel Prize

in Chemistry for developing radioactive tracer analysis, used in chemistry and medicine.

Peter Higgs*: British physicist Peter Higgs proposed in 1964 the existence of a subatomic particle to account for the origin of mass in other subatomic particles such as protons and neutrons. In July 2012, his predictions were verified, providing an experimental basis for a complete revolution in unified field theory.

James Hillier: With Albert Prebus, scientist James Hillier built a successful high-resolution electron microscope in 1938, the first in the United States.

Hipparchus*: Hipparchus was one of the greatest astronomers of ancient times. He was the founder of trigonometry, which he used to determine the distances from Earth to the moon and sun. He was also the first to consistently use the idea of latitude and longitude to describe locations on Earth and in the sky.

Hippocrates*: Hippocrates, known as the "father of medicine," is credited with separating the practice of medicine from magic and superstition, inaugurating the modern practice of scientific observation, and setting high standards for ethical medical practice.

David D. Ho: As a physician specializing in infectious diseases, David D. Ho is best known for his groundbreaking work uncovering the mechanism of how HIV replicates. This research was instrumental in creating new antiretroviral therapies to treat HIV/AIDS.

Dorothy Crowfoot Hodgkin: An expert in X-ray crystallography, Hodgkin received the 1964 Nobel Prize in Chemistry for defining the structure of cholesterol, penicillin, vitamin B12, and insulin.

Felix Hoffmann: In 1897, chemist Felix Hoffmann synthesized acetyl salicylic acid (aspirin), which Bayer first distributed to doctors as a pain reliever two years later.

Roald Hoffmann*: A theoretical chemist particularly known for his research in the field of organometallic chemistry, Roald Hoffmann won the 1981 Nobel Prize in Chemistry for his work on the course of chemical reactions.

Robert Hofstadter*: American physicist Robert Hofstadter was awarded the 1961 Nobel Prize in Physics for his discoveries about the fundamental composition and structure of the atomic nucleus. His other contributions include a series of investigations into the hydrogen bond and the development of several instruments for measuring radiation and electron scattering.

J. Paul Hogan: In 1951, chemist John Paul Hogan and Robert Banks invented crystalline and high-density polyethylene (HDPE), plastics since used in common products such as milk jugs and indoor-outdoor carpeting.

Robert William Holley: Holley determined the sequence of nucleotide bases in transfer RNA (tRNA), the molecule that carries amino acids to ribosomes for protein synthesis. Holley's work provided a means for demonstrating the reading of the genetic code. He was awarded the Nobel Prize in Physiology or Medicine in 1968.

Leroy E. Hood: Biologist Leroy Hood is renowned for the automatic DNA sequencer, with which the entire genome of a human being was decoded in 2003.

Robert Hooke*: As curator of experiments for England's Royal Society, Robert Hooke proved to be one of the most influential experimentalists and inventors of the seventeenth century, contributing to a wide range of scientific fields.

Grace Murray Hopper*: Grace Murray Hopper was a US naval officer who ultimately rose to the rank of rear admiral. She is best known for her pioneering work on the development of COBOL, the first user-friendly computer programming language. She also created a variety of innovative computer software that was instrumental to the evolution of the information age.

Jeremiah Horrocks: Horrocks's observation of the transit of Venus, in 1639, is the earliest on record. He applied Kepler's laws of planetary motion to the moon, comets, and planets.

Robert E. Horton*: Twentieth-century American Earth scientist Robert Elmer Horton made significant contributions to the development of the field of hydrology in the United States. During a fifty-year career as a civil engineer, working with various government agencies and as an independent consultant, he analyzed and helped define many concepts related to rainfall, runoff, and water flow.

H. Robert Horvitz: Horvitz won the Nobel Prize in 2002 for his work on nematode worms, which helped advance research in cell death, or apoptosis, and organ regulation in humans.

Godfrey Newbold Hounsfield: Hounsfield invented computed tomography, a method of producing detailed images of internal body tissues that provides physicians with much more information than ordinary X-rays can supply. Computed tomography inspired the development of other advanced methods of medical imaging in the late twentieth century.

Freeman S. Howlett: A horticulturist born in New York, Howlett was associated with the Ohio State University as teacher, administrator, and researcher for more than forty-five years and was considered an expert on the history of horticulture. His investigations focused on plant hormones, embryology, fruit setting, reproductive physiology, and foliation for a variety of crops, including fruits, vegetables, and nuts. He created five new varieties of apples popular among consumers. A horticulture and food science building at Ohio State is named in his honor.

Fred Hoyle*: British astrophysicist Fred Hoyle established the theory of stellar nucleosynthesis to explain the chemical processes within stars, advocated for the steady-state theory of the universe, and extended the panspermia hypothesis. Hoyle also published numerous books that helped popularize science.

Edwin Powell Hubble*: Twentieth-century American astronomer Edwin Hubble is credited with the discovery that countless galaxies exist beyond the Milky Way, previously believed to be the only galaxy in the universe. He also identified the outward expansion of those galaxies, disproving the centuries-old belief that the universe was static. He produced the first outline of the observable universe, revolutionizing conceptions of its size, structure, processes, and history.

Margaret Lindsay Huggins*: Astronomer Margaret Lindsay Huggins and her husband, William Huggins, did pioneering work in astronomical spectroscopy, which they employed to study planets, stars, and nebulae. Together, they established the gaseous nature of the Orion Nebula and published an atlas of stellar spectra.

Alexander von Humboldt*: German naturalist Alexander von Humboldt was one of the most influential scientists and explorers of his day. Among his various accomplishments were his development of comparative climatology and his discovery of the Humboldt Current and worldwide magnetic storms.

Timothy R. Hunt: Hunt discovered the existence and role of proteins called cyclins, which regulate the cell cycle in eukaryotic cells. With Leland Hartwell and Sir Paul Nurse, he won the Nobel Prize in Physiology or Medicine in 2001.

James Hutton*: Eighteenth-century Scottish geologist James Hutton is remembered as the father of geology for promoting the theory of uniformitarianism and for recognizing the natural processes that create igneous, metamorphic, and sedimentary rocks. By adding tens of thousands of years onto the six thousand years then believed to represent the age of the Earth, he effectively separated geology from Genesis and proved the Neptunists wrong.

Thomas Henry Huxley: As the first and most influential defender of Darwin's theory of evolution, Huxley forcefully articulated its implications in the fields of religion, philosophy, and ethics.

Christiaan Huygens: An astronomer, mathematician, and physicist, Huygens developed an improved method for grinding telescope lenses, invented the pendulum clock, and proposed a wave theory of light.

I

Sumio Iijima: Physicist Sumio Iijima synthesized the first nanotubes in 1991, a basic advance in the development of nanotechnology.

Jan Ingenhousz*: Jan Ingenhousz began his scientific career by traveling throughout Europe administering smallpox inoculations. After settling in England, he performed botanical experiments that demonstrated the process of photosynthesis and respiration in plants, and was an early investigator of what became known as Brownian motion.

J

Abū Mūsā Jābir ibn Hayyān: The greatest alchemist of Islam, Jābir is regarded as the father of Arabian chemistry. His many works influenced later Arabian and European chemists considerably, and his alchemical ideas and recipes helped advance chemical theory and experimentation.

Shirley Ann Jackson*: American physicist Shirley Ann Jackson is best known for her contributions to theoretical physics, including polaronic aspects of electrons in two-dimensional systems. Jackson's prolific career has paved the way for many African American women in science.

François Jacob: Jacob shared the 1965 Nobel Prize in Physiology or Medicine with André Lwoff and Jacques Monod for their collaborative discoveries concerning the genetic control of enzyme and virus synthesis. These studies were landmarks in the evolving area of molecular biology. Jacob's work spanned virology, biochemistry, and microbiology.

Joseph Marie Jacquard: A French inventor, Jacquard created a series of mechanical looms in the early nineteenth century. His experiments culminated in the Jacquard loom attachment, which could be programmed, via punch cards, to weave silk in various patterns, colors, and textures automatically. The labor-saving device became highly popular in the silk-weaving industry, and its inventor received royalties on each unit sold and became wealthy in the process. The loom inspired scientists to incorporate the concept of punch cards for computer information storage.

Karl Guthe Jansky*: Twentieth-century American physicist and engineer Karl Guthe Jansky spent his career at Bell Telephone Laboratories. In the course of completing an assignment for the company, he detected radio signals emanating from the center of the Milky Way Galaxy, laying the foundation for a new branch of astronomy.

Thomas Jefferson: A versatile, practical scientist, the third US president produced an improved ox plow, lap desk, and mechanical copier, as well as innovations in agriculture.

Alec Jeffreys: Geneticist Alec Jeffreys gave a powerful new tool to forensic science with his development of DNA profiling, also known as DNA fingerprinting, in 1984.

György Jendrassik: In 1937, Hungarian physicist György Jendrassik designed the Jendrassik Cs-1 turboprop, the prototype of engines used on many long-distance aircraft.

Edward Jenner: Scientist Edward Jenner's great discovery, vaccination against disease, helped eradicate smallpox and started a revolution in public health.

J. Hans D. Jensen*: In 1949, Hans Jensen discovered that if one allowed for strong spin-orbit coupling among nucleons, the nuclear shell model explained accurately the structure of the nucleus. Jensen and Maria Goeppert-Mayer, who independently discovered this at the same time, shared half of the 1963 Nobel Prize in Physics for the achievement.

Steven Jobs: An inventor and entrepreneur of Syrian and American heritage born in San Francisco, Jobs worked at Hewlett-Packard as a teenager and was later employed at Atari designing circuit boards. In 1976, he and coworker Steve Wozniak (b. 1950) and others founded Apple, which designed, built, and sold a popular and highly successful line of personal computers. A multibillionaire and holder of more than 200 patents, Jobs continued to make innovations in interfacing, speakers, keyboards, power adaptation, and myriad other components related to modern computer science until his death in late 2011.

Carl Edvard Johansson: Inventor and scientist Johansson produced lengths of steel, called a gauge block set (patented in 1901), that provided exact standards of measurement and are widely used in machine shops and industry.

Wilhelm L. Johannsen: Danish botanist Wilhelm Johannsen introduced the term "genes," derived from "pangenes," factors suggested by Hugo de Vries to determine hereditary characteristics in plants. Johannsen also introduced the concepts of phenotype and genotype to distinguish between physical and hereditary traits.

Katherine G. Johnson: A pioneering space scientist who broke racial and gender barriers, Johnson specialized in mathematics and physics during a career spanning more than thirty years with the National Aeronautics and Space Administration (NASA). She was an indispensable member of teams that launched some of America's most successful exploratory programs, including the Mercury, Apollo, and space shuttle missions.

Frédéric and Irène Joliot-Curie*: Frédéric and Irène Joliot-Curie continued the work that Irène's parents, Pierre and Marie Curie, had begun on radioactivity, researching such elements as radium and polonium. They received the Nobel Prize in Chemistry in 1935 for discovering the process of inducing artificial radioactivity.

James Prescott Joule*: James Prescott Joule was a nineteenth-century physicist who studied heat and energy. His work as a brewer inspired him to study the nature of heat and led to his discovery of the first law of thermodynamics. The international unit used to measure energy is named the joule in his honor.

Percy Lavon Julian: Julian, a chemist, produced several therapeutic drugs from plants, including the arthritis-relieving cortisone and the glaucoma medicine physostigmine.

Ernest Everett Just: Just's extensive zoological research advanced knowledge of fertilization in marine invertebrates. Limited by racial discrimination in Depression-era America, he spent several years in Europe, where he was able to clarify the role of cell surfaces in the development of organisms.

K

Bob Kahn: Kahn and Vinton Gray Cerf developed the packet network interconnection protocols (TCP/IP), the system of technical rules used to transfer information though the Internet.

Michio Kaku*: Michio Kaku codeveloped string field theory. A popular futurologist and best-selling author, Kaku has linked issues at the cutting edge of theoretical physics to visions of human life in the near- to mid-future.

Hartmut Kallmann: Physicist Hartmut Kallmann invented the scintillation counter, which measures ionizing radiation.

Heike Kamerlingh Onnes: A pioneer in ultra-low temperature physics, Kamerlingh Onnes liquefied helium and discovered superconductivity, for which he was honored with the 1913 Nobel Prize in Physics.

Hiroo Kanamori*: To better measure the energy released by major earthquakes, Japanese seismologist Hiroo Kanamori helped develop the moment magnitude scale in 1979, which has replaced the Richter scale for earthquakes above a 3.5 magnitude. Kanamori also contributed to research on earthquake predictions and the development of real-time seismology for earthquake responses.

Pyotr Leonidovich Kapitsa: Kapitsa received the 1978 Nobel Prize in Physics for his investigations into the superfluidity of liquid helium and basic inventions in low-temperature physics.

Jerome Karle: Karle, a renowned chemist, was awarded a Nobel Prize for pioneering a technique for using X-rays to investigate crystal structures.

Lord Kelvin*: Lord Kelvin, born William Thomson, devoted himself to the study of thermodynamics. He devised an absolute temperature scale that measured temperature according to a general standard and went down to absolute zero. He is sometimes credited with the formulation of the second law of thermodynamics.

Johannes Kepler*: Johannes Kepler was a German astronomer and mathematician whose three laws of planetary motion helped to popularize the Copernican view of a heliocentric universe and disprove the ancient idea that planetary orbits are perfect circles.

Har Gobind Khorana: Biochemist Har Gobind Khorana shared the 1968 Nobel Prize in Physiology or Medicine for his work in protein synthesis and in 1970 was the first to synthesize a gene.

al-Khwarizmi*: The early Persian mathematician and astronomer al-Khwarizmi has been considered by some scholars to be the founder of algebra, the branch of mathematics that deals with equations containing unknown quantities and variables. His publications on the subject were among the earliest available to the Arab world and were highly influential among later scholars.

Jack St. Clair Kilby: Kilby received the 2000 Nobel Prize in Physics as the inventor of the integrated circuit; he also developed a hand calculator and thermal printer.

Gustav Robert Kirchhoff*: German theoretical physicist Gustav Robert Kirchhoff developed a series of physical laws that synthesized knowledge in different fields of physics, including thermodynamics and optics. With Robert Bunsen, Kirchhoff carried out experiments that founded the field of spectroscopy.

Fritz Klatte: German chemist Fritz Klatte patented his process for synthesizing vinyl acetate in 1913, also known as polyvinyl chloride (PVC).

Felix Klein*: Nineteenth-century German mathematician Felix Klein discovered many new non-Euclidean geometric systems. He established their consistency with traditional Euclidean geometry through applying algebra to the study of symmetry.

Leonard Kleinrock*: One of a handful of individuals most frequently called the "father of the Internet," Leonard Kleinrock has made many significant contributions in the area of computer networking. He is most famous for developing a new technology in the mid-1960s called packet switching, which sent messages from one computer to another and was the precursor for email messages and the Internet.

Thomas Andrew Knight: Plant biologist Thomas Andrew Knight first recognized the usefulness of the garden pea for genetic studies because of its distinctive traits. He was the first to characterize dominant and recessive traits in the pea, though, unlike Gregor Mendel, he never determined the mathematical relationships among his crosses.

Makoto Kobayashi: Makoto Kobayashi is a Japanese scientist and Nobel laureate. In October 2008, the Royal Swedish Academy of Sciences announced that Kobayashi would jointly share, together with fellow researcher Toshihide Maskawa, one half of the 2008 Nobel Prize in Physics. The other half of the award was given to Yoichiro Nambu. The three scientists won the award for their explanations of key anomalies in the laws of particle physics. Maskawa and Kobayashi were honored specifically for their discovery of the origin of broken symmetry—a process by which matter acquires mass—at the subatomic level of the cosmos.

Robert Koch*: Physician, bacteriologist, and Nobel laureate Robert Koch is remembered as one of the founders of medical bacteriology. He was a pioneer in the development of public health and hygiene programs and traveled the world studying epidemiology and bacterial hygiene.

Josef Gottlieb Kölreuter: A forerunner of Gregor Mendel, Kölreuter demonstrated the sexual nature of plant fertilization, in which characteristics were derived from each member of the parental generation in equivalent amounts.

Roscoe Koontz: Koontz was a pioneer in creating safety procedures to protect workers from radiation at nuclear reactors, thereby helping to establish the field of health physics.

Arthur Kornberg: Kornberg isolated the enzyme DNA polymerase, with which he made copies of DNA. He shared the 1959 Nobel Prize in Physiology or Medicine for his work.

Sergey Korolyov: Sometimes called the "father of practical astronautics," Korolyov led the team that developed the first intercontinental ballistic missile (ICBM) and was chief designer of the rockets in the Soviet space program from 1953 until his death.

Albrecht Kossel: Kossel won the 1910 Nobel Prize in Physiology or Medicine. He isolated and described molecular constituents of the cell's nucleus, notably cytosine, thymine, and uracil. These molecules later proved to be constituents of the codons in DNA and RNA. Thus, Kossel's research prepared the way for understanding the biochemistry of genetics.

Hans Adolf Krebs*: Krebs elucidated some of the key cycles of metabolic chemical reactions that support living organisms. The most important of these, the citric

acid cycle, is found in all living organisms. Also known as the Krebs cycle, this complex sequence of reactions is central to the study of metabolism.

August Krogh: Krogh, who had been aided by co-researcher Marie (Jorgensen) Krogh in his studies, won the 1920 Nobel Prize in Physiology or Medicine for his investigations into how the capillaries regulate the flow of blood, and thus oxygen, in the body. The married couple also made important advances in the understanding of how the lungs exchange oxygen from the air into the bloodstream.

William Kroll: In 1932, Kroll developed a process for mass producing ductile metallic titanium, later a key material in aircraft.

Gerard Peter Kuiper*: Twentieth-century Dutch American astronomer Gerard Peter Kuiper was a leading planetary scientist. He taught and conducted research at a number of major American astronomical installations, inspired the construction of several observatories, contributed significantly to early NASA moon-exploration projects, and made many discoveries within the solar system.

Igor Kurchatov: Nuclear physicist Igor Kurchatov led the Soviet program to develop nuclear weapons, beginning in 1943. He also oversaw construction of a Russian cyclotron (1949) and its first nuclear power plant (1954).

Ray Kurzweil: Inventor, scientist, and writer Ray Kurzweil developed computer programs to recognize patterns in sounds (speech recognition) and images (character recognition). He also designed musical synthesizers and wrote prolifically on artificial intelligence (AI) and the role of technology in the expansion and extension of human life.

Stephanie Kwolek: Chemist Stephanie Kwolek discovered liquid crystalline polymers, which made possible the development of the high-performance fiber Kevlar.

L

Alexandre Lacassagne: Sometimes referred to as the father of forensic science, Lacassagne concluded that bullets could be connected to the firearms that discharged them based on the grooves etched into bullets

by the weapons' barrels, providing the theoretical basis for the science of ballistics. Lacassagne also investigated the physical evidence used to prove that people were dead, noting that the skin appears purple when blood stops circulating. His investigations of rigor mortis and body temperature contributed to the forensic techniques used to calculate time since death when bodies are discovered.

Joseph-Louis Lagrange*: Particularly known for his work in fields such as mathematical analysis and mechanics, Joseph-Louis Lagrange synthesized the mathematical innovations of his predecessors and reshaped the systems underlying classical physics.

Georges Lakhovsky: Working with Nikola Tesla, Lakhovsky developed the multiple-wave oscillator, used in alternative medicine for electromagnetic therapy.

Jean-Baptiste Lamarck*: Jean-Baptiste Lamarck was a French botanist and biologist during the late eighteenth and early nineteenth centuries. He was one of the first scientists to advance a theory of evolution. Though later discredited by Charles Darwin and modern genetics, Lamarck's ideas were revolutionary at the time.

Lev Davidovich Landau*: Landau contributed to the development of quantum mechanics and its applications to the physical world. Among his major achievements are the development of the theory of phase transitions and his explanation of the behavior of quantum liquids such as liquid helium in the superfluid state. Landau's contributions to the theory of quantum liquids earned him the Nobel Prize in Physics in 1962.

Karl Landsteiner*: Remembered for his discovery of blood groups, Landsteiner also worked in immunology and immunochemistry and helped found the science of serology, the study of blood serum. A significant result of his discovery of blood groups was an increase in the safety of blood transfusions. His discoveries relating to syphilis, poliomyelitis, and various blood diseases eventually led to their control or cure.

Robert S. Langer: A leader in biomedical engineering, Langer developed controlled drug delivery in 1986 and pioneered remotely controlled drug delivery and tissue engineering.

Paul Langevin: Physicist Paul Langevin was a central figure in the development of submarine detection by echolocation during World War I, a technology later called sonar.

Samuel Pierpont Langley: A pioneer in aviation and an astronomer, Langley was also the inventor of the bolometer, which measures radiant electromagnetic energy.

Irving Langmuir: Langmuir developed a successful type of incandescent bulb, and his work in surface chemistry brought him the 1932 Nobel Prize in Chemistry.

Edwin Ray Lankester*: Ray Lankester systematized the field of embryology and researched major groups of living and fossil animals. He is the author of over one hundred scientific essays on comparative anatomy and paleontology, as well as books that make science accessible to nonscientists.

Pierre-Simon Laplace*: Pierre-Simon Laplace made groundbreaking mathematical contributions to probability theory and statistical analysis. Using Isaac Newton's theory of gravitation, he performed detailed mathematical analyses of the shape of the Earth and the orbits of comets, planets, and their moons.

Leone Lattes: A contributor to the science of the forensic analysis of blood evidence; while experimenting with blood flakes mixed with fresh blood, Lattes noted that the blood became lumpy if the samples were not of the same blood type. Forensic scientists recognized the value of Lattes's method for quick assessment of bloodstains, and that technique has retained its investigative value.

Max von Laue*: German physicist and crystallographer Max von Laue was the first to demonstrate X-ray diffraction in crystals. For this work, he was awarded the 1914 Nobel Prize in Physics.

Paul Lauterbur: Chemist Paul Lauterbur conceived the nuclear magnetic resonance in magnetic resonance imaging (MRI), for which he shared the 2003 Nobel Prize in Physiology or Medicine.

Antoine-Laurent Lavoisier*: French chemist Antoine Lavoisier is generally regarded as the founder of modern chemistry. In addition to discovering oxygen, he developed a system of chemical nomenclature, defined what an element is, and studied the nature of chemical compounds.

John Bennet Lawes: In 1842, agricultural scientist John Bennet Lawes perfected his process for making the chemical fertilizer superphospate and launched the artificial fertilizer industry.

Ernest Lawrence : Lawrence invented the cyclotron, a circular particle accelerator that made possible the direct investigation of the atomic nucleus and produced new radioactive isotopes; he received the Nobel Prize in Physics in 1939.

Henri Louis Le Chatelier*: Nineteenth-century French chemist Henri Louis Le Chatelier discovered the response of a chemical equilibrium to outside disturbances, and Le Chatelier's principle was subsequently named in his honor. His principle has become important to the chemical industry for developing efficient chemical processes. Le Chatelier also contributed to knowledge in metallurgy and cement compounds.

Louis S. B. Leakey*: Louis Leakey's lifelong examinations of the fossil remains near Lake Victoria and in the Olduvai Gorge in East Africa have provided clues as to the origin of the human species. His work and his support of the study of animal behavior in the wild have significantly advanced understanding of both how evolution occurred and how prehistoric humans managed to survive and eventually prevail.

Mary Leakey*: Mary Leakey's disciplined approach to fossil records supplied empirical support for the theory that Africa was the cradle of humankind. Her discoveries in East Africa included the approximately 1.75-million-year-old fossils of Homo habilis at Olduvai Gorge and the approximately 3.6-million-year-old footprints of three fully upright, bipedal hominids in Laetoli.

Henrietta Swan Leavitt*: While studying Cepheid variable stars, American astronomer Henrietta Swan Leavitt discovered the period-luminosity law, which is the relationship between a star's brightness and its distance. Leavitt also established the Harvard Standard for the photographic measurement of stars.

Sergei Vasilyevich Lebedev: Chemist Sergei Vasilyevich Lebedev produced a synthetic elastic rubber from polybutadiene in 1910.

Joshua Lederberg*: Joshua Lederberg discovered that genetic material is exchanged between bacteria by both conjugation and transduction. These discoveries were particularly significant for explaining the spread of antibiotic resistance among bacteria.

Leon M. Lederman*: Experimental physicist Leon M. Lederman won the Nobel Prize for his studies of neutrinos and discovery of the muon neutrino. Lederman also played a role in discovering the bottom quark and has written a number of popular science texts that help to explain the discoveries of particle physicists to a general audience.

Tsung-Dao Lee: Physicist Tsung-Dao Lee is most famous for his discovery, in collaboration with Chen-Ning Yang, that certain elementary-particle processes violate the long-established rule that physical laws make no distinction between right and left. Lee also contributed significantly to such fields as astrophysics as well as to science policies in the United States and China.

Yuan T. Lee: Yuan T. Lee is a Nobel Prize–winning chemist known for his work in the field of reaction dynamics (the study of chemical reactions) and his development of techniques and apparatuses for crossed molecular beam experimentation. After many years of research, he redirected his energy to bolstering the educational system in Taiwan and promoting science and education worldwide.

Antoni van Leeuwenhoek*: Dutch naturalist Antoni van Leeuwenhoek, sometimes known as the father of microbiology, was a pioneer in the construction and use of microscopes. He was the first person to observe bacteria, spermatozoa, and protozoa—creatures that he called animalcules, or tiny animals.

Inge Lehmann: Inge Lehmann's hypothesis that the Earth has an inner and outer core led to investigations that confirmed her theory.

Gottfried Wilhelm Leibniz*: Gottfried Wilhelm Leibniz developed both differential and integral calculus and is recognized today as the founder of symbolic logic. He also invented the stepped reckoner, an early calculator, and devised binary arithmetic.

Georges Lemaître*: The Belgian physicist Georges Lemaître established the foundation for modern cosmology. He was the first to theorize the big bang, the idea that the universe came into being at a specific point in time and expanded outward.

Leonardo da Vinci*: In the pursuit of art, Leonardo da Vinci studied many sciences, including anatomy, engineering, and botany, and is considered the ideal model of the Renaissance man.

Leonardo of Pisa (Fibonacci)*: Leonardo of Pisa introduced the Hindu-Arabic number system and its computational methods to Western Europe. He contributed substantially to the acceptance of the Arabic algebraic system and called European attention to a revolutionary mathematical technique that came to be known as the Fibonacci sequence.

Phoebus Aaron Levene: American biochemist Phoebus Aaron Levene determined the components found in DNA and RNA. Levene described the presence of ribose sugar in RNA and of 2'-deoxyribose in DNA, thereby differentiating the two molecules. He also identified the nitrogen bases found in nucleic acid, though he was never able to determine the acid's molecular structure.

Rita Levi-Montalcini*: Rita Levi-Montalcini is best known for her work concerning growth factors in cells. Her research into nerve and cell growth has created a better understanding of how embryos develop.

Edward B. Lewis*: Twentieth-century American geneticist Edward B. Lewis shared the Nobel Prize in Medicine for discovering the genetic aspects of embryo development. His work laid the foundation for developmental genetics and demonstrated the relationship between radiation and cancer at the genetic level.

Gilbert N. Lewis*: Physical chemist Gilbert Lewis is known for his contributions to the chemical study of thermodynamics, the discovery of the covalent bond, and his contributions to the discovery of deuterium and heavy water. Lewis spent most of his career teaching at the University of California, Berkeley where he trained a number of doctoral students who went on to make other major contributions to the field of chemistry.

Willard F. Libby: Libby postulated that the radioactive isotope of the element carbon, those atoms having a mass number 14, is incorporated into living matter at a steady rate until its demise. He developed an ultrasensitive device for the detection of the disintegration of this radioactive isotope. Building upon the newly determined half-life of carbon 14, he was able to create, for the first time, a reliable measure of the age of archeological materials.

By numerous experiments he established the validity and extended the useful range of his method.

Justus von Liebig*: One of the most important chemists of the nineteenth century, Justus von Liebig conducted pioneering experimental research that transformed modern organic chemistry. His studies in agriculture led to the development of agricultural chemistry, and his systematic methods for training students became institutionalized within the German research university.

Carolus Linnaeus*: Carl Linnaeus dedicated his life to classifying plants, animals, minerals, and even diseases. His extensive contributions to scientific classification have established him as the father of taxonomy. Linnaeus is best known for standardizing binomial nomenclature, the two-word system used to name species. He also implemented a set of naming rules and procedures and prepared an inventory of all the known species in the mid-eighteenth century. He remains one of the most celebrated botanists in history.

Hans Lippershey: A maker of eyeglasses, Lippershey also made an early refracting telescope, which many scholars believe was the first.

Gabriel Lippmann: Lippmann's color photography process based on the interference phenomenon brought him the 1908 Nobel Prize in Physics.

M. Stanley Livingston: Livingston worked with Ernest Orlando Lawrence to build the first cyclotron and later designed other particle accelerators used in nuclear research.

Edmond Locard: Originator of the principle of forensic science that holds that "every contact leaves a trace," Locard focused on dust as essential forensic trace evidence, studying variations and specifying how investigators should collect it. He also developed poroscopy, or the assessment of the distribution of pores in fingerprints.

Oliver Lodge: Physicist Oliver Joseph Lodge invented the coherer—the radio-wave detector in early radiotelegraph receivers—in 1894.

Mikhail Vasilyevich Lomonosov*: Russian scientist Mikhail Vasilyevich Lomonosov made significant contributions to a number of scientific fields, including chemistry, astronomy, and mineralogy. A prominent member of the Saint Petersburg Academy of Sciences, he was in charge of the academy's mineral collection and chemical laboratory.

Hendrik Lorentz*: Dutch physicist Hendrik Lorentz helped discover the existence of electrons within atoms and developed Lorentz contractions and Lorentz transformations. For his work, Lorentz shared the 1902 Nobel Prize in Physics with fellow physicist Pieter Zeeman.

Konrad Lorenz*: A key figure in the study of animal behavior, Konrad Lorenz was one of the first biologists to combine behavioral science with evolutionary theory, and his controversial views on human behavior are among the earliest examples of evolutionary psychology.

Oleg Losev: Scientists and inventor Oleg Losev independently discovered the principle of the light-emitting diode in the early 1920s.

Ada Lovelace*: During an age when women were rarely acknowledged for their scientific and technological pursuits, the Countess of Lovelace wrote a paper describing how to program a forerunner of modern computers. As a result, she is regarded as the first computer programmer.

James Lovelock: Lovelock is best known for his Gaia hypothesis, which suggests that the Earth itself is the source of life and that all living things on the planet have coevolved and therefore are inextricably intertwined.

Amory Lovins: Physicist and environmental scientist Amory Lovins, cofounder of the Rocky Mountain Institute, has worked to promote the use of sustainable and clean energy, particularly as a means to attain global stability and security.

Archibald Montgomery Low: A research physicist and inventor, Low invented a forerunner of the television and guidance systems for torpedoes, airplanes, and rockets.

Jane Lubchenco: An environmental scientist, Lubchenco is the first woman to serve as the administrator of the National Oceanic and Atmospheric Administration. Previously, she was a member of a team of researchers who conducted the first National Academy of Sciences study on the policy implications of global warming and provided advice on that topic to President George H. W. Bush and the US Congress.

Salvador E. Luria: Alvador Luria was a pioneer in understanding replication and genetic structure in viruses. The Luria-Delbrück fluctuation test, developed by Luria and Max Delbrück, demonstrated that genetic mutations precede environmental selection. Luria was awarded the 1969 Nobel Prize in Physiology or Medicine.

Jane X. Luu*: American astronomer Jane X. Luu is a codiscoverer, together with English astronomer David Jewitt, of the first Kuiper Belt trans-Neptunian Object in the solar system, thereby confirming the existence of the Kuiper Belt.

André Lwoff: French biochemist and protozoologist. Lwoff's early work demonstrated that vitamins function as components of living organisms. He is best known for demonstrating that the genetic material of bacteriophage can become part of the host bacterium's DNA, a process known as lysogeny. Lwoff was awarded the 1965 Nobel Prize in Physiology or Medicine.

Charles Lyell*: Charles Lyell is considered the father of modern geology. His Principles of Geology countered the dominant nineteenth-century belief that the Earth had been formed by a series of massive cataclysms, arguing convincingly that it had been formed over millions of years by gradual, ongoing changes.

Mary Frances Lyon: British cytogeneticist Mary Frances Lyon proposed what became known as the Lyon hypothesis, that only a single X chromosome is active in a cell. Any other X chromosomes are observed as Barr bodies.

M

Ernst Mach*: Ernst Mach lived and worked during the nineteenth century, when the study of science was closely related to the study of philosophy, especially in German-speaking countries. Mach was influential in both disciplines but is probably best remembered for his contributions to the development of Einstein's theories

of relativity. His ideas also contributed to the fields of physiology and psychology, and he is notorious for having stubbornly denied the existence of the atom.

John J. R. Macleod*: As the leader of a physiology research laboratory at the University of Toronto in

Canada, Macleod shared the 1923 Nobel Prize in Physiology or Medicine with Frederick G. Banting for the discovery of insulin as a treatment for diabetes.

Theodore Maiman: Physicist Theodore Maiman designed and built the first operable laser, using a synthetic ruby as the amplifier, and he foresaw many applications for the laser.

Marcello Malpighi: Malpighi's microscopic anatomy led him to discover the blood capillaries and demonstrate the fine structure of the lungs, thus laying the foundation for knowledge of the physiology of respiration. His other important studies were in embryology, plant anatomy, and invertebrate zoology.

Syukuro Manabe: A meteorological scientist, Manabe's research using computer modeling has improved humankind's understanding of the role that the oceans play in the global climate.

Gideon Mantell: A British surgeon, geologist, and paleontologist, Mantell began collecting fossil specimens from quarries as a child. As an adult, he was a practicing physician and pursued geology in his spare time. He discovered fossils that were eventually identified as belonging to the Iguanodon and Hylaeosaurus—which he named Megalosaurus and Pelorosaurus—and he became a recognized authority on dinosaurs. His major works were *The Fossils of South Downs: Or, Illustrations of the Geology of Sussex* (1822) and *Notice on the Iguanodon: A Newly Discovered Fossil Reptile* (1825).

Guglielmo Marconi: Marconi shared the 1909 Nobel Prize in Physics for his improvements in wireless telegraphy and his long-distance wireless transmission across the Atlantic Ocean.

Rudolph A. Marcus: A Nobel Prize-winning chemist, Marcus is known for his work on electron transfers within chemical systems. He also described the form of interaction between the driving force of an electron transfer and the rate of the reaction as being parabolic.

Andreas Sigismund Marggraf: A pioneer German analytic chemist, Marggraf is most famous for discovering sugar in the beet, for discovering the element zinc, and for realizing commercially applicable ways of extracting each. By the mid-eighteenth century he was Germany's most famous chemist.

Lynn Margulis*: Lynn Margulis confirmed and expanded endosymbiotic theory by concluding that eukaryotic cells originated by a series of symbioses. Initially rejected by the scientific majority, her work on endosymbiotic theory was eventually accepted by the greater scientific community worldwide. She is remembered for collecting convincing evidence that symbiogenesis is a major factor of evolution leading to the origin of new species.

James Marsh: An English chemist, Marsh devised a technique and testing device that forensic investigators could use to determine whether arsenic was present in organisms. The technique, known as the Marsh test, employed zinc and either sulfuric or hydrochloric acid to form hydrogen gas, which reacts with arsenic.

Othniel Charles Marsh*: Nineteenth-century American paleontologist Othniel Marsh was a pioneer of American paleontological exploration. He provided important contributions to the study of dinosaurs and other extinct species. Marsh's professional and personal rivalry with fellow paleontologist E. D. Cope helped to define the gilded age of paleontology in the United States.

Toshihide Maskawa: Toshihide Maskawa is a Japanese scientist and Nobel laureate. In October 2008, the Royal Swedish Academy of Sciences announced that Maskawa would jointly share, with fellow researcher Makoto Kobayashi, one half of the 2008 Nobel Prize in Physics. The other half of the award was given to Yoichiro Nambu. The three scientists won the award for their explanations of key anomalies in the laws of particle physics.

Matthew Fontaine Maury: A universal scientist, Maury did not limit his endeavors to one field; instead, he researched the land, sea, and air and showed how they are inextricably linked to one another. He brought the study of physical geography and oceanography into the modern age.

James Clerk Maxwell*: James Clerk Maxwell contributed several important scientific findings, particularly in the fields of electromagnetism and thermodynamics. He also predicted the theoretical existence of radio waves before they were produced or observed in the laboratory and is remembered as the first person to discover the true nature of Saturn's rings.

Barbara McClintock*: A pioneer in classical and molecular genetics, McClintock won the Nobel Prize in

Physiology or Medicine in 1983. Her theories that patterns of genetic traits caused by mutations do not follow the accepted rules of genetics, and that sections of chromosomes detach and move to a new location during development, were far ahead of contemporary genetic research.

Edwin Mattison McMillan*: Twentieth-century American physicist and chemist Edwin McMillan discovered the radioactive metal neptunium and codiscovered plutonium, which is fundamental to nuclear power and nuclear weapons. He also discovered the important principle of phase stability, which made possible the high-energy accelerators of the late twentieth century and allowed for fundamental advances in the understanding of the nature of matter.

Ronald E. McNair: McNair was the second African American astronaut to fly into space. He was a mission specialist on the Challenger flight, mission 51-L, that exploded just after liftoff, killing everyone onboard. McNair also published an array of research on laser and satellite innovation with the National Aeronautics and Space Administration (NASA).

Lise Meitner*: Physicist Lise Meitner's joint research with chemist Otto Hahn, and later Fritz Strassmann, yielded the discovery of new radioactive elements and their properties and paved the way for the discovery of uranium fission.

Craig Mello*: Biologist Craig Mello and his colleague, biologist Andrew Fire, were jointly awarded the 2006 Nobel Prize in Physiology or Medicine for their work in discovering the process of RNA interference. This process is now used to develop drug therapies for cancer and other diseases.

Gregor Mendel*: Nineteenth-century monk and teacher Gregor Mendel's pea plant experiments demonstrated principles of heredity that would eventually evolve into the new disciplines of genetics and molecular biology. His work not only helped solve the mysteries of diseases such as cystic fibrosis, Tay-Sachs disease, sickle cell anemia, and hemophilia, it also laid the foundation for the Human Genome Project.

Dmitry Ivanovich Mendeleyev*: Dmitry Mendeleyev is best known for his discovery of the periodic law, which states that the properties of the chemical elements vary with their atomic weights in a systematic way. His

periodic table of the elements became the standard model for organizing and displaying the various chemical elements.

Dorothy Reed Mendenhall: Best known for her medical research identifying the cell responsible for Hodgkin's disease, Mendenhall spent most of her career as a physician interested in maternal and child health. As one of the first doctors employed by the U.S. Children's Bureau, she merged social welfare and preventive health strategies as the best approach for reducing maternal and infant mortality and morbidity.

Marin Mersenne: Mersenne is best known as the priest-scientist who facilitated the cross-fertilization of the most eminent minds of his time. He is widely commemorated for helping to establish modern science by promoting the new ideas of Nicolaus Copernicus, Galileo, and René Descartes and by attacking what he believed to be the pseudo- sciences of alchemy, astrology, and natural magic.

Matthew Meselson: Meselson demonstrated the nature of DNA replication, in which the two parental DNA strands are separated, each passing into one of the two daughter molecules. He was also noted as a social activist.

Albert A. Michelson*: Albert A. Michelson made important contributions in the field of optics, particularly relating to the velocity of light. He is perhaps best remembered for the 1887 "Michelson-Morley experiment" he conducted with chemist Edward Williams Morley, which established the speed of light as a constant.

Friedrich Miescher: In 1869, Miescher discovered and purified DNA from cell-free nuclei obtained from white blood cells and gave the name "nuclein" to the extract. The substance was later known as nucleic acid.

Milutin Milankovitch*: Milutin Milankovitch was a Serbian physicist whose studies of climate change and weather patterns in Earth's history led to an understanding of the links between long-term astronomical phenomena and global cooling. The Milankovitch cycles are used to explain the cyclic ice ages during the quaternary period.

Stanley Miller*: American chemist Stanley Miller opened new avenues of inquiry into the origins of life when he published the results of a groundbreaking experiment showing how amino acids, the building blocks of life, could have formed on primitive Earth.

Robert Andrews Millikan*: As a skilled and meticulous experimenter, Millikan made major contributions to twentieth-century physics. As a textbook author, university teacher, and supervisor of research, he greatly influenced the way that physics is studied in the United States.

John Milne: Milne devised a seismograph and established the first international seismological network for detecting and measuring earthquakes.

Maria Mitchell*: Maria Mitchell was the first known astronomer to observe the comet C/1847 T1, which became known as Miss Mitchell's Comet in her honor. As the United States' first female professional astronomer, she played a key role in encouraging women to enter scientific professions.

August Ferdinand Möbius*: Nineteenth-century mathematician August Ferdinand Möbius is best known for his discovery of the Möbius strip, a unique, twisting surface with only one side. Although much of his work took place within the field of astronomy, he made invaluable contributions to a wide range of scientific disciplines.

Andrija Mohorovičić*: Andrija Mohorovičić's research on the structure and makeup of the Earth's crust contributed to the rise of seismology, the scientific study of earthquakes, in the twentieth century. The disparate geological region that separates the Earth's crust and mantle layers is dubbed the "Mohorovičić discontinuity," or Moho, in his honor.

Friedrich Mohs*: Nineteenth-century German geologist/mineralogist Friedrich Mohs developed a system for classifying minerals based upon their physical characteristics. This method is still in use today.

Mario Molina*: Mario Molina received the Nobel Prize in Chemistry in 1995 for his discovery of the connection between the release of chlorofluorocarbons and the depletion of the ozone layer.

Gaspard Monge: Monge founded modern descriptive geometry and revitalized analytic geometry. An enthusiastic supporter of the French Revolution, he helped establish the metric system and the École Polytechnique, an important engineering school.

Jacques Lucien Monod: With François Jacob, French geneticist and molecular biologist Jacques Lucien Monod demonstrated a method of gene regulation in bacteria that came to be known as the Jacob-Monod model. Jacob and Monod were jointly awarded the 1965 Nobel Prize in Physiology or Medicine.

Luc Montagnier*: French biologist and virologist Luc Montagnier began studying cancer-causing viruses in the late 1950s. His research in the 1980s led to the isolation of the human immunodeficiency virus (HIV), which was later determined to be the cause of acquired immunodeficiency syndrome (AIDS).

Stanford Moore: Moore won the 1972 Nobel Prize in Chemistry, with William H. Stein. Moore and Stein supplemented Alfinsen's research by identifying the sequence of amino acids in ribonuclease, a clue to the structure of the gene responsible for it.

Lilian Vaughan Morgan: Morgan discovered the attached X and ring X chromosomes in Drosophila (fruit flies). She later contributed to studying the effects of polio vaccines in primates. She was married to Thomas Hunt Morgan.

Thomas Hunt Morgan*: Nineteenth-century geneticist and embryologist Thomas Hunt Morgan developed the gene-chromosome theory of inheritance—the idea that genes located on chromosomes encode information inherited by the next generation. Morgan and his research team also confirmed the roles of the X and Y chromosomes in determining gender at fertilization.

Samuel F. B. Morse: An artist and inventor born in Massachusetts, Morse painted portraits and taught art at the City University of New York before experimenting with electricity. In the mid-1830s, he designed the components of a practical telegraph—a sender, receiver, and a code to translate signals into numbers and words—and in 1844 sent the first message via wire. Within a decade, the telegraph had spread across America and subsequently around the world. The invention would inspire such later advancements in communication as radio, the Teletype, and the fax machine.

Henry Gwyn Jeffreys Moseley*: Physicist Henry Moseley demonstrated the physics behind the chemical concept of the atomic number using X-ray spectroscopy.

His discovery helped to define the modern periodic table, and helped to create a more complete understanding of the relationship between elements and atoms.

Erwin Wilhelm Müller: Physicist Erwin Wilhelm Müller invented the field-emission microscope, field-ion microscope, and atom-probe microscope.

Hermann Joseph Muller*: As the first scientist to induce mutations with X-rays, Hermann Joseph Muller founded the field of radiation genetics. He later became a crusader for radiation protection.

Karl Alexander Müller: With J. Georg Bednorz, Müller discovered high-temperature superconductivity in novel ceramic materials, receiving the 1987 Nobel Prize in Physics for their work.

Paul Müller: Müller discovered that dichlorodiphenyl-trichloroethane (DDT) was a powerful insecticide, for which he received the 1948 Nobel Prize in Physiology or Medicine.

Kary Mullis*: Geneticist and biochemist Kary Mullis conceived, designed, and developed the polymerase chain reaction, or PCR, which revolutionized the study of the biological and medical sciences. PCR allows for one DNA molecule to be amplified to billions of copies in a short period of time in a lab, making analysis of specific DNA targets possible. This technique is used in the diagnosis of various infectious and genetic diseases and has been widely used in forensic analysis.

Makio Murayama: Makio Murayama's biochemical research on sickle-cell anemia led to his uncovering the molecular mechanism of the disease. This discovery subsequently allowed for the creation of a new diagnostic test. Murayama was among the first medical researchers to propose using urea in the treatment of sickle-cell anemia.

N

Nabu-rimanni: Babylonian astronomer and mathematician Nabu-rimanni copied and preserved astronomical tables for the computation of lunar, solar, and planetary phenomena. These accurate numerical parameters for the prediction of astronomical phenomena furthered the development and success of Greek spherical astronomy, developed to its fullest in the Ptolemaic system.

Yoichiro Nambu*: Yoichiro Nambu shared the Nobel Prize in Physics in 2008 for his work related to the mechanism of broken symmetry in matter at the subatomic level. He is also known for his pioneering work in string theory.

John Napier*: Scottish mathematician John Napier invented logarithms, revolutionizing arithmetic calculation and providing astronomers and other scientists with simpler ways of analyzing mathematical data. His invention of the abacus system known as Napier's bones further influenced developments in the field of mathematics.

Daniel Nathans: Nathans applied the use of restriction enzymes to the study of genetics. He developed the first genetic map of SV40, among the first DNA viruses shown to transform normal cells into cancer. Nathans was awarded the 1978 Nobel Prize in Physiology or Medicine.

Giulio Natta: Natta shared the 1963 Nobel Prize in Chemistry for research on high polymers, including production of polypropylene.

James Van Gundia Neel: Neel is considered to be the father of human genetics. Among his discoveries was the recognition of the genetic basis of sickle-cell disease. He was also noted for his study of the aftereffects of radiation on survivors of the atomic attack on Hiroshima and Nagasaki in World War II. He was the first to propose what was referred to as the thrifty-gene hypothesis, the idea that potentially lethal genes may have been beneficial to the human population earlier in evolution.

Louis Néel*: Louis Néel was awarded the 1970 Nobel Prize in Physics for his discovery of new forms of magnetism, including antiferromagnetism and ferrimagnetism. His work greatly strengthened magnetic theory and contributed fundamentally to the development of computer-memory technology.

Walther Nernst*: Walther Nernst was awarded the Nobel Prize in Chemistry in 1920 for developing the third law of thermodynamics. However, he is perhaps best known for his equation for the electrode potential of a voltaic cell.

Elizabeth F. Neufeld: French-born biochemist Elizabeth Neufeld found that many mucopolysaccharide storage diseases resulted from the absence of certain metabolic enzymes. Her work opened the way for prenatal diagnosis of such diseases.

John von Neumann*: A brilliant mathematician who formulated the mathematical foundations of quantum theory and computer science, John von Neumann affirmed the importance of independent scientific research during the anti-Communist McCarthy era.

Thomas Newcomen: Thomas Newcomen built the first steam engine, providing the power to operate pumps, mostly those needed to remove water from the coal mines that had penetrated ever deeper into the English landscape. (Newcomen appears to have been working on a steam engine at the same time as Thomas Savery, but Savery, more attuned to the corridors of power, secured a patent on his device in 1698, and its broad description gave him an effective monopoly over the steam engine and its development until the patent expired in 1733.)

Isaac Newton: Newton's contributions to science were varied and profound, among them the nature of optics, celestial mechanics, and the calculus, arrived at independently of Gottfried Wilhelm Leibniz.

Marshall Warren Nirenberg: Molecular biologist Marshall Warren Nirenberg was among the first to decipher the genetic code. He later demonstrated the process of ribosome binding in protein synthesis and carried out the first cell-free synthesis of protein. Nirenberg was awarded the 1968 Nobel Prize in Physiology or Medicine.

Alfred Nobel: Nobel's invention of dynamite was important to heavy construction and warfare. The international prizes given in his name for chemistry, economics, medicine, physics, literature, and peace became the modern emblems of genius.

Emmy Noether*: As one of the founders of the study of abstract algebra, German mathematician Emmy Noether formulated Noether's theorem, an important development in the theory of general relativity that has become fundamental in the study of classical and quantum physics.

John Howard Northrop: Northrop received the 1946 Nobel Prize in Chemistry for his research on enzymes, proteins, and viruses. He also invented a fermentation process for acetone.

Robert Norton Noyce: The digital revolution of mass-produced computer circuitry proceeded from Noyce's development of the integrated circuit.

Paul M. Nurse: British scientist Paul M. Nurse discovered the role of chemical modification (phosphorylation) in regulation of the cell cycle. With Tim Hunt and Leland Hartwell, he was awarded the Nobel Prize in Physiology or Medicine in 2001.

Christiane Nüsslein-Volhard*: German biologist Christiane Nüsslein-Volhard is best known for her study of the genes of Drosophila melanogaster, also known as the fruit fly. In recognition of her genetics research, Nüsslein-Volhard shared the Nobel Prize in Physiology or Medicine in 1995.

O

Adriana Ocampo Uria*: Planetary geologist Adriana Ocampo Uria became intrigued by the stars and space travel at a young age, and she used to make toy spaceships and imagine exploring distant planets with her dog and dolls as fellow astronauts. She has worked for the United States National Aeronautics Space Administration (NASA) on several missions dealing with the terrain of other planets.

Hermann Oberth: Oberth is one of the three great pioneers of the sciences of astronautics and modern rocketry. Along with Konstantin Tsiolkovsky and Robert H.

Goddard, he is credited with developing the principles behind rocket-powered flight beyond Earth's atmosphere, liquid-fueled rockets, a piloted Earth orbital space station, and piloted interplanetary flight.

Severo Ochoa*: Biochemist Severo Ochoa was awarded the 1959 Nobel Prize in Physiology or Medicine for his isolation of polynucleotide phosphorylase from bacteria, an enzyme that could be used to synthesize RNA (ribonucleic acid). Ochoa's discovery helped scientists understand how genetic information is transmitted.

Georg Simon Ohm*: Nineteenth-century German mathematician and physicist Georg Simon Ohm was responsible for the discovery of Ohm's law, which describes the exact relationship of potential, or voltage, and current in electric conduction. The international unit of resistance, the ohm, is named after him.

Jan Hendrik Oort*: Dutch astronomer Jan Hendrik Oort postulated the existence of the vast swarm of comets known subsequently as the Oort cloud. One of the pioneers of radio astronomy, he also proposed the existence of dark matter and helped establish the structure of the Milky Way Galaxy.

Aleksandr Ivanovich Oparin: Oparin was the principal pioneer in theorizing on the origins of life on Earth from inorganic matter. Of major importance also were his works that dealt with the biochemistry of plant material, from which he successfully developed the principles of Soviet biochemistry based on biocatalysis.

J. Robert Oppenheimer*: J. Robert Oppenheimer was an American physicist noted for his work during World War II as scientific director of the Manhattan Project, which developed the first atomic bomb. After the war, he became director of the Institute for Advanced Study in Princeton, New Jersey. Before joining the Manhattan Project, Oppenheimer worked as a physics professor, with a joint appointment to the University of California, Berkeley, and the California Institute of Technology.

Hans Christian Ørsted*: Hans Christian Ørsted, an early nineteenth-century physicist and chemist, is most famous for discovering electromagnetism—the phenomenon of electric currents producing magnetic fields. Nearly all modern electrical technologies are based on this discovery.

Wilhelm Ostwald: Ostwald's most notable work was in the field of chemistry, in which he is considered to be the founder of physical chemistry and in which he was awarded the 1909 Nobel Prize. He was later nominated for a second Nobel Prize, this time in physics, for his work in the field of color science.

Stanford Ovshinsky: Ovshinsky pioneered ovonics, the study of disordered materials, and developed the ovonic switch in 1957, which rendered amorphous materials suitable to a variety of technologies.

Richard Owen*: Nineteenth century English anatomist, naturalist, and paleontologist Richard Owen was a controversial figure with an interest in numerous areas of science. He lectured widely on anatomy, catalogued fossils, and classified numerous extinct species. Owen was a prominent voice in the debate over evolution, and successfully championed the establishment of the Natural History Museum.

P

David Pall: An innovator in filtration systems, chemist David Boris Pall invented filters that remove oil impurities from engines and hydraulics and a filter that reduces the number of white blood cells in blood transfusion.

Luigi Palmieri: Physicist and meteorologist Luigi Palmieri invented a mercury seismometer in 1855 that detected and measured ground movement with great sensitivity. With it, he was able to predict volcanic eruptions.

Paracelsus: Paracelsus has been hailed as the founder of biochemistry. He also made major contributions to the development of modern chemistry and made revolutionary changes in Renaissance medical theory and practice.

Ambroise Paré: A French royal surgeon, Paré revolutionized battlefield medicine, developing techniques and instruments for the treatment of gunshot wounds and for performing amputations. He greatly advanced knowledge of human anatomy by studying the effects of violent death on internal organs. He pioneered the lifesaving practices of vascular ligating and herniotomies, designed prosthetics to replace amputated limbs, and was the first to create realistic artificial eyes from such substances as glass, porcelain, silver, and gold.

Alexander Parkes: Metallurgist Alexander Parkes invented Parkesine, a form of cellulose nitrate, in 1862; it was an early artificial plastic.

Blaise Pascal*: Mathematician and physicist Blaise Pascal invented an early form of the calculator, developed studies of conics and atmospheric pressure, and, with Pierre de Fermat, devised an early version of the theory of probability.

Louis Pasteur: Pasteur's work in microbiology established the germ theory of disease, which afforded new medical treatments, such as vaccines, and he made dairy products safer through his pasteurization process.

Ruth Patrick: A pioneer in freshwater biology, Patrick developed tests for assessing the pollution levels in lakes and rivers.

Wolfgang Pauli*: Pauli's discovery of the exclusion principle, which asserts the individuality of electrons, revolutionized atomic physics. He is also responsible for the electron theory of metals, which led to the development of transistors, and for proposing the existence of neutrinos.

Linus Pauling*: In addition to his work with chemical bonds, noted American chemist Linus Pauling made significant contributions to the fields of quantum mechanics and molecular biology. He is the only person to have won two unshared Nobel Prizes. After World War II, Pauling became an outspoken critic of nuclear armaments.

Ivan Pavlov*: Winner of the Nobel Prize in Physiology or Medicine in 1904, Ivan Pavlov was one of Russia's most prominent physiologists. Best known for his investigation of the conditioned reflexes of animals, Pavlov was a skilled surgeon and clinician whose experiments greatly influenced both modern physiology and psychology.

Cecilia Payne-Gaposchkin*: Astronomer Cecilia Payne-Gaposchkin was the first person to receive a PhD in astronomy from Harvard University and the first female professor there. While studying stellar atmospheres and the composition of stars, she suggested that their most abundant element is hydrogen.

Gerald Pearson: Pearson coinvented the silicon photovoltaic (solar) cell at Bell Telephone Laboratories in 1954.

William Henry Perkin: Chemist William Henry Perkin produced the first synthetic dye, patented in 1856. It was aniline purple, better known as mauve.

Max Perutz*: Max Perutz developed the procedure by which the atomic structure of proteins can be determined by the pattern of X-ray diffraction they produce.

He later applied similar techniques of X-ray diffraction to explain the structure of hemoglobin.

Petrus Peregrinus de Maricourt: Petrus was the author of the first Western scientific treatise on the principles of magnetism. His practical inventions included a floating compass and a pivoted compass, both of which were used for finding the meridian and the azimuths of heavenly bodies.

William Petty: A distinguished physician and scientist, Petty made demographic and economic surveys of Ireland that constituted the first practical implementation of population studies. He is also credited with introducing the labor theory of value to economics.

Georg von Peuerbach: A pre-Copernican astronomer, Peuerbach accepted, reintroduced, and extended the ideas of Ptolemy and made original astronomical observations. His published works include a look at new theories of the planets, which became a standard astronomy textbook, and an aid for the calculation of eclipses.

Auguste Piccard: Physicist and explorer Auguste Piccard built the first bathyscaphe in 1948, a submersible for deep sea exploration.

Max Planck*: Planck's 1900 discovery that light consists of infinitesimal "quanta" and his articulation of quantum theory replaced classical physics with modern quantum physics. This work not only resulted in Planck's receiving the Nobel Prize in Physics in 1918 but also laid the groundwork for the achievements of many other Nobel laureates.

Joseph Plateau: Belgian physicist Plateau and his sons invented the phenakistoscope, otherwise known as the stroboscope, in 1832.

Roy J. Plunkett : Chemist Roy J. Plunkett synthesized Teflon, patented in 1941. Its nonstick, nonreactive properties transformed the plastics industry.

Siméon Denis Poisson*: Nineteenth-century French mathematician Siméon Denis Poisson made important contributions in the areas of statistics and physics. A student of French astronomer Pierre Laplace, Poisson is one of seventy-two French scientists, engineers, and notables who have their names engraved on the Eiffel Tower in recognition of their work.

Alexander Stepanovich Popov: Russian physicist Alexander Stepanovich Popov has a claim as the inventor of radio, since he demonstrated radio reception with a coherer in 1895. He also used his device as a lightning detector.

Freda Porter-Locklear*: Environmental scientist Freda Porter-Locklear is widely known for her application of mathematical models in groundwater analysis and water pollution control systems. A member of the Lumbee American Indian tribe, Porter has also played a well-publicized role in the advocacy of science and mathematics education for students in the United States, particularly for those of American Indian and minority descent.

Ludwig Prandtl*: One of the fathers of theoretical aerodynamics, Ludwig Prandtl is credited with discovering many of the pivotal concepts on which modern aviation is based. He was also the founder of the highly acclaimed school of aerodynamics and hydrodynamics at the University of Göttingen and the first director of what would become the Max Planck Institute for Dynamics and Self-Organization.

Joseph Priestly: A master chemist, Priestley devised lab equipment, discovered oxygen, and invented soda water and an eraser.

Joseph Louis Proust*: French chemist Joseph Louis Proust flourished during the late eighteenth and early nineteenth centuries. He spent more than twenty years teaching and researching at institutions in Spain, where he conducted numerous experiments with various metals that ultimately resulted in the development of a universal principle in analytical chemistry.

Stanley B. Prusiner: Prusiner discovered prions, proteins that can reproduce and cause fatal degenerative neurological diseases. His discovery challenged biological notions that all infectious agents contain either DNA or RNA.

Ptolemy: Ptolemy defined the universe for more than a millennium with his Earth-centered cosmology, but he also wrote about geography and optics.

Mihajlo I. Pupin: In 1893, scientist Mihajlo Idvorski Pupin invented the resonator, which was subsequently used to tune radios, and in 1894 the Pupin coil, which facilitated long-distance telephone calling.

Reginald C. Punnett: English biologist Reginald C. Punnett collaborated with William Bateson in a series of important breeding experiments that confirmed the principles of Mendelian inheritance. Punnett also introduced the Punnett square, the standard graphical method of depicting hybrid crosses.

Pythagoras*: Pythagoras set an inspiring example with his energetic search for knowledge and universal order. His many discoveries and accomplishments in philosophy, mathematics, astronomy, and music theory make him an important figure in Western intellectual history.

R

Isidor Isaac Rabi*: Austrian-born physicist Isidor Isaac Rabi developed the magnetic-resonance method to measure the properties of atomic nuclei with unprecedented accuracy. After World War II, he used the idea of science's universality to bring peoples of the globe together.

Venkatraman Ramakrishnan*: Indian-born biologist Venkatraman Ramakrishnan shared the 2009 Nobel Prize in Chemistry for his contribution to mapping the atomic structure of the ribosome, thus enabling close study of how proteins are built from genetic information. His discovery also led to research into a new generation of antibiotics.

Chandrasekhara Venkata Raman*: Chandrasekhara Venkata Raman, the first internationally acclaimed Indian physicist to be entirely educated within India, was awarded the Nobel Prize in Physics in 1930 for his discovery of important characteristics of light scattering. Raman also made significant contributions to Indian education, establishing the Raman Research Institute in Bangalore in 1948.

Srinivasa Ramanujan*: Self-taught Indian mathematician Srinivasa Ramanujan, a famous collaborator of the English mathematician G. H. Hardy, became a Fellow of the Royal Society in 1918 in recognition of his many contributions to the study of pure mathematics, including an approximate formula for deriving the number of partitions of an integer.

Norman F. Ramsey*: American physicist Norman F. Ramsey was an influential researcher, teacher, and administrator. He contributed to the development of radar and the atomic bomb, served with a number of agencies, and won the Nobel Prize for the Ramsey method of separated oscillatory fields.

John Ray*: Seventeenth-century naturalist John Ray made major contributions to the fields of botany, zoology, and natural theology. With his adaptation of a taxonomical scheme based on such factors as habitat and anatomy, Ray pushed the study of flora and fauna toward modern scientific thinking. His comprehensive field guides set new standards for rigor of methodology and precision of content.

René-Antoine Ferchault de Réaumur*: Réaumur markedly improved metallurgical technology in France and performed groundbreaking experiments involving limb regeneration in crustaceans. As a result of his observations of insects, he is considered by some to be the founder of animal-behavior studies.

Karl von Reichenbach: Reichenbach produced several commercially valuable substances from coal and wood tar, including creosote, paraffin, and phenol.

Frederick Reines: Beginning with his codiscovery of the neutrino in 1956, Reines pioneered the developments leading to an understanding of the properties and the interactions of this elementary particle. His subsequent work led to the field of neutrino astronomy and to an understanding of the role played by neutrinos in generating the elements heavier than iron during stellar collapse and explosion.

Archibald Rodolphe Reiss: A chemist, photographer, teacher, and natural scientist born in Germany, Reiss founded the world's first school of forensic science at the University of Lausanne, Switzerland, in 1909. He published numerous works that greatly influenced the new discipline, including *La photographie judiciaire* (Forensic photography, 1903) and *Manuel de police scientifique. I Vols et homicides* (Handbook of forensic science: thefts and homicides, 1911). During World War I he investigated alleged atrocities in Serbia and lived there for the rest of his life. The institute he founded more than a century ago has become a major school offering numerous courses in various forensic sciences, criminology, and criminal law.

Ira Remsen: With Constantin Fahlberg, Remsen synthesized the artificial sweetener saccharin in 1879.

Rheticus: Rheticus was instrumental in spreading the heliocentric theory of Nicolaus Copernicus, which argued that the sun rotated around the Earth. Rheticus also prepared the first set of mathematical tables with all six trigonometric functions.

Ellen Swallow Richards*: Nineteenth-century scientist Ellen Swallow Richards is considered the first female American chemist. In addition to being the first woman admitted to MIT, she is known for her work in environmental chemistry, sanitary engineering, public health, and home economics.

Charles Francis Richter: A pioneering seismologist, Richter invented the scale for measuring the intensity of earthquakes.

Sally Ride: NASA astronaut Ride was the first American woman to fly in space when she flew aboard space shuttle Challenger in 1983 as a mission specialist. She was one of the first of a new breed of astronauts who were, primarily, scientists, and who were called mission specialists. Ride later founded NASA's Office of Exploration.

Bernhard Riemann*: Nineteenth-century German mathematician Bernhard Riemann built on the work of German mathematician Gottfried Leibniz and Swiss mathematician Leonhard Euler to define position mathematically, as a corollary to defining magnitude algebraically. Riemann's algebraic functions and Riemannian geometry laid the foundations of the field of topology, central to physics, quantum theory, and general relativity.

David R. Rittenhouse: A celebrated astronomer, Rittenhouse also was an inventor, producing an accurate orrery about 1767 and improving Benjamin Franklin's stove in 1790 by adding an L-shaped chimney.

Richard J. Roberts: Roberts discovered that genes in eukaryotic cells and animal viruses are often discontinuous, with intervening sequences between segments of genetic material. With Philip Sharp, Roberts received the Nobel Prize in Physiology or Medicine in 1993.

Eugene G. Rochow: Inorganic chemist Eugene G. Rochow developed a method to produce silicone polymers in 1940.

Martin Rodbell: Rodbell discovered the role of membrane-bound "G" proteins in regulation of signal transduction in eukaryotic cells. With Alfred Gilman, Rodwell was awarded the Nobel Prize in Physiology or Medicine in 1994.

John Roebuck: After learning chemistry as a medical student, Roebuck introduced a new method for manufacturing sulfuric acid on a large scale and a new method of smelting iron.

Heinrich Rohrer: The scanning tunneling microscope, which Rohrer developed with Gerd Binnig, gives scientists three-dimensional images of objects as small as a single atom.

Ole Christensen Rømer*: Seventeenth-century Danish astronomer and mathematician Ole Christensen Rømer was the first scientist to demonstrate that light was not instantaneous and the first scientist to attempt to measure its speed. In addition to his work as a teacher, observatory builder, and instrument maker, he served two kings of Denmark in a number of important and influential posts.

Wilhelm Conrad Röntgen*: Wilhelm Conrad Röntgen made important contributions to several areas of physics but is best known for his revolutionary discovery of X-rays and his investigations of their properties.

Irwin Rose: Rose won the Nobel Prize in Chemistry for his research of protein regulation and the polypeptide ubiquitin. His discoveries led to a better understanding of how the human body works at the molecular level and how the human immune system fights diseases.

Joseph Rotblat: Rotblat's work in nuclear physics and on the Manhattan Project led to his postwar crusade to denuclearize the world and end all wars. As a medical researcher he pioneered radiation therapy for certain cancers, and in 1995 he won the Nobel Peace Prize, sharing the award with the peace organization Pugwash, which he helped to found.

F. Sherwood Rowland*: F. Sherwood Rowland was a key figure in global political efforts to control and reverse the pollution of Earth's atmosphere by chlorofluorocarbon (CFC) gases. He found that in addition to depleting ozone, CFCs also contribute to the greenhouse effect, leading to global warming and climate change.

Ernst Ruska: Ruska received the 1986 Nobel Prize in Physics for his investigations into electron optics and in particular his design for the electron microscope in 1933.

Henry Norris Russell*: Henry Norris Russell was among the first astrophysical theorists in the United States. Seeking to explain his observations and to understand the physics of stars, he incorporated theory into the descriptive science of astronomy. He is best known for his work in developing the Hertzsprung-Russell (H-R) diagram, a major tool used to understand the composition and evolution of stars.

Ernest Rutherford*: British physicist Ernest Rutherford is known as the father of nuclear physics. His experiments with radiation, description of the structure of the atom, and initial success at artificially splitting the atom laid the foundation for nuclear weapons and power generation.

Johannes Robert Rydberg*: Johannes Robert Rydberg was a Swedish physicist best known for his studies on the spectral analysis of chemicals. He discovered formulas for predicting spectral lines of chemicals and metals before atomic structure was properly understood. The Rydberg constant is named for him.

S

Albert Bruce Sabin: A microbiologist born of Jewish heritage as Albert Saperstein in Russia, Sabin later became an American citizen and changed his name. Trained in internal medicine, he conducted research into infectious diseases and assisted in the development of a vaccine to combat encephalitis. His major contribution to medicine was an effective oral polio vaccine, which was administered in mass immunizations during the 1950s and 1960s and eventually led to the eradication of the disease worldwide. Among other honors, he received the Presidential Medal of Freedom in 1986.

Florence R. Sabin*: Eminent anatomist Florence R. Sabin did important research into brain development and the lymphatic system. She also worked in immunology, especially focusing on tuberculosis. She was the first woman to graduate from the Johns Hopkins School of Medicine, as well as the school's first female faculty member and first female full professor.

Julius von Sachs: A German botanist, writer, and teacher, Sachs made great strides in the investigation of plant physiology, morphology, heliotropism, and germination while professor of botany at the University of Würzburg. In addition to numerous written works on photosynthesis, water absorption, and chloroplasts that significantly advanced the science of botany, he also invented a number of devices useful to research, including an auxanometer to measure growth rates, and the clinostat, a device that rotates plants to compensate for the effects of gravitation on botanical growth.

Carl Sagan*: One of the best-known scientists of the twentieth century, Carl Sagan had the unique ability to conduct significant astronomical and planetary research and make science interesting and accessible to the public. He inspired the catch phrase "billions and billions of stars" after his memorable description of the universe and its objects in his television series Cosmos.

Andrei Sakharov: As well as a Nobel Peace Prize (1975) laureate, Sakharov was a central figure in the Soviet program that developed the hydrogen bomb and conceived of the tokamak nuclear fusion reactor in 1950.

Abdus Salam*: Twentieth-century theoretical physicist Muhammad Abdus Salam became the first Muslim scientist to win a Nobel Prize in 1979 for his codevelopment of a theory unifying electromagnetic and weak nuclear forces. Salam was also involved in Pakistan's efforts to build a nuclear bomb.

Jonas Salk: The Salk vaccine was the first safe, effective killed-virus polio vaccine and contributed to the near elimination of the disease in the United States and many other countries.

Frederick Sanger*: Twentieth-century biochemist Frederick Sanger was awarded the Nobel Prize in Chemistry in 1958 for his discovery of the structure of the insulin molecule and again in 1980 for his invention of a technique for determining the sequence of DNA.

Santorio Santorio: Santorio was an innovator in physiology, applied medicine, and the use of instruments of precision in the practice of medicine. By quantitative experimentation, he encouraged the use of mathematics and experimentation as analytical tools in the study of physiology and pathology. He also is considered the father of scientific metabolism for his studies in "insensible perspiration" and was likely an inventor of the thermometer.

Thomas Savery: Savery invented the first steam engine, patented in England in 1698. Thomas Newcomen, whose steam engine was a modified version of Savery's, worked closely with Savery during the first decade of the eighteenth century.

Arthur L. Schawlow: Schawlow received a share of the 1981 Nobel Prize in Physics for his work in laser spectroscopy.

Carl Wilhelm Scheele: A chemist born in a Swedish-controlled area of Germany, Scheele became a pharmacist at an early age. Though he discovered oxygen through experimentation, he did not publish his findings immediately, and the discovery was credited to Antoine-Laurent Lavoisier (1743–1794) and Joseph Priestly (1733–1804), though science later gave Scheele the recognition he deserved. Scheele also discovered the elements barium, manganese, and tungsten, identified such chemical compounds as citric acid, glycerol, and hydrogen cyanide, experimented with heavy metals, and devised a method of producing phosphorus in quantity for the manufacture of matches.

Wilhelm Schickard: Schickard was the first individual to construct an automated calculating, or adding, machine; was one of the first strong advocates of the laws of planetary motion that had been proposed by Johannes Kepler; and employed fundamental principles of cartography to produce some of the seventeenth century's most accurate geographical maps.

Matthias Jacob Schleiden*: Nineteenth-century biologist Matthias Jacob Schleiden contributed to the concept of cell theory through his observations that plants are composed of cells, and that such cells represent the fundamental structure of plants.

Bernhard Voldemar Schmidt: Schmidt's telescope, invented in 1930, allowed a large field of view without the distortion of traditional Newtonian telescopes.

Maarten Schmidt*: Astronomer Maarten Schmidt measured the distance and luminosity of quasars, some of the oldest and most distant objects in the universe. He then led the study of radio sources, gamma rays, and X-rays generated by galaxies and other cosmological matter.

Christian Friedrich Schönbein: Schönbein discovered ozone in 1840 and synthesized guncotton (nitrocellulose), which is used in explosives, in 1845.

Erwin Schrödinger*: Erwin Schrödinger invented wave mechanics in 1926, for which he received the Nobel Prize in Physics in 1933, and he helped develop the formal equations that are central to quantum mechanics. His pioneering work on the relationship between physics and living systems influenced the growth of molecular biology.

Theodor Schwann*: Nineteenth-century biologist Theodor Schwann contributed to the development of cell theory through his observations of the notochord in animals. He also helped to uncover the role played by pepsin in digestions, and discovered the cell covering on nerves, now called Schwann cells.

Karl Schwarzschild*: Karl Schwarzschild developed a new use for photography as a tool for measuring the brightness of stars, particularly variable objects. He was the first to develop a solution for Albert Einstein's general relativity field equations, dealing with gravity around a star of such intensity that it becomes a black hole.

Glenn Theodore Seaborg: Seaborg shared the 1951 Nobel Prize in Chemistry for synthesizing transuranic elements and was the first scientist to chair the Atomic Energy Commission.

Gerhard Sessler: In 1962, Sessler and James E. West invented the foil electret microphone with high sensitivity and broad frequency range, and Sessler invented the silicon microphone in 1983.

Claude Shannon*: Twentieth-century American mathematician and computer scientist Claude Shannon is often called "the father of information theory" in recognition of his pioneering work in the field of networked electronic communications and his application of Boolean logic to computer design. He is also credited with the creation of digital computers and their binary circuit design.

Phillip A. Sharp: Sharp discovered that genes in eukaryotic cells or animal viruses are discontinuous, with segments divided by sections separated by intervening sequences of genetic material. With Richard Roberts, received the Nobel Prize in Physiology or Medicine in 1993.

William Shockley: Shockley shared the 1956 Nobel Prize in Physics for the invention of the junction transistor, which transformed the electronics industry and hastened the trend of miniaturization.

Carolyn Shoemaker*: Twentieth-century American astronomer Carolyn Shoemaker has discovered more than thirty comets, including Shoemaker-Levy 9, which struck Jupiter in 1994. Over the course of her career, Shoemaker discovered more than eight hundred asteroids and thirty-two comets. Her work in astronomy began when she started working as a field assistant for her husband, geologist Eugene Shoemaker.

Eugene M. Shoemaker*: Twentieth-century geologist and planetary scientist Eugene Shoemaker pioneered the field of astrogeology, the study of the geological makeup of celestial bodies. In the 1960s, he was involved with the first unmanned missions to the moon and provided geological training to Apollo astronauts. He and his wife discovered numerous comets and asteroids during their careers, including the Shoemaker-Levy 9 comet that collided with Jupiter in 1994.

Igor Sikorsky: A Ukrainian engineer and test pilot, Igor Sikorsky immigrated to the United States and became a naturalized American citizen, Sikorsky was a groundbreaking designer of both airplanes and helicopters. Inspired as a child by the drawings of Leonardo da Vinci (1452–1519), he created and flew the first multi-engine fixed-wing aircraft and the first airliner in the 1910s. He built the first flying boats in the 1930s—the famous Pan Am Clippers—and in 1939 designed the first practical helicopter, which introduced the system of rotors still used in modern helicopters.

George Gaylord Simpson: American paleontologist George Gaylord Simpson applied population genetics to the study of the evolution of animals. Simpson was instrumental in establishing a neo-Darwinian theory of evolution (the rejection of Lamarck's inheritance of acquired characteristics) during the early twentieth century.

Maxine Singer: Singer applied the use of the newly discovered restriction enzymes in formation of recombinant DNA. Singer is most noted as a "voice of calm" in the debate over genetic research, emphasizing the application of such research, and the self-policing of scientists carrying out such work.

John Brooks Slaughter: Educator and scientist John Brooks Slaughter enjoyed a distinguished career in the field of electrical engineering and served with distinction as the first African American director of the National Science Foundation. It was his tireless work for more than three decades promoting diversity in American universities that established for him a national reputation as a visionary educator.

Hamilton Othanel Smith: Smith pioneered the purification of restriction enzymes, winning the 1978 Nobel Prize in Physiology or Medicine, with Werner Arber and Daniel Nathans. Arber and the team of Nathans and Smith separately described the restriction-modification system by studying bacteria and bacteriophages; the system involves the action of site-specific endonuclease and other enzymes that cleave DNA into segments.

Michael Smith: Smith won the 1995 Nobel Prize in Chemistry. He developed site-directed mutagenesis, a means for reconfiguring genes in order to create altered proteins with distinct properties. Smith's genetic engineering tool made it possible to treat genetic disease and cancer and to create novel plant strains.

George D. Snell*: George Snell discovered the presence of histocompatibility antigens on the surface of cells, and provided a molecular explanation for rejection of tissue transplants. His work contributed to understanding the role played by these proteins in immune cell interactions.

Frederick Soddy*: Frederick Soddy received a Nobel Prize in Chemistry for revolutionizing the understanding of the nature of radioactive particles, specifically by proposing the existence of isotopes—atoms of the same chemical element that have the same atomic number but different radioactive properties and atomic weights. His theory ran counter to the long-held assumption that all atoms of a particular element were identical in size and atomic weight.

Mary Somerville*: After preparing a celebrated translation and explanation of Pierre-Simon Laplace's *Traité de mécanique céleste*, Somerville became a central figure in British and American scientific networks, and her widely read books helped define the disciplines within the physical sciences.

Mary Spaeth: Physicist Mary Spaeth, along with D. P. Bortfield, developed the tunable dye laser in 1966, which became important to the production of atomic isotopes.

Lazzaro Spallanzani*: Spallanzani conducted important studies in bodily regeneration and fertilization. He also challenged the theory of spontaneous generation—the idea that microbial life-forms could arise from decaying matter—helping to overturn an assumption that had dominated science and popular imagination for centuries.

Hans Spemann*: In a career that spanned the late nineteenth and early twentieth century, German biologist Hans Spemann taught zoology and comparative anatomy for forty years and conducted influential research at several German universities. In the course of transplantation experiments, he was the first scientist to create a clone. Spemann received the Nobel Prize in Physiology or Medicine for his discovery of the principle of embryonic induction.

Herbert Spencer: Spencer was an English philosopher influenced by the work of Charles Darwin. Spencer proposed the first general theory of inheritance, postulating the existence of self-replicating units within the individual which determine the traits. Spencer is more popularly known as the source of the notion of "survival of the fittest" as applied to natural selection.

Bernard Henry Spilsbury: The first British forensic pathologist, Spilsbury began performing postmortems in 1905. He investigated cause of death in many spectacular homicide cases—including those of Dr. Crippen and the Brighton trunk murders—that resulted in convictions and enhanced the science of forensics. He was a consultant to Operation Mincemeat, a successful World War II ruse (dramatized in the 1956 film The Man Who Never Was) involving the corpse of an alleged Allied courier, which deceived the Axis powers about the invasion of Sicily. Spilsbury was found dead in his laboratory—a victim of suicide.

Georg Ernst Stahl: Stahl was a physician who developed the phlogiston theory, modern chemistry's first great explanatory system. The theory provided chemists with a framework for understanding reactions such as combustion and the smelting of metal ores, and it guided research into productive discoveries such as new gases and the composition of chemical molecules.

Wendell Stanley: Stanley's crystallization of the tobacco mosaic virus in the mid-1930s illustrated the ability to purify viruses in large quantities for subsequent study and also demonstrated the protein nature of viruses.

Johannes Stark*: Stark's detection of the Doppler effect in a terrestrially generated light source led to his discovery that a strong electric field will split the spectral lines of chemical elements. Stark's experiments provided confirmation of Albert Einstein's special theory of relativity and evidence for the controversial quantum theories of Max Planck.

Ernest Henry Starling*: Starling discovered the mechanisms that regulate the output of the heart and the flow of lymphatic fluid and discovered the role of hormones in the control of organ function.

Hermann Staudinger: Staudinger became the founder of a novel branch of chemistry when he conceived of and proved the existence of macromolecules. This work laid the foundation for the technological achievements in the plastics and high polymer synthetics industries. In addition, Staudinger contributed to the fields of organic chemistry and molecular biology.

William H. Stein: Stein won the 1972 Nobel Prize in Chemistry, with Stanford Moore. Stein and Moore supplemented Alfinsen's research by identifying the sequence of amino acids in ribonuclease, a clue to the structure of the gene responsible for it.

Nicolaus Steno*: Considered by many to be the founder of geology, Nicolaus Steno provided scientific explanations for the existence of fossils, stratification, and the constancy of crystal angles. As an anatomist, he made important discoveries regarding glands, muscles, the heart, and the brain.

Nettie Stevens: Stevens discovered the existence of the specific chromosomes that determine sex, now known as the X and Y chromosomes. She described the existence of chromosomes as paired structures within the cell.

Simon Stevin: Stevin formulated the law of inclined planes and laws of hydraulics, and in 1599 he described a twenty-six-seat, self-propelled land yacht—a carriage with sails for use on beaches.

Aurel Stodola: In 1915, Stodola and surgeon Ferdinand Sauerbruch created the first artificial hand, but Stodola is better known as an expert in thermodynamics and its application in designing steam and gas turbines.

William Sturgeon: Physicist William Sturgeon is credited with building the first electromagnet, and he invented an electric motor, galvanometer, and long-lasting battery cell.

Alfred Henry Sturtevant: Sturtevant was a colleague of Thomas Hunt Morgan and among the pioneers in the application of the fruit fly (Drosophila) in the study of genetics. In 1913, Sturtevant constructed the first genetic map of a fruit fly chromosome. His work became a major factor in chromosome theory. In the 1930s, his work with George Beadle led to important observations of meiosis.

Yellapragada SubbaRow*: During the 1930s, Yellapragada SubbaRow determined the roles of phosphocreatine and adenosine triphosphate as the energy "currency" in cells. Later, he helped explain the role of the vitamin folic acid in cell metabolism. He and pathologist Sidney Farber devised a way to apply the folic acid antagonist methotrexate in the treatment of cancer.

John E. Sulston: Sulston developed the first map of cell lineages in the model nematode Caenorhabditis, leading to the discovery of the first gene associated with programmed cell death. Sulston was also part of the team that sequenced the worm's genome. With Sydney Brenner and H. Robert Horvitz, he was awarded the Nobel Prize in Physiology or Medicine in 2002.

James B. Sumner*: Sumner crystallized the enzyme urease in 1926, the first successful example of such a chemical process. Subsequently, he was able to demonstrate that urease is a protein, providing the first evidence that enzymes are members of that organic category.

Ivan Sutherland*: Computer scientist Ivan Sutherland pioneered advances in artificial intelligence, simulation programming, and advanced circuitry. His work with computer graphics led to the development of the graphical user interface.

Walter Stanborough Sutton: Biologist and geneticist Walter Stanborough Sutton demonstrated the role of chromosomes during meiosis in gametes, and demonstrated their relationship to Mendel's laws. Sutton observed that chromosomes form homologous pairs during meiosis, with one member of each pair appearing in gametes. The particular member of each pair was subject to Mendel's law of independent assortment.

David Suzuki: Canadian genetics scientist and environmentalist David Suzuki is known for his activism regarding climate change and for his television and radio programs that have addressed various issues related to science and the environment. He became the host of the Canadian Broadcasting Corporation television series, *The Nature of Things* in 1979; this widely viewed program has focused on the topics of nature, wildlife, and sustainable human societies. Suzuki was awarded the United Nations Environment Programme Medal for his 1985 series, *A Planet for the Taking*, in which he called for a change in the way human beings relate to nature.

Michael Sveda: Chemist Michael Sveda invented the noncaloric artificial sweetener cyclamate in 1937, widely used until 1969, when the US government banned it on suspicion that it was a carcinogen.

Theodor Svedberg: The 1926 Nobel laureate in chemistry, Svedberg invented the ultracentrifuge in 1924, which is capable of separating out very small particles, and a device for measuring low osmotic pressure.

Jan Swammerdam: Swammerdam was among the earliest scientists to apply microscopic techniques to the study of anatomy and physiology in diverse organisms, ranging from insects to human beings. His work marked the beginning of the scientific study of insects, and he is most likely the first to observe red blood cells.

Joseph Swan: Swan was the first to patent an incandescent lamp, which he demonstrated in 1878, and contributed to the development of photographic printing.

Emanuel Swedenborg: Swedenborg was first a mechanical prodigy, then a scientist and philosopher, then an anatomist, and finally a theologian. His peers saw him as a genius in science and invention, but it was only much later that his anatomical studies were appreciated. His many contributions to Christian religious thought are still not widely known.

Thomas Sydenham: Sydenham laid the foundations for modern clinical, scientific, and public-health medicine, and he has been credited with the invention of the modern conception of disease, understood as a morbid entity in nature with its own history. This conception replaced the earlier model of disease as a set of peculiar events in people's lives with only particular case histories.

Leo Szilard: Szilard conceived the chain reaction necessary for nuclear reactors and bombs. He also developed a refrigerator in collaboration with Albert Einstein.

Jack W. Szostak*: Biologist Jack W. Szostak has led many groundbreaking investigations into the origins of life and genetic solutions to disease. His scientific contributions have earned him many honors, including the Nobel Prize for Physiology or Medicine in 2009.

T

Henry Fox Talbot: In 1834 and 1835, Talbot experimented with paper coated with salt and silver nitrate until he had created a negative photographic image, from which many positive prints could be made, known as the collotype process.

Igor Tamm: A 1956 Nobel laureate in physics, Tamm was also a central theoretician behind the first Soviet thermonuclear bomb and attempts to use fusion peacefully with the tokamak system.

Tan Jiazhen: Jiazhan is considered the father of Chinese genetics. In a career spanning more than seven decades, Tan studied genetic structure and variation in a wide range of organisms. His most important work involved the study of evolution of genetic structures in Drosophila (fruit flies), as well as the concept of mosaic dominance in the beetle.

Toyoichi Tanaka: Following Tanaka's discovery of "smart gels," scientists were able to track microscopic changes in a macroscopic way; the polymer gels also had a wide range of practical applications.

Arthur G. Tansley: Tansley, who coined the term "ecosystem," published scholarly articles and books on natural processes that have become central to ecological theory.

Terence Tao*: Australian-born mathematician Terence Tao has made significant contributions to areas such as harmonic analysis and number theory. He is particularly known for his in-depth study of prime numbers.

Edward Tatum*: American biochemist and geneticist Edward Tatum, in collaboration with Stanford University colleague George Beadle, conducted experiments in which the bread mold Neurospora crassa was exposed to X-rays, resulting in mutant strains. In 1941, they published an important paper explaining their "one gene–one enzyme" hypothesis: the idea that genes encode enzymes that accelerate chemical reactions in cells. The hypothesis is considered the first significant concept in molecular biology.

Edward Teller: Teller played a leading role in the design and development of the fusion bomb and vigorously argued that it should be part of the United States' arsenal of weapons.

Howard Martin Temin*: Howard Temin discovered the presence of a reverse transcriptase enzyme in the capsid of ribonucleic acid (RNA) tumor viruses, providing an explanation for how their genome is copied into deoxyribonucleic acid (DNA). His work greatly influenced the development of treatments for deadly viruses.

Nikola Tesla: Tesla brought many theoretical and applied innovations to electromagnetism, notably his brushless alternating current induction motor (1888).

Thales of Miletus: Through his various theories, Thales countered supernatural and mythical explanations of nature, attempting to replace them with empirically derived answers. He became a transitional figure between the worlds of philosophy and science.

Max Theiler : Theiler received the 1951 Nobel Prize in Physiology or Medicine for creating a vaccine against yellow fever.

Theophrastus*: Theophrastus was an ancient Greek philosopher and scholar. Over the course of his long life, he wrote many treatises on logic, science, ethics, politics, and rhetoric. He is considered one of the founders of botany and taxonomy.

Hugo Theorell: Theorell received the 1955 Nobel Prize in Physiology or Medicine for his work on the nature and action of oxidation enzymes. He was the first to produce a pure enzyme in the laboratory and the first to produce myoglobin in a pure form. His discoveries found wide scientific application in the study of cancer and tuberculosis, among other diseases.

Benjamin Thompson: Thompson (Count Rumford) was a leading eighteenth-century scientific investigator and invented an improved oven, lamp, and fireplace and a drip coffee maker.

J. J. Thomson*: J. J. Thomson discovered the electron, for which he received the Nobel Prize in Physics in 1906, and subsequently proposed a model for the interior of the atom. His discovery rendered false the belief in the atom as the indivisible building block of matter.

Samuel C. C. Ting*: Ting discovered the high-energy particle J/psi in 1974, with a different method used simultaneously by Burton Richter at Stanford; both physicists received the 1976 Nobel Prize in Physics for their independent discovery. In the 1990s and early 2000s, Ting led the Alpha Magnetic Spectrometer project designed to measure cosmic rays.

Max Tishler: Tishler led research into the synthesis of ascorbic acid (vitamin C), cortisone, riboflavin, vitamin B_{12}, streptomycin, and other compounds valuable to medicine.

Alexander Robertus Todd: Todd won the 1957 Nobel Prize in Chemistry. As part of wide-ranging research in organic chemistry, Todd revealed how ribose and deoxyribose bond to the nitrogenous bases on one side of a nucleotide unit and to the phosphate group on the other side. These discoveries provided necessary background for work by others that explained the structure of the DNA molecule.

Clyde W. Tombaugh*: Clyde W. Tombaugh discovered the dwarf planet Pluto and several star clusters and galaxies, studied the distribution of extragalactic nebulas, searched for small natural Earth satellites, and made observations of the surfaces of several planets and of Earth's moon.

Susumu Tonegawa: Tonegawa discovered the role of genetic rearrangement of DNA in lymphocytes, which plays a key role in generation of antibody diversity. In 1987, he was awarded the Nobel Prize in Physiology or Medicine.

Evangelista Torricelli: A mathematician and physicist, Torricelli invented the barometer in 1644.

Charles Hard Townes: Townes invented microwave amplification by stimulated emission of radiation (maser), a precursor of the laser. For it he shared the 1964 Nobel Prize in Physics.

Roger Y. Tsien: A pioneer in biological imaging, Roger Tsien characterized and exploited green fluorescent protein from jellyfish as an agent for visualizing biological processes within living cells. Tsien's ingenious use of the protein and its variants revolutionized the ability of scientists to visualize a broad range of biological processes that were thought to be beyond imaging technologies.

Konstantin Tsiolkovsky: A visionary advocate of space travel, Tsiolkovsky designed space stations and rocket-powered vehicles with life-support systems.

Daniel Chee Tsui: Best known for his work associated with the fractional quantum Hall effect, Tsui, along with colleagues, was awarded the 1998 Nobel Prize in physics for the discovery of a new form of quantum fluid with fractionally charged excitations. Tsui's research focuses on the electrical properties of thin films, microstructures of semiconductors, and solid-state physics.

Mikhail Tsvet: In 1901, Tsvet pioneered chromatography, a technique for separating chemical mixtures and analyzing them.

Alan Turing*: Twentieth-century British mathematician Alan Turing is regarded as one of the founders of modern computing. His research into machines and human thought helped shape the field of artificial intelligence.

John Tyndall: An early atmospheric scientist, Tyndall conceived the idea of the "atmospheric envelope," which implied that sunlight could be trapped in the Earth's atmosphere (the greenhouse effect). He also developed a respirator for firemen in 1871.

Neil deGrasse Tyson: Tyson, an accomplished astrophysicist, became one of the most visible and respected scientists of the early twenty-first century. Through his numerous books, television appearances, public lectures, and radio shows, he has done much to popularize astronomy.

U

Harold C. Urey*: Urey discovered deuterium, the heavy isotope of hydrogen, as well as methods of isotope separation. He founded the modern science of

cosmochemistry, devoted to understanding the origin and development of the solar system.

V

James Van Allen*: James Van Allen pioneered the use of artificial satellites for Earth studies, applying his expertise to help deploy planetary probes to enhance space exploration and knowledge. His discovery of radiation belts around the Earth initiated the field of magnetospheric physics.

Robert Jemison Van de Graaff: The Van de Graaff generator (1929), standard equipment in school physics labs, accumulates electrical charge on a moving belt and deposits it in a hollow glass sphere at the top.

Harold E. Varmus*: Oncogenes, genetic information associated with the conversion of normal cells into cells that are malignant, had been found in viruses during the 1960s and 1970s. In 1975, Varmus and his colleague, J. Michael Bishop, discovered that viral oncogenes actually originated from normal cells, where they played a role in regulating cell division.

Nikolai Ivanovich Vavilov: Vavilov is noted for his pioneering work on the origins, distribution, and genetics of crop plants. He postulated a law of homologous series in variation whereby variation (and thus characteristics of possible cultivars) of a plant could be predicted from variation in related species. He also mapped centers of origin and genetic diversity of cultivated plants on a worldwide scale as well as personally organizing and leading numerous botanical expeditions and establishing a network of agricultural experiment stations in the Soviet Union.

J. Craig Venter*: Prominent genomics researcher and entrepreneur, J. Craig Venter is recognized for a wide array of accomplishments that includes the first complete sequencing of the human genome, as well as his 2010 creation of the first self-replicating bacterial cell with synthetic DNA.

Giovanni Battista Venturi*: Italian priest, physicist, teacher, and diplomat Giovanni Battista Venturi's career spanned the late eighteenth century to the early nineteenth century. In addition to exploring optics and acoustics, Venturi discovered a hydraulic principle that provided multiple practical—and commercial—applications. He also published works on the scientific contributions of Leonardo da Vinci and Galileo Galilei.

Vladimir Vernadsky: Russian geochemist and mineralogist Vladimir Vernadsky developed the concepts of the biosphere and the noosphere, and his 1926 book *The Biosphere* inspired a new vision of humankind's role in shaping the earth's environment.

Andreas Vesalius*: Sixteenth-century Flemish physician Andreas Vesalius published the first modern comprehensive text of human anatomy. His accurate description of the structure of the human body, which was the result of firsthand dissection, is the basis of the modern scientific study of human anatomy.

Rudolf Virchow*: Nineteenth-century German pathologist Rudolf Virchow is known as the "father of pathology" for his pioneering use of cell theory to analyze and explain the body's response to disease. As a politician, he instituted many public health reforms. He also helped advance the organization of anthropology within Germany.

Alessandro Volta: Volta is best known for inventing the voltaic pile, an electric battery, in 1799, but he also produced several other instruments, such as a eudiometer for measuring the purity of air.

Hugo de Vries*: Working in the late nineteenth and early twentieth centuries, Dutch botanist Hugo de Vries was instrumental in rediscovering geneticist Gregor Mendel's laws of heredity. In addition, de Vries helped establish the modern science of genetics with his theory of intracellular pangenesis, and his mutation theory paved the way for debates about the nature of evolutionary change.

W

Johannes Diderik van der Waals*: Educator and physicist Johannes Diderik van der Waals received the Nobel Prize in Physics in 1910 for his work showing the continuity of state between liquids and gases. The weak electric forces that attract neutral molecules to one another are named after him.

Selman Abraham Waksman: From his studies of soil microorganisms, Waksman developed numerous antibiotics, most notably streptomycin (1943), which greatly enhanced public health worldwide. He received the 1952 Nobel Prize in Physiology or Medicine for his work.

Alfred Russel Wallace*: Nineteenth-century naturalist and explorer Alfred Russel Wallace developed a theory of evolution based on the principle of natural selection at the same time as fellow investigator and theorist

Charles Darwin. Wallace also made significant contributions in the field of biogeography.

John Wallis: Wallis made advances in mathematical notation and created new methods for making mathematical discoveries. He paved the way for the work of Sir Isaac Newton and consequently for the invention of the calculus.

Alan Walsh: Walsh invented atomic absorption spectroscopy, enabling scientists to identify quickly the chemical elements present in a sample.

Ernest Thomas Sinton Walton: Working with John Cockroft, Walton built the first high-energy particle accelerator in 1932 and produced the first human-made nuclear reaction. They shared the 1951 Nobel Prize in Physics for their work.

Taylor Gunjin Wang: Wang became the first Chinese American astronaut when he flew on space shuttle Challenger in 1985, before which he invented novel methods of acoustic manipulation of matter and designed drop dynamics experiments in zero gravity.

James D. Watson*: James Watson, working with British biologist Francis Crick, helped identify the double-helix structure of the deoxyribonucleic acid (DNA) molecule, and codiscovered the process of replication responsible for heredity. He also conducted significant research on protein synthesis and the role of viruses in cancer.

Robert Watson-Watt: Watson-Watt developed the physics of radar, and his administrative efforts helped in producing a radar-based air defense system for England during World War II.

Alfred Wegener*: Wegener's theories gave scientific credence to the idea of continental drift. Wegener concluded that the continents were once part of a so-called supercontinent known as Pangaea sometime during the Mesozoic era.

Karl Weierstrass*: A pioneer in the field of mathematics, Weierstrass is often called the "father of modern analysis" for having provided a solid arithmetical foundation for calculus.

Robert Weinberg: Molecular biologist Robert Weinberg isolated the first human oncogene, the ras gene, associated with a variety of cancers, including those of the colon and brain. Weinberg later isolated the first tumor suppressor gene, the retinoblastoma gene. Weinberg is considered among the leading researchers in understanding the role played by oncogenes in development of cancer.

Steven Weinberg*: Weinberg, along with Sheldon Glashow and Abdus Salam, developed the theory that unified the electromagnetic and weak nuclear interactions into the electroweak force. Weinberg also helped develop the theory of strong nuclear interactions known as quantum chromodynamics, or QCD. The electroweak theory and QCD provide the foundation for the standard model of matter.

August Weismann*: Weismann is most noted for his development and refinement of the theory of the continuity of the germplasm, his devout support of Darwinism and the principle of natural selection, and his discrediting of the idea of the inheritance of acquired characteristics.

George Westinghouse: Westinghouse was an engineer, inventor, entrepreneur, and a rival of Thomas Edison (1847–1931). He built a rotary steam engine while still a teenager and in his youth patented several devices—including a fail-safe compressed-air braking system—to improve railway safety. He developed an alternating-current power distribution network that proved superior to Edison's direct-current scheme, invented a power meter still in use, built several successful hydroelectric generating plants, and devised shock absorbers for automobiles.

Charles Wheatstone: Physicist Charles Wheatstone who produced inventions in acoustic and telegraph technology, Wheatstone invented an eerie musical instrument, the enchanted lyre (or acoucryptophone, 1821).

John Archibald Wheeler*: American physicist John Archibald Wheeler made important contributions to the theories of general relativity, quantum gravity, and quantum electrodynamics. He is known for his role in the development of both the atomic and the hydrogen bombs, as well as for naming one of the strangest astronomical bodies known to science: the black hole.

Otto Wichterle: Chemist Otto Wichterle discovered the hydrogel polyhydroxyethyl methacrylate (poly-HEMA) in 1952 and in 1957 how to mold it into flexible contact lenses.

Norbert Wiener: Wiener was a distinguished American mathematician credited with a founding of cybernetics, a science that facilitates comparison of biological and electronic systems by focusing on communication, feedback, and control.

Eric F. Wieschaus*: American molecular biologist Eric Francis Wieschaus has been involved in the study of genetics as a researcher and teacher since the 1960s. His collaborative experiments on the mutation of genes of fruit flies aided in understanding the process of embryonic development across the animal kingdom, and earned him a share of the Nobel Prize.

Eugene P. Wigner*: Wigner applied quantum theory to theoretical physics and focused on group theory in quantum mechanics. During World War II, he joined with other physicists in an effort to convince President Franklin D. Roosevelt of the need to develop nuclear weapons.

Maurice Vincent Wilkes*: Maurice Wilkes designed and built the EDSAC computer, the first computer to combine mercury delay line memory with stored program instructions. He later developed WISP, one of the first high-level programming languages.

Maurice Wilkins*: Maurice Wilkins's X-ray diffraction studies were instrumental in determining the double-helical structure of DNA. He came to regard DNA's simplicity as symbolizing the underlying simplicity of all biological phenomena.

Robert R. Williams, Jr. : Williams isolated vitamin B1 (thiamine) in 1933 and two years later found a method to synthesize it.

Ian Wilmut: In 1996, Wilmut became the first scientist to clone a mammal, a Finn Dorset ewe named Dolly, from differentiated adult mammary cells.

Edmund Beecher Wilson*: American zoologist Edmund Beecher Wilson is considered one of most influential cell biologists in history. During a career that spanned the late nineteenth and early twentieth centuries, he conducted multiple studies on the cellular division of eggs in insects and marine creatures, and helped define the vital role of chromosomes in determining gender across the animal kingdom.

Edward O. Wilson: Wilson described many new species of ants and discovered the chemical nature of ant communication. He synthesized the patterns of social behavior in insects and other organisms, including humans, into a new field of life science called sociobiology. Wilson's biogeographical work demonstrated the direct relationship between habitat size and biological diversity, leading him to become an advocate for biological conservation.

Edward Witten*: Sometimes called the successor to Albert Einstein, Edward Witten has developed numerous theories in advanced mathematics, often borrowing concepts from biology, physics, and other branches of science. He is best known for proposing superstring theory, which seeks to reconcile Einsteinian relativity with Newtonian gravitation.

Carl Woese: Based on his studies of ribosomal RNA differences in prokaryotes and eukaryotes, Woese proposed that all life forms exist in one of three domains: Bacteria, Archaea ("ancient" bacteria), and Eukarya (eukaryotic organisms, from microscopic plants to large animals). Woese expanded his theory in arguing that the Archaea represent the earliest form of life on Earth, and that they later formed a branch which became the eukaryotes.

Friedrich Wöhler*: In synthesizing urea, Wöhler was the first scientist to demonstrate that organic materials—which had previously been believed to possess a vital force—need not be made exclusively within living organisms. He also isolated aluminum metal and discovered the elements beryllium and yttrium.

Max Wolf: Wolf was the first astronomer to use an astronomical camera to discover asteroids by combining the camera with a mechanical telescope. During his very full career, Wolf discovered 582 asteroids with 228 of these receiving general recognition. This figure is a personal record of discoveries in astronomy that has been difficult to surpass.

Abel Wolman: Wolman was a pioneer in the field of sanitary engineering. His innovations and advocacy influenced the establishment of sound water-resource management strategies by American cities during the twentieth century.

Flossie Wong-Staal*: Molecular biologist Flossie Wong-Staal conducted important research into retroviruses while working at the National Cancer Institute and was part of a team that discovered a link between HIV and AIDS. Considered a leading authority on HIV, she headed America's first university-affiliated department established to research AIDS and founded a cutting-edge pharmaceutical company.

John Woodward: An English naturalist, physician, paleontologist, and geologist, Woodward was an early collector of fossils, which served as the basis for his *Classification of English Minerals and Fossils* (1729), a work that influenced geology for many years. He also conducted pioneering research into the science of hydroponics. His collection of specimens formed the foundation of Cambridge University's Sedgwick Museum, and his estate was sold to provide a post in natural history, now the Woodwardian Chair of Geology at Cambridge.

Robert Burns Woodward: Woodward received the 1965 Nobel Prize in Chemistry for his work in organic chemistry, including his synthesis of complex substances, such as cholesterol, cortisone, vitamin B12, and quinine.

Jane Cooke Wright: Scientist and physician Jane Cooke Wright revolutionized the field of chemother-

apy. Her research on chemotherapy agents and their administration continued to be used in clinical practice decades later. She also became the highest-ranking African American woman at a medical institution when she was appointed associate dean at New York Medical College.

Chien-Shiung Wu*: Nuclear physicist Chien-Shiung Wu disproved the principle of conservation of parity and proved the law of vector current in beta decay. Wu was the first woman elected president of the American Physical Society and honored with Israel's Wolf Prize.

Y

Rosalyn Yalow*: Yalow helped develop the radioimmunoassay technique for the measurement of minute quantities of biological materials in blood. This technique was established after her research determined that people who had received injections of the polypeptide hormone insulin for conditions such as diabetes developed antibodies against the hormone. For her work, Yalow was awarded a Nobel Prize in Physiology or Medicine in 1977.

Chen Ning Yang*: Chinese-born American physicist Chen Ning Yang was awarded the Nobel Prize in Physics in 1957 together with Tsung-Dao Lee for their research into universal parity conservation. Yang is also known for his work on the Yang–Mills theory and Yang–Baxter equation.

Charles Yanofsky: Yanofsky confirmed that the genetic code involved groups of three bases by demonstrating colinearity of the bases and amino acid sequences. He applied this work in demonstrating similar colinearity of mutations in the tryptophan operon and changes in amino acid sequences.

Ada E. Yonath*: In 2009, Israeli biochemist Ada E. Yonath became the first woman from her country to win a

Nobel Prize for her work on ribosome structure and function. Yonath pioneered the use of cryo-biocrystallography, which she used to determine the ribosome's complex structure. Her work has implications for the development of antibiotics and the search for the origin of life in the universe.

Roger Arliner Young*: An African American woman, Roger Arliner Young rose from poverty to become a respected biologist and zoologist. The first black female in the United States to earn a doctoral degree in zoology, she began her career as a researcher, but spent most of her adult life teaching at historically black colleges and universities.

Thomas Young*: British scientist Thomas Young is known for his contributions to the fields of physics, optics, and medicine. He proposed a wave theory of light, challenging the particle theory of earlier scientist Isaac Newton.

Hideki Yukawa*: When Hideki Yukawa won the 1949 Nobel Prize in Physics, he became the first Japanese person to win a Nobel Prize. Though he was often regarded as soft-spoken and shy, his ideas about the nature of atoms spoke loudly, forming the foundation for modern particle studies.

Z

Paolo Zacchia: Considered a forensic medicine pioneer, Zacchia was employed as the Vatican's physician, providing medical care for popes. Historians credit him with writing the first known scientific text discussing issues that formed the foundation of forensic medicine.

Hajib Zaid: Zaid patented his corrosion inhibitor industrial chemical mixtures in 1987. Mixtures of oil- and water-soluble compounds, they keep oil wells and pipes free from bacteria and corrosion.

Pieter Zeeman*: Pieter Zeeman shared the Nobel Prize in Physics in 1902 with Hendrik A. Lorentz. Zeeman is remembered for discovering that spectral lines could be split when placed in a magnetic field. This "Zeeman effect" aided in the discovery of the electron and helped lead to the development of magnetic resonance imaging, among many other advances.

Karl Ziegler: Ziegler shared the 1963 Nobel Prize in Chemistry for developing catalysts that are widely used in the plastics industry.

Norton David Zinder*: As a graduate student, twentieth-century American virologist Norton Zinder discovered transduction, the process by which genetic material is transferred between bacteria by bacteriophage (bacterial viruses). Later in his career, he discovered the first bacteriophage in which RNA was the genetic material.

Hans Zinsser: In 1932, bacteriologist Hans Zinsser proved that typhus is caused by the microorganism Rickettsia prowazekii and with M. Ruiz Castañeda developed a vaccine.

Richard Zsigmondy: Zsigmondy developed the ultramicroscope in 1903 for his foundational investigation into colloids, for which he received the 1925 Nobel Prize in Chemistry.

Konrad Zuse: Zuse designed and built early computers and wrote the first book about digital physics.

Fritz Zwicky*: Astronomer and physicist Fritz Zwicky observed and named the supernova phenomenon. He also theorized the existence of neutron stars and dark matter, and patented numerous inventions related to jet propulsion.

Vladimir Zworykin: A Russian who emigrated to the United States after World War I, Zworykin worked at the Westinghouse laboratories in Pittsburgh. An engineer and inventor who patented a cathode ray tube television transmitting and receiving system in 1923, he later worked in development for the Radio Corporation of America (RCA) in New Jersey, where his inventions were perfected in time to be used to telecast the 1936 Olympic Games in Berlin. He also contributed to the development of the electron microscope.

NOBEL PRIZE SCIENCE LAUREATES

CHEMISTRY

1901	Jacobus Henricus van't Hoff	1951	Edwin Mattison McMillan, Glenn Theodore Seaborg
1902	Hermann Emil Fischer	1952	Archer John Porter Martin, Richard Laurence Millington Synge
1903	Svante August Arrhenius		
1904	Sir William Ramsay	1953	Hermann Staudinger
1905	Johann Friedrich Wilhelm Adolf von Baeyer	1954	Linus Carl Pauling
		1955	Vincent du Vigneaud
1906	Henri Moissan	1956	Sir Cyril Norman Hinshelwood, Nikolay Nikolaevich Semenov
1907	Eduard Buchner		
1908	Ernest Rutherford	1957	Lord (Alexander R.) Todd
1909	Wilhelm Ostwald	1958	Frederick Sanger
1910	Otto Wallach	1959	Jaroslav Heyrovsky
1911	Marie Curie née Sklodowska	1960	Willard Frank Libby
1912	Victor Grignard, Paul Sabatier	1961	Melvin Calvin
1913	Alfred Werner	1962	John Cowdery Kendrew, Max Ferdinand Perutz
1914	Theodore William Richards	1963	Guilio Natta, Karl Ziegler
1915	Richard Martin Willstätter	1964	Dorothy Crowfoot Hodgkin
1918	Fritz Haber	1965	Robert Burns Woodward
1920	Walther Hermann Nernst	1966	Robert S. Mulliken
1921	Frederick Soddy	1967	Manfred Eigen, Ronald George Wreyford Norrish, George Porter
1922	Francis William Aston		
1923	Fritz Pregl	1968	Lars Onsager
1925	Richard Adolf Zsigmondy	1969	Derek H. R. Barton, Odd Hassel
1926	The (Theodor) Svedberg	1970	Luis F. Leloir
1927	Heinrich Otto Wieland	1971	Gerhard Herzberg
1928	Adolf Otto Reinhold Windaus	1972	Christian B. Anfinsen, Stanford Moore, William H. Stein
1929	Arthur Harden, Hans Karl August Simon von Euler-Chelpin		
		1973	Ernst Otto Fischer, Geoffrey Wilkinson
1930	Hans Fischer	1974	Paul J. Flory
1931	Carl Bosch, Friedrich Bergius	1975	John Warcup Cornforth, Vladimir Prelog
1932	Irving Langmuir	1976	William N. Lipscomb
1934	Harold Clayton Urey	1977	Ilya Prigogine
1935	Frédéric Joliot, Irène Joliot-Curie	1978	Peter D. Mitchell
1936	Petrus (Peter) Josephus Wilhelmus Debye	1979	Herbert C. Brown, Georg Wittig
1937	Walter Norman Haworth, Paul Karrer	1980	Paul Berg, Walter Gilbert, Frederick Sanger
1938	Richard Kuhn	1981	Kenichi Fukui, Roald Hoffman
1939	Adolf Friedrich Johann Butenandt, Leopold Ruzicka	1982	Aaron Klug
		1983	Henry Taube
1943	George de Hevesy	1984	Robert Bruce Merrifield
1944	Otto Hahn	1985	Herbert A. Hauptman, Jerome Karle
1945	Artturi Ilmari Virtanen	1986	Dudley R. Herschbach, Yuan T. Lee, John C. Polanyi
1946	John Howard Northrop, Wendell Meredith Stanley, James Batcheller Sumner		
		1987	Donald J. Cram, Jean-Marie Lehn, Charles J. Pedersen
1947	Sir Robert Robinson		
1948	Arne Wilhelm Kaurin Tiselius	1988	Johann Deisenhofer, Robert Huber, Hartmur Michel
1949	William Francis Giauque		
1950	Otto Paul Hermann Diels, Kurt Alder		

1989	Thomas R. Cech, Sidney Altman	2002	John B. Fenn, Koichi Tanaka, Kurt Wüthrich
1990	Elias James Corey	2003	Peter Agre, Roderick MacKinnon
1991	Richard R. Ernst	2004	Aaron Ciechanover, Avram Hershko, Irwin Rose
1992	Rudolph A. Marcus		
1993	Kary B. Mullis, Michael Smith	2005	Yves Chauvin, Robert H. Grubbs, Richard R. Schrock
1994	George A. Olah		
1995	Paul J. Crutzen, Mario J. Molina, F. Sherwood Rowland	2006	Roger D. Kornberg
		2007	Gerhard Ertl
1996	Robert F. Curl Jr., Sir Harold W. Kroto, Richard E. Smalley	2008	Martin Chalfie, Osamu Shimomura, Roger Y. Tsien
1997	Paul D. Boyer, Jens C. Skou, John E. Walker	2009	Venkatraman Ramakrishnan, Thomas A. Steitz, Ada E. Yonath
1998	Walter Kohn, John A. Pople		
1999	Ahmed H. Zewail	2010	Richard F. Heck, Ei-ichi Negishi, Akira Suzuki
2000	Alan J. Heeger, Alan G. MacDiarmid, Hideki Shirakawa	2011	Dan Shechtman
		2012	Robert J. Lefkowitz, Brian K. Kobilk
2001	William S. Knowles, Ryoji Noyori, K. Barry Sharpless		

PHYSICS

1901	Wilhelm Conrad Röntgen	1928	Owen Willans Richardson
1902	Hendrik Antoon Lorentz, Pieter Zeeman	1929	Prince Louis-Victor Pierre Raymond de Broglie
1903	Antoine Henri Becquerel, Pierre Curie, Marie Curie née Sklodowska	1930	Sir Chandrasekhara Venkata Raman
1904	Lord Rayleigh (John William Strutt)	1932	Werner Karl Heisenberg
1905	Philipp Eduard Anton von Lenard	1933	Erwin Schrödinger, Paul Adrien Maurice Dirac
1906	Joseph John Thomson	1935	James Chadwick
1907	Albert Abraham Michelson	1936	Victor Franz Hess, Carl David Anderson
1908	Gabriel Lippman	1937	Clinton Joseph Davisson, George Paget Thomson
1909	Guglielmo Marconi, Karl Ferdinand Braun		
1910	Johannes Diderik van der Waals	1938	Enrico Fermi
1911	Wilhelm Wien	1939	Ernest Orlando Lawrence
1912	Nils Gustaf Dalén	1943	Otto Stern
1913	Heike Kamerlingh Onnes	1944	Isidor Isaac Rabi
1914	Max von Laue	1945	Wolfgang Pauli
1915	Sir William Henry Bragg, William Lawrence Bragg	1946	Percy Williams Bridgman
		1947	Sir Edward Victor Appleton
1917	Charles Glover Barkla	1948	Patrick Maynard Stuart Blackett
1918	Max Karl Ernst Ludwig Planck	1949	Hideki Yukawa
1919	Johannes Stark	1950	Cecil Frank Powell
1920	Charles Edouard Guillaume	1951	Sir John Douglas Cockcroft, Ernest Thomas Sinton Walton
1921	Albert Einstein		
1922	Niels Henrik David Bohr	1952	Felix Bloch, Edward Mills Purcell
1923	Robert Andrews Millikan	1953	Frits (Frederik) Zernike
1924	Karl Manne Georg Siegbahn	1954	Max Born, Walther Bothe
1925	James Franck, Gustav Ludwig Hertz	1955	Polykarp Kusch, Willis Eugene Lamb
1926	Jean Baptiste Perrin	1956	John Bardeen, William Bradford Shockley, Walter Houser Brattain
1927	Arthur Holly Compton, Charles Thomson Rees Wilson		
		1957	Tsung-Dao (T.D.) Lee, Chen Ning Yang

1958	Pavel Alekseyevich Cherenkov, Il´ja Mikhailovich Frank, Igor Yevgenyevich Tamm		1985	Klaus von Klitzing
1959	Owen Chamberlain, Emilio Gino Segrè		1986	Gerd Binnig, Heinrich Rohrer, Ernst Ruska
1960	Donald Arthur Glaser		1987	J. Georg Bednorz, K. Alexander Müller

1958   Pavel Alekseyevich Cherenkov, Il´ja Mikhailovich Frank, Igor Yevgenyevich Tamm
1959   Owen Chamberlain, Emilio Gino Segrè
1960   Donald Arthur Glaser
1961   Robert Hofstadter, Rudolph Ludwig Mössbauer
1962   Lev Davidovich Landau
1963   J. Hans D. Jensen, Maria Goeppert-Mayer, Eugene Paul Wigner
1964   Nicolay Gennadiyevich Basov, Aleksandr Mikhailovich Prokhorov, Charles Hard Townes
1965   Richard P. Feynman, Julian Schwinger, Sin-Itiro Tomonaga
1966   Alfred Kastler
1967   Hans Albrecht Bethe
1968   Luis Walter Alvarez
1969   Murray Gell-Mann
1970   Hannes Olof Gösta Alfvén, Louis Eugène Félix Néel
1971   Dennis Gabor
1972   John Bardeen, Leon Neil Cooper, John Robert Schrieffer
1973   Leo Esaki, Ivar Giaever, Brian David Josephson
1974   Antony Hewish, Sir Martin Ryle
1975   Aage Niels Bohr, Ben Roy Mottelson, Leo James Rainwater
1976   Burton Richter, Samuel Chao Chung Ting
1977   Philip Warren Anderson, Sir Nevill Francis Mott, John Hasbrouck van Vleck
1978   Pyotr Leonidovich Kapitsa, Arno Allan Penzias, Robert Woodrow Wilson
1979   Sheldon Lee Glashow, Abdus Salam, Steven Weinberg
1980   James Watson Cronin, Val Logsdon Fitch
1981   Nicolaas Bloembergen, Arthur Leonard Schawlow, Kai M. Siegbahn
1982   Kenneth G. Wilson
1983   Subramanyan Chandrasekhar, William Alfred Fowler
1984   Carlo Rubbia, Simon van der Meer

1985   Klaus von Klitzing
1986   Gerd Binnig, Heinrich Rohrer, Ernst Ruska
1987   J. Georg Bednorz, K. Alexander Müller
1988   Leon M. Lederman, Melvin Schwartz, Jack Steinberger
1989   Hans G. Dehmelt, Wolfgang Paul, Norman F. Ramsey
1990   Jerome I. Friedman, Henry W. Kendall, Richard E. Taylor
1991   Pierre-Gilles de Gennes
1992   Georges Charpak
1993   Russell A. Hulse, Joseph H. Taylor Jr.
1994   Bertram N. Brockhouse, Clifford G. Shull
1995   Martin L. Perl, Frederick Reines
1996   David M. Lee, Douglas D. Osheroff, Robert C. Richardson
1997   Steven Chu, Claude Cohen-Tannoudji, William D. Phillips
1998   Robert B. Laughlin, Horst L. Störmer, Daniel C. Tsui
1999   Gerardus 't Hooft, Martinus J. G. Veltman
2000   Zhores I. Alferov, Jack S. Kilby, Herbert Kroemer
2001   Eric A. Cornell, Wolfgang Ketterle, Carl E. Wieman
2002   Raymond Davis Jr., Masatoshi Koshiba, Riccardo Giacconi
2003   Alexei A. Abrikosov, Vitaly L. Ginzburg, Anthony J. Leggett
2004   David J. Gross, H. David Politzer, Frank Wilczek
2005   Roy J. Glauber, John L. Hall, Theodore W. Hänsch
2006   John C. Mather, George F. Smoot
2007   Albert Fert, Peter Grünberg
2008   Makoto Kobayashi, Yoichiro Nambu, Toshihide Maskawa
2009   Willard S. Boyle, Charles Kuen Kao, George E. Smith
2010   Andre Geim, Konstanin Novoselov
2011   Saul Perlmutter, Brian P. Schmidt, Adam G. Riess
2012   Serge Haroche, David J. Wineland

Physiology or Medicine

1901   Emil Adolf von Behring
1902   Ronald Ross
1903   Niels Ryberg Finsen

1904   Ivan Petrovich Pavlov
1905   Robert Koch
1906   Camillo Golgi, Santiago Ramón y Cajal

1907	Charles Louis Alphonse Laveran
1908	Paul Ehrlich, Ilya Ilyich Mechnikov
1909	Emil Theodor Kocher
1910	Albrecht Kossel
1911	Allvar Gullstrand
1912	Alexis Carrel
1913	Charles Robert Richet
1914	Robert Bárány
1919	Jules Bordet
1920	Schack August Steenberg Krogh
1922	Archibald Vivian Hill, Otto Fritz Meyerhof
1923	Frederick Grant Banting, John James Rickard Macloed
1924	Willem Einthoven
1926	Johannes Andreas Grib Fibiger
1927	Julius Wagner-Jauregg
1928	Charles Jules Henri Nicolle
1929	Christiaan Eijkman, Sir Frederick Gowland Hopkins
1930	Karl Landsteiner
1931	Otto Heinrich Warburg
1932	Edgar Douglas Adrian, Sir Charles Scott Sherrington
1933	Thomas Hunt Morgan
1934	George Richards Minot, William Parry Murphy, George Hoyt Whipple
1935	Hans Spemann
1936	Sir Henry Hallett Dale, Otto Loewi
1937	Albert von Szent-Györgyi Nagyrápolt
1938	Corneille Jean François Heymans
1939	Gerhard Domagk
1943	Henrik Carl Peter Dam, Edward Adelbert Doisy
1944	Joseph Erlanger, Herbert Spencer Gasser
1945	Ernst Boris Chain, Sir Alexander Fleming, Sir Howard Walter Florey
1946	Hermann Joseph Muller
1947	Carl Ferdinand Cori, Bernardo Alberto Houssay, Gerty Theresa Cori née Radnitz
1948	Paul Hermann Müller
1949	Walter Rudolph Hess, Antonio Caetano de Abreu Freire Egas Moniz
1950	Edward Calvin Kendall, Philip Showalter Hench, Tadeus Reichstein
1951	Max Theiler
1952	Selman Abraham Waksman
1953	Fritz Albert Lipmann, Hans Adolf Krebs
1954	John Franklin Enders, Frederick Chapman Robbins, Thomas Huckle Weller
1955	Axel Hugo Theodor Theorell
1956	André Frédéric Cournand, Werner Forssmann, Dickinson W. Richards
1957	Daniel Bovet
1958	George Wells Beadle, Joshua Lederberg, Edward Lawrie Tatum
1959	Arthur Kornberg, Severo Ochoa
1960	Sir Frank Macfarlane Burnet, Peter Brian Medawar
1961	Georg von Békésy
1962	Francis Harry Compton Crick, James Dewey Watson, Maurice Hugh Frederick Wilkins
1963	Sir John Carew Eccles, Alan Lloyd Hodgkin, Andrew Fielding Huxley
1964	Konrad Bloch, Feodor Lynen
1965	François Jacob, André Lwoff, Jacques Monod
1966	Charles Brenton Huggins, Peyton Rous
1967	Ragnar Granit, Haldan Keffer Hartline, George Wald
1968	Robert W. Holley, Har Gobind Khorana, Marshall W. Nirenberg
1969	Max Delbrück, Alfred D. Hershey, Salvador E. Luria
1970	Julius Axelrod, Sir Bernand Katz, Ulf von Euler
1971	Earl W. Sutherland, Jr.
1972	Gerald M. Edelman, Rodney R. Porter
1973	Karl von Frisch, Konrad Lorenz, Nikolaas Tinbergen
1974	Albert Claude, Christian de Duve, George E. Palade
1975	David Baltimore, Renato Dulbecco, Howard Martin Temin
1976	Baruch S. Blumberg, D. Carleton Gajdusek
1977	Roger Guillemin, Andrew V. Schally, Rosalyn Yalow
1978	Werner Arber, Daniel Nathans, Hamilton O. Smith
1979	Allan M. Cormack, Godfrey N. Hounsfield
1980	Baruj Benacerraf, Jean Dausset, George D. Snell
1981	David H. Hubel, Roger W. Sperry, Torsten N. Wiesel
1982	Sune K. Bergström, Bengt I. Samuelsson, John R. Vane
1983	Barbara McClintock
1984	César Milstein, Niels K. Jerne, Georges J.K. Köhler

1985	Michael S. Brown, Joseph L. Goldstein		2001	Leland H. Hartwell, Tim Hunt, Sir Paul M. Nurse
1986	Stanley Cohen, Rita Levi-Montalcini		2002	Sydney Brenner, H. Robert Horvitz, John E. Sulston
1987	Susumu Tonegawa		2003	Paul C. Lauterbur, Sir Peter Mansfield
1988	Sir James W. Black, Gertrude B. Elion, George H. Hitchings		2004	Richard Axel, Linda B. Buck
1989	J. Michael Bishop, Harold E. Varmus		2005	Barry J. Marshall, J. Robin Warren
1990	Joseph E. Murray, E. Donnall Thomas		2006	Andrew Z. Fire, Craig C. Mello
1991	Erwin Neher, Bert Sakmann		2007	Mario R. Capecchi, Sir Martin J. Evans, Oliver Smithies
1992	Edmond H. Fischer, Edwin G. Krebs		2008	Françoise Barré-Sinoussi, Harald zur Hausen, Luc Montagnier
1993	Richard J. Roberts, Phillip A. Sharp		2009	Elizabeth H. Blackburn, Carol W. Greider, Jack W. Szostak
1994	Alfred G. Gilman, Martin Rodbell		2010	Robert G. Edwards
1995	Edward B. Lewis, Christiane Nüsslein-Volhard, Eric F. Wieschaus		2011	Bruce A. Beutler, Jules A. Hoffmann, Ralph M. Steinman
1996	Peter C. Doherty, Rolf M. Zinkernagel		2012	Sir John B. Gurdon, Shinya Yamanaka
1997	Stanley B. Prusiner			
1998	Louis J. Ignarro, Ferid Murad, Robert F. Ruchgott			
1999	Günter Blobel			
2000	Arvid Carlsson, Paul Greengard, Eric R. Kandel			

ELECTRONIC RESOURCES

The following sites were visited by editors in 2012. Because URLs frequently change, the accuracy of these addresses cannot be guaranteed; however, long-standing sites, such as those of colleges and universities, national organizations, and government agencies, generally maintain links when sites are moved or updated.

GENERAL INFORMATION

How Stuff Works: Science
http://Science.HowStuffWorks.com/

How Stuff Works presents a wide variety of science-related material, with wide-ranging subjects from military to environmental sciences. Within these subject areas, topics become more specific and students can find detailed explanations as to "how stuff works." For example, students can find out how a rocket engine works through seven pages of detailed text and diagrams, with related articles and links at the end. Other articles include "How the Dyson Bladeless Fan Works" and "How Time Travel Works." Students can also find puzzles, games, and videos such as "Ten Silly Inventions That Became Wildly Famous."

Marian Koshland Science Museum of the National Academy of Sciences
http://www.Koshland-Science-Museum.org/

The Marian Koshland Science Museum of the National Academy of Sciences offers many online exhibits and experiences with hands-on science activities for visitors. Also included are online galleries where students can find information on things such as infectious diseases. Within this portal, students can view online exhibits on global disease distribution, vaccines, emerging diseases, and much more. Under the teach-and-learn tab, there is a list of educational activities with descriptions, appropriate grade level, additional links, science standards, and teacher comments and ratings.

The Official Site of the Nobel Prize
http://www.NobelPrize.org/

NobelPrize.org, the official web site of the Nobel Prize, contains a great deal of general scientific material. Within the site's specific award areas (physics, chemistry, medicine, literature, peace, and economic sciences) are facts, winners, nomination and selection history, interviews, articles, and general videos. Under the educational tab are games and simulations to help students learn based on "Nobel Prize–awarded achievements." There are also educational videos that explain complicated subjects in depth and in a way that students can understand.

Scientific American
http://www.ScientificAmerican.com/

The web site for Scientific American magazine, a past recipient of the National Magazine Award for General Excellence, offers a wealth of science-related resources to the general user, covering general and emerging topics such as health, technology, sustainability, evolution, neuroscience, and extraterrestrial life. Supplementing this content is a variety of blogs, podcasts, interactive online exhibits, and slide shows; additionally, featured portals such as "Bring Science Home" bring together scientists and educators and offer educational resources such as science-related activities for the home that teach basic science concepts.

Science Fair Projects World
http://www.ScienceFair-Projects.org/

This web site offers a large collection of illustrated, detailed science projects for both teachers and students ranging from elementary school to the high-school level. The projects are diagrammed and sorted by a range of categories, including technology, physics, chemistry, math, and biology. The projects are designed to help foster a better understanding of basic science principles and laws, and thus maintain a relative ease of application at home or in the classroom.

Science Learning Network (SLN)
http://www.sln.org/sln.html

The Science Learning Network is an online network of community-oriented institutions dedicated to the study of science. The network is represented by numerous science museums, including the Museum of Science in Boston and the Franklin Institute in Philadelphia; at the international level, member institutions include the Science Museum in London, the Heureka science center in Finland, and science museums and centers in Japan, Singapore, and France. The site offers a wealth of science-related resources, including collaborative online exhibits, interviews with scientists in the field, and numerous image galleries. A sampling of online exhibits includes "Contemporary Issues in Science," "Hurricane: Storm Science," "Monarch and Migration," and "Science of Cycling."

ASTRONOMY

Cosmic Journey: A History of Scientific Cosmology
http://www.aip.org/history/cosmology/

Presented by the American Institute of Physics, this web site is an interactive study of the history of cosmology, from the astronomers of ancient Greece to the development of galaxy-probing high-tech space telescopes. Biographies of famous scientists and astronomers, including Nicholas Copernicus, Galileo Galilei, and George Ellery Hale, add to the in-depth historical content offered on the site. The web site also offers a list of reliable sources for further reading, categorized by history and modern cosmology.

Harvard-Smithsonian Center for Astrophysics
http://www.CFA.Harvard.edu/

The Harvard-Smithsonian Center for Astrophysics sets out to advance awareness and comprehension of the universe through research and education in the fields of astronomy and astrophysics. From the main page, visitors can browse through an image gallery highlighting the wonders of space, as well as view stargazing information for the current night sky. Under the research tab, interested persons can find out specific astronomy information within six general categories. For educators, a list of "Fun Things to Do and See" is included with various activities and simulations. Also provided for educators is information on professional development, curricula, informal education, and research.

Space Technology Hall of Fame
http://www.SpaceTechHallOfFame.org/

The Space Technology Hall of Fame honors organizations and individuals who have converted technology originally intended for space exploration into products that advance the quality of life for the general public. The site presents a list of inducted technologies with further information about them. The option of nominating an organization is included through the use of the site's official nomination form. There is also a media center with videos and photos of past inductions.

BIOLOGY

Centre of the Cell
http://www.CentreOfTheCell.org/

Centre of the Cell is an educational charity that aims to incite curiosity and learning by connecting science to daily life. The web site has a section dedicated to teachers that allows them to give students access to key, stage-specific data and to allocate assessments and other educational material to students. There is also a student-specific page that gives students their own password-protected "locker room" to communicate with their teacher and complete quizzes. Also for students is a game section to test their knowledge and have fun at the same time.

eSkeletons Project
http://www.eSkeletons.org/

eSkeletons from The University of Texas at Austin provides an interactive atmosphere to study and learn about skeletal composition. Visitors can view the bones of human and nonhuman primates to acquire information about them. Under the "Comparative Anatomy" tab, students can view pictures of the bones of thirteen different primates, including humans. Under the "Taxonomic Tree" tab, evolutionary trees of various suborder and infraorders are visible with diagrams and informative text.

Famous Biologists: A History of Biology in Biography
http://www.Macroevolution.net/Famous-Biologists.html

Famous Biologists: A History of Biology in Biography offers biographies that depict the lives, contributions, and findings of various distinguished biologists throughout the extensive history of the field. The site is organized alphabetically by last name, with biologists ranging from the well-known "father of biology," Aristotle, to the lesser-known Hungarian naturalist John Xantus.

MendelWeb
http://www.MendelWeb.org/

MendelWeb is an educational resource for both educators and students alike to explore the origins of classical genetics, data analysis, botany, and the history of science. The site is structured around one of Mendel's papers "Experiments in Plant Hybridization" and is offered as a public sourcebook. His paper is presented in its original German, English, and in English with annotations. This site also contains essays and commentary, as well as additional reference material for Mendel.

UCMP Exhibit Hall: Evolution Wing
http://www.UCMP.Berkeley.edu/History/Evolution.html

The Evolution Wing of the University of California Museum of Paleontology has multiple online exhibits that trace the development of evolutionary thought over time, with additional information regarding specific scientists such as Aristotle, Darwin, Wallace, and others. The "tree of life" link will bring visitors to a classification chart of all forms of life, with specific information on various classifications. Another portion of the web site is titled "time periods," and contains a geologic time scale with information about ancient life, climates, and geography from the Hadean time to the present Cenozoic Era.

CHEMISTRY

Chemical Heritage Foundation
http://www.ChemHeritage.org/

The Chemical Heritage Foundation prides itself in the saying "we tell the story of chemistry." The CHF has a library, museum, and numerous online resources that explore the role of chemistry in everyday life. One such resource is called "Chemistry in History" and contains detailed accounts on important people and themes in the field of chemistry, as well as a hands-on activity center to test students' knowledge. The "Thanks to Chemistry" section contains detailed explanations into the role that chemistry plays in day-to-day life. The CHF web site also includes a periodic table with each element linked to informational videos from a nationwide contest.

Periodic Table of Elements
http://Periodic.LANL.gov/index.shtml

This page is part of the official site of the Los Alamos National Laboratory and enables users to explore the periodic table of elements. The site, which presents an interactive periodic table, details the history of each element, sources where the element is found, and the element's properties and uses. Downloadable versions of the table are available as a resource for students and teachers alike.

COMPUTER SCIENCE

Computer History Museum
http://www.ComputerHistory.org/

The museum, located in Mountain View, California, maintains a timeline of computer history and a number of online exhibits on its web site. Exhibits include "The Silicon Engine," which chronicles the history of semiconductors in computers, "The Babbage Engine," a biographical exhibit on computer pioneer Charles Babbage, and "Mastering the Game," which provides an overview of computer chess. Other exhibits outline the milestones

of Internet history from 1962 through 1992, detail the early history of microprocessors, and display a historical overview of computer marketing brochures. Additional information about computer scientists and other computer industry leaders can be found in the biographies of persons inducted into the museum's Hall of Fame.

EARTH SCIENCES

Geology.com
http://Geology.com/

Geology.com provides a great deal of useful information on geology. The web site contains an alphabetical list of diverse categories to explore, ranging from astronomy, climate change, gemstones, and volcanoes, to careers in geology, teacher resources, and a collection of US geological maps. Users can also access an archived news section, a database of global satellite images, and a dictionary of geological and earth science terms and definitions. A database of rocks, encompassing igneous, metamorphic, and sedimentary rocks, is also available.

Earth Science World
http://www.EarthScienceWorld.org/

An educational portal maintained by the American Geological Institute (AGI). Users can access a wide range of interactive features on the site, including an interactive geological time scale, a digitized collection of earth science images, and an interactive game concerning the exploration for oil. The web site also contains career-focused content related to the field of geosciences, as well as information pertaining to Earth Science Week, an annual event organized at the international level by the AGI.

MATHEMATICS

The Story of Mathematics
http://www.StoryOfMathematics.com/

This web site approaches the "story of mathematics" in essay form, beginning in the prehistoric era and ending in the twentieth century. Supplementing the historical overview of mathematics that forms the focal point of the site is a list of significant mathematicians throughout history, an alphabetized glossary of mathematical terms, and a search function that allows users to search by important mathematical theorems or periods in history. A reference page presents important linked web sites and other sources used to create the site's content.

The MacTutor History of Mathematics Archive

http://www-History.MCS.St-Andrews.ac.uk/index.html

The MacTutor History of Mathematics Archive contains indices regarding specific mathematicians throughout history as well as mathematics in different cultures and other mathematical topics. The mathematician index includes a wide variety of influential figures in the field of mathematics starting from Ahmes in 1680 BCE all the way to Terence Tao in 1975 CE. For each mathematician there is an article as well as a list of honors they received, other web sites, and a list of references.

PHYSICS

American Institute of Physics Center for History of Physics

http://www.AIP.org

This web portal, maintained by the American Institute of Physics, is the online presence for the Center for History of Physics, which operates as an archival historical record of modern physics and related sciences. Users can access extensive online resources, including a collection of teaching syllabi, a collection of oral history interviews, and an extensive collection of short biographies of contemporary American physicists. Users also have catalog access to the Niels Bohr Library and Archives, which maintains an extensive collection of photographs and visual materials. Online exhibits include "Bright Idea: The First Lasers," a history of laser technology; "Albert Einstein: Image and Impact," a detailed perspective of the famed physicist; and "The Discover of Global Warming," which collects thirty essays on the topic.

PhysicsCentral

http://www.PhysicsCentral.com/

Sponsored by the American Physical Society, this site explores physics through current research, pictures, podcasts, book excerpts, and profiles of physicists at work. Topics of discovery highlighted at the site include compression waves and sound, electricity and magnetism, light and optics, quantum mechanics, space and the universe, and thermodynamics and heat. The site also provides resources for educators, such as posters and outreach guides, and an online exhibit dedicated to Albert Einstein.

Physics.org

http://www.Physics.org/

This educational web portal, maintained by the Institute of Physics (IOP), is one of the premier physics guides on the Internet. Users can access practical information and instructions on at-home physics experiments, while aspiring physicists can access a comprehensive list of college physics courses and career-related resources. The site also provides a database of other physics sites, searchable by age level and knowledge level, an archived news section, and online exhibits and links dedicated to the exploration of physics in sports and other areas.

Encyclopedia of Earth

http://www.eoEarth.org/

Supported by the National Council for Science and the Environment and the Environmental Information Coalition, the Encyclopedia of Earth is an all-encompassing reference center for our planet that contains expert-reviewed information and reference materials. The site has resources for all fields of science including other science-related topics such as environmental law, agricultural resources, and more. Within these broad topics are more specific fields of study, each containing an overview, further reading section, and expert-reviewed articles.

BIBLIOGRAPHY

Abir-Am, Pnina G., and Dorinda Outram. *Uneasy Careers and Intimate Lives: Women in the Sciences, 1789–1979.* Piscataway, NJ: Rutgers UP, 1987. Print. A pioneering collection of chapter-length biographical studies of women scientists, some familiar, most not.

Alic, Margaret. *Hypatia's Heritage: A History of Women in Science from Antiquity through the Nineteenth Century.* Boston: Beacon Press, 1986. Print. A collection of relatively brief biographies, indispensable for its scope and completeness. Shows, in considerable detail, that there is more to the subject than Marie Curie and Rachel Carson.

Asimov, Isaac. *Asimov's Biographical Dictionary of Science and Technology.* 2nd ed. New York: Doubleday, 1982. Print. Brief biographical sketches of more than one thousand individuals—mostly male physical scientists from the last two centuries. Entries provide little social or intellectual context, and minimal cross-referencing, but basic data is reliable.

---. *Asimov's Chronology of Science and Discovery.* Rev. ed. Harper, 1994. Print. Presents scientific and technological breakthroughs from antiquity to the present, narrated in Asimov's characteristic (learned, breezy, accessible) style. Treats discoveries in social and cultural context.

Bass, Thomas A. *Reinventing the Future: Conversations with the World's Leading Scientists.* Reading, MA: Addison-Wesley, 1994. Print. Includes eleven interviews with leading scientists, some controversial. A biographical sketch precedes the question-and-answer segment.

Beek, Leo. *Dutch Pioneers of Science.* Assen, Neth.: Van Gorcum, 1985. Print. Spanning five centuries, Beek's work discusses noteworthy Dutch inventions and inventors, from Gerardus Mercator, the cartographer, to Frits Zernike, inventor of the phase-contrast microscope.

Bertolotti, Mario. *The History of the Laser.* Philadelphia: Institute of Physics, 2005. Print. Covers not only the laser but also the history of optics.

Bird, Kai, and Martin J. Sherman. *American Prometheus: The Triumph and Tragedy of J. Robert Oppenheimer.* New York: Knopf, 2005. Print. A new biography of Oppenheimer emphasizing his work on the atomic bomb at Los Alamos Laboratory.

Bowler, Peter J. *The Norton History of the Environmental Sciences.* New York: Norton, 1993. Print. Despite its title, primarily a history of ideas about the history of Earth and of its living inhabitants, with some attention to ecology, meteorology, and oceanography. Probably the best single-volume treatment of its chosen subjects.

Brennan, Richard. *Heisenberg Probably Slept Here.* Hoboken, NJ: Wiley, 1996. Print. Chapter-length biographies of seven major twentieth-century physicists, treating their ideas as well as their careers. Covers, in addition to the title character, Einstein, Feynmann, Planck, and others.

Brian, Dennis. *Albert Einstein: A Life.* Hoboken, NJ: Wiley, 1996. Print. Written by an outsider after the recent, full disclosure of Einstein's personal papers. Elementary explanations of his science punctuate a survey of his public and personal lives. Balanced on controversial issues.

Brooke, John Hedley. *Science and Religion: Some Historical Perspectives.* New York: Cambridge UP, 1991. Print. A comprehensive narrative and analysis of the changing relationship between scientific and religious ideas, set in the context of recent history-of-science scholarship. Dense, detailed, and demanding, but written with acute insight and brilliant clarity of expression.

Bryson, Bill. *A Really Short History of Everything.* New York: Delacorte Books, 2009. Print. An abbreviated version of Bryson's bestseller for younger readers.

---. *A Short History of Nearly Everything: Special Illustrated Edition.* New York: Broadway Books, 2010. Print. This bestseller is a very readable and comprehensive account of the history of science including full-color artwork to illustrate the concepts.

Burlingame, Roger. *Out of Silence into Sound.* New York: Harcourt, Brace & World, 1960. Print. Identifies those who provided insights in detecting and producing sound, including Dr. Joseph Black, James Watt; Benjamin Silliman, Charles Goodyear, Joseph Henry, Michael Faraday, Michael Pupin, and Thomas Alva Edison.

Byers, Nina, and Gary Williams, eds. *Out of the Shadows: Contributions of 20th Century Women to Physics.* New York: Cambridge UP, 2006. Print. Covers the scientific achievements of women scientists, putting their contributions to the field of physics in social and historical context.

Bynum, W. F., E. J. Browne, and Roy Porter. *Dictionary of the History of Science*. Princeton, NJ: Princeton UP, 1984. Print. Seven hundred articles dealing with the history of specific scientific ideas and concepts. Extensive cross-referencing, indexing, and bibliographies make this a useful supplement to individual- and event-oriented works.

Cardwell, D. S. L. *Turning Points in Western Technology: A Study of Technology, Science, and History*. New York: Science History Publications, 1972. Print. Identifies four stages in the development of science and technology. The first coincided with the rise of European technics during the Middle Ages; the second began in the early seventeenth century; the third at the time of the Industrial Revolution; and the fourth at the time of the establishment of industrial research laboratories, with the renaissance of German technology and science, and with the rise of new technological powers—the United States and Japan.

Cassidy, David. *Einstein and Our World*. Amherst, NY: Humanities Press, 1995. Print. Brief, nontechnical survey of Einstein's ideas, scientific and otherwise, and their impact on the first half of the twentieth century. A compact case study of the intersection of science and culture.

Chang, Hasok. *Inventing Temperature: Measurement and Scientific Progress*. New York: Oxford UP, 2004. Print. Philosophical survey and critique of the whole history of the study of temperature.

Christianson, Gale E. *Edwin Hubble: Mariner of the Nebulae*. Chicago: U of Chicago P, 1996. Print. The first full-scale biography of a man whose work transformed twentieth-century astronomy by establishing solid evidence for the expansion of the universe. Also deals squarely with Hubble's less-than-attractive personality.

Conner, Clifford D. *A People's History of Science: Miners, Midwives, and Low Mechanicks*. New York: Nation Books, 2005. Print. A proletarian history of science emphasizing the contributions of common folks in the history of science.

Croft, William J. *Under the Microscope: A Brief History of the Microscope*. Hackensack, NJ: World Scientific, 2006. Print. A brief history of the development and evolution of the microscope and microscopy, from the use of water drops by the ancient Greeks to recent innovations in electron and confocal microscopy.

Crombie, A. C. *The History of Science from Augustine to Galileo*. Mineola, NY: Dover, 1996. Print. One of the definitive works on the history of medieval science, originally published in 1952. Strong focus on scientific ideas, with comparatively less attention to social context than other books.

Crowe, Michael J. *Modern Theories of the Universe from Herschel to Hubble*. Mineola, NY: Dover, 1994. Print. Scientific, historical, and philosophical introduction to modern astronomy and cosmology. Assumes a high-school level grasp of mathematics.

---. *Theories of the World from Antiquity to the Copernican Revolution*. Mineola, NY: Dover, 1990. Print. Leads the reader through the internal logic of Aristotelian, Ptolemaic, Copernican, and other cosmologies. History of astronomy is seen from the inside, for those comfortable with high-school level math, geometry, and algebra.

Darrow, Floyd L. *Masters of Science and Invention*. New York: Harcourt, 1951. Print. Provides inspirational, readable biographical sketches of thirty-six scientists and inventors, some of whom are less well known.

Davis, Kenneth S. *The Cautionary Scientists: Priestley, Lavoisier, and the Founding of Modern Chemistry*. New York: G. P. Putnam's Sons, 1966. Print. This dual biography emphasizes, besides Joseph Priestley's and Antoine Lavoisier's scientific accomplishments, the social, political, and religious contexts within which each lived and worked.

Degler, Carl N. *In Search of Human Nature*. New York: Oxford UP, 1992. Print. A survey of the history of the social sciences in (mostly) twentieth century America, using the decline and revival of Darwinism as a central organizing theme.

Desmond, Adrian, and James R. Moore. *Darwin*. New York: Norton, 1991. Print. A comprehensive, readable one-volume biography placing Darwin's scientific work firmly in its Victorian social and cultural context. Janet Browne's *Charles Darwin: Voyaging* (1996), the first of a projected two-volume work, is also excellent.

Dupree, A. Hunter. *Science in the Federal Government: A History of Policies and Activities*. 1957. Baltimore: Johns Hopkins UP, 1986. Print. Still the standard source for the period up to World War II; comprehensive and detailed without sacrificing readability. For the post-WWII period, see Greenberg (1967).

Fortey, Jacqueline. *Great Scientists*. New York: Dorling Kindersley, 2007. Print. This book, written for young people, includes profiles of several eminent scientists.

Geison, Gerald L. *The Private Science of Louis Pasteur*. Princeton, NJ: Princeton UP, 1995. Print. Detailed study of Pasteur's life and work, rooted in the author's careful analysis of his laboratory notebooks. Careful and even-handed in placing Pasteur's ideas and methods in the context of his times, but topples a number of cherished Pasteur myths.

Gillispie, Charles Coulston, ed. *Dictionary of Scientific Biography*. 16 vols. Scribner's, 1970–80. Print. Easily the most complete history-of-science reference source available. Multipage entries on major scientists are frequently the best work available on their subjects, and can serve as useful introductions to major periods and subjects.

Gordon, Scott. *The History and Philosophy of Social Science*. London: Routledge, 1991. Print. Intellectual history of social scientists' attempts to develop comprehensive explanations of human behavior. Chronologically organized, with additional chapters on topics of long-term interest to social scientists, such as the relationship between the social and the biological in shaping human culture.

Grant, Edward. *Physical Science in the Middle Ages*. New York: Cambridge UP, 1978. Print. Covers the origins of medieval science and its institutions [treated in more depth in Grant (1996)] and basic medieval ideas about the motion of celestial and terrestrial bodies.

---. *The Foundations of Modern Science in the Middle Ages: Their Religious, Institutional, and Intellectual Contexts*. New York: Cambridge UP, 1996. Print. Traces the rediscovery, translation, and transformation of ancient Greek science by medieval scholars, and the intersection of Aristotelian and Christian thought.

Gribbin, John. *The Scientists: A History of Science Told Through the Lives of Its Greatest Inventors*. New York: Random House, 2003. Print. A well-written biographical narrative that clearly explains scientific theories.

Haber, Louis. *Black Pioneers of Science and Invention*. New York: Harcourt, 1970. Print. Includes fourteen chapters on African American innovators, inventors, and scientists.

Hall, A. Rupert. *The Revolution in Science, 1500–1750*. 3rd ed. Boston: Addison-Wesley, 1983. Print. Comprehensive, densely written history of the origins of modern science, originally published in the 1950s. Focuses on ideas more than social institutions, and physical more than biological sciences.

Hankins, Thomas L. *Science in the Enlightenment*. New York: Cambridge UP, 1985. Print. Comprehensive, balanced survey of scientific ideas, organized roughly by discipline.

Hoffman, Banesh, and Helen Dukas. *Albert Einstein: Creator and Rebel*. New York: New American Library, 1989. Print. Short, fond biography of Einstein by two colleagues, with dense-but-comprehensible explanations of his science interspersed with rose-colored stories of his personal life.

Hudson, Wade. *Book of Black Heroes: Scientists, Healers, and Inventors*. East Orange, NJ: Just Us Books, 2003. Print. Covers many lesser-known African American scientists and inventors. Written for a juvenile audience.

Isaacson, Walter. *Einstein: His Life and Universe*. New York: Simon, 2010. Print. A new biography of Einstein based on recently released personal papers.

Jacob, Margaret. *Scientific Culture and the Making of the Industrial West*. New York: Oxford UP, 1996. Print. Surveys the interrelations of science, industry, and society in France and, particularly, in Britain. Begins with the cultural and scientific legacies of Newton and Descartes and ends in the early stages of industrialization.

Judson, Horace Freeland. *The Eighth Day of Creation: Makers of the Revolution in Biology*. Rev. ed. Cold Spring Harbor, NY: Cold Spring Harbor Laboratory, 1996. Print. Long and detailed, but non-technical, history of twentieth century molecular biology.

Keller, Evelyn Fox. *A Feeling for the Organism: The Life and Work of Barbara McClintock*. New York: W. H. Freeman, 1983. Print. Award-winning biography of pioneer geneticist Barbara McClintock, whose studies of corn—unconventional by the standards of the time—eventually won her the Nobel Prize.

Kessler, James H., J. S. Kidd, Renée A. Kidd, and Katherine A. Morin. *Distinguished African American Scientists of the Twentieth Century*. Phoenix, AZ: Oryx Press, 1996. Print. Encyclopedic book covers the lives and accomplishments of one hundred African American scientists and inventors. Full of biographical data, arranged alphabetically and including a photograph of each profiled person. Written for young readers in clear and rather plain language.

Kevles, Daniel J. *In the Name of Eugenics: Genetics and the Uses of Human Heredity*. Berkeley: U of

California P, 1985. Print. History of Anglo-American attempts to improve the human race through selective breeding, from the late nineteenth to the mid-twentieth century. Sober, scrupulously detailed, and often frightening.

Knight, David. *Ideas in Chemistry*. Piscataway, NJ: Rutgers UP, 1992. Print. Big-picture history of chemistry from its origins in medieval alchemy through its glory days in the eighteenth and early nineteenth century to its reduced, twentieth-century status as a "service science." Covers key people, ideas, and experiments, but not a comprehensive "names and dates" compendium.

Kohn, David, ed. *The Darwinian Heritage*. Princeton, NJ: Princeton UP, 1985. Print. The vast literature on Darwin and Darwinism embraces a great variety of subjects and approaches. This thick collection of articles provides a representative cross-section. Its table of contents could serve as an impromptu "Who's Who" of the "Darwin Industry."

Kuhn, Thomas S. *The Structure of Scientific Revolutions*. 2nd ed. Chicago: U of Chicago P, 1970. Print. Landmark theoretical study of how scientific communities function and how new scientific ideas become accepted. Among the most influential history-of-science studies ever written.

Landau, Misia. *Narratives of Human Evolution*. New Haven: Yale UP, 1991. Print. A unique perspective on narratives of human evolution from Darwin to the present, arguing that they mirror the structure of hero-on-a-quest folktales. An elegant argument for literature's impact on science.

Larson, Edward J. *Summer for the Gods: The Scopes Trial and America's Continuing Debate over Science and Religion*. New York: Basic Books, 1997. Print. Detailed narrative and analysis of perhaps the single most famous collision of science and American culture: the Scopes "Monkey Trial" of 1925. Illuminates the roots and continuing relevance of the trial, while debunking the simplistic "Ignorance vs. Truth" interpretation enshrined by the play and film *Inherit the Wind*.

---. *Trial and Error: The American Controversy over Creation and Evolution*. Rev. ed. New York: Oxford UP, 1989. Print. A history of anti-evolution and pro-creationist legislation in the United States, and the court battles that resulted. Elegantly written and incisively argued by a lawyer-historian.

Levine, George. *Darwin and the Novelists: Patterns of Science in Victorian Fiction*. Chicago: U of

Chicago P, 1991. Print. A pioneering study of science's influence on major literary figures, and an introduction to the rapidly growing science-and-literature field.

Lewin, Roger. *Bones of Contention*. 2nd ed. Chicago: U of Chicago P, 1997. Print. Episodes in the history of twentieth-century paleoanthropology, chosen to illustrate the contentious nature of the field. Highly readable, with anecdotes and character sketches leavening the explanations of competing theories.

Lindberg, David C., ed. *Cambridge History of Science: The Middle Ages*. Vol. 2. New York: Cambridge UP, 2010. Print. An authoritative account of science in the Middle Ages by a leading historian of science.

---, and Ronald L. Numbers. *God and Nature: Historical Perspectives on the Encounter Between Science and Christianity*. Berkeley: U of California P, 1986. Print. A collection of essays by an all-star team of historians of science that collectively revise the old "warfare" model of science's relationship to religion. Many of the individual essays remain the best treatments of their subjects.

Lloyd, G. E. R. *Early Greek Science: Thales to Aristotle and Greek Science After Aristotle*. New York: Norton, 1974. Print. Compact, wide-ranging surveys of ancient Greek scientific ideas from their origins in the sixth century BCE to their absorption by the Romans.

Magner, Lois. *A History of the Life Sciences*. 2nd ed. New York: Marcel Dekker, 1994. Print. Comprehensive history of the biological sciences from the ancient world to the present day. Divided chronologically for the period through the Renaissance, thematically thereafter.

Margulis, Lynn, and Eduardo Punset, eds. *Mind, Life, and Universe: Conversations with Great Scientists of Our Time*. White River Junction, VT: Chelsea Green, 2007. Print. The authors interviewed thirty-six scientists about their thoughts and ideas regarding some of the most important concepts influencing their fields today. An index and bibliographical references are included.

McGrayne, Sharon Bertsch. *Nobel Prize Women in Science: Their Lives, Struggles, and Momentous Discoveries*. Secaucus, NJ: Carol, 1993. Print. Very readable and well-researched biographies of fourteen female scientists who overcame gender discrimination as both students and researchers to accomplish groundbreaking scientific work.

Merchant, Carolyn. *The Death of Nature: Women, Ecology, and the Scientific Revolution*. New York:

Harper, 1990. Print. Provocative re-examination of the Scientific Revolution, arguing that the rise of a mechanical worldview sanctioned the exploitation of nature and the subordination of women.

Morgan, Michael Hamilton. *Lost History: The Enduring Legacy of Muslim Scientists, Thinkers, and Artists*. Washington, DC: National Geographic, 2007. Print. Morgan includes biographies of a variety of Muslim figures whose works would leave a mark on Western endeavors in fields as diverse as medicine, astronomy, and mathematics.

Nachmansohn, David. *German-Jewish Pioneers in Science, 1900–1930: Highlights in Atomic Physics, Chemistry, and Biochemistry*. New York: Springer-Verlag, 1979. Print. While some familiar names appear, the book treats some of the amazing scientific discoveries of a number of lesser-known scientists in chemistry, biochemistry, physiology in particular. Provides a historical background and ends with a chapter on the worldwide effects on biochemistry due to persecution and subsequent flight from Germany.

Nelkin, Dorothy, and M. Susan Lindee. *The DNA Mystique: The Gene as a Cultural Icon*. New York: W. H. Freeman, 1995. Print. Surveys the nature and impact of popular ideas about scientific issues connected with genetics, including DNA fingerprinting, the Human Genome Project, and genetic testing.

Nye, Mary Jo, ed. *The Cambridge History of Science*. New York: Cambridge UP, 2003. Print. An acclaimed series and international standard in the history of science.

Olby, R. C., et al. *Companion to the History of Modern Science*. London: Routledge, 1990. Print. Not a reference book in the conventional sense, but a collection of sixty-seven authoritative essays on the methods and contents of the history of science. The essays are grouped into six broad sections: Neighboring Disciplines, Analytical Perspectives, Philosophical Problems, Turning Points, Topics and Interpretations, and Themes.

Oleksy, Walter. *Hispanic-American Scientists*. New York: Facts On File, 1998. Print. Brief biographical sketches with a few photos and a useful chronology.

Park, Katharine, and Lorraine Daston, eds. *The Cambridge History of Science: Early Modern Science*. 3rd vol. New York: Cambridge UP, 2006. Print. An authoritative account of science in the early modern period by a leading historian of science.

Paul, Diane B. *Controlling Human Heredity*. Amherst, NY: Humanities Press, 1995. Print. The history of late nineteenth- and early twentieth-century attempts to create a better human race by applying scientists' emerging knowledge of genetics. Briefly links its main story to present-day concerns, but useful primarily as a brief synopsis of material covered at length by Gould (1981) and Kevles (1985).

Pickover, Clifford A. *Archimedes to Hawking: Laws of Science and the Great Minds behind Them*. New York: Oxford UP, 2008. Print. An exploration of the physical laws that have dominated the history of science and the scientists who established them.

Porter, Theodore M. *The Rise of Statistical Thinking, 1820–1900*. Princeton, NJ: Princeton UP, 1985. Print. Though not limited to the social sciences, this work examines the rise of a most powerful and versatile intellectual tool.

Primack, Joel. *History of Cosmic Inquiry*. Philadelphia: Franklin Institute, 2007. Print. A history of early twentieth-century cosmology, including pioneers such as Michelson, Einstein, Millikan, and Hubble.

Pycior, Helena M., et al., eds. *Creative Couples in the Sciences*. Piscataway, NJ: Rutgers UP, 1996. Print. Twenty-four studies of collaborative work by scientists who were married to each other. Explores the ways in which gender roles, marital dynamics, and social expectations shaped these collaborations.

Rhodes, Richard. *The Making of the Atomic Bomb*. 1987. New York: Touchstone, 1995. Print. Massive, prize-winning history of the design, building, testing, and aftermath of the first atomic bombs. An unmatched treatment of the subject, coupled with a substantial history of pre-WWII nuclear physics and detailed portraits of Niels Bohr and J. Robert Oppenheimer, among others.

Ross, Dorothy. *Origins of American Social Science*. New York: Cambridge UP, 1991. Print. Surveys the history of the social sciences in their American cultural context, arguing for the central role of an ideology of American exceptionalism in shaping them.

Rudy, Lisa Jo. *The Ben Franklin Book of Easy and Incredible Experiments*. Hoboken, NJ: Wiley, 1995. Print. Includes a brief biographical sketch of Benjamin Franklin and provides interesting juvenile experiments involving weather, electricity, music, printing, light, and sound.

Shectman, Jonathan. *Groundbreaking Scientific Experiments, Inventions, and Discoveries of the Eighteenth Century*. Westport, CT: Greenwood Press,

2003. Print. The introduction gives an overview of the eighteenth-century interest in science; several essays discuss scientific discoveries, applications, and investigations to provide background on the impact of scientific advances, such as the Leiden jar, on social and political history.

Schiebinger, Londa. *The Mind Has No Sex?: Women in the Origins of Modern Science.* Cambridge, MA: Harvard UP, 1989. Print. Examines both the role of women in seventeenth- and eighteenth-century science and the scientific attitudes toward women that emerged during the same period.

Serafini, Anthony. *The Epic History of Biology.* New York: Perseus Publishing, 1993. Print. Sweeping, popular history of Western biology and medicine from the ancient Near East to the present. Old-fashioned emphasis on the role of "revolutionary" thinkers challenging "prejudices and dogmas" of their times in order to advance knowledge.

Sime, Ruth Lewin. *Lise Meitner: A Life in Physics.* U of California P, 1997. Print. Extensively detailed effort to rescue the codiscoverer of nuclear fission from the historical oblivion to which politics, sexism, and less-than-generous colleagues consigned her. Covers both Meitner's physics and her personal life.

Smith, Crosbie, and M. Norton Wise. *Energy and Empire: A Biographical Study of Lord Kelvin.* New York: Cambridge UP, 1989. Print. Definitive biography of one of the most influential figures in nineteenth-century physics, covering his contributions to thermodynamics and other fields in considerable technical depth.

Spangenburg, Ray, and Kit Moser. *African Americans in Science, Math, and Invention.* New York: Facts On File, 2003. Print. Outlines the lives of 160 African American scientists since 1731, highlighting not only the challenges and difficulties the subjects encountered in their scientific pursuits but also the barriers to their formal education and training. Includes a bibliography, special categorical index, and black-and-white photographs.

Stableford, Brian. *Science Fact and Science Fiction: An Encyclopedia.* New York: Routledge, 2006. Print. Focusing on the nineteenth century to the present,

Stableford examines how science has influenced science fiction and vice versa.

Stiebing, William. *Uncovering the Past: A History of Archaeology.* New York: Oxford UP, 1994. Print. Half a history of archaeology, half an introduction to the current "state of the art." Less comprehensive and scholarly than Bruce Trigger's *A History of Archaeological Thought* (Cambridge UP, 1989), but more accessible to nonarchaeologists.

Sullivan, Otha Richard, and James Haskins. *African American Women Scientists and Inventors.* New York: Wiley, 2002. Print. A simple, straightforward presentation of African American women who have influenced science and technology. Written for a juvenile audience.

Tuomey, Christopher. *Conjuring Science: Scientific Symbols and Cultural Meanings in American Life.* Piscataway, NJ: Rutgers UP, 1996. Print. Analyzes the impact on public policy of most Americans' willingness to grant science great cultural authority while remaining vaguely aware, at best, of science's methods and results.

Westfall, Richard S. *The Life of Isaac Newton.* New York: Cambridge UP, 1994. Print. A compact distillation of the author's definitive Newton biography *Never at Rest.* Covers Newton's relationship with colleagues as well as his ideas, and assumes some basic knowledge of the Scientific Revolution.

Wilson, Mitchell. *American Science and Invention: A Pictorial History.* New York: Simon, 1954. Print. A large volume that relies on period illustrations and photographs to describe the course of American invention.

Windelspecht, Michael. *Groundbreaking Scientific Experiments, Inventions, and Discoveries of the Nineteenth Century.* Westport, CT: Greenwood, 2003. Print. A book in a series spanning the modern centuries. Describes more than sixty major inventions of the nineteenth century.

Worster, Donald. *Nature's Economy: A History of Ecological Ideas.* New York: Cambridge UP, 1994. Print. The most recent edition of the classic history of ecological ideas and their cultural impact, by a leading figure in the study of environmental history.

Indexes

CATEGORY INDEX

GEOGRAPHICAL INDEX

SUBJECT INDEX